Modern Chemistry®

Solutions Manual

HOLT, RINEHART AND WINSTON

A Harcourt Education Company

Orlando • **Austin** • New York • San Diego • Toronto • London

ISBN 0-03-036782-4

11 12 13 1417 13 12 11 10

4500244864

TABLE OF CONTENTS

Section I Pupil's Edition Solutions

Note: Chapters 5, 8, and 23 contain no quantitative problems, so solutions are not provided for these chapters.

Section II Problem Bank Solutions

CONTENTS

CHAPTER 1

Matter and Change

Math Tutor, p. 24

1. a. Given: 42.200 L

   Unknown: number of significant figures

   All figures (5) are significant as per rules.

b. Given: 0.055 00 mol.

   Unknown: number of significant figures

   Four figures are significant. The first two zeroes are not: they are placeholders.

2. a. Given: 56.05 g ÷ 13.3 cm³

   Unknown: number of significant figures in answer

   There are 3 significant figures in the answer (4.21 g/cm³): the same as in 13.3 g/cm³

b. Given: 1.057 g + 3.02 g + 12.4 g

   Unknown: number of significant figures in answer

   The answer is 16.5 g. Keep one digit to the right of the decimal point, as in 12.4 g, and round off 16.477 in the calculation up to 16.5.

CHAPTER 2

Measurements and Calculations

Practice, p. 40

1. Given: $V = 310 \text{ cm}^3$
$m = 853 \text{ g}$
Unknown: D

$$D = \frac{m}{V} = \frac{853 \text{ g}}{310 \text{ cm}^3} = 2.75 \text{ g/cm}^3$$

2. Given: $D = 3.26 \text{ g/cm}^3$
$V = 0.351 \text{ cm}^3$
Unknown: m

$$D = \frac{m}{V}$$

$$m = DV = (3.26 \text{ g/cm}^3)(0.351 \text{ cm}^3) = 1.14 \text{ g}$$

3. Given: $m = 76.2 \text{ g}$
$D = 13.6 \text{ g/mL}$
Unknown: V

$$D = \frac{m}{V}$$

$$V = \frac{m}{D} = \frac{76.2 \text{ g}}{13.6 \text{ g/mL}} = 5.60 \text{ mL}$$

ATE, Additional Sample Problems, p. 40

A-1. Given: $m = 74.0 \text{ g}$
$V = 20.3 \text{ cm}^3$
Unknown: D

$$D = \frac{m}{V} = \frac{74.0 \text{ g}}{20.3 \text{ cm}^3} = 3.65 \text{ g/cm}^3$$

A-2. Given: $m = 95.1 \text{ g}$
$D = 0.857 \text{ g/cm}^3$
Unknown: V

$$D = \frac{m}{V}$$

$$V = \frac{m}{D} = \frac{95.1 \text{ g}}{0.857 \text{ g/cm}^3} = 111 \text{ cm}^3$$

ATE, Additional Sample Problems, p. 41

B-1. Given: 1.00 day
Unknown: time in s

1 day = 24 h

1 h = 60 min

1 min = 60 s

$$1.00 \text{ day} \times \frac{24 \text{ h}}{\text{day}} \times \frac{60 \text{ min}}{\text{h}} \times \frac{60 \text{ s}}{\text{min}} = 86\ 400 \text{ s}$$

B-2. Given: 6.25 kg
Unknown: mass in cg

1 g = 100 cg

1 kg = 1000 g

$$6.25 \text{ kg} \times \frac{1000 \text{ g}}{\text{kg}} \times \frac{100 \text{ cg}}{\text{g}} = 625\ 000 \text{ cg}$$

Practice, p. 42

1. Given: 16.45 m

Unknown: length in cm and km

$1\ m = 100\ cm$

$16.45\ m \times \dfrac{100\ cm}{m} = 1645\ cm$

$1\ km = 1000\ m$

$16.45\ m \times \dfrac{1\ km}{1000\ m} = 0.016\ 45\ km$

2. Given: 0.014 mg

Unknown: mass in g

$1\ g = 1000\ mg$

$0.014\ mg \times \dfrac{1\ g}{1000\ mg} = 0.000\ 014\ g$

Section Review, p. 42

3. a. Given: 10.5 g

Unknown: mass in kg

$10.5\ g \times \dfrac{1\ kg}{1000\ g} = 0.0105\ kg$

b. Given: 1.57 km

Unknown: length in m

$1.57\ km \times \dfrac{1000\ m}{km} = 1570\ m$

c. Given: 3.54 µg

Unknown: mass in g

$3.54\ µg \times \dfrac{1\ g}{1\ 000\ 000\ µg} = 0.000\ 003\ 54\ g$

d. Given: 3.5 mol

Unknown: amount of substance in µmol

$3.5\ mol \times 1\ 000\ 000\ µmol = 3\ 500\ 000\ µmol$

e. Given: 1.2 L

Unknown: volume in mL

$1.2\ L \times \dfrac{1000\ mL}{L} = 1200\ mL$

f. Given: 358 cm³

Unknown: volume in m³

$358\ cm^3 \times \dfrac{1\ m^3}{1\ 000\ 000\ cm^3} = 0.000\ 358\ m^3$

g. Given: 548.6 mL

Unknown: volume in cm³

$548.6\ mL \times \dfrac{1\ cm^3}{mL} = 548.6\ cm^3$

5. a. Given: $m = 84.7\ g$
$V = 49.6\ cm^3$

Unknown: D

$D = \dfrac{m}{V}$

$= \dfrac{84.7\ g}{49.6\ cm^3} = 1.71\ g/cm^3$

b. Given: $m = 7.75\ g$
$D = 1.71\ g/cm^3$

Unknown: V

$D = \dfrac{m}{V}$

$V = \dfrac{m}{D}$

$= \dfrac{7.75\ g}{1.71\ g/cm^3} = 4.53\ cm^3$

Practice, p. 45

1. Given: $\text{Value}_{\text{experimental}} =$ 17.7 g
Value$_{\text{accepted}} =$ 21.2 g
Unknown: Percent error

$$\text{Percent error} = \frac{\text{Value}_{\text{experimental}} - \text{Value}_{\text{accepted}}}{\text{Value}_{\text{accepted}}} \times 100$$

$$\text{Percent error} = \frac{17.7\ \text{g} - 21.2\ \text{g}}{21.2\ \text{g}} \times 100 = -17\%$$

2. Given: $\text{Value}_{\text{experimental}} =$ 4.26 mL
Value$_{\text{accepted}} =$ 4.15 mL
Unknown: Percent error

$$\text{Percent error} = \frac{\text{Value}_{\text{experimental}} - \text{Value}_{\text{accepted}}}{\text{Value}_{\text{accepted}}} \times 100$$

$$\text{Percent error} = \frac{4.26\ \text{mL} - 4.15\ \text{mL}}{4.15\ \text{mL}} \times 100 = 2.7\%$$

ATE, Additional Sample Problems, p. 45

C-1. Given: $\text{Value}_{\text{accepted}} =$ 7.44 g/cm^3
Value$_{\text{experimental}} =$ 7.30 g/cm^3
Unknown: Percent error

$$\text{Percent error} = \frac{\text{Value}_{\text{experimental}} - \text{Value}_{\text{accepted}}}{\text{Value}_{\text{accepted}}} \times 100$$

$$\text{Percent error} = \frac{7.30\ \text{g/cm}^3 - 7.44\ \text{g/cm}^3}{7.44\ \text{g/cm}^3} \times 100 = -1.9\%$$

Practice, p. 50

1. Given: 2.099 g
0.05681 g
Unknown: sum of given values

2.099 g + 0.05681 g = 2.156 g

2. Given: 87.3 cm
1.655 cm
Unknown: difference between first and second given value

87.3 cm − 1.655 cm = 85.6 cm

3. Given: length = 1.34 μm
width = 0.7488 μm
Unknown: area

area = length × width

area = 1.34 μm × 0.7488 μm = 1.00 μm^2

4. Given: D = 1.2 g/cm^3
length = 28 cm
width = 22 cm
height = 2×3.0 mm = 6.0 mm = 0.60 cm
Unknown: m

$$D = \frac{m}{V}$$

$V = \text{length} \times \text{width} \times \text{height}$

$m = DV = D \times \text{length} \times \text{width} \times \text{height}$

$m = 1.2\ \text{g/cm}^3 \times 28\ \text{cm} \times 22\ \text{cm} \times 0.60\ \text{cm} = 440\ \text{g}$

ATE, Additional Sample Problems, p. 50

E-1. Given: length = width = height = 3.23 cm
Unknown: V

$V = \text{length} \times \text{width} \times \text{height}$

$V = (3.23\ \text{cm})^3 = 33.7\ \text{cm}^3$

E-2. Given: 67.14 kg $67.14 \text{ kg} + 8.2 \text{ kg} = 75.3 \text{ kg}$
            8.2 kg

       Unknown: sum of given
                 values

E-3. Given: $m = 17.982$ g
            $V = 4.13 \text{ cm}^3$ $D = \dfrac{m}{V} = \dfrac{17.982 \text{ g}}{4.13 \text{ cm}^3} = 4.35 \text{ g/cm}^3$

       Unknown: D

Practice, p. 54

1. Given: $m = 1.73 \times 10^{-3}$ g $D = \dfrac{m}{V}$
            $D = 0.178\ 47$ g/L

       Unknown: V $V = \dfrac{m}{D} = \dfrac{1.73 \times 10^{-3} \text{ g}}{0.178\ 47 \text{ g/L}} = 0.00969 \text{ L}$

                            $V = 9.69 \times 10^{-3} \text{ L} \times \dfrac{1000 \text{ mL}}{\text{L}} = 9.69 \text{ mL}$

2. Given: $m = 6.25 \times 10^5$ g
            $V = 92.5 \text{ cm} \times$ $D = \dfrac{m}{V} = \dfrac{6.25 \times 10^5 \text{ g}}{92.5 \text{ cm} \times 47.3 \text{ cm} \times 85.4 \text{ cm}} = 1.67 \text{ g/cm}^3$
                $47.3 \text{ cm} \times 85.4 \text{ cm}$

       Unknown: D

3. Given: 5.12×10^5 km
       Unknown: length in mm $5.12 \times 10^5 \text{ km} \times \dfrac{10^6 \text{ mm}}{\text{km}} = 5.12 \times 10^{11} \text{ mm}$

4. Given: A clock gains
             0.020 sec/min $6 \text{ mo} \times 30 \dfrac{\text{dy}}{\text{mo}} \times 24 \dfrac{\text{hr}}{\text{dy}} \times 60 \dfrac{\text{min}}{\text{hr}} \times 0.02 \dfrac{\text{sec}}{\text{min}}$

       Unknown: The error
               after six $5184 \text{ s} = 5.2 \times 10^3 \text{ s}$
               months

ATE, Additional Sample Problems, p. 54

F-1. Given: $V = 41.4$ mL
            $m = 58.24$ g $D = \dfrac{m}{V} = \dfrac{58.24 \text{ g}}{41.4 \text{ mL}} = 1.41 \text{ g/mL}$

       Unknown: D

F-2. Given: 6.2×10^7 cm
       Unknown: length in km $6.2 \times 10^7 \text{ cm} \times \dfrac{1 \text{ m}}{10^2 \text{ cm}} \times \dfrac{1 \text{ km}}{10^3 \text{ m}} = 6.2 \times 10^2 \text{ km}$

F-3. Given: 3 weeks (exactly)
       Unknown: time in hours $3 \text{ weeks} \times \dfrac{7 \text{ day}}{\text{week}} \times \dfrac{24 \text{ h}}{\text{day}} = 504 \text{ h}$

Section Review, p. 57

4. a. Given: 52.13 g + $52.13 \text{ g} + 1.7502 \text{ g} = 53.88 \text{ g}$
               1.7502 g

        Unknown: sum of
                 values

4. b. Given: $12 \text{ m} \times 6.41 \text{ m}$

Unknown: product of values

$12 \text{ m} \times 6.41 \text{ m} = 77 \text{ m}^2$

c. Given: $\dfrac{16.25 \text{ g}}{5.1442 \text{ mL}}$

Unknown: quotient of values

$\dfrac{16.25 \text{ g}}{5.1442 \text{ mL}} = 3.159 \text{ g/mL}$

---

5. a. Given: $(1.54 \times 10^{-2} \text{ g}) + (2.86 \times 10^{-1} \text{ g})$

Unknown: sum of values

$1.54 \times 10^{-2} \text{ g} = 0.154 \times 10^{-1} \text{ g}$

$(0.154 \times 10^{-1} \text{ g}) + (2.86 \times 10^{-1} \text{ g}) = 3.01 \times 10^{-1} \text{ g}$

b. Given: $(7.023 \times 10^{9} \text{ g}) - (6.62 \times 10^{7} \text{ g})$

Unknown: difference between values

$6.62 \times 10^{7} \text{ g} = 0.0662 \times 10^{9} \text{ g}$

$(7.023 \times 10^{9} \text{ g}) - (0.0662 \times 10^{9} \text{ g}) = 6.96 \times 10^{9} \text{ g}$

c. Given: $(8.99 \times 10^{-4} \text{ m}) \times (3.57 \times 10^{4} \text{ m})$

Unknown: product of values

$(8.99 \times 10^{-4} \text{ m}) \times (3.57 \times 10^{4} \text{ m}) = 3.21 \times 10^{1} \text{ m}^2$

d. Given: $\dfrac{2.17 \times 10^{-3} \text{ g}}{5.022 \times 10^{4} \text{ mL}}$

Unknown: quotient of values

$\dfrac{2.17 \times 10^{-3} \text{ g}}{5.022 \times 10^{4} \text{ mL}} = 4.32 \times 10^{-8} \text{ g/mL}$

---

7. a. Given: $m_{total} = 215.6 \text{ g}$
$m_{beaker} = 110.4 \text{ g}$

Unknown: m_{oil}

$m_{total} = m_{oil} + m_{beaker}$

$m_{oil} = m_{total} - m_{beaker} = 215.6 \text{ g} - 110.4 \text{ g} = 105.2 \text{ g}$

b. Given: $V_{oil} = 114 \text{ cm}^3$
$m_{oil} = 105.2 \text{ g}$

Unknown: D_{oil}

$D = \dfrac{m}{V}$

$D_{oil} = \dfrac{m_{oil}}{V_{oil}} = \dfrac{105.2 \text{ g}}{114 \text{ cm}^3} = 0.923 \text{ g/cm}^3$

---

8. Given: $V = 5.0 \times 10^{-3} \text{ cm}^3$
$D = 19.3 \text{ g/cm}^3$

Unknown: m

$D = \dfrac{m}{V}$

$m = DV = (19.3 \text{ g/cm}^3)(5.00 \times 10^{-3} \text{ cm}^3) = 9.6 \times 10^{-2} \text{ g}$

Chapter Review

16. Given: length = 0.25 m
width = 6.1 m
height = 4.9 m

Unknown: V

$V = \text{length} \times \text{width} \times \text{height}$

$V = 0.25 \text{ m} \times 6.1 \text{ m} \times 4.9 \text{ m} = 7.5 \text{ m}^3$

17. Given: $m = 5.03$ g
$V = 3.24$ mL

Unknown: D

$$D = \frac{m}{V} = \frac{5.03 \text{ g}}{3.24 \text{ mL}} = 1.55 \text{ g/mL}$$

---

18. Given: $V = 55.1$ cm^3
$D = 6.72$ g/cm^3

Unknown: m

$$D = \frac{m}{V}$$

$$m = DV = (6.72 \text{ g/cm}^3)(55.1 \text{ cm}^3) = 3.70 \times 10^2 \text{ g}$$

---

19. Given: $D = 0.824$ g/mL
$m = 0.451$ g

Unknown: V

$$D = \frac{m}{V}$$

$$V = \frac{m}{D} = \frac{0.451 \text{ g}}{0.824 \text{ g/mL}} = 0.547 \text{ mL}$$

---

20. Given: 882 µg

Unknown: mass in g

$$882 \text{ µg} \times \frac{1 \text{ g}}{1\,000\,000 \text{ µg}} = 8.82 \times 10^{-4} \text{ g}$$

---

21. Given: 0.603 L

Unknown: volume in mL

$$0.603 \text{ L} \times \frac{1000 \text{ mL}}{\text{L}} = 603 \text{ mL} = 6.03 \times 10^2 \text{ mL}$$

---

22. a. Given: $D = 19.3$ g/cm^3
$m = 0.715$ kg

Unknown: V

$$D = \frac{m}{V}$$

$$V = \frac{m}{D} = \frac{0.715 \text{ kg}}{19.3 \text{ g/cm}^3} \times \frac{1000 \text{ g}}{\text{kg}} = 37.0 \text{ cm}^3$$

b. Given: $V = 37.0$ cm^3

Unknown: length of cube's edge

$$V = \text{length}^3$$

$$\text{length} = \sqrt[3]{V} = \sqrt[3]{37.0 \text{ cm}^3} = 3.33 \text{ cm}$$

---

23. a. Given: 92.25 m

Unknown: length in km

$$92.25 \text{ m} \times \frac{1 \text{ km}}{10^3 \text{ m}} = 9.225 \times 10^{-2} \text{ km}$$

b. Given: 9.225×10^{-2} km

Unknown: length in cm

$$9.225 \times 10^{-2} \text{ km} \times \frac{10^3 \text{ m}}{\text{km}} \times \frac{10^2 \text{ cm}}{\text{m}} = 9.225 \times 10^3 \text{ cm}$$

---

35. Given: Value$_\text{experimental}$ = 9.67 g
Value$_\text{accepted}$ = 9.82 g

Unknown: Percent error

$$\text{Percent error} = \frac{\text{Value}_\text{experimental} - \text{Value}_\text{accepted}}{\text{Value}_\text{accepted}} \times 100$$

$$\text{Percent error} = \frac{9.67 \text{ g} - 9.82 \text{ g}}{9.82 \text{ g}} \times 100 = -1.5\%$$

---

36. Given: Value$_\text{accepted}$ = 1.54 g/cm^3
Value$_\text{experimental}$ = 1.25 g/cm^3

Unknown: Percent error

$$\text{Percent error} = \frac{\text{Value}_\text{experimental} - \text{Value}_\text{accepted}}{\text{Value}_\text{accepted}} \times 100$$

$$\text{Percent error} = \frac{1.25 \text{ g/cm}^3 - 1.54 \text{ g/cm}^3}{1.54 \text{ g/cm}^3} \times 100 = -19\%$$

---

37. Given: Value$_\text{experimental}$ = 0.229 cm
Value$_\text{accepted}$ = 0.225 cm

Unknown: Percent error

$$\text{Percent error} = \frac{\text{Value}_\text{experimental} - \text{Value}_\text{accepted}}{\text{Value}_\text{accepted}} \times 100$$

$$\text{Percent error} = \frac{0.229 \text{ cm} - 0.225 \text{ cm}}{0.225 \text{ cm}} \times 100 = 2\%$$

39. Given: 6.078 g
         0.3329 g

    Unknown: sum of given
            values

$6.078 \text{ g} + 0.3329 \text{ g} = 6.411 \text{ g}$

---

40. Given: 7.11 cm
         8.2 cm

    Unknown: difference
            between sec-
            ond and first
            given value

$8.2 \text{ cm} - 7.11 \text{ cm} = 1.1 \text{ cm}$

---

41. Given: 0.8102 m
         3.44 m

    Unknown: product of
            given values

$0.8102 \text{ m} \times 3.44 \text{ m} = 2.79 \text{ m}^2$

---

42. Given: 94.20 g
         3.167 22 mL

    Unknown: first given
            value divided
            by second
            given value

$$\frac{94.20 \text{ g}}{3.167\ 22 \text{ mL}} = 29.74 \text{ g/mL}$$

---

45. Given: 0.002115 m
         0.0000405 m

    Unknown: product of
            values in
            scientific
            notation with
            the correct
            number of
            significant
            figures

$0.002115 \text{ m} \times 0.0000405 \text{ m} = 8.57 \times 10^{-8} \text{ m}^2$

---

46. Given: $m = 2.03 \times 10^{-3}$ g
         $D = 9.133 \times$
            10^{-1} g/cm^3

    Unknown: V

$D = \dfrac{m}{V}$

$V = \dfrac{m}{D}$

$V = \dfrac{2.03 \times 10^{-3} \text{ g}}{9.133 \times 10^{-1} \text{ g/cm}^3} = 2.22 \times 10^{-3} \text{ cm}^3$

The unit of volume, cm^3, is correct. An order-of-magnitude estimate would put the answer at about 1/1000 cm^3. The correct number of significant digits is three.

---

47. Given: $m_1 = 100.6$ kg
         $m_2 = 96.4$ kg

    Unknown: given values
            expressed in
            scientific
            notation,
            difference
            between first
            and second
            given values

$m_1 = 1.006 \times 10^2$ kg

$m_2 = 9.64 \times 10^1$ kg

$m_1 - m_2 = 100.6 \text{ kg} - 96.41 \text{ kg} = 4.2 \text{ kg}$

48. Given: length = 1.07×10^2 m
width = 31 m
height = 4.25×10^2 m

Unknown: V

$V = \text{length} \times \text{width} \times \text{height}$

$V = (1.07 \times 10^2 \text{ m})(31 \text{ m})(4.25 \times 10^2 \text{ m})$

$V = 1.4 \times 10^6 \text{ m}^3$

---

49. Given: $m = 57.6$ g
$V = 40.25 \text{ cm}^3$

Unknown: D

$D = \dfrac{m}{V} = \dfrac{57.6 \text{ g}}{40.25 \text{ cm}^3} = 1.43 \text{ g/cm}^3$

---

50. Given: 0.947 mg

Unknown: mass in g and kg

$0.947 \text{ mg} \times \dfrac{1 \text{ g}}{10^3 \text{ mg}} = 9.47 \times 10^{-4} \text{ g}$

$9.47 \times 10^{-4} \text{ g} \times \dfrac{1 \text{ kg}}{10^3 \text{ g}} = 9.47 \times 10^{-7} \text{ kg}$

---

51. Given: $\text{Value}_{\text{experimental}} = 6.80 \text{ g/cm}^3$
$\text{Value}_{\text{accepted}} = 7.86 \text{ g/cm}^3$

Unknown: Percent error

$\text{Percent error} = \dfrac{\text{Value}_{\text{experimental}} - \text{Value}_{\text{accepted}}}{\text{Value}_{\text{accepted}}} \times 100$

$\text{Percent error} = \dfrac{6.80 \text{ g/cm}^3 - 7.86 \text{ g/cm}^3}{7.86 \text{ g/cm}^3} \times 100 = -13.5\%$

---

52. Given: $r_{\text{Li}} = 152$ pm
$r_{\text{Na}} = 186$ pm
$r_{\text{K}} = 235$ pm
$r_{\text{Rb}} = 248$ pm
$r_{\text{Cs}} = 265$ pm
$r_{\text{Fr}} = 270$ pm

Unknown: $V_{\text{Li}}, V_{\text{Na}}, V_{\text{K}}, V_{\text{Rb}}, V_{\text{Cs}}, V_{\text{Fr}},$

$V = \frac{4}{3} \pi r^3$

$V_{\text{Li}} = \frac{4}{3} \pi (r_{\text{Li}})^3 = \frac{4}{3} \pi (152 \text{ pm})^3 = 1.47 \times 10^7 \text{ pm}^3$

$V_{\text{Na}} = \frac{4}{3} \pi (r_{\text{Na}})^3 = \frac{4}{3} \pi (186 \text{ pm})^3 = 2.70 \times 10^7 \text{ pm}^3$

$V_{\text{K}} = \frac{4}{3} \pi (r_{\text{K}})^3 = \frac{4}{3} \pi (235 \text{ pm})^3 = 5.44 \times 10^7 \text{ pm}^3$

$V_{\text{Rb}} = \frac{4}{3} \pi (r_{\text{Rb}})^3 = \frac{4}{3} \pi (248 \text{ pm})^3 = 6.39 \times 10^7 \text{ pm}^3$

$V_{\text{Cs}} = \frac{4}{3} \pi (r_{\text{Cs}})^3 = \frac{4}{3} \pi (265 \text{ pm})^3 = 7.80 \times 10^7 \text{ pm}^3$

$V_{\text{Fr}} = \frac{4}{3} \pi (r_{\text{Fr}})^3 = \frac{4}{3} \pi (270 \text{ pm})^3 = 8.24 \times 10^7 \text{ pm}^3$

---

53. Given: $r_{\text{Na}} = 186$ pm
length = 5.00 cm

Unknown: number of Na atoms

length = (number of Na atoms)(diameter of one Na atom)

$\quad$ = (number of Na atoms)$(2r_{\text{Na}})$

$\text{number of Na atoms} = \dfrac{\text{length}}{2r_{\text{Na}}}$

$1 \text{ cm} = 10^{10} \text{ pm}$

$\text{number of Na atoms} = \dfrac{5.00 \text{ cm}}{(2)(186 \text{ pm})} \times \dfrac{10^{10} \text{ pm}}{\text{cm}} = 1.34 \times 10^8 \text{ Na atoms}$

---

54. a. Given: $V_{\text{Na}} = 3.00 \text{ cm} \times 5.00 \text{ cm} \times 5.00 \text{ cm} = 75.0 \text{ cm}^3$
$m_{\text{Na}} = 75.5$ g

Unknown: D_{Na}

$D = \dfrac{m}{V}$

$D_{\text{Na}} = \dfrac{m_{\text{Na}}}{V_{\text{Na}}} = \dfrac{75.5 \text{ g}}{75.0 \text{ cm}^3} = 1.01 \text{ g/cm}^3$

54. b. Given: $\text{Value}_{\text{experimental}} =$ 1.01 g/cm³
Value$_{\text{accepted}} =$ 0.971 g/cm³

Unknown: Percent error

$$\text{Percent error} = \frac{\text{Value}_{\text{experimental}} - \text{Value}_{\text{accepted}}}{\text{Value}_{\text{accepted}}} \times 100$$

$$\text{Percent error} = \frac{1.01 \text{ g/cm}^3 - 0.971 \text{ g/cm}^3}{0.971 \text{ g/cm}^3} \times 100 = 4\,\%$$

58. a. Given: Total fat per serving = 2 g
Calories from fat per serving = 15 Calories

Unknown: conversion factor in Calories per gram

15 Cal = 2 g fat

$$\frac{15 \text{ Cal}}{2 \text{ g}} = 8 \text{ Cal/g}$$

b. Given: Serving size = 30 g
Number of servings = 20

Unknown: mass of total in kg

total mass = m_{tot} = Serving size × Number of servings

$$m_{\text{tot}} = (30 \text{ g})(20) \times \frac{1 \text{ kg}}{1000 \text{ g}} = 0.6 \text{ kg}$$

c. Given: 2 g
Unknown: mass in μg

$$2 \text{ g} \times \frac{10^6 \text{ μg}}{\text{g}} = 2 \times 10^6 \text{ μg}$$

Standardized Test Prep, p. 63

8. Given: 23 456 mg
Unknown: this quantity expressed in grams

$$23\,456 \text{ mg} \times \frac{0.001 \text{ g}}{1 \text{ mg}} = 23.456 \text{ g}$$

9. Given: a mass of 45.65 g and a volume of 16.9 cm³

Unknown: the density of the metal

$$\text{density} = \frac{\text{mass}}{\text{volume}} = \frac{45.65 \text{ g}}{16.9 \text{ cm}^3}$$

$$\text{density} = 2.70 \text{ g/cm}^3$$

CHAPTER 3

Atoms: the Building Blocks of Matter

Practice, p. 80

1. Given: name and mass number of bromine-80

Unknown: number of protons, electrons, and neutrons

atomic number = number of protons = number of electrons
mass number = number of neutrons + number of protons.

For bromine, the atomic number = 35
For bromine-80, the mass number = 80

number of protons = 35 protons
number of electrons = 35 electrons

number of neutrons = mass number − atomic number = 80 − 35
number of neutrons = 45 neutrons

2. Given: name and mass number of carbon-13

Unknown: nuclear symbol for carbon-13

chemical symbol for carbon: C
atomic number for carbon = 6 (located at lower left of symbol)
mass number for carbon-13 = 13 (located at upper left of symbol)

carbon-13: $^{13}_{6}\text{C}$

3. Given: element that has 15 electrons and 15 neutrons

Unknown: hyphen notation for given element nuclide

atomic number = number of protons = number of electrons
mass number = number of protons + number of neutrons

atomic number = 15 (element is phosphorus)

mass number = 15 protons + 15 neutrons = 30

nuclide is phosphorus-30

ATE, Additional Sample Problems, p. 80

A-1. Given: name and mass number of carbon-13

Unknown: number of protons, electrons, and neutrons

atomic number = number of protons = number of electrons
mass number = number of neutrons + number of protons

For carbon, the atomic number = 6
For carbon-13, the mass number = 13

number of protons = 6 protons
number of electrons = 6 electrons
number of neutrons = mass number − atomic number = 13 − 6
number of neutrons = 7 neutrons

A-2. Given: name and mass number of oxygen-16

Unknown: nuclear symbol for oxygen-16

chemical symbol for oxygen: O

atomic number for oxygen = 8 (located at lower left of symbol)
mass number for oxygen-16 = 16 (located at upper left of symbol)

oxygen-18: $^{16}_{8}\text{O}$

A-3. Given: element that has 7 electrons and 9 neutrons

Unknown: hyphen notation for given nuclide

atomic number = number of protons = number of electrons

mass number = number of protons + number of neutrons
atomic number = 7 (element is nitrogen)
mass number = 7 protons + 9 neutrons = 16
nuclide is nitrogen-16

ATE, Additional Sample Problems, p. 84

B-1. Given: 3.6 mol C

Unknown: mass of C in grams

$$3.6 \text{ mol C} \times \frac{12.01 \text{ g C}}{\text{mol C}} = 43 \text{ g C}$$

B-2. Given: 0.733 mol S

Unknown: mass of S in grams

$$0.733 \text{ mol S} \times \frac{32.07 \text{ g S}}{\text{mol S}} = 23.5 \text{ g S}$$

Practice B, p. 85

1. Given: 2.25 mol Fe

Unknown: mass of Fe in grams

$$2.25 \text{ mol Fe} \times \frac{55.85 \text{ g Fe}}{\text{mol Fe}} = 126 \text{ g Fe}$$

2. Given: 0.375 mol K

Unknown: mass of K in grams

$$0.375 \text{ mol K} \times \frac{39.10 \text{ g K}}{\text{mol K}} = 14.7 \text{ g K}$$

3. Given: 0.0135 mol Na

Unknown: mass of Na in grams

$$0.0135 \text{ mol Na} \times \frac{22.99 \text{ g Na}}{\text{mol Na}} = 0.310 \text{ g Na}$$

4. Given: 16.3 mol Ni

Unknown: mass of Ni in grams

$$16.3 \text{ mol Ni} \times \frac{58.69 \text{ g Ni}}{\text{mol Ni}} = 957 \text{ g Ni}$$

Practice C, p. 85

1. Given: 5.00 g Ca

Unknown: amount of Ca in moles

$$5.00 \text{ g Ca} \times \frac{\text{mol Ca}}{40.08 \text{ g Ca}} = 0.125 \text{ mol Ca}$$

2. Given: 3.60×10^{-5} g Au

Unknown: amount of Au in moles

$$3.60 \times 10^{-5} \text{ g Au} \times \frac{\text{mol Au}}{196.97 \text{ g Au}} = 1.83 \times 10^{-7} \text{ mol Au}$$

3. Given: 0.595 g of Zn

Unknown: Number of mols of Zn

$$0.535 \text{ g} \times \frac{1 \text{ mol}}{65.38 \text{ g Zn}} = 8.18 \times 10^{-3} \text{ mol Zn}$$

ATE, Additional Sample Problems, p. 85

C-1. Given: 3.22 g Cu
Unknown: amount of Cu in moles

$$3.22 \text{ g Cu} \times \frac{\text{mol Cu}}{63.55 \text{ g Cu}} = 0.0507 \text{ mol Cu}$$

C-2. Given: 2.72×10^{-4} g Li
Unknown: amount of Li in moles

$$2.72 \times 10^{-4} \text{ g Li} \times \frac{\text{mol Li}}{6.94 \text{ g Li}} = 3.92 \times 10^{-5} \text{ mol Li}$$

Practice, p. 86

1. Given: 1.50×10^{12} atoms Pb
Unknown: amount of Pb in moles

$$1.50 \times 10^{12} \text{ Pb atoms} \times \frac{\text{mol Pb}}{6.022 \times 10^{23} \text{ Pb atoms}} = 2.49 \times 10^{-12} \text{ mol Pb}$$

2. Given: 2500 atoms Sn
Unknown: amount of Sn in moles

$$2500 \text{ Sn atoms} \times \frac{\text{mol Sn}}{6.022 \times 10^{23} \text{ Sn atoms}} = 4.2 \times 10^{-21} \text{ mol Sn}$$

3. Given: 2.75 mol Al
Unknown: number of Al atoms

$$2.75 \text{ mol Al} \times \frac{6.022 \times 10^{23} \text{ Al atoms}}{\text{mol Al}} = 1.66 \times 10^{24} \text{ Al atoms}$$

ATE, Additional Sample Problems, p. 86

D-1. Given: 2.25×10^{22} atoms C
Unknown: amount of C in moles

$$2.25 \times 10^{22} \text{ C atoms} \times \frac{\text{mol C}}{6.022 \times 10^{23} \text{ C atoms}} = 0.0374 \text{ mol C}$$

D-2. Given: 2×10^{6} atoms O
Unknown: amount of O in moles

$$2 \times 10^{6} \text{ O atoms} \times \frac{\text{mol O}}{6.022 \times 10^{23} \text{ O atoms}} = 3 \times 10^{-18} \text{ mol O}$$

D-3. Given: 3.80 mol Na
Unknown: number of Na atoms

$$3.80 \text{ mol Na} \times \frac{6.022 \times 10^{23} \text{ Na atoms}}{\text{mol Na}} = 2.29 \times 10^{24} \text{ Na atoms}$$

E-1. Given: 5.0×10^{9} atoms Ne
Unknown: mass of Ne in grams

$$5.0 \times 10^{9} \text{ Ne atoms} \times \frac{\text{mol Ne}}{6.022 \times 10^{23} \text{ Ne atoms}} \times \frac{20.18 \text{ g Ne}}{\text{mol Ne}}$$
$$= 1.7 \times 10^{-13} \text{ g Ne}$$

E-2. Given: 0.020 g C
Unknown: number of C atoms

$$0.020 \text{ g C} \times \frac{\text{mol C}}{12.01 \text{ g C}} \times \frac{6.022 \times 10^{23} \text{ C atoms}}{\text{mol C}} = 1.0 \times 10^{21} \text{ C atoms}$$

E-3. Given: 10.0 g B
Unknown: mass of Ag with same number of atoms as 10.0 g B

One mole of boron has the same number of atoms as one mole of silver. Therefore

1 mol B = 1 mol Ag

$$10.0 \text{ g B} \times \frac{\text{mol B}}{10.87 \text{ g B}} \times \frac{\text{mol Ag}}{\text{mol B}} \times \frac{107.87 \text{ g Ag}}{\text{mol Ag}} = 99.8 \text{ g Ag}$$

Practice, p. 87

1. Given: 7.5×10^{15} atoms Ni

Unknown: mass of Ni in grams

$$7.5 \times 10^{15} \text{ Ni atoms} \times \frac{\text{mol Ni}}{6.022 \times 10^{23} \text{ Ni atoms}} \times \frac{58.69 \text{ g Ni}}{\text{mol Ni}}$$

$$= 7.3 \times 10^{-7} \text{ g Ni}$$

2. Given: 4.00 g S
Unknown: number of S atoms

$$4.00 \text{ g S} \times \frac{\text{mol S}}{32.07 \text{ g S}} \times \frac{6.022 \times 10^{23} \text{ S atoms}}{\text{mol S}} = 7.51 \times 10^{22} \text{ S atoms}$$

3. Given: 9.0 g Al
Unknown: mass of Au with same number of atoms as 9.0 g Al

1 mol Al = 1 mol Au

$$9.0 \text{ g Al} \times \frac{\text{mol Al}}{26.98 \text{ g Al}} \times \frac{\text{mol Au}}{\text{mol Al}} \times \frac{196.97 \text{ g Au}}{\text{mol Au}} = 66 \text{ g Au}$$

Section Review, p. 87

2. a. Given: name and mass number of sodium-23

Unknown: number of protons, electrons, and neutrons

atomic number = number of protons = number of electrons
mass number = number of neutrons + number of protons

For sodium, the atomic number = 11
For sodium-23, the mass number = 23

number of protons = 11 protons
number of electrons = 11 electrons
number of neutrons = mass number – atomic number = 23 – 11
number of neutrons = 12 neutrons

b. Given: name and mass number of calcium-40

Unknown: number of protons, electrons, and neutrons

atomic number = number of protons = number of electrons
mass number = number of neutrons + number of protons

For calcium, the atomic number = 20
For calcium-40, the mass number = 40

number of protons = 20 protons
number of electrons = 20 electrons

number of neutrons = mass number – atomic number = 40 – 20
number of neutrons = 20 neutrons

c. Given: $^{64}_{29}Cu$

Unknown: number of protons, electrons, and neutrons

atomic number = number of protons = number of electrons = 29
mass number = number of neutrons + number of protons = 64

number of neutrons = mass number − atomic number = 64 − 29 = 35
number of protons = 29 protons
number of electrons = 29 electrons
number of neutrons = 35 neutrons

d. Given: $^{108}_{47}Ag$

Unknown: number of protons, electrons, and neutrons

atomic number = number of protons = number of electrons = 47

mass number = number of neutrons + number of protons = 108
number of neutrons = mass number − atomic number = 108 − 47 = 61

number of protons = 47 protons
number of electrons = 47 electrons
number of neutrons = 61 neutrons

3. a. Given: mass number = 28, atomic number = 14

Unknown: nuclear symbol and hyphen notation for given nuclide

atomic number = number of protons
element with 14 protons: silicon, Si

nuclear symbol → $^{28}_{14}Si$

hyphen notation → Silicon-28

b. Given: element that has 26 protons and 30 neutrons

Unknown: nuclear symbol and hyphen notation for given nuclide

atomic number = number of protons = 26
element with 26 protons: iron, Fe
mass number = number of neutrons + number of protons = 30 + 26 = 56

nuclear symbol → $^{56}_{26}Fe$

hyphen notation → iron-56

5. a. Given: 2.00 mol N

Unknown: mass of N in grams

$2.00 \text{ mol N} \times \dfrac{14.01 \text{ g N}}{\text{mol N}} = 28.0 \text{ g N}$

b. Given: 3.01×10^{23} atoms Cl

Unknown: mass of Cl in grams

$3.01 \times 10^{23} \text{ Cl atoms} \times \dfrac{\text{mol Cl}}{6.022 \times 10^{23} \text{ Cl atoms}} \times \dfrac{35.45 \text{ g Cl}}{\text{mol Cl}} = 17.7 \text{ g Cl}$

6. a. Given: 12.15 g Mg

Unknown: amount of Mg in moles

$12.15 \text{ g Mg} \times \dfrac{\text{mol Mg}}{24.30 \text{ g Mg}} = 0.5000 \text{ mol Mg}$

b. Given: 1.50×10^{23} atoms F

Unknown: amount of F in moles

$1.50 \times 10^{23} \text{ F atoms} \times \dfrac{\text{mol F}}{6.022 \times 10^{23} \text{ F atoms}} = 0.249 \text{ mol F}$

7. Given: 2.06 mol Cu + 222 g Ag

Unknown: which is the greater mass; which has the greater number of atoms

$$2.06 \text{ mol} \times \frac{63.55 \text{ g}}{1 \text{ mol}} = 131 \text{ g of Cu}$$

222 g > 131 g Beaker B.

$$222 \text{ g} \times \frac{1 \text{ mol Ag}}{107.87 \text{ g}} = 2.06 \text{ mol Ag}$$

Equal numbers of mols means equal numbers of atoms.

Chapter Review

2. Given: element A with 2 mass units element B with 3 mass units

Unknown: masses of compounds AB and A_2B_3

mass of AB = mass A + mass B = 2 mass units + 3 mass units = 5 mass units

mass of A_2B_3 = (2 × mass A) + (3 × mass B)

mass of A_2B_3 = (2)(2 mass units) + (3)(3 mass units) = 13 mass units

8. Given: isotopes Si-28, Si-29, and Si-30

Unknown: number of protons, electrons, and neutrons

atomic number = number of protons = number of electrons
mass number = number of neutrons + number of protons
number of neutrons = mass number − atomic number
atomic number for Si (silicon) = 14

all Si isotopes have 14 protons and 14 electrons

mass number for Si-28 = 28
number of neutrons = 28 − 14 = 14

mass number for Si-29 = 29
number of neutrons = 29 − 14 = 15

mass number for Si-30 = 30
number of neutrons = 30 − 14 = 16

11. a. Given: atomic number = 2, mass number = 4

Unknown: hyphen notation for given isotope

atomic number = 2 → element is helium

isotope is helium-4

b. Given: atomic number = 8, mass number = 16

Unknown: hyphen notation for given isotope

atomic number = 8 → element is oxygen

isotope is oxygen-16

c. Given: atomic number = 19, mass number = 39

Unknown: hyphen notation for given isotope

atomic number = 19 → element is potassium
isotope is potassium-39

13. a. Given: atom with $\frac{1}{3}$ mass of carbon-12

Unknown: atomic mass of given atom

mass of carbon-12 = 12 amu

mass of given element = $\frac{1}{3}$(12 amu) = 4 amu

b. Given: atom with 4.5 times mass of carbon-12

Unknown: atomic mass of given atom

mass of carbon-12 = 12 amu

mass of given element = (4.5)(12 amu) = 54 amu

---

17. a. Given: 1.00 mol Li

Unknown: mass of Li in grams

$$1.00 \text{ mol Li} \times \frac{6.94 \text{ g Li}}{\text{mol Li}} = 6.94 \text{ g Li}$$

b. Given: 1.00 mol Al

Unknown: mass of Al in grams

$$1.00 \text{ mol Al} \times \frac{26.98 \text{ g Al}}{\text{mol Al}} = 27.0 \text{ g Al}$$

c. Given: 1.00 molar mass Ca

Unknown: mass of Ca in grams

$$\frac{40.08 \text{ g Ca}}{\text{mol Ca}} \times 1.00 \text{ mol Ca} = 40.1 \text{ g Ca}$$

d. Given: 1.00 molar mass Fe

Unknown: mass of Fe in grams

$$\frac{55.85 \text{ g Fe}}{\text{mol Fe}} \times 1.00 \text{ mol Fe} = 55.8 \text{ g Fe}$$

e. Given: 6.022×10^{23} atoms C

Unknown: mass of C in grams

$$6.022 \times 10^{23} \text{ C atoms} \times \frac{\text{mol C}}{6.022 \times 10^{23} \text{ C atoms}} \times \frac{12.01 \text{ g C}}{\text{mol C}} = 12.01 \text{ g C}$$

f. Given: 6.022×10^{23} atoms Ag

Unknown: mass of Ag in grams

$$6.022 \times 10^{23} \text{ Ag atoms} \times \frac{\text{mol Ag}}{6.022 \times 10^{23} \text{ Ag atoms}} \times \frac{107.87 \text{ g Ag}}{\text{mol Ag}}$$

$$= 107.9 \text{ g Ag}$$

---

18. a. Given: 6.022×10^{23} atoms Ne

Unknown: amount of Ne in moles

$$6.022 \times 10^{23} \text{ Ne atoms} \times \frac{\text{mol Ne}}{6.022 \times 10^{23} \text{ Ne atoms}} = 1.000 \text{ mol Ne}$$

b. Given: 3.011×10^{23} atoms Mg

Unknown: amount of Mg in moles

$$3.011 \times 10^{23} \text{ Mg atoms} \times \frac{\text{mol Mg}}{6.022 \times 10^{23} \text{ Mg atoms}} = 0.5000 \text{ mol Mg}$$

c. Given: 3.25×10^5 g Pb

Unknown: amount of Pb in moles

$$3.25 \times 10^5 \text{ g Pb} \times \frac{\text{mol Pb}}{207.2 \text{ g Pb}} = 1.57 \times 10^3 \text{ mol Pb}$$

d. Given: 4.50×10^{-12} g O

Unknown: amount of O in moles

$$4.50 \times 10^{-12} \text{ g O} \times \frac{\text{mol O}}{16.00 \text{ g O}} = 2.81 \times 10^{-13} \text{ mol O}$$

---

19. Given: mass of argon-36 = 35.97 amu, abundance = 0.337 %
mass of argon-38 = 37.96 amu, abundance = 0.063 %
mass of argon-40 = 39.96 amu, abundance = 99.600 %

Unknown: average atomic mass of Ar to two decimal places

average atomic mass Ar = (mass argon-36)(abundance argon-36)
+ (mass argon-38)(abundance argon-38)
+ (mass argon-40)(abundance argon-40)

average atomic mass Ar = (35.97 amu)(0.00337) + (37.96 amu)(0.00063)
+ (39.96 amu)(0.99600)

average atomic mass Ar = 0.121 amu + 0.024 amu + 39.80 amu = 39.95 amu

---

20. Given: mass of boron-11 = 11.01 amu, abundance = 80.20 %
abundance of unknown isotope = 19.80 %
average atomic mass B = 10.81 amu

Unknown: atomic mass of unknown isotope

average atomic mass B = (mass boron-11)(abundance boron-11) + (mass unknown isotope)(abundance unknown isotope)

mass unknown isotope

$$= \frac{\text{average atomic mass B} - (\text{mass boron-11})(\text{abundance boron-11})}{\text{abundance unknown isotope}}$$

$$\text{mass unknown isotope} = \frac{10.81 \text{ amu} - (11.01 \text{ amu})(0.8020)}{0.1980} = \frac{1.98 \text{ amu}}{0.1980}$$

mass unknown isotope of boron = 10.00 amu

---

21. a. Given: 1.50 mol Na

Unknown: number of Na atoms

$$1.50 \text{ mol Na} \times \frac{6.022 \times 10^{23} \text{ Na atoms}}{\text{mol Na}} = 9.03 \times 10^{23} \text{ Na atoms}$$

b. Given: 6.755 mol Pb

Unknown: number of Pb atoms

$$6.755 \text{ mol Pb} \times \frac{6.022 \times 10^{23} \text{ Pb atoms}}{\text{mol Pb}} = 4.068 \times 10^{24} \text{ Pb atoms}$$

c. Given: 7.02 g Si

Unknown: number of Si atoms

$$7.02 \text{ g Si} \times \frac{\text{mol Si}}{28.09 \text{ g Si}} \times \frac{6.022 \times 10^{23} \text{ Si atoms}}{\text{mol Si}} = 1.50 \times 10^{23} \text{ Si atoms}$$

---

22. a. Given: 3.011×10^{23} atoms F

Unknown: mass of F in grams

$$3.011 \times 10^{23} \text{ F atoms} \times \frac{\text{mol F}}{6.022 \times 10^{23} \text{ F atoms}} \times \frac{19.00 \text{ g F}}{\text{mol F}} = 9.500 \text{ g F}$$

b. Given: 1.50×10^{23} atoms Mg

Unknown: mass of Mg in grams

$$1.50 \times 10^{23} \text{ Mg atoms} \times \frac{\text{mol Mg}}{6.022 \times 10^{23} \text{ Mg atoms}} \times \frac{24.30 \text{ g Mg}}{\text{mol Mg}} = 6.05 \text{ g Mg}$$

c. Given: 4.50×10^{12} atoms Cl

Unknown: mass of Cl in grams

$$4.50 \times 10^{12} \text{ Cl atoms} \times \frac{\text{mol Cl}}{6.022 \times 10^{23} \text{ Cl atoms}} \times \frac{35.45 \text{ g Cl}}{\text{mol Cl}}$$

$$= 2.65 \times 10^{-10} \text{ Cl}$$

d. Given: 8.42×10^{18} atoms Br

Unknown: mass of Br in grams

$$8.42 \times 10^{18} \text{ Br atoms} \times \frac{\text{mol Br}}{6.022 \times 10^{23} \text{ Br atoms}} \times \frac{79.90 \text{ g Br}}{\text{mol Br}}$$

$$= 1.12 \times 10^{-3} \text{ g Br}$$

e. Given: 25 atoms W

Unknown: mass of W in grams

$$25 \text{ W atoms} \times \frac{\text{mol W}}{6.022 \times 10^{23} \text{ W atoms}} \times \frac{183.84 \text{ g W}}{\text{mol W}} = 7.6 \times 10^{-21} \text{ W}$$

f. Given: 1 atom Au

Unknown: mass of Au in grams

$$1 \text{ Au atom} \times \frac{\text{mol Au}}{6.022 \times 10^{23} \text{ Au atoms}} \times \frac{196.97 \text{ g Au}}{\text{mol Au}} = 3 \times 10^{-22} \text{ g Au}$$

---

23. a. Given: 5.40 g B

Unknown: number of B atoms

$$5.40 \text{ g B} \times \frac{\text{mol B}}{10.81 \text{ g B}} \times \frac{6.022 \times 10^{23} \text{ B atoms}}{\text{mol B}} = 3.01 \times 10^{23} \text{ B atoms}$$

b. Given: 0.250 mol S

Unknown: number of S atoms

$$0.250 \text{ mol S} \times \frac{6.022 \times 10^{23} \text{ S atoms}}{\text{mol S}} = 1.51 \times 10^{23} \text{ S atoms}$$

c. Given: 0.0384 mol K

Unknown: number of K atoms

$$0.0384 \text{ mol K} \times \frac{6.022 \times 10^{23} \text{ K atoms}}{\text{mol K}} = 2.31 \times 10^{22} \text{ K atoms}$$

d. Given: 0.025 50 g Pt

Unknown: number of Pt atoms

$$0.025 \, 50 \text{ g Pt} \times \frac{\text{mol Pt}}{195.08 \text{ g Pt}} \times \frac{6.022 \times 10^{23} \text{ Pt atoms}}{\text{mol Pt}}$$

$$= 7.872 \times 10^{19} \text{ Pt atoms}$$

e. Given: 1.00×10^{-10} g Au

Unknown: number of Au atoms

$$1.00 \times 10^{-10} \text{ g Au} \times \frac{\text{mol Au}}{196.97 \text{ g Au}} \times \frac{6.022 \times 10^{23} \text{ Au atoms}}{\text{mol Au}}$$

$$= 3.06 \times 10^{11} \text{ Au atoms}$$

---

24. a. Given: 3.00 mol Al

Unknown: mass of Al in grams

$$3.00 \text{ mol Al} \times \frac{26.98 \text{ g Al}}{\text{mol Al}} = 80.9 \text{ g Al}$$

b. Given: 2.56×10^{24} atoms Li

Unknown: mass of Li in grams

$$2.56 \times 10^{24} \text{ Li atoms} \times \frac{\text{mol Li}}{6.022 \times 10^{23} \text{ Li atoms}} \times \frac{6.94 \text{ g Li}}{\text{mol Li}} = 29.5 \text{ g Li}$$

c. Given: 1.38 mol N

Unknown: mass of N in grams

$$1.38 \text{ mol N} \times \frac{14.01 \text{ g N}}{\text{mol N}} = 19.3 \text{ g N}$$

d. Given: 4.86×10^{24} atoms Au

Unknown: mass of Au in grams

$$4.86 \times 10^{24} \text{ Au atoms} \times \frac{\text{mol Au}}{6.022 \times 10^{23} \text{ Au atoms}} \times \frac{196.97 \text{ g Au}}{\text{mol Au}} = 1590 \text{ g Au}$$

e. Given: 6.50 mol Cu

Unknown: mass of Cu in grams

$$6.50 \text{ mol Cu} \times \frac{63.55 \text{ g Cu}}{\text{mol Cu}} = 413 \text{ g Cu}$$

f. Given: 2.57×10^8 mol S

Unknown: mass of S in grams

$$2.57 \times 10^8 \text{ mol S} \times \frac{32.07 \text{ g S}}{\text{mol S}} = 8.24 \times 10^9 \text{ g S}$$

g. Given: 1.05×10^{18} atoms Hg

Unknown: mass of Hg in grams

$$1.05 \times 10^{18} \text{ Hg atoms} \times \frac{\text{mol Hg}}{6.022 \times 10^{23} \text{ Hg atoms}} \times \frac{200.59 \text{ g Hg}}{\text{mol Hg}}$$

$$= 3.50 \times 10^{-4} \text{ g Hg}$$

---

28. a. Given: 40.1 g Ca

Unknown: amount of Ca in moles

$$40.1 \text{ g Ca} \times \frac{\text{mol Ca}}{40.08 \text{ g Ca}} = 1.00 \text{ mol Ca}$$

b. Given: 11.5 g Na

Unknown: amount of Na in moles

$$11.5 \text{ g Na} \times \frac{\text{mol Na}}{22.99 \text{ g Na}} = 0.500 \text{ mol Na}$$

c. Given: 5.87 g Ni

Unknown: amount of Ni in moles

$$5.87 \text{ g Ni} \times \frac{\text{mol Ni}}{58.69 \text{ g Ni}} = 0.100 \text{ mol Ni}$$

d. Given: 150 g S

Unknown: amount of S in moles

$$150 \text{ g S} \times \frac{\text{mol S}}{32.07 \text{ g S}} = 4.7 \text{ mol S}$$

e. Given: 2.65 g Fe

Unknown: amount of Fe in moles

$$2.65 \text{ g Fe} \times \frac{\text{mol Fe}}{55.85 \text{ g Fe}} = 0.0474 \text{ mol Fe}$$

f. Given: 0.007 50 g Ag

Unknown: amount of Ag in moles

$$0.007\,50 \text{ g Ag} \times \frac{\text{mol Ag}}{107.87 \text{ g Ag}} = 6.95 \times 10^{-5} \text{ mol Ag}$$

g. Given: 2.25×10^{25} atoms Zn

Unknown: amount of Zn in moles

$$2.25 \times 10^{25} \text{ Zn atoms} \times \frac{\text{mol Zn}}{6.022 \times 10^{23} \text{ Zn atoms}} = 37.4 \text{ mol Zn}$$

h. Given: 50.0 atoms Ba

Unknown: amount of Ba in moles

$$50.0 \text{ Ba atoms} \times \frac{\text{mol Ba}}{6.022 \times 10^{23} \text{ Ba atoms}} = 8.30 \times 10^{-23} \text{ mol Ba}$$

---

30. a. Given: atom with mass 12 times that of carbon-12

Unknown: approximate atomic mass of given atom

atomic mass of carbon-12 = 12.0 amu

unknown mass = (12)(12.0 amu) = 144 amu

b. Given: atom with mass $\frac{1}{2}$ that of carbon-12

Unknown: approximate atomic mass of given atom

atomic mass of carbon-12 = 12.0 amu

unknown mass $= \frac{1}{2}(12.0 \text{ amu}) = 6.0 \text{ amu}$

---

34. Given: 22.58 g/cm³ and 2×10^8 metric tons/cm³

1 metric ton = 1000 kg

Unknown: comparison of the two densities

$$\frac{2 \times 10^8 \text{ m.t.}}{1 \text{ cm}^3} \times \frac{10^3 \text{ kg}}{1 \text{ m.t.}} \times \frac{10^3 \text{ g}}{1 \text{ kg}} = 2 \times 10^{14} \text{ g/cm}^3$$

$$\frac{2 \times 10^{14} \text{ g/cm}^3}{22.58 \text{ g/cm}^3} = 9 \times 10^{12} \text{ times as great}$$

Math Tutor, p. 92

1. a. Given: 2250 mg

Unknown: value in grams

$$2250 \text{ mg} \times \frac{1 \text{ g}}{1000 \text{ mg}} = 2.250 \text{ g}$$

b. Given: 59.3 kL

Unknown: value in liters

$$59.3 \text{ kL} \times \frac{1000 \text{ L}}{1 \text{ kL}} = 5.93 \times 10^4 \text{ L}$$

---

2. a. Given: 0.000072 g

Unknown: value in μg in scientific notation

$$0.000072 \text{ g} \times \frac{10^6 \ \mu\text{g}}{1 \text{ g}} = 7.2 \times 10^{-5} \times 10^6 \ \mu\text{g}$$

$$7.2 \times 10^1 \ \mu\text{g}$$

b. Given: 3.98×10^6 m

Unknown: number of km in scientific notation

$$3.98 \times 10^6 \text{ m} \times \frac{1 \text{ km}}{1000 \text{ m}} = 3.98 \times 10^3 \text{ km}$$

Standardized Test Prep, p. 93

7. Given: atomic number = 50

mass number 119

Unknown: number of neutrons

$$119(n^0 + p^t) - 50(p^t) = 69 \ n^0$$

---

8. Given: 1.50 mol of Na

Unknown: mass of Na

$$1.50 \text{ mol} \times 22.99 \ \frac{\text{g}}{\text{mol}} = 34.485 \text{ g} = 34.5 \text{ g}$$

---

9. Given: 28.0 g of C

Unknown: number of mols

$$28.0 \text{ g} \times \frac{1 \text{ mol}}{12 \text{ g}} = 2.33 \text{ mol}$$

10. Given: K-40 and A-40

Unknown: the element with the most neutrons

Both have the same total number of neutrons plus protons. Since argon has one less proton, it has one more neutron.

---

11. Given: 1.2×10^{23} atoms of P

Unknown: mass of P

$$1.2 \times 10^{23} \text{ atoms} \times \frac{1 \text{ mol}}{6.02 \times 10^{23} \text{ atom}} = 0.199 \text{ mol}$$

$$0.199 \text{ mol} \times 30.97 \frac{\text{g}}{\text{mol}} = 6.16$$

---

13. Given: 19.9% of atomic mass 10.013
80.1% of atomic mass 11.009

Unknown: the average atomic mass

$$10.013 \text{ amu} \times 0.199 + 11.009 \text{ amu} \times 0.801$$

$$1.9925 \text{ amu} + 8.8182 \text{ amu} = 10.811 \text{ amu}$$

CHAPTER 4

Arrangement of Electrons in Atoms

Chapter Review

10. Given: $\lambda = 4.257 \times 10^{-7}$ cm

Unknown: ν

$$c = \lambda \nu$$

$$\nu = \frac{c}{\lambda} = \frac{3.00 \times 10^8 \text{ m/s}}{(4.257 \times 10^{-7} \text{ cm})(10^{-2} \text{ m/cm})}$$

$$\nu = 7.0 \times 10^{16} \text{ Hz}$$

11. Given: $\nu = 3.55 \times 10^{17}$ Hz

Unknown: E_{photon}

$$E_{photon} = h\nu = (6.626 \times 10^{-34} \text{ J} \cdot \text{s})(3.55 \times 10^{17} \text{ Hz})$$

$$E_{photon} = 2.35 \times 10^{-16} \text{ J}$$

12. Given: $E = h\nu$

$$c = \lambda \nu$$

Unknown: equation expressing E in terms of h, c, and λ

$$c = \lambda \nu$$

$$\nu = \frac{c}{\lambda}$$

$$E = h\nu = \frac{hc}{\lambda}$$

$$E = \frac{hc}{\lambda}$$

13. Given: distance = 8.00×10^7 km

Unknown: time that it takes radio wave to travel given distance

$$\text{speed} = c = \frac{\text{distance}}{\text{time}}$$

$$\text{time} = \frac{\text{distance}}{c} = \frac{(8.00 \times 10^7 \text{ km})(10^3 \text{ m/km})}{3.00 \times 10^8 \text{ m/s}}$$

$$\text{time} = 267 \text{ s}$$

14. Given: $\lambda = 1.00 \times 10^{-3}$ nm

Unknown: E_{photon}

$$E_{photon} = h\nu = \frac{hc}{\lambda} = \frac{(6.626 \times 10^{-34} \text{ J} \cdot \text{s})(3.00 \times 10^8 \text{ m/s})}{(1.00 \times 10^{-3} \text{ nm})(10^{-9} \text{ m/nm})}$$

$$E_{photon} = 1.99 \times 10^{-13} \text{ J}$$

44. Given: $c = 3.00 \times 10^8$ m/s

$\nu = 7.500 \times 10^{12}$ Hz

Unknown: λ

$$c = \lambda \nu$$

$$\lambda = \frac{c}{\nu} = \frac{3.00 \times 10^8 \text{ m/s}}{7.500 \times 10^{12} \text{ Hz}}$$

$$\lambda = 4.00 \times 10^{-5} \text{ m}$$

47. Given: $E_{photon} = 1.55 \times 10^{-24}$ J

Unknown: ν

$$E_{photon} = h\nu$$

$$\nu = \frac{E_{photon}}{h} = \frac{1.55 \times 10^{-24} \text{ J}}{6.626 \times 10^{-34} \text{ J} \cdot \text{s}}$$

$$\nu = 2.34 \times 10^9 \text{ Hz}$$

50. a. Given: $E_{photon} = 3.37 \times 10^{-19}$ J

Unknown: ν

$E_{photon} = h\nu$

$\nu = \dfrac{E_{photon}}{h} = \dfrac{3.37 \times 10^{-19} \text{ J}}{6.626 \times 10^{-34} \text{ J} \cdot \text{s}}$

$\nu = 5.09 \times 10^{14}$ Hz

b. Given: $\nu = 5.09 \times 10^{14}$ Hz

Unknown: λ

$c = \lambda\nu$

$\lambda = \dfrac{c}{\nu} = \dfrac{3.00 \times 10^{8} \text{ m/s}}{5.09 \times 10^{14} \text{ Hz}}$

$\lambda = 5.90 \times 10^{-7}$ m

53. Given: $\lambda_{max} = 284$ nm

Unknown: threshold energy of chromium

threshold energy $= E_{photon,\ min} = h\nu_{min}$

$c = \lambda\nu = \lambda_{max}\ \nu_{min}$

$\nu_{min} = \dfrac{c}{\lambda_{max}}$

threshold energy $= h\nu_{min} = \dfrac{hc}{\lambda_{max}} = \dfrac{(6.626 \times 10^{-34} \text{ J} \cdot \text{s})(3.00 \times 10^{8} \text{ m/s})}{(284 \text{ nm})(10^{-9} \text{ m/nm})} =$

7.00×10^{-19} J

Math Tutor, p. 128

1. Given: 72.17% Rb
84.911 amu
27.83% Rb
86.909 amu

Unknown: the average atomic mass

84.911 amu $\times$ 0.7217 + 86.909 amu $\times$ 0.2783

61.28 amu + 24.19 amu

85.47 amu

2. Given: 92.22%
27.976826 amu
4.69%
28.976495 amu
3.09%
29.973773 amu

Unknown: the average atomic mass

0.9222×27.976926 amu $= 25.80$ amu

0.0469×28.976495 amu $= 1.359$ amu

0.0309×29.973770 amu $= \underline{0.9262 \text{ amu}}$

28.12 amu

Standardized Test Prep, p. 129

3. Given: frequency = 88.5 MHz
$c = 3.00 \times 10^{8}$ m/s

Unknown: wavelength

3.00×10^{8} m/s $= \lambda \times 88.5 \times 10^{6}$ s^{-1}

$\lambda = 3.00 \times 10^{8}$ m/s/88.5 $\times 10^{6}$ s^{-1}

$\lambda = 3.4$ m

CHAPTER 6

Chemical Bonding

Practice, p. 177

Given: bonding between Cl and Ca, Cl and O, and Cl and Br

Unknown: classification of each given bond and indication of the more-negative atom in each pair

Using Figure 20 in Chapter 5, the electronegativities of the elements are:

Cl $\rightarrow$ 3.0

Ca $\rightarrow$ 1.0

O $\rightarrow$ 3.5

Br $\rightarrow$ 2.8

In each bonded pair, the element with the greater electronegativity is the more-negative atom.

For each bond, the electronegativity difference is:

Cl and Ca	$3.0 - 1.0 = 2.0$
O and Cl	$3.5 - 3.0 = 0.5$
Cl and Br	$3.0 - 2.8 = 0.2$

Bond type can be determined from Figure 2.

Bonded atoms	Bond type	More-negative atom
Cl and Ca	ionic	Cl ($3.0 > 1.0$)
O and Cl	polar-covalent	O ($3.5 > 3.0$)
Cl and Br	nonpolar-covalent	Cl ($3.0 > 2.8$)

ATE, Additional Sample Problem A-1, p. 217A

Given: table of bonded elements and electronegativity differences

Unknown: bond types and more electronegative of the given atoms in each pair

Elements bonded	Electronegativity difference
a. C and H	0.4
b. C and S	0.0
c. O and H	1.4
d. Na and Cl	2.1
e. Cs and S	1.8

Bond type can be determined from Figure 2.

Elements from Groups 13 through 17 have higher electronegativities than elements from Groups 1 and 2.

Elements bonded	Electronegativity difference	Bond type	More-negative atom
a. C and H	0.4	polar-covalent	C
b. C and S	0.0	nonpolar-covalent	same electronegativity
c. O and H	1.4	polar-covalent	O
d. Na and Cl	2.1	ionic	Cl
e. Cs and S	1.8	ionic	S

3a. Given: H and F

Unknown: type of bond between given atoms

According to Figure 20 in Chapter 5, H and F have electronegativities of 2.1 and 4.0, respectively. The difference in the electronegativities is

$$4.0 - 2.1 = 1.9,$$

which, according to Figure 2, corresponds to an ionic bond.

b. Given: Cu and S

Unknown: type of bond between given atoms

According to Figure 20 in Chapter 5, Cu and S have electronegativities of 1.9 and 2.5, respectively. The difference in the electronegativities is

$$2.5 - 1.9 = 0.6,$$

which, according to Figure 2, corresponds to a polar-covalent bond.

c. Given: I and Br

Unknown: type of bond between given atoms

According to Figure 20 in Chapter 5, I and Br have electronegativities of 2.5 and 2.8, respectively. The difference in the electronegativities is

$$2.8 - 2.5 = 0.3,$$

which, according to Figure 2, corresponds to a polar-covalent bond.

ATE, Additional Sample Problem B-1, p. 184

a. Given: phosphorus

Unknown: electron-dot notation for given element

According to its electron configuration ($[Ne]3s^23p^3$), P has 5 valence electrons (2 + 3). The electron-dot notation for P is therefore

$\cdot\text{P}:$

b. Given: silicon

Unknown: electron-dot notation for given element

According to its electron configuration ($[Ne]3s^23p^2$), Si has 4 valence electrons (2 + 2). The electron-dot notation for Si is therefore

$\cdot\text{Si}\cdot$

c. Given: sulfur

Unknown: electron-dot notation for given element

According to its electron configuration ($[Ne]3s^23p^4$), S has 6 valence electrons (2 + 4). The electron-dot notation for S is therefore

$:\text{S}:$

d. Given: chlorine

Unknown: electron-dot notation for given element

According to its electron configuration ($[Ne]3s^23p^5$), Cl has 7 valence electrons (2 + 5). The electron-dot notation for Cl is therefore

$:\overset{..}{\text{Cl}}:$

e. Given: xenon

Unknown: electron-dot notation for given element

According to its electron configuration ($[Kr]4d^{10}5s^25p^6$), Xe has 8 valence electrons (2 + 6). The electron-dot notation for Xe is therefore

$:\overset{..}{\text{Xe}}:$

a. Given: H_2O

Unknown: the Lewis structure for the given molecule

O has 6 valence electrons. H has one valence electron.

:Ö: H·

Total number of valence electrons:

O $1 \times 6e^- = 6e^-$

H $2 \times 1e^- = 2e^-$
                        $8e^-$

H:Ö:H

b. Given: CH_4

Unknown: the Lewis structure for the given molecule

C has 4 valence electrons. H has one valence electron.

·Ċ·   H·

Total number of valence electrons:

C $1 \times 4e^- = 4e^-$

H $4 \times 1e^- = 4e^-$
                        $8e^-$

        H
H:C:H
        H

c. Given: CH_4O

Unknown: the Lewis structure for the given molecule

C has 4 valence electrons. H has one valence electron. O has 6 valence electrons.

·Ċ·   H·   :Ö:

Total number of valence electrons:

C $1 \times 4e^- = 4e^-$

H $4 \times 1e^- = 4e^-$

O $1 \times 6e^- = 6e^-$
                        $14e^-$

        H
H:C:O:H
        H

d. Given: HCl

Unknown: the Lewis structure for the given molecule

Cl has 7 valence electrons. H has one valence electron.

:C̈l: H·

Total number of valence electrons:

Cl $1 \times 7e^- = 7e^-$

H $1 \times 1e^- = 1e^-$
                        $8e^-$.

H:C̈l:

Practice, p. 186

1. Given: NH_3

Unknown: the Lewis structure for the given molecule

N has 5 valence electrons. H has one valence electron.

·N̈·   H·

Total number of valence electrons:

N $1 \times 5e^- = 5e^-$

H $3 \times 1e^- = 3e^-$
                        $8e^-$

H:N̈:H
  Ḧ

2. Given: H_2S

Unknown: the Lewis structure for the given molecule

S has 6 valence electrons. H has one valence electron.

·S̈·   H·

Total number of valence electrons:

S $1 \times 6e^- = 6e^-$

H $2 \times 1e^- = 2e^-$
                        $8e^-$

H:S̈:H

3. Given: SiH_4

Unknown: the Lewis structure

·Si·   Si has 4 valence electrons.

H·   H has 1 valence electron.

Total = 8 electrons

      H
H:S̈i:H
      H

Octet rule is satisfied for Si.

2 electrons satisfy H.

4. Given: PF_3

Unknown: the Lewis structure

$\cdot \overset{\displaystyle \cdot}{P} \cdot$ P has 5 valence electrons.

$\cdot \overset{\displaystyle \cdot \cdot}{\underset{\displaystyle \cdot \cdot}{F}} \cdot$ Each F has 7 valence electrons.

Total $= 5e^- + (3 \times 7e^-) = 5e^- + 21e^- = 26$ electrons

$$\overset{\displaystyle \cdot \cdot}{\underset{\displaystyle \cdot \cdot}{:F:}}$$
$:\overset{\cdot \cdot}{F} : \overset{\cdot \cdot}{P} : \overset{\cdot \cdot}{F} :$ The octet rule is satisfied for all atoms.

Practice, p. 188

1. Given: CO_2

Unknown: the Lewis structure for the given molecule

C has 4 valence electrons. O has 6 valence electrons.

$\cdot \overset{\displaystyle \cdot}{C} \cdot$ $: \overset{\displaystyle \cdot \cdot}{O} :$

Total number of valence electrons:

C $1 \times 4e^- =\ \ 4e^-$

O $2 \times 6e^- = 12e^-$
$$\overline{\ 16e^-}$$

$\overset{\cdot \cdot}{O} :: \overset{}{C} :: \overset{\cdot \cdot}{O}$, or $\overset{\cdot \cdot}{O} {=} C {=} \overset{\cdot \cdot}{O}$

This configuration gives each atom the correct number of valence electrons (C = 4, O = 6).

2. Given: hydrogen cyanide (HCN)

Unknown: the Lewis structure for the given molecule

C has 4 valence electrons. N has 5 valence electrons. H has one valence electron.

$\cdot \overset{\displaystyle \cdot}{C} :$ $\cdot \overset{\displaystyle \cdot \cdot}{N} \cdot$ $H \cdot$

Total number of valence electrons:

C $1 \times 4e^- = 4e^-$

N $1 \times 5e^- = 5e^-$

H $1 \times 1e^- = 1e^-$
$$\overline{\ 10e^-}$$

$H:C:::N:$, or $H{-}C{\equiv}N:$

This configuration gives each atom the correct number of valence electrons (H = 1, C = 4, N = 5).

ATE, Additional Sample Problem D-1, p. 217A

a. Given: O_2

Unknown: the Lewis structure for the given molecule

O has 6 valence electrons.

$: \overset{\displaystyle \cdot}{O} :$

Total number of valence electrons:

O $2 \times 6e^- = 12e^-$

$\overset{\cdot \cdot}{O} :: \overset{\cdot \cdot}{O}$, or $\overset{\cdot \cdot}{O} {=} \overset{\cdot \cdot}{O}$

This configuration gives each O atom the correct number of valence electrons, 6.

b. Given: C_2H_4

Unknown: the Lewis structure for the given molecule

C has 4 valence electrons. H has one valence electron.

$\cdot\overset{\displaystyle\cdot}{C}\cdot$ $H\cdot$

Total number of valence electrons:

C $2 \times 4e^- = 8e^-$

H $\underline{4 \times 1e^- = 4e^-}$

                $12e^-$

$\begin{matrix} H & H \\ \overset{\displaystyle\cdots}{C} & \overset{\displaystyle\cdots}{C} \\ H & H \end{matrix}$,   or $\begin{matrix} H & & H \\ | & & | \\ C & = & C \\ | & & | \\ H & & H \end{matrix}$

This configuration gives each atom the correct number of valence electrons (C = 4, H = 1).

c. Given: C_2H_2

Unknown: the Lewis structure for the given molecule

C has 4 valence electrons. H has one valence electron.

$\cdot\overset{\displaystyle\cdot}{C}\cdot$ $H\cdot$

Total number of valence electrons:

C $2 \times 4e^- = 8e^-$

H $\underline{2 \times 1e^- = 2e^-}$

                $10e^-$

$H{:}C{:::}C{:}H$,   or $H—C{\equiv}C—H$

This configuration gives each atom the correct number of valence electrons (C = 4, H = 1).

Section Review, p. 189

4a. Given: IBr

Unknown: the Lewis structure for the given molecule

I has 7 valence electrons. Br has 7 valence electrons.

$:\overset{\displaystyle\cdot\cdot}{I}$ $:\overset{\displaystyle\cdot\cdot}{Br}\cdot$

Total number of valence electrons:

I $1 \times 7e^- = 7e^-$

Br $\underline{1 \times 7e^- = 7e^-}$

                $14e^-$

$:\overset{\displaystyle\cdot\cdot}{\underset{\displaystyle\cdot\cdot}{I}}{:}\overset{\displaystyle\cdot\cdot}{\underset{\displaystyle\cdot\cdot}{Br}}{:}$

b. Given: CH_3Br

Unknown: the Lewis structure for the given molecule

C has 4 valence electrons. H has one valence electron. Br has 7 valence electrons.

$\cdot \ddot{C} \cdot$ $H \cdot$ $: \ddot{Br} :$

Total number of valence electrons:

C $1 \times 4e^- = 4e^-$

H $3 \times 1e^- = 3e^-$

Br $1 \times 7e^- = \underline{7e^-}$

$14e^-$

$$\begin{array}{c} H \\ \ddot{} \\ H : C : \ddot{Br} : \\ \\ H \end{array}$$

c. Given: C_2HCl

Unknown: the Lewis structure for the given molecule

C has 4 valence electrons. H has one valence electron. Cl has 7 valence electrons.

$\cdot \dot{C} \cdot$ $H \cdot$ $: \ddot{Cl} :$

Total number of valence electrons:

C $2 \times 4e^- = 8e^-$

H $1 \times 1e^- = 1e^-$

Cl $1 \times 7e^- = \underline{7e^-}$

$16e^-$

$H : C ::: C : \ddot{Cl} :$,   or $H—C≡C—Cl$

This configuration gives each atom the correct number of valence electrons (C = 4, H = 1, Cl = 7).

d. Given: $SiCl_4$

Unknown: the Lewis structure for the given molecule

Si has 4 valence electrons. Cl has 7 valence electrons.

$\cdot \dot{Si} \cdot$ $: \ddot{Cl} :$

Total number of valence electrons:

Si $1 \times 4e^- = 4e^-$

Cl $4 \times 7e^- = 28e^-$

$32e^-$

$$\begin{array}{c} : \ddot{Cl} : \\ : \ddot{Cl} : Si : \ddot{Cl} : \\ : \ddot{Cl} : \end{array}$$

e. Given: F_2O

Unknown: the Lewis structure for the given molecule

F has 7 valence electrons. O has 6 valence electrons.

$: \ddot{F} :$ $: \dot{O} :$

Total number of valence electrons:

F $2 \times 7e^- = 14e^-$

O $1 \times 6e^- = \underline{6e^-}$

$20e^-$

$: \ddot{F} : \ddot{O} : \ddot{F} :$

5. Given: H_2NNH_2 and HNNH

Unknown: the relative strengths of the N–N bonds

$:\overset{\cdot}{N}\cdot$ N has 5 valence electrons.

$H\cdot$ H has 1 valence electron.

$(2 \times 5e^-) + (4 \times 1e^-) = 14e^-$ for H_2NNH_2

$H:\overset{\cdot\cdot}{N}:\overset{\cdot\cdot}{N}:H$ This satisfies the octet and duet rules for 14 electrons.
$\quad\ H\ H$

$(2 \times 5e^-) + (2 \times 1e^-) = 12e^-$ for HNNH

$H:\overset{\cdot\cdot}{N}::\overset{\cdot\cdot}{N}:H$ This satisfies the octet and duet rules for $12e^-$.
The double bond in HNNH is the stronger of the two.

Section Review, p. 194

2a. Given: Li and Cl

Unknown: ionic compounds formed, using electron-dot notation

$Li\cdot$ gives up an electron to form the Li^+ cation. $:\overset{\cdot\cdot}{Cl}:$ acquires an electron to form the $:\overset{\cdot\cdot}{Cl}:^-$ anion.

$Li\cdot + :\overset{\cdot\cdot}{Cl}: \rightarrow Li^+ + :\overset{\cdot\cdot}{Cl}:^- \rightarrow LiCl$

b. Given: Ca and I

Unknown: ionic compounds formed, using electron-dot notation

$\cdot Ca\cdot$ gives up two electrons to form the Ca^{2+} cation. $:\overset{\cdot\cdot}{I}:$ acquires an electron to form the $:\overset{\cdot\cdot}{I}:^-$ anion.

Two iodine anions combine with one calcium cation to form an electrically neutral compound.

$\cdot Ca\cdot + :\overset{\cdot\cdot}{I}: + :\overset{\cdot\cdot}{I}: \rightarrow Ca^{2+} + :\overset{\cdot\cdot}{I}:^- + :\overset{\cdot\cdot}{I}:^- \rightarrow CaI_2$

Practice, p. 199

1a. Given: HI

Unknown: geometry of the given molecule, using VSEPR theory

The molecule has only two atoms, and therefore must be linear.

b. Given: CBr_4

Unknown: geometry of the given molecule, using VSEPR theory

The Lewis structure for CBr_4 is

$\quad\ :\overset{\cdot\cdot}{Br}:$
$:\overset{\cdot\cdot}{Br}:C:\overset{\cdot\cdot}{Br}:$
$\quad\ :\overset{\cdot\cdot}{Br}:$

The octet of electrons around C indicates that the molecule is of the AB_4 type. Its geometry is therefore tetrahedral.

c. Given: $AlBr_3$

Unknown: geometry of the given molecule, using VSEPR theory

The Lewis structure for $AlBr_3$ is

$:\overset{\cdot\cdot}{Br}:Al:\overset{\cdot\cdot}{Br}:$
$\quad\ :\overset{\cdot\cdot}{Br}:$

The molecule is an exception to the octet rule because Al forms only three bonds. Therefore, the molecule is of the AB_3 type and its geometry is trigonal-planar.

d. Given: CH_2Cl_2

Unknown: geometry of the given molecule, using VSEPR theory

The Lewis structure for CH_2Cl_2 is

$$\overset{\displaystyle H}{\underset{\displaystyle H}{:\!\overset{..}{\underset{..}{Cl}}\!:\!\overset{..}{C}\!:\!\overset{..}{\underset{..}{Cl}}\!:}}$$

The octet of electrons around C indicates that the molecule is of the AB_4 type. Its geometry is therefore tetrahedral.

ATE, Additional Sample Problem E-1, p. 199

a. Given: CCl_4

Unknown: geometry of the given molecule, using VSEPR theory

The Lewis structure for CCl_4 is

$$\begin{array}{c} :\overset{..}{Cl}: \\ :\overset{..}{Cl}:\overset{..}{C}:\overset{..}{Cl}: \\ :\overset{..}{Cl}: \end{array}$$

The octet of electrons around C indicates that the molecule is of the AB_4 type. Its geometry is therefore tetrahedral.

b. Given: HCN

Unknown: geometry of the given molecule, using VSEPR theory

The Lewis structure for HCN is

$$H:C:::N:$$

Although there is an octet of electrons around C, six electrons are combined to form a triple bond. The remaining electron pair in the C–H bond is located opposite the triple bond, so that the molecule is of the AB_2 type. Its geometry is therefore linear.

c. Given: $SiBr_4$

Unknown: geometry of the given molecule, using VSEPR theory

The Lewis structure for $SiBr_4$ is

$$\begin{array}{c} :\overset{..}{Br}: \\ :\overset{..}{Br}:\overset{..}{Si}:\overset{..}{Br}: \\ :\overset{..}{Br}: \end{array}$$

The octet of electrons around Si indicates that the molecule is of the AB_4 type. Its geometry is therefore tetrahedral.

Practice, p. 201

1a. Given: $:\overset{..}{F}\!-\!\overset{..}{S}\!-\!\overset{..}{F}:$

Unknown: geometry of the given molecule, using VSEPR theory

The Lewis structure for F_2S indicates that there are two unshared electron pairs on the S atom, as well as two F atoms bonded to the S atom. This arrangement is of the AB_2E_2 type, whose shape is bent or angular.

b. Given: $:\overset{..}{Cl}\!-\!P\!-\!\overset{..}{Cl}:$
$\qquad\qquad |$
$\qquad\quad :\overset{..}{Cl}:$

Unknown: geometry of the given molecule, using VSEPR theory

The Lewis structure for PCl_3 indicates one unshared electron pair and three atoms bonded to the P atom. This arrangement is of the AB_3E type, which has a geometry that is trigonal-pyramidal.

a. Given: AsF_5

Unknown: geometry of the given molecule, using VSEPR theory

The Lewis structure for AsF_5 is

$$\begin{array}{c} :\ddot{F}: \\ | \quad \ddot{F}: \\ :\ddot{F}-As \diagup \\ | \diagdown \ddot{F}: \\ :\ddot{F}: \quad \end{array}$$

The molecule with five single bonds to and no unshared electron pairs on the central atom is of the AB_5 type. Its geometry is trigonal-bipyramidal.

b. Given: SeF_6

Unknown: geometry of the given molecule, using VSEPR theory

The Lewis structure for SeF_6 is

$$\begin{array}{c} :\ddot{F}: \\ :\ddot{F} \diagdown | \diagup \ddot{F}: \\ Se \\ :\ddot{F} \diagup | \diagdown \ddot{F}: \\ :\ddot{F}: \end{array}$$

The molecule with six single bonds to and no unshared electron pairs on the central atom is of the AB_6 type. Its geometry is octahedral.

c. Given: CF_4

Unknown: geometry of the given molecule, using VSEPR theory

The Lewis structure for CF_4 is

$$\begin{array}{c} :\ddot{F}: \\ | \\ :\ddot{F}-C-\ddot{F}: \\ | \\ :\ddot{F}: \end{array}$$

The molecule with four single bonds to and no unshared electron pairs on the central atom is of the AB_4 type. Its geometry is tetrahedral.

d. Given: NO_3^-

Unknown: geometry of the given ion, using VSEPR theory

The Lewis structure of NO_3^- is

$$\left[:\ddot{O}:N:\ddot{O}: \atop :\ddot{O}: \right]^- , \quad \text{or} \quad \left[\begin{array}{c} :\ddot{O} \diagdown \quad \diagup \ddot{O}: \\ N \\ \| \\ :\ddot{O}: \end{array} \right]^-$$

The molecule or ion with three bonds to and no unshared electron pairs on the central atom is of the AB_3 type. Its geometry is trigonal-planar.

Section Review, p. 207

2a. Given: SO_2

Unknown: the Lewis structure and geometry of the given molecule

S and O have 6 valence electrons each. The total number of valence electrons in the molecule is

$$6 + (2 \times 6) = 6 + 12 = 18$$

$$:\ddot{O}:S::\ddot{O}, \quad \text{or} \quad :\ddot{O}-\ddot{S}=\ddot{O}$$

The molecule with two bonds to and one unshared electron pair on the central atom is of the AB_2E type. Its geometry is bent or angular.

b. Given: CI_4

Unknown: the Lewis structure and geometry of the given molecule

C has 4 valence electrons. I has 7 valence electrons. The total number of valence electrons in the molecule is

$$4 + (4 \times 7) = 4 + 28 = 32$$

The Lewis structure for CI_4 is

The molecule with four bonds to and no unshared electron pairs on the central atom is of the AB_4 type. Its geometry is tetrahedral.

c. Given: BCl_3

Unknown: the Lewis structure and geometry of the given molecule

B has 3 valence electrons. Cl has 7 valence electrons. The total number of valence electrons in the molecule is

$$3 + (3 \times 7) = 3 + 21 = 24$$

The Lewis structure for BCl_3 is

The molecule with three bonds to and no unshared electron pairs on the central atom is of the AB_3 type. Its geometry is trigonal-planar.

Chapter Review

6. For each pair of atoms, determine their electronegativities from Figure 20 in Chapter 5, and subtract the smaller from the larger to obtain the electronegativity difference. Refer to Figure 2 and use the electronegativity difference to determine bond type. The more negative atom is the atom with the higher electronegativity.

Example:

a. H and I

electronegativity difference = 2.5 − 2.1 = 0.4

A bond with an electronegativity difference of 0.4 is of the *polar-covalent* type.

I is the more negative atom since its electronegativity is 2.5, greater than that of H, 2.1.

7. Given: H and I, S and O, K and Br, Si and Cl, K and Cl, Se and S, C and H

Unknown: order of bonded pairs from least to most covalent

Using the electronegativity differences from item 33, noting that the lower the number the more covalent the bond is, the results are tabulated below.

Bonded atoms	Electronegativity difference
K and Cl	2.2
K and Br	2.0
Si and Cl	1.2
S and O	1.0
H and I, C and H	0.4
Se and S	0.1

15a. Given: H

Unknown: number of valence electrons in given atom

The electron configuration for H is $1s^1$. H therefore has 1 valence electron.

b. Given: F

Unknown: number of valence electrons in given atom

The electron configuration for F is $[He]2s^22p^5$. Counting the outer-shell superscripts, F has 7 valence electrons.

c. Given: Mg

Unknown: number of valence electrons in given atom

The electron configuration for Mg is $[Ne]3s^2$. Counting the outer-shell superscripts, Mg has 2 valence electrons.

d. Given: O

Unknown: number of valence electrons in given atom

The electron configuration for O is $[He]2s^22p^4$. Counting the outer-shell superscripts, O has 6 valence electrons.

e. Given: Al

Unknown: number of valence electrons in given atom

The electron configuration for Al is $[Ne]3s^23p^1$. Counting the outer-shell superscripts, Al has 3 valence electrons.

f. Given: N

Unknown: number of valence electrons in given atom

The electron configuration for N is $[He]2s^22p^3$. Counting the outer-shell superscripts, N has 5 valence electrons.

g. Given: C

Unknown: number of valence electrons in given atom

The electron configuration for C is $[He]2s^22p^2$. Counting the outer-shell superscripts, C has 4 valence electrons.

19a. Given: Li

Unknown: electron-dot notation for given element

According to its electron configuration ($[He]2s^1$), Li has 1 valance electron. The electron-dot notation for Li is therefore

Li·

b. Given: Ca

Unknown: electron-dot notation for given element

According to its electron configuration ($[Ar]4s^2$), Ca has 2 valance electrons. The electron-dot notation for Ca is therefore

·Ca·

c. Given: Cl

Unknown: electron-dot notation for given element

According to its electron configuration ($[Ne]3s^23p^5$), Cl has 7 valance electrons (2 + 5). The electron-dot notation for Cl is therefore

:Cl:

d. Given: O

Unknown: electron-dot notation for given element

According to its electron configuration ($[He]2s^2 2p^4$), O has 6 valance electrons (2 + 4). The electron-dot notation for O is therefore

$:\overset{\displaystyle .}{O}:$

e. Given: C

Unknown: electron-dot notation for given element

According to its electron configuration ($[He]2s^2 2p^2$), C has 4 valance electrons (2 + 2). The electron-dot notation for C is therefore

$\cdot \overset{\displaystyle .}{C} \cdot$

f. Given: P

Unknown: electron-dot notation for given element

According to its electron configuration ($[Ne]3s^2 3p^3$), P has 5 valance electrons (2 + 3). The electron-dot notation for P is therefore

$\cdot \overset{\displaystyle .}{P}:$

g. Given: Al

Unknown: electron-dot notation for given element

According to its electron configuration ($[Ne]3s^2 3p^1$), Al has 3 valance electrons (2 + 1). The electron-dot notation for Al is therefore

$\cdot Al \cdot$

h. Given: S

Unknown: electron-dot notation for given element

According to its electron configuration ($[Ne]3s^2 3p^4$), S has 6 valance electrons (2 + 4). The electron-dot notation for S is therefore

$:\overset{\displaystyle .}{S}:$

20a. Given: Na and S

Unknown: ionic compound formed, using electron-dot notation

Na· gives up an electron to form the Na^+ cation.

:S: acquires two electrons to form the $:\overset{..}{S}:^{2-}$ anion.

$Na\cdot + Na\cdot + :\overset{\displaystyle .}{S}: \rightarrow Na^+ + Na^+ + :\overset{..}{S}:^{2-} \rightarrow Na_2S$

b. Given: Ca and O

Unknown: ionic compound formed, using electron-dot notation

·Ca· gives up two electrons to form the Ca^{2+} cation.

:O: acquires two electrons to form the $:\overset{..}{O}:^{2-}$ anion.

$\cdot Ca \cdot + :\overset{\displaystyle .}{O}: \rightarrow Ca^{2+} + :\overset{..}{O}:^{2-} \rightarrow CaO$

c. Given: Al and S

Unknown: ionic compound formed, using electron-dot notation

$\cdot\dot{Al}\cdot$ gives up three electrons to form the Al^{3+} cation.

$:\dot{\underset{\cdot}{S}}:$ acquires two electrons to form the $:\overset{..}{\underset{..}{S}}:^{2-}$ anion.

$\cdot\dot{Al}\cdot + \cdot\dot{Al}\cdot + :\dot{\underset{\cdot}{S}}: + :\dot{\underset{\cdot}{S}}: + :\dot{\underset{\cdot}{S}}: \rightarrow Al^{3+} + Al^{3+} + :\overset{..}{\underset{..}{S}}:^{2-} + :\overset{..}{\underset{..}{S}}:^{2-} + :\overset{..}{\underset{..}{S}}:^{2-} \rightarrow Al_2S_3$

21a. Given: compound containing one C atom and four F atoms

Unknown: the Lewis structure for the given molecule

C has 4 valence electrons. F has 7 valence electrons.

$\cdot\dot{C}\cdot \qquad :\dot{\underset{\cdot}{F}}:$

Total number of valence electrons:

C	$1 \times 4e^- =$	$4e^-$
F	$4 \times 7e^- =$	$28e^-$
		$\overline{32e^-}$

$\begin{array}{c} :\overset{..}{F}: \\ :\overset{..}{F}:\overset{..}{C}:\overset{..}{F}: \\ :\overset{..}{F}: \end{array}$

b. Given: compound containing two H atoms and one Se atom

Unknown: the Lewis structure for the given molecule

Se has 6 valence electrons. H has one valence electron.

$:\dot{\underset{\cdot}{Se}}: \qquad H\cdot$

Total number of valence electrons:

Se	$1 \times 6e^- =$	$6e^-$
H	$2 \times 1e^- =$	$2e^-$
		$\overline{8e^-}$

$H:\overset{..}{Se}:H$

c. Given: compound containing one N atom and three I atoms

Unknown: the Lewis structure for the given molecule

N has 5 valence electrons. I has 7 valence electrons.

$:\dot{N}\cdot \qquad :\overset{..}{\underset{..}{I}}\cdot$

Total number of valence electrons:

N	$1 \times 5e^- =$	$5e^-$
I	$3 \times 7e^- =$	$21e^-$
		$\overline{26e^-}$

$\begin{array}{c} :\overset{..}{I}:\overset{..}{N}:\overset{..}{I}: \\ :\overset{..}{I}: \end{array}$

d. Given: compound containing one Si atom and four Br atoms

Unknown: the Lewis structure for the given molecule

Si has 4 valence electrons. Br has 7 valence electrons.

$\cdot \overset{\cdot}{\underset{\cdot}{Si}} \cdot$ $:\overset{\cdot \cdot}{\underset{\cdot \cdot}{Br}}:$

Total number of valence electrons:

Si $1 \times 4e^- = 4e^-$

Br $4 \times 7e^- = 28e^-$

$\overline{32e^-}$

$$:\overset{\cdot \cdot}{\underset{\cdot \cdot}{Br}}: $$
$$:\overset{\cdot \cdot}{Br}:\overset{\cdot \cdot}{Si}:\overset{\cdot \cdot}{Br}:$$
$$:\overset{\cdot \cdot}{\underset{\cdot \cdot}{Br}}:$$

e. Given: compound containing one C atom, one Cl atom, and three H atoms

Unknown: the Lewis structure for the given molecule

C has 4 valence electrons. Cl has 7 valence electrons. H has one valence electron.

$\cdot \overset{\cdot}{\underset{\cdot}{C}} \cdot$ $:\overset{\cdot \cdot}{\underset{\cdot \cdot}{Cl}}:$ $H \cdot$

Total number of valence electrons:

C $1 \times 4e^- = 4e^-$

Cl $1 \times 7e^- = 7e^-$

H $3 \times 1e^- = 3e^-$

$\overline{14e^-}$

$$H$$
$$H:\overset{\cdot \cdot}{\underset{\cdot \cdot}{C}}:\overset{\cdot \cdot}{\underset{\cdot \cdot}{Cl}}:$$
$$H$$

---

22. Given: BF_3

Unknown: type of hybrid orbitals in given molecule

B has 3 valence electrons. F has 7 valence electrons. The total number of valence electrons in the molecule is

$3 + (3 \times 7) = 3 + 21 = 24$

The Lewis structure for BF_3 is

$:\overset{\cdot \cdot}{F}:B:\overset{\cdot \cdot}{F}:,$ or

$:\overset{\cdot \cdot}{\underset{\cdot \cdot}{F}}:$

According to VSEPR theory, a molecule with three single bonds to and no unshared electron pairs on the central atom is of the AB_3 type, and therefore has trigonal-planar geometry. According to Table 6-6, this geometry is achieved with sp^2 hybridization.

BF_3 therefore has sp^2 hybrid orbitals.

23a. Given: O_2

Unknown: the Lewis structure for the given molecule

O has 6 valence electrons.

$:\overset{\cdot}{\underset{\cdot}{O}}:$

Total number of valence electrons:

O $2 \times 6e^- = 12e^-$

$\overset{\cdot \cdot}{O}::\overset{\cdot \cdot}{O},$ or $\overset{\cdot \cdot}{O}=\overset{\cdot \cdot}{O}$

This configuration gives each atom the correct number of valence electrons, 6.

b. Given: N_2

Unknown: the Lewis structure for the given molecule

N has 5 valence electrons.

$\cdot \overset{\cdot}{\underset{\cdot}{N}} :$

Total number of valence electrons:

N $2 \times 5e^- = 10e^-$

$:N:::N:$,   or $:N \equiv N:$

This configuration gives each atom a complete octet.

c. Given: CO

Unknown: the Lewis structure for the given molecule

C has 4 valence electrons. O has 6 valence electrons.

$\cdot \overset{\cdot}{C} \cdot$ $\cdot \overset{\cdot\cdot}{\underset{\cdot\cdot}{O}} \cdot$

Total number of valence electrons:

C $1 \times 4e^- = \ \ 4e^-$

O $1 \times 6e^- = \ \underline{\ 6e^-}$

$10e^-$

$:C:::O:$,   or $:C \equiv O:$

This configuration gives each atom a complete octet.

d. Given: SO_2

Unknown: the Lewis structure for the given molecule

S has 6 valence electrons. O has 6 valence electrons.

$\cdot \overset{\cdot\cdot}{\underset{\cdot}{S}} \cdot$ $\cdot \overset{\cdot\cdot}{\underset{\cdot}{O}} \cdot$

Total number of valence electrons:

S $1 \times 6e^- = \ \ 6e^-$

O $2 \times 6e^- = \underline{12e^-}$

$18e^-$

A lone electron pair from either oxygen atom can be moved to the bond between that oxygen atom and the sulfur atom, giving the sulfur atom a complete octet. This forms a double bond. Because neither oxygen atom is favored for the double bond, the Lewis structure is represented as two resonance structures.

$:\overset{\cdot\cdot}{\underset{\cdot\cdot}{O}}:\overset{\cdot\cdot}{S}::\overset{\cdot\cdot}{\underset{\cdot\cdot}{O}}: \leftrightarrow :\overset{\cdot\cdot}{\underset{\cdot\cdot}{O}}::\overset{\cdot\cdot}{S}:\overset{\cdot\cdot}{\underset{\cdot\cdot}{O}}:$

or

$:\overset{\cdot\cdot}{\underset{\cdot\cdot}{O}}-\overset{\cdot\cdot}{S}=\overset{\cdot\cdot}{\underset{\cdot\cdot}{O}}: \leftrightarrow :\overset{\cdot\cdot}{\underset{\cdot\cdot}{O}}=\overset{\cdot\cdot}{S}-\overset{\cdot\cdot}{\underset{\cdot\cdot}{O}}:$

24a. Given: OH^-

Unknown: the Lewis structure for the given ion

O has 6 valence electrons. H has one valence electron.

$\cdot \overset{\cdot\cdot}{\underset{\cdot\cdot}{O}} \cdot$ $H \cdot$

Total number of valence electrons:

O $1 \times 6e^- = 6e^-$

H $1 \times 1e^- = 1e^-$

ion's negative charge $1 \times 1e^- = \underline{1e^-}$

$8e^-$

$\left[:\overset{\cdot\cdot}{\underset{\cdot\cdot}{O}}:H \right]^-$

b. Given: $H_3C_2O_2^-$

Unknown: the Lewis structure for the given ion

C has 4 valence electrons. H has one valence electron. O has 6 valence electrons.

$$\cdot \overset{\cdot}{\underset{\cdot}{C}} \cdot \qquad H \cdot \qquad \overset{\cdot \cdot}{\underset{\cdot \cdot}{O}} \cdot$$

Total number of valence electrons:

C	$2 \times 4e^- =$	$8e^-$
O	$2 \times 6e^- =$	$12e^-$
H	$3 \times 1e^- =$	$3e^-$
ion's negative charge	$1 \times 1e^- =$	$\underline{1e^-}$
		$24e^-$

A double bond is formed between the carbon atom and one of the oxygen atoms in order to give each atom a complete octet. Because neither oxygen atom is favored for the double bond, the Lewis structure is represented as two resonance structures.

$$\left[\begin{array}{c} H \\ H\!:\!\overset{\cdot\cdot}{C}\!:\!C\!:\!:\!\overset{\cdot\cdot}{O} \\ H\!:\!\overset{\cdot\cdot}{O}\!: \end{array} \right]^- \ \leftrightarrow\ \left[\begin{array}{c} H \\ H\!:\!\overset{\cdot\cdot}{C}\!:\!C\!:\!\overset{\cdot\cdot}{O}\!: \\ H\!:\!\overset{\cdot\cdot}{O}\!: \end{array} \right]^-$$

c. Given: BrO_3^-

Unknown: the Lewis structure for the given ion

Br has 7 valence electrons. O has 6 valence electrons.

$$:\overset{\cdot\cdot}{\underset{\cdot}{Br}}: \qquad \cdot \overset{\cdot\cdot}{\underset{\cdot}{O}} \cdot$$

Total number of valence electrons:

Br	$1 \times 7e^- =$	$7e^-$
O	$3 \times 6e^- =$	$18e^-$
ion's negative charge	$1 \times 1e^- =$	$\underline{1e^-}$
		$26e^-$

$$\left[\begin{array}{c} :\overset{\cdot\cdot}{O}: \\ :\overset{\cdot\cdot}{O}\!:\!\overset{\cdot\cdot}{Br}\!:\!\overset{\cdot\cdot}{O}: \end{array} \right]^-$$

33b. Given: F_2 and HF

Unknown: geometry of the given molecules, using VSEPR theory

There are only two atoms in each molecule; therefore both molecules are linear.

---

46. Given: H–H, H–O, H–F, Br–Br, H–Cl, H–N

Unknown: whether bonds in the given molecules are polar or nonpolar

Diatomic molecules have polar bonds if the two atoms are different and nonpolar bonds if the two atoms are the same.

	Molecule	Bond polarity
a.	H–H	nonpolar
b.	H–O	polar
c.	H–F	polar
d.	Br–Br	nonpolar
e.	H–Cl	polar
f.	H–N	polar

47a. Given: H_2O

Unknown: polarity of given molecule

In the molecule there are eight valence electrons in the outer shell of oxygen. Four electrons are used in the covalent bonds with hydrogen, while four exist as unshared electron pairs.

According to Table 5, a molecule whose central atom has two bonds and two lone electron pairs is of the AB_2E_2 type, and has bent or angular geometry. The bent shape causes electric charge to be unevenly distributed, and so H_2O is polar.

b. Given: I_2

Unknown: polarity of given molecule

I_2 has two atoms, and therefore is linear. Because the atoms are identical, there is zero difference in electronegativity, so the molecule is nonpolar.

c. Given: CF_4

Unknown: polarity of given molecule

In the molecule there are eight valence electrons in the outer shell of carbon, all of which are used in bonds to the four fluorine atoms.

According to Table 5, a molecule with four bonds to the central atom and no unshared pairs is of the type AB_4 which has a tetrahedral geometry. Electric charge is evenly distributed over this molecule when all four bonded atoms are identical, so CF_4 is nonpolar.

d. Given: NH_3

Unknown: polarity of given molecule

In the molecule there are eight valence electrons in the outer shell of nitrogen. Six electrons are used in the covalent bonds with hydrogen, while two exist as an unshared electron pair.

According to Table 5, a molecule whose central atom has three bonds and one lone electron pair is of the AB_3E type, and has a trigonal-pyramidal geometry. Electric charge is unevenly distributed over this molecule, so NH_3 is polar.

e. Given: CO_2

Unknown: polarity of given molecule

In the molecule there are eight valence electrons in the outer shell of carbon. All electrons are used to form two double bonds.

According to Table 5, a molecule whose central atom has two bonds and no unshared electron pairs is of the AB_2 type, and has linear geometry. Electric charge is evenly distributed over this molecule when the two bonded atoms are identical, so CO_2 is nonpolar.

48a. Given: SCl_2

Unknown: the Lewis structure and molecular geometry of the given molecule

S has 6 valence electrons. Cl has 7 valence electrons. The total number of valence electrons in the molecule is

$6 + (2 \times 7) = 6 + 14 = 20$

The Lewis structure for SCl_2 is

$$:\overset{..}{\underset{..}{Cl}}:\overset{..}{\underset{..}{S}}:\overset{..}{\underset{..}{Cl}}:$$

The molecule with two bonds to and two unshared electron pairs on the central atom is of the AB_2E_2 type. Its geometry is bent or angular.

b. Given: PI_3

Unknown: the Lewis structure and molecular geometry of the given molecule

P has 5 valence electrons. I has 7 valence electrons. The total number of valence electrons in the molecule is

$5 + (3 \times 7) = 5 + 21 = 26$

The Lewis structure for PI_3 is

$$:\overset{..}{\underset{..}{I}}:\overset{..}{P}:\overset{..}{\underset{..}{I}}:$$
$$:\overset{..}{\underset{..}{I}}:$$

The molecule with three bonds to and one unshared electron pair on the central atom is of the AB_3E type. Its geometry is trigonal-pyramidal.

c. Given: Cl_2O

Unknown: the Lewis structure and molecular geometry of the given molecule

O has 6 valence electrons. Cl has 7 valence electrons. The total number of valence electrons in the molecule is

$$6 + (2 \times 7) = 6 + 14 = 20$$

The Lewis structure for Cl_2O is

:C̈l:Ö:C̈l:

The molecule with two bonds to and two unshared electron pairs on the central atom is of the AB_2E_2 type. Its geometry is bent or angular.

d. Given: NH_2Cl

Unknown: the Lewis structure and molecular geometry of the given molecule

N has 5 valence electrons. H has one valence electron. Cl has 7 valence electrons. The total number of valence electrons in the molecule is

$$5 + (2 \times 1) + 7 = 5 + 2 + 7 = 14$$

The Lewis structure for NH_2Cl is

:C̈l:
H:N̈:H

The molecule with three bonds to and one unshared electron pair on the central atom is of the AB_3E type. Its geometry is trigonal-pyramidal.

e. Given: $SiCl_3Br$

Unknown: the Lewis structure and molecular geometry of the given molecule

Si has 4 valence electrons. Cl and Br both have 7 valence electrons. The total number of valence electrons in the molecule is

$$4 + (4 \times 7) = 4 + 28 = 32$$

The Lewis structure for $SiCl_3Br$ is

:C̈l:
:C̈l:Si:C̈l:
:B̈r:

The molecule with four bonds to and no unshared electron pairs on the central atom is of the AB_4 type. Its geometry is tetrahedral.

f. Given: ONCl

Unknown: the Lewis structure and molecular geometry of the given molecule

O has 6 valence electrons. N has 5 valence electrons. Cl has 7 valence electrons. The total number of valence electrons in the molecule is

$$6 + 5 + 7 = 18$$

The Lewis structure for ONCl is

Ö::N:C̈l:

This configuration gives each atom a complete octet. The molecule with two bonds to and one unshared electron pair on the central atom is of the AB_2E type. Its geometry is bent or angular.

49a. Given: NO_3^-

Unknown: the Lewis structure and geometry of the given ion

N has 5 valence electrons. O has 6 valence electrons. The total number of valence electrons in the ion (plus one to account for the ion's negative charge) is

$$5 + (3 \times 6) + 1 = 24$$

The Lewis structure for NO_3^- is

$$\left[\begin{array}{c} :\ddot{O}:N:\ddot{O}: \\ :\vdots: \\ :\ddot{O}: \end{array} \right]^-$$

This configuration gives each atom a complete octet. The molecule or ion with three bonds to and no unshared electron pairs on the central atom is of the AB_3 type. Its geometry is trigonal-planar.

b. Given: NH_4^+

Unknown: the Lewis structure and geometry of the given ion

N has 5 valence electrons. H has one valence electron. The total number of valence electrons in the ion (minus one to account for the ion's positive charge) is

$$5 + (4 \times 1) - 1 = 8$$

The Lewis structure for NH_4^+ is

$$\left[\begin{array}{c} H \\ H\!:\!\overset{\displaystyle ..}{\underset{\displaystyle ..}{N}}\!:\!H \\ H \end{array} \right]^+$$

The molecule or ion with four bonds to and no unshared electron pairs on the central atom is of the AB_4 type. Its geometry is tetrahedral.

c. Given: SO_4^{2-}

Unknown: the Lewis structure and geometry of the given ion

S and O both have 6 valence electrons. The total number of valence electrons in the ion (plus two to account for the ion's negative charge) is

$$6 + (4 \times 6) + 2 = 32$$

The Lewis structure for SO_4^{2-} is

$$\left[\begin{array}{c} :\!\overset{..}{O}\!: \\ :\!\overset{..}{O}\!:\!S\!:\!\overset{..}{O}\!: \\ :\!\overset{..}{O}\!: \end{array} \right]^{2-}$$

The molecule or ion with four bonds to and no unshared electron pairs on the central atom is of the AB_4 type. Its geometry is tetrahedral.

d. Given: ClO_2^-

Unknown: the Lewis structure and geometry of the given ion

Cl has 7 valence electrons. O has 6 valence electrons. The total number of valence electrons in the ion (plus one to account for the ion's negative charge) is

$$7 + (2 \times 6) + 1 = 20$$

The Lewis structure for ClO_2^- is

$$\left[:\!\overset{..}{O}\!:\!\overset{..}{\underset{..}{Cl}}\!:\!\overset{..}{O}\!: \right]^-$$

The molecule or ion with two bonds to and two unshared electron pairs on the central atom is of the AB_2E_2 type. Its geometry is bent or angular.

---

50. Given: list of pairs of molecule types

Unknown: order of molecule pairs from strongest to weakest attraction

a. polar molecule and polar molecule

b. nonpolar molecule and nonpolar molecule

c. polar molecule and ion

d. ion and ion

The stronger the electric charge for each molecule, the stronger the attractive force on another molecule. Ions have the greatest electrical charge, followed by polar molecules. Nonpolar molecules exert the weakest forces. The order of the molecule pairs from strongest attraction to weakest is therefore

d., c., a., b.

51a. Given: CCl_4

Unknown: geometry of given molecule

There are four atoms bonded covalently to the central carbon atom. There are no lone electron pairs on the carbon atom. The molecule is therefore of the AB_4 type and its geometry is tetrahedral.

b. Given: $BeCl_2$

Unknown: geometry of given molecule

There are two atoms bonded covalently to the central beryllium atom, which does not obey the octet rule and has only a total of four valence electrons in its outer shell. There are no unshared electron pairs on the Be atom, so the molecule is of the AB_2 type. Its geometry is therefore linear.

c. Given: PH_3

Unknown: geometry of given molecule

There are three atoms bonded covalently to the central phosphorus atom. There is one lone electron pair on the phosphorus atom. The molecule is therefore of the AB_3E type and its geometry is trigonal-pyramidal.

---

54. Given: SO_3

Unknown: three resonance structures for given molecule

S has 6 valence electrons. O has 6 valence electrons. The total number of valence electrons in the molecule is

$6 + (3 \times 6) = 24$

The Lewis structure for SO_3 is

:O:S:O:

:O:

To provide an electron octet to the sulfur atom, the sulfur atom can form a double bond with any of the three oxygen atoms. The three possible resonance structures are therefore

---

56a. Given: He

Unknown: electron-dot notation for given element

According to its electron configuration ($1s^2$), He has 2 valence electrons. The electron-dot notation for He is therefore

:He

b. Given: Cl

Unknown: electron-dot notation for given element

According to its electron configuration ($[Ne]3s^23p^5$), Cl has 7 valence electrons $(2 + 5)$. The electron-dot notation for Cl is therefore

:Cl:

c. Given: O

Unknown: electron-dot notation for given element

According to its electron configuration ($[He]2s^22p^4$), O has 6 valence electrons $(2 + 4)$. The electron-dot notation for O is therefore

:O:

d. Given: P

Unknown: electron-dot notation for given element

According to its electron configuration ($[Ne]3s^23p^3$), P has 5 valence electrons $(2 + 3)$. The electron-dot notation for P is therefore

.P:

e. Given: B

Unknown: electron-dot notation for given element

According to its electron configuration ($[He]2s^22p^1$), B has 3 valence electrons. The electron-dot notation for B is therefore

.B·

57. Given: CH_3OH

Unknown: structural formula for the given molecule

C has 4 valence electrons and is the central molecule. H has one valence electron. O has 6 valence electrons. The total number of valence electrons is

$$4 + 4 + 6 = 14$$

The Lewis structure for CH_3OH is

$$
\begin{array}{c}
\text{H} \\
\text{H}\!:\!\ddot{\text{C}}\!:\!\ddot{\text{O}}\!:\!\text{H,} \\
\text{H}
\end{array}
$$

which has the correct number of valence electrons and an electron octet around the carbon and oxygen atoms. The structural formula contains single bonds throughout.

$$
\begin{array}{c}
\quad\ \ \text{H} \\
\quad\ \ | \\
\text{H}-\text{C}-\text{O}-\text{H} \\
\quad\ \ | \\
\quad\ \ \text{H}
\end{array}
$$

63a. Given: Zn and O

Unknown: electronegativity difference, probable bonding type, and more-electronegative atom of given pair of atoms

Using Figure 20 in Chapter 5, the electronegativities of the two given elements

Zn → 1.6
O → 3.5

The more-electronegative atom is O.

The electronegativity difference is $3.5 - 1.6 = 1.9$

The bond in ZnO, according to Figure 2, is probably ionic.

b. Given: Br and I

Unknown: electronegativity difference, probable bonding type, and more-electronegative atom of given pair of atoms

Using Figure 20 in Chapter 5, the electronegativities of the two given elements are as follows:

Br → 2.8
I → 2.5

The more-electronegative atom is Br.

The electronegativity difference is $2.8 - 2.5 = 0.3$

The bond in BrI, according to Figure 2, is probably polar-covalent.

c. Given: S and Cl

Unknown: electronegativity difference, probable bonding type, and more-electronegative atom of given pair of atoms

Using Figure 20 in Chapter 5, the electronegativities of the two given elements are as follows:

S → 2.5
Cl → 3.0

The more-electronegative atom is Cl.

The electronegativity difference is $3.0 - 2.5 = 0.5$

The bond between the S and Cl atoms, according to Figure 2, is probably polar-covalent.

64a. Given: PCl_3

Unknown: the Lewis structure for the given molecule

The electron-dot notations for P, which has 5 valence electrons, and Cl, which has 7 valence electrons, are

$$\cdot \overset{\cdot\cdot}{\underset{}{P}} \cdot \qquad :\overset{\cdot\cdot}{\underset{\cdot\cdot}{Cl}}:$$

The total number of valence electrons in the molecule's atoms is

$$1 \times 5e^- = 5e^-$$

$$3 \times 7e^- = \underline{21e^-}$$

$$26e^-$$

The resulting Lewis structure is:

$$:\overset{\cdot\cdot}{\underset{\cdot\cdot}{Cl}}:\overset{\cdot\cdot}{\underset{}{P}}:\overset{\cdot\cdot}{\underset{\cdot\cdot}{Cl}}:$$
$$:\overset{\cdot\cdot}{\underset{\cdot\cdot}{Cl}}:$$

b. Given: CCl_2F_2

Unknown: the Lewis structure for the given molecule

The electron-dot notations for C, which has 4 valence electrons, Cl, which has 7 valence electrons, and F, which also has 7 valence electrons, are

$$\cdot \overset{\cdot}{\underset{}{C}} \cdot \qquad :\overset{\cdot\cdot}{\underset{\cdot\cdot}{Cl}}: \qquad :\overset{\cdot\cdot}{\underset{\cdot\cdot}{F}}:$$

The total number of valence electrons in the molecule's atoms is

$$1 \times 4e^- = 4e^-$$

$$2 \times 7e^- = 14e^-$$

$$2 \times 7e^- = \underline{14e^-}$$

$$32e^-$$

The resulting Lewis structure is:

$$:\overset{\cdot\cdot}{\underset{\cdot\cdot}{F}}:$$
$$:\overset{\cdot\cdot}{\underset{\cdot\cdot}{Cl}}:\overset{}{\underset{}{C}}:\overset{\cdot\cdot}{\underset{\cdot\cdot}{Cl}}:$$
$$:\overset{\cdot\cdot}{\underset{\cdot\cdot}{F}}:$$

c. Given: CH_3NH_2

Unknown: the Lewis structure for the given molecule

The electron-dot notations for C, which has 4 valence electrons, N, which has 5 valence electrons, and H, which has 1 valence electron, are

$$\cdot \overset{\cdot}{\underset{}{C}} \cdot \qquad \cdot \overset{\cdot\cdot}{\underset{}{N}} \cdot \qquad H \cdot$$

The total number of valence electrons in the molecule's atoms is

$$1 \times 4e^- = 4e^-$$

$$1 \times 5e^- = 5e^-$$

$$1 \times 5e^- = \underline{5e^-}$$

$$14e^-$$

The resulting Lewis structure is:

$$\begin{array}{c} H \phantom{:\overset{\cdot\cdot}{N}} \\ H:\overset{}{\underset{}{C}}:\overset{\cdot\cdot}{\underset{}{N}}:H \\ H \;\; H \end{array}$$

65. Given: $BeCl_2$

Unknown: the Lewis structure for the given molecule

The electron-dot notations for Be, which has 2 valence electrons, and Cl, which has 7 valence electrons, are

$\cdot Be\cdot$ $:\overset{..}{\underset{.}{Cl}}:$

The total number of valence electrons in the molecule's atoms is

$1 \times 2e^- = 2e^-$

$2 \times 7e^- = 14e^-$

$\overline{16e^-}$

$:\overset{..}{\underset{..}{Cl}}:Be:\overset{..}{\underset{..}{Cl}}:$

66a. Given: NO_2^-

Unknown: the Lewis structure and geometry of the given ion

N has 5 valence electrons. O has 6 valence electrons. The total number of valence electrons in the ion (plus one to account for the ion's negative charge) is

$5 + (2 \times 6) + 1 = 18$

The Lewis structure for NO_2^- can be found by connecting the oxygen atoms to nitrogen and placing eight electrons around each atom.

$\left[:\overset{..}{\underset{..}{O}}::\overset{..}{N}:\overset{..}{\underset{..}{O}}:\right]^-$

This configuration gives each atom a complete octet. The molecule or ion with two bonds to and one unshared electron pair on the central atom is of the AB_2E type. Its geometry is bent or angular.

b. Given: NO_3^-

Unknown: the Lewis structure and geometry of the given ion

N has 5 valence electrons. O has 6 valence electrons. The total number of valence electrons in the ion (plus one to account for the ion's negative charge) is

$5 + (3 \times 6) + 1 = 24$

$\left[\begin{array}{c} :\overset{..}{\underset{..}{O}}:\overset{..}{N}:\overset{..}{\underset{..}{O}}: \\ :\overset{..}{\underset{..}{O}}: \end{array}\right]^-$

This configuration gives each atom a complete octet. The molecule or ion with three bonds to and no unshared electron pair on the central atom is of the AB_3 type. Its geometry is trigonal-planar.

c. Given: NH_4^+

Unknown: the Lewis structure and geometry of the given ion

N has 5 valence electrons. H has one valence electron. The total number of valence electrons in the ion (minus one to account for the ion's positive charge) is

$5 + (4 \times 1) - 1 = 8$

The Lewis structure for NH_4^+ is

$\left[\begin{array}{c} H \\ H:\overset{..}{\underset{..}{N}}:H \\ H \end{array}\right]^+$

The molecule or ion with four bonds to and no unshared electron pairs on the central atom is of the AB_4 type. Its geometry is tetrahedral.

1. Given: Si and Sr atoms
    Unknown: the electron
              dot notation
              for both atoms

Si has electron configuration ($[Ne]3s^2 3p^2$). There are 4 valence electrons. Therefore the electron dot notation is

·S̈i·

Sr has electron configuration ($[Kr] 5s^2$) There are 2 valence electrons. The electron dot notation therefore is

·Sr·

---

2. Given: H_2S and HCO_2H
    Unknown: the Lewis
              structure
              for each
              compound

:S̈·   Has 6 valence electrons

H·   Has 1 valence electron

$6e^- + (2 \times 1e^-) = 8$ total electrons

H:S̈:H   This satisfies the octet and duet rule for 8 electrons.

·C̈·   Has 4 valence electrons

H·   Has 1 valence electron

:Ö·   Has 6 valence electrons

$4e^- + (2 \times 1e^- + 2 \times 6e^-) = 18$ electrons

H:C̈:Ö:H   This satisfies the octet and duet rules for 18 electrons.
  :Ö:

CHAPTER 7

Chemical Formulas and Chemical Compounds

Practice, p. 238

1. a. Given: H_2SO_4

Unknown: the formula mass of the given compound

$$2 \text{ H atoms} \times \frac{1.01 \text{ amu}}{\text{H atom}} = 2.02 \text{ amu}$$

$$1 \text{ S atom} \times \frac{32.07 \text{ amu}}{\text{S atom}} = 32.07 \text{ amu}$$

$$4 \text{ O atoms} \times \frac{16.00 \text{ amu}}{\text{O atom}} = 64.00 \text{ amu}$$

formula mass of H_2SO_4 = 98.09 amu

b. Given: $Ca(NO_3)_2$

Unknown: the formula mass of the given compound

$$1 \text{ Ca atom} \times \frac{40.08 \text{ amu}}{\text{Ca atom}} = 40.08 \text{ amu}$$

$$2 \text{ N atoms} \times \frac{14.01 \text{ amu}}{\text{N atom}} = 28.02 \text{ amu}$$

$$6 \text{ O atoms} \times \frac{16.00 \text{ amu}}{\text{O atom}} = 96.00 \text{ amu}$$

formula mass of $Ca(NO_3)_2$ = 164.10 amu

c. Given: PO_4^{3-}

Unknown: the formula mass of the given ion

$$1 \text{ P atom} \times \frac{30.97 \text{ amu}}{\text{P atom}} = 30.97 \text{ amu}$$

$$4 \text{ O atoms} \times \frac{16.00 \text{ amu}}{\text{O atom}} = 64.00 \text{ amu}$$

formula mass of PO_4^{3-} = 94.97 amu

d. Given: $MgCl_2$

Unknown: the formula mass of the given compound

$$1 \text{ Mg atom} \times \frac{24.305 \text{ amu}}{\text{Mg atom}} = 24.305 \text{ amu}$$

$$2 \text{ Cl atoms} \times \frac{35.45 \text{ amu}}{\text{Cl atom}} = 70.90 \text{ amu}$$

formula mass of $MgCl_2$ = 95.21 amu

ATE, Additional Sample Problem, p. 238

F-1. a. Given: Na_2SO_3

Unknown: the formula mass of the given compound

$$2 \text{ Na atoms} \times \frac{22.99 \text{ amu}}{\text{Na atom}} = 45.98 \text{ amu}$$

$$1 \text{ S atom} \times \frac{32.07 \text{ amu}}{\text{S atom}} = 32.07 \text{ amu}$$

$$3 \text{ O atoms} \times \frac{16.00 \text{ amu}}{\text{O atom}} = 48.00 \text{ amu}$$

formula mass of Na_2SO_3 = 126.05 amu

b. Given: $HClO_3$

Unknown: the formula mass of the given compound

$$1 \text{ H atom} \times \frac{1.01 \text{ amu}}{\text{H atom}} = 1.01 \text{ amu}$$

$$1 \text{ Cl atom} \times \frac{35.45 \text{ amu}}{\text{Cl atom}} = 35.45 \text{ amu}$$

$$3 \text{ O atoms} \times \frac{16.00 \text{ amu}}{\text{O atom}} = 48.00 \text{ amu}$$

formula mass of $HClO_3$ = 84.46 amu

c. Given: MnO_4^-

Unknown: the formula mass of the given ion

$$1 \text{ Mn atom} \times \frac{54.94 \text{ amu}}{\text{Mn atom}} = 54.94 \text{ amu}$$

$$4 \text{ O atoms} \times \frac{16.00 \text{ amu}}{\text{O atom}} = 64.00 \text{ amu}$$

formula mass of MnO_4^- = 118.94 amu

d. Given: C_2H_6O

Unknown: the formula mass of the given compound

$$2 \text{ C atoms} \times \frac{12.01 \text{ amu}}{\text{C atom}} = 24.02 \text{ amu}$$

$$6 \text{ H atoms} \times \frac{1.01 \text{ amu}}{\text{H atom}} = 6.06 \text{ amu}$$

$$1 \text{ O atom} \times \frac{16.00 \text{ amu}}{\text{O atom}} = 16.00 \text{ amu}$$

formula mass of C_2H_6O = 46.08 amu

Practice, p. 239

2. a. Given: Al_2S_3

Unknown: the molar mass of the given compound

$$2 \text{ mol Al} \times \frac{26.98 \text{ g Al}}{\text{mol Al}} = 53.96 \text{ g Al}$$

$$3 \text{ mol S} \times \frac{32.07 \text{ g S}}{\text{mol S}} = 96.21 \text{ g S}$$

molar mass of Al_2S_3 = 150.17 g/mol

b. Given: $NaNO_3$

Unknown: the molar mass of the given compound

$$1 \text{ mol Na} \times \frac{22.99 \text{ g Na}}{\text{mol Na}} = 22.99 \text{ g Na}$$

$$1 \text{ mol N} \times \frac{14.01 \text{ g N}}{\text{mol N}} = 14.01 \text{ g N}$$

$$3 \text{ mol O} \times \frac{16.00 \text{ g O}}{\text{mol O}} = 48.00 \text{ g O}$$

molar mass of $NaNO_3$ = 85.00 g/mol

c. Given: $Ba(OH)_2$

Unknown: the molar mass of the given compound

$$1 \text{ mol Ba} \times \frac{137.33 \text{ g Ba}}{\text{mol Ba}} = 137.33 \text{ g Ba}$$

$$2 \text{ mol O} \times \frac{16.00 \text{ g O}}{\text{mol O}} = 32.00 \text{ g O}$$

$$2 \text{ mol H} \times \frac{1.01 \text{ g H}}{\text{mol H}} = 2.02 \text{ g H}$$

molar mass of $Ba(OH)_2$ = 171.35 g/mol

G-2. a. Given: K_2SO_4

Unknown: the molar mass of the given compound

$$2 \text{ mol K} \times \frac{39.10 \text{ g K}}{\text{mol K}} = 78.20 \text{ g K}$$

$$1 \text{ mol S} \times \frac{32.07 \text{ g S}}{\text{mol S}} = 32.07 \text{ g S}$$

$$4 \text{ mol O} \times \frac{16.00 \text{ g O}}{\text{mol O}} = 64.00 \text{ g O}$$

molar mass of K_2SO_4 = 174.27 g/mol

b. Given: $(NH_4)_2CrO_4$

Unknown: the molar mass of the given compound

$$2 \text{ mol N} \times \frac{14.01 \text{ g N}}{\text{mol N}} = 28.02 \text{ g N}$$

$$8 \text{ mol H} \times \frac{1.01 \text{ g H}}{\text{mol H}} = 8.08 \text{ g H}$$

$$1 \text{ mol Cr} \times \frac{52.00 \text{ g Cr}}{\text{mol Cr}} = 52.00 \text{ g Cr}$$

$$4 \text{ mol O} \times \frac{16.00 \text{ g O}}{\text{mol O}} = 64.00 \text{ g O}$$

molar mass of $(NH_4)_2CrO_4$ = 152.10 g/mol

ATE, Additional Sample Problems, p. 240

H-1. Given: 3.04 mol NH_3

Unknown: mass of NH_3

$$1 \text{ mol N} \times \frac{14.01 \text{ g N}}{\text{mol N}} = 14.01 \text{ g N}$$

$$3 \text{ mol H} \times \frac{1.01 \text{ g H}}{\text{mol H}} = 3.03 \text{ g H}$$

molar mass of NH_3 = 17.04 g/mol

$$\text{mass } NH_3 = \frac{17.04 \text{ g } NH_3}{\text{mol } NH_3} \times 3.04 \text{ mol } NH_3 = 51.8 \text{ g}$$

H-2. Given: 0.257 mol $Ca(NO_3)_2$

Unknown: mass of $Ca(NO_3)_2$

$$1 \text{ mol Ca} \times \frac{40.08 \text{ g Ca}}{\text{mol Ca}} = 40.08 \text{ g Ca}$$

$$2 \text{ mol N} \times \frac{14.01 \text{ g N}}{\text{mol N}} = 28.02 \text{ g N}$$

$$6 \text{ mol O} \times \frac{16.00 \text{ g O}}{\text{mol O}} = 96.00 \text{ g O}$$

molar mass of $Ca(NO_3)_2$ = 164.10 g/mol

$$\text{mass } Ca(NO_3)_2 = \frac{164.10 \text{ g } Ca(NO_3)_2}{\text{mol } Ca(NO_3)_2} \times 0.257 \text{ mol } Ca(NO_3)_2 = 42.2 \text{ g}$$

ATE, Additional Sample Problems, p. 241

I-1. a. Given: 3.82 g SO_2

Unknown: number of moles SO_2

$$1 \text{ mol S} \times \frac{32.07 \text{ g S}}{\text{mol S}} = 32.07 \text{ g S}$$

$$2 \text{ mol O} \times \frac{16.00 \text{ g O}}{\text{mol O}} = 32.00 \text{ g O}$$

molar mass of SO_2 = 64.07 g/mol

$$\text{mol } SO_2 = \frac{3.82 \text{ g}}{64.07 \text{ g/mol}} = 0.0596 \text{ mol}$$

b. Given: 4.15×10^{-3} g $C_6H_{12}O_6$

Unknown: number of moles $C_6H_{12}O_6$

$6 \text{ mol C} \times \dfrac{12.01 \text{ g C}}{\text{mol C}} = 72.06 \text{ g C}$

$12 \text{ mol H} \times \dfrac{1.01 \text{ g H}}{\text{mol H}} = 12.1 \text{ g H}$

$6 \text{ mol O} \times \dfrac{16.00 \text{ g O}}{\text{mol O}} = 96.00 \text{ g O}$

molar mass of $C_6H_{12}O_6 = 180.2$ g/mol

$\text{mol } C_6H_{12}O_6 = \dfrac{4.15 \times 10^{-3} \text{ g}}{180.2 \text{ g/mol}} = 2.30 \times 10^{-5} \text{ mol}$

c. Given: 77.1 g Cl_2

Unknown: number of moles Cl_2

$2 \text{ mol Cl} \times \dfrac{35.45 \text{ g Cl}}{\text{mol Cl}} = 70.90 \text{ g Cl}$

molar mass of $Cl_2 = 70.90$ g/mol

$\text{mol } Cl_2 = \dfrac{77.1 \text{ g}}{70.90 \text{ g/mol}} = 1.09 \text{ mol}$

I-2. a. Given: 5.96×10^{-2} mol SO_2

Unknown: n; number of molecules SO_2

$n = \dfrac{6.022 \times 10^{23} \text{ molecules}}{\text{mol}} \times (5.96 \times 10^{-2} \text{ mol } SO_2)$

$= 3.59 \times 10^{22} \text{ molecules}$

b. Given: 2.30×10^{-5} mol $C_6H_{12}O_6$

Unknown: n; number of molecules $C_6H_{12}O_6$

$n = \dfrac{6.022 \times 10^{23} \text{ molecules}}{\text{mol}} \times (2.30 \times 10^{-5} \text{ mol } C_6H_{12}O_6)$

$= 1.39 \times 10^{19} \text{ molecules}$

c. Given: 1.09 mol Cl_2

Unknown: n; number of molecules Cl_2

$n = \dfrac{6.022 \times 10^{23} \text{ molecules}}{\text{mol}} \times 1.09 \text{ mol } Cl_2 = 6.56 \times 10^{23} \text{ molecules}$

Practice, p. 242

1. a. Given: 6.60 g $(NH_4)_2SO_4$

Unknown: number of moles $(NH_4)_2SO_4$

$2 \text{ mol N} \times \dfrac{14.01 \text{ g N}}{\text{mol N}} = 28.02 \text{ g N}$

$8 \text{ mol H} \times \dfrac{1.01 \text{ g H}}{\text{mol H}} = 8.08 \text{ g H}$

$1 \text{ mol S} \times \dfrac{32.07 \text{ g S}}{\text{mol S}} = 32.07 \text{ g S}$

$4 \text{ mol O} \times \dfrac{16.00 \text{ g O}}{\text{mol O}} = 64.00 \text{ g O}$

molar mass of $(NH_4)_2SO_4 = 132.17$ g/mol

$\text{mol } (NH_4)_2SO_4 = \dfrac{6.60 \text{ g } (NH_4)_2SO_4}{132.17 \text{ g/mol } (NH_4)_2SO_4} = 4.99 \times 10^{-2} \text{ mol}$

b. Given: 4.5 kg $Ca(OH)_2$

Unknown: number of moles $Ca(OH)_2$

$$1 \text{ mol Ca} \times \frac{40.08 \text{ g Ca}}{\text{mol Ca}} = 40.08 \text{ g Ca}$$

$$2 \text{ mol} \times \frac{16.00 \text{ g O}}{\text{mol O}} = 32.00 \text{ g O}$$

$$2 \text{ mol H} \times \frac{1.01 \text{ g H}}{\text{mol H}} = 2.02 \text{ g H}$$

molar mass of $Ca(OH)_2$ = 74.10 g/mol

$$\text{mol } Ca(OH)_2 = 4.5 \text{ kg } Ca(OH)_2 \times \frac{1000 \text{ g}}{\text{kg}} \times \frac{1 \text{ mol}}{74.10 \text{ g } Ca(OH)_2} = 61 \text{ mol}$$

---

2. a. Given: 25.0 g H_2SO_4

Unknown: n; number of molecules H_2SO_4

$$2 \text{ mol H} \times \frac{1.01 \text{ g H}}{\text{mol H}} = 2.02 \text{ g H}$$

$$1 \text{ mol S} \times \frac{32.07 \text{ g S}}{\text{mol S}} = 32.07 \text{ g S}$$

$$4 \text{ mol O} \times \frac{16.00 \text{ g O}}{\text{mol O}} = 64.00 \text{ g O}$$

molar mass of H_2SO_4 = 98.09 g/mol

$$n = 25.0 \text{ g } H_2SO_4 \times \frac{1 \text{ mol}}{98.07 \text{ g } H_2SO_4} \times \frac{6.022 \times 10^{23} \text{ molecules}}{\text{mol}}$$

$$= 1.53 \times 10^{23} \text{ molecules}$$

b. Given: 125 g of $C_{12}H_{22}O_{11}$

Unknown: n; number of molecules $C_{12}H_{22}O_{11}$

$$12 \text{ mol C} \times \frac{12.01 \text{ g C}}{\text{mol C}} = 144.1 \text{ g C}$$

$$22 \text{ mol H} \times \frac{1.01 \text{ g H}}{\text{mol H}} = 22.2 \text{ g H}$$

$$11 \text{ mol O} \times \frac{16.00 \text{ g O}}{\text{mol O}} = 176.0 \text{ g O}$$

molar mass of $C_{12}H_{22}O_{11}$ = 342.3 g/mol

$$n = 125 \text{ g } C_{12}H_{22}O_{11} \times \frac{1 \text{ mol}}{342.3 \text{ g } C_{12}H_{22}O_{11}} \times \frac{6.022 \times 10^{23} \text{ molecules}}{\text{mol}}$$

$$= 2.20 \times 10^{23} \text{ molecules}$$

---

3. Given: 6.25 mol of $Cu(NO_3)_2$

Unknown: mass of $Cu(NO_3)_2$

$$1 \text{ mol Cu} \times \frac{63.55 \text{ g Cu}}{\text{mol Cu}} = 63.55 \text{ g Cu}$$

$$2 \text{ mol N} \times \frac{14.01 \text{ g N}}{\text{mol N}} = 28.02 \text{ g N}$$

$$6 \text{ mol O} \times \frac{16.00 \text{ g O}}{\text{mol O}} = 96.00 \text{ g O}$$

molar mass of $Cu(NO_3)_2$ = 187.57 g/mol

$$\text{mass } Cu(NO_3)_2 = \frac{187.57 \text{ g } Cu(NO_3)_2}{\text{mol } Cu(NO_3)_2} \times 6.25 \text{ mol } Cu(NO_3)_2 = 1170 \text{ g}$$

J-1. Given: $NaNO_3$
Unknown: percentage composition of given compound

$$1 \text{ mol Na} \times \frac{22.99 \text{ g Na}}{\text{mol Na}} = 22.99 \text{ g Na}$$

$$1 \text{ mol N} \times \frac{14.01 \text{ g N}}{\text{mol N}} = 14.01 \text{ g N}$$

$$3 \text{ mol O} \times \frac{16.00 \text{ g O}}{\text{mol O}} = 48.00 \text{ g O}$$

molar mass of $NaNO_3$ = 85.00 g

$$\frac{22.99 \text{ g Na}}{85.00 \text{ g NaNO}_3} \times 100 = 27.05\% \text{ Na}$$

$$\frac{14.01 \text{ g N}}{85.00 \text{ g NaNO}_3} \times 100 = 16.48\% \text{ N}$$

$$\frac{48.00 \text{ g O}}{85.00 \text{ g NaNO}_3} \times 100 = 56.47\% \text{ O}$$

J-2. Given: Ag_2SO_4
Unknown: percentage composition of given compound

$$2 \text{ mol Ag} \times \frac{107.87 \text{ g Ag}}{\text{mol Ag}} = 215.74 \text{ g Ag}$$

$$1 \text{ mol S} \times \frac{32.07 \text{ g S}}{\text{mol S}} = 32.07 \text{ g S}$$

$$4 \text{ mol O} \times \frac{16.00 \text{ g O}}{\text{mol O}} = 64.00 \text{ g O}$$

molar mass of Ag_2SO_4 = 311.81 g

$$\frac{215.74 \text{ g Ag}}{311.81 \text{ g Ag}_2SO_4} \times 100 = 69.19\% \text{ Ag}$$

$$\frac{32.07 \text{ g S}}{311.81 \text{ g Ag}_2SO_4} \times 100 = 10.29\% \text{ S}$$

$$\frac{64.00 \text{ g O}}{311.81 \text{ g Ag}_2SO_4} \times 100 = 20.53\% \text{ O}$$

Practice, p. 244

1. a. Given: $PbCl_2$
Unknown: percentage composition of given compound

$$1 \text{ mol Pb} \times \frac{207.2 \text{ g Pb}}{\text{mol Pb}} = 207.2 \text{ g Pb}$$

$$2 \text{ mol Cl} \times \frac{35.45 \text{ g Cl}}{\text{mol Cl}} = 70.90 \text{ g Cl}$$

molar mass of $PbCl_2$ = 278.1 g

$$\frac{207.2 \text{ g Pb}}{278.1 \text{ g PbCl}_2} \times 100 = 74.51\% \text{ Pb}$$

$$\frac{70.90 \text{ g Cl}}{278.1 \text{ g PbCl}_2} \times 100 = 25.49\% \text{ Cl}$$

b. Given: $Ba(NO_3)_2$

Unknown: percentage composition of given compound

$$1 \text{ mol Ba} \times \frac{137.33 \text{ g Ba}}{\text{mol Ba}} = 137.33 \text{ g Ba}$$

$$2 \text{ mol N} \times \frac{14.01 \text{ g N}}{\text{mol N}} = 28.02 \text{ g N}$$

$$6 \text{ mol O} \times \frac{16.00 \text{ g O}}{\text{mol O}} = 96.00 \text{ g O}$$

molar mass of $Ba(NO_3)_2 = 261.35$ g

$$\frac{137.33 \text{ g Ba}}{261.35 \text{ g Ba(NO}_3)_2} \times 100 = 52.546\% \text{ Ba}$$

$$\frac{28.02 \text{ g N}}{261.35 \text{ g Ba(NO}_3)_2} \times 100 = 10.72\% \text{ N}$$

$$\frac{96.00 \text{ g O}}{261.35 \text{ g Ba(NO}_3)_2} \times 100 = 36.73\% \text{ O}$$

---

2. Given: $ZnSO_4 \cdot 7H_2O$

Unknown: mass percentage of H_2O in given compound

$$\text{mass } H_2O = 7 \text{ mol } H_2O \times \frac{18.02 \text{ g } H_2O}{\text{mol } H_2O} = 126.1 \text{ g } H_2O$$

1 mol $ZnSO_4 \cdot 7H_2O$ contains 1 mol Zn, 1 mol S, and 4 mol O in the zinc sulfate molecule proper.

$$1 \text{ mol Zn} \times \frac{65.41 \text{ g Zn}}{\text{mol Zn}} = 65.41 \text{ g Zn}$$

$$1 \text{ mol S} \times \frac{32.07 \text{ g S}}{\text{mol S}} = 32.07 \text{ g S}$$

$$4 \text{ mol O} \times \frac{16.00 \text{ g O}}{\text{mol O}} = 64.00 \text{ g O}$$

molar mass of $ZnSO_4 \cdot 7H_2O = 287.6$ g

$$\text{mass percentage of } H_2O \text{ in } ZnSO_4 \cdot 7H_2O = \frac{126.1 \text{ g } H_2O}{287.6 \text{ g } ZnSO_4 \cdot 7H_2O} \times 100$$

$$= 43.85\% \text{ } H_2O$$

---

3. Given: 54.87% O by mass in $Mg(OH)_2$

Unknown: mass of O in 175 g of $Mg(OH)_2$

mass O in $Mg(OH)_2$ = mass percentage of O in $Mg(OH)_2$ × mass

$Mg(OH)_2 = 0.5487 \times 175$ g

mass O in $Mg(OH)_2 = 96.0$ g O

$$\text{mol O} = \frac{\text{mass O}}{\text{molar mass of O}} = \frac{96.0 \text{ g O}}{16.00 \text{ g/mol O}} = 6.00 \text{ mol O}$$

K-1. Given: $CuSO_4 \cdot 5H_2O$

Unknown: mass percentage of H_2O in given compound

$\text{mass } H_2O = 5 \text{ mol } H_2O \times \dfrac{18.02 \text{ g } H_2O}{\text{mol } H_2O} = 90.10 \text{ g } H_2O$

$1 \text{ mol Cu} \times \dfrac{63.55 \text{ g Cu}}{\text{mol Cu}} = 63.55 \text{ g Cu}$

$1 \text{ mol S} \times \dfrac{32.07 \text{ g S}}{\text{mol S}} = 32.07 \text{ g S}$

$4 \text{ mol O} \times \dfrac{16.00 \text{ g O}}{\text{mol O}} = 64.00 \text{ g O}$

molar mass of $CuSO_4 \cdot 5H_2O = 249.72$ g

mass percentage of H_2O in $CuSO_4 \cdot 5H_2O$

$= \dfrac{90.10 \text{ g } H_2O}{249.72 \text{ g } CuSO_4 \cdot 5H_2O}$

$\times 100 = 36.08\% \ H_2O$

K-2. a. Given: 52.02% Cl by mass in $ZnCl_2$

Unknown: mass of Cl in 80.3 g of $ZnCl_2$

mass Cl in $ZnCl_2$ = mass percentage of Cl in $ZnCl_2 \times$ mass $ZnCl_2$
$= 0.5202 \times 80.3$ g

mass Cl in $ZnCl_2 = 41.8$ g Cl

b. Given: 41.8 g Cl

Unknown: number of moles in sample

molar mass of Cl = 35.45 g/mol

$\text{mol Cl} = \dfrac{\text{mass Cl}}{\text{molar mass of Cl}} = \dfrac{41.08 \text{ g Cl}}{35.45 \text{ g/mol}} = 1.18 \text{ mol Cl}$

Section Review, p. 244

1. Given: $(NH_4)_2CO_3$

Unknown: the formula and molar masses of the given compound

$2 \text{ N atoms} \times \dfrac{14.01 \text{ amu}}{\text{N atom}} = 28.02 \text{ amu}$

$8 \text{ H atoms} \times \dfrac{1.01 \text{ amu}}{\text{H atom}} = 8.08 \text{ amu}$

$1 \text{ C atom} \times \dfrac{12.01 \text{ amu}}{\text{C atom}} = 12.01 \text{ amu}$

$3 \text{ O atoms} \times \dfrac{16.00 \text{ amu}}{\text{O amu}} = 48.00 \text{ amu}$

formula mass of $(NH_4)_2CO_3 = 96.11$ amu

molar mass of $(NH_4)_2CO_3 = 96.11 \text{ amu} \times \dfrac{1 \text{ g/mol}}{1 \text{ amu}} = 96.11 \text{ g/mol}$

3. Given: 3.25 mol $Fe_2(SO_4)_3$
Unknown: mass of $Fe_2(SO_4)_3$

$$2 \text{ mol Fe} \times \frac{55.85 \text{ g Fe}}{\text{mol Fe}} = 111.7 \text{ g Fe}$$

$$3 \text{ mol S} \times \frac{32.07 \text{ g S}}{\text{mol S}} = 96.21 \text{ g S}$$

$$12 \text{ mol O} \times \frac{16.00 \text{ g O}}{\text{mol O}} = 192.0 \text{ g O}$$

molar mass of $Fe_2(SO_4)_3$ = 399.9 g/mol

$$\text{mass } Fe_2(SO_4)_3 = \frac{399.9 \text{ g } Fe_2(SO_4)_3}{\text{mol } Fe_2(SO_4)_3} \times 3.25 \text{ mol } Fe_2(SO_4)_3 = 1.30 \times 10^3 \text{ g}$$

---

4. Given: 100.0 mg of $C_9H_8O_4$
Unknown: n; number of molecules $C_9H_8O_4$

$$9 \text{ mol C} \times \frac{12.01 \text{ g C}}{\text{mol C}} = 108.1 \text{ g C}$$

$$8 \text{ mol H} \times \frac{1.01 \text{ g H}}{\text{mol H}} = 8.08 \text{ g H}$$

$$4 \text{ mol O} \times \frac{16.00 \text{ g O}}{\text{mol O}} = 64.00 \text{ g O}$$

molar mass of $C_9H_8O_4$ = 180.2 g/mol

$$n = 100.0 \text{ mg } C_9H_8O_4 \times \frac{1 \text{ g}}{1000 \text{ mg}} \times \frac{1 \text{ mol}}{180.2 \text{ g } C_9H_8O_4} \times \frac{6.022 \times 10^{23} \text{ molecules}}{\text{mol}}$$

$$= 3.342 \times 10^{20} \text{ molecules}$$

---

5. Given: $(NH_4)_2CO_3$
Unknown: percentage composition of given compound

$$2 \text{ mol N} \times \frac{14.01 \text{ g N}}{\text{mol N}} = 28.02 \text{ g N}$$

$$8 \text{ mol H} \times \frac{1.01 \text{ g H}}{\text{mol H}} = 8.08 \text{ g H}$$

$$1 \text{ mol C} \times \frac{12.01 \text{ g C}}{\text{mol C}} = 12.01 \text{ g C}$$

$$3 \text{ mol O} \times \frac{16.00 \text{ g O}}{\text{mol O}} = 48.00 \text{ g O}$$

molar mass of $(NH_4)_2CO_3$ = 96.11 g

$$\frac{28.02 \text{ g N}}{96.11 \text{ g } (NH_4)_2CO_3} \times 100 = 29.15\% \text{ N}$$

$$\frac{8.08 \text{ g H}}{96.11 \text{ g } (NH_4)_2CO_3} \times 100 = 8.407\% \text{ H}$$

$$\frac{12.01 \text{ g C}}{96.11 \text{ g } (NH_4)_2CO_3} \times 100 = 12.50\% \text{ C}$$

$$\frac{48.00 \text{ g O}}{96.11 \text{ g } (NH_4)_2CO_3} \times 100 = 49.94\% \text{ O}$$

6. Given: $CuSO_4 \cdot nH_2O \rightarrow$
103.74 g of $CuSO_4$
and 58.55 g H_2O

Unknown: value of n

molecular weights: $H_2O \rightarrow 18 \frac{g}{mol}$; $CuSO_4 \rightarrow 159.55 \frac{g}{mol}$

$\frac{58.55\ g}{18\ g/mol} = 3.25\ mol \quad \frac{103.74\ g}{159.55\ g/mol} = 0.65\ mol$

$3.25\ mol/0.65\ mol = 5 = n$

ATE, Additional Sample Problems, p. 246

L-1. Given: percentage composition: 36.70% K, 33.27% Cl, and 30.03% O

Unknown: empirical formula

mass composition in 100.00 g sample: 36.70 g K, 33.27 g Cl, 30.03 g O

composition in moles:

$36.70\ g\ K \times \frac{1\ mol\ K}{39.10\ g\ K} = 0.9386\ mol\ K$

$33.27\ g\ Cl \times \frac{1\ mol\ Cl}{35.45\ g\ Cl} = 0.9385\ mol\ Cl$

$30.03\ g\ O \times \frac{1\ mol\ O}{16.00\ g\ O} = 1.877\ mol\ O$

smallest whole-number ratio of atoms:

$\frac{0.9386\ mol\ K}{0.9385} : \frac{0.9385\ mol\ Cl}{0.9385} : \frac{1.877\ mol\ O}{0.9385} = 1\ mol\ K : 1\ mol\ Cl : 2\ mol\ O$

The empirical formula is therefore $KClO_2$.

L-2. Given: percentage composition: 17.15% C, 1.44% H, and 81.41% F

Unknown: empirical formula

mass composition in 100.00 g sample: 17.15 g C, 1.44 g H, 81.41 g F

composition in moles:

$17.15\ g\ C \times \frac{1\ mol\ C}{12.01\ g\ C} = 1.428\ mol\ C$

$1.44\ g\ H \times \frac{1\ mol\ H}{1.01\ g\ H} = 1.43\ mol\ H$

$81.41\ g\ F \times \frac{1\ mol\ F}{19.00\ g\ F} = 4.285\ mol\ F$

smallest whole-number ratio of atoms:

$\frac{1.428\ mol\ C}{1.428} : \frac{1.43\ mol\ H}{1.428} : \frac{4.285\ mol\ F}{1.428} = 1\ mol\ C : 1\ mol\ H : 3\ mol\ F$

The empirical formula is therefore CHF_3.

1. Given: percentage composition: 63.52% Fe and 36.48% S

Unknown: empirical formula

mass composition in 100.00 g sample: 63.52 g Fe, 36.48 g S

composition in moles:

$$63.52 \text{ g Fe} \times \frac{1 \text{ mol Fe}}{55.85 \text{ g Fe}} = 1.137 \text{ mol Fe}$$

$$36.48 \text{ g S} \times \frac{1 \text{ mol S}}{32.07 \text{ g S}} = 1.138 \text{ mol S}$$

smallest whole-number ratio of atoms:

$$\frac{1.137 \text{ mol Fe}}{1.137} : \frac{1.138 \text{ mol S}}{1.137} = 1 \text{ mol Fe} : 1 \text{ mol S}$$

The empirical formula is therefore FeS.

2. Given: percentage composition: 26.56% K, 35.41% Cr, and the remainder is O

Unknown: empirical formula

% O = 100.00% − 26.56% − 35.41% = 38.03%

mass composition in 100.00 g sample: 26.56 g K, 35.41 g Cr, 38.03 g O

composition in moles:

$$26.56 \text{ g K} \times \frac{1 \text{ mol K}}{39.10 \text{ g K}} = 0.6793 \text{ mol K}$$

$$35.41 \text{ g Cr} \times \frac{1 \text{ mol Cr}}{52.00 \text{ g Cr}} = 0.6810 \text{ mol Cr}$$

$$38.03 \text{ g O} \times \frac{1 \text{ mol O}}{16.00 \text{ g O}} = 2.377 \text{ mol O}$$

smallest whole-number ratio of atoms:

$$\frac{0.6793 \text{ mol K}}{0.6793} : \frac{0.6810 \text{ mol Cr}}{0.6793} : \frac{2.377 \text{ mol O}}{0.6793}$$

= 1.000 mol K : 1.003 mol Cr : 3.499 mol O

= 2.000 mol K : 2.006 mol Cr : 6.998 mol O

= 2 mol K : 2 mol Cr : 7 mol O

The empirical formula is therefore $K_2Cr_2O_7$.

3. Given: sample mass = 20.0 g
calcium mass = 4.00 g

Unknown: empirical formula

bromine mass = sample mass − calcium mass = 20.0 g − 4.00g = 16.0 g

composition in moles:

$$4.00 \text{ g Ca} \times \frac{1 \text{ mol Ca}}{40.08 \text{ g Ca}} = 0.0998 \text{ mol Ca}$$

$$16.0 \text{ g Br} \times \frac{1 \text{ mol Br}}{79.90 \text{ g Br}} = 0.200 \text{ mol Br}$$

smallest whole-number ratio of atoms:

$$\frac{0.0998 \text{ mol Ca}}{0.0998} : \frac{0.200 \text{ mol Br}}{0.0998}$$

= 1 mol Ca : 2 mol Br

The empirical formula is therefore $CaBr_2$.

M-1. Given: sample mass
= 60.00 g
lead mass
= 38.43 g
carbon mass
= 17.83 g
hydrogen mass
= 3.74 g
Unknown: empirical
formula

composition in moles:

$$38.43 \text{ g Pb} \times \frac{1 \text{ mol Pb}}{207.2 \text{ g Pb}} = 0.1855 \text{ mol Pb}$$

$$17.83 \text{ g C} \times \frac{1 \text{ mol C}}{12.01 \text{ g C}} = 1.485 \text{ mol C}$$

$$3.74 \text{ g H} \times \frac{1 \text{ mol H}}{1.01 \text{ g H}} = 3.70 \text{ mol H}$$

smallest whole-number ratio of atoms:

$$\frac{0.1855 \text{ mol Pb}}{0.1855} : \frac{1.485 \text{ mol C}}{0.1855} : \frac{3.70 \text{ mol H}}{0.1855}$$

= 1 mol Pb : 8.005 mol C : 19.9 mol H

= 1 mol Pb : 8 mol C : 20 mol H

The empirical formula is therefore PbC_8H_{20}.

M-2. Given: sample mass
= 170.00 g
sodium mass
= 29.84 g
chromium mass
= 67.49 g
oxygen mass
= 72.67 g
Unknown: empirical
formula

composition in moles:

$$29.84 \text{ g Na} \times \frac{1 \text{ mol Na}}{22.99 \text{ g Na}} = 1.298 \text{ mol Na}$$

$$67.49 \text{ g Cr} \times \frac{1 \text{ mol Cr}}{52.00 \text{ g Cr}} = 1.298 \text{ mol Cr}$$

$$72.67 \text{ g O} \times \frac{1 \text{ mol O}}{16.00 \text{ g O}} = 4.542 \text{ mol O}$$

smallest whole-number ratio of atoms:

$$\frac{1.298 \text{ mol Na}}{1.298} : \frac{1.298 \text{ mol Cr}}{1.298} : \frac{4.542 \text{ mol O}}{1.298}$$

= 1 mol Na : 1 mol Cr : 3.499 mol O

= 2 mol Na : 2 mol Cr : 6.998 mol O

= 2 mol Na : 2 mol Cr : 7 mol O

The empirical formula is therefore $Na_2Cr_2O_7$.

Practice, p. 249

1. Given: empirical formula: CH
molecular
formula mass =
78.110 amu
Unknown: molecular
formula

$$x = \frac{\text{molecular formula mass}}{\text{empirical formula mass}}$$

empirical formula mass of CH = 12.01 amu + 1.01 amu = 13.02 amu

$$x = \frac{78.110 \text{ amu}}{13.02 \text{ amu}} = 6$$

molecular formula: $C_xH_x = C_6H_6$

2. Given: molecular formula mass = 34.00 amu
hydrogen mass = 0.44 g
oxygen mass = 6.92 g

Unknown: molecular formula

composition in moles:

$$0.44 \text{ g H} \times \frac{1 \text{ mol H}}{1.01 \text{ g H}} = 0.44 \text{ mol H}$$

$$6.92 \text{ g O} \times \frac{1 \text{ mol O}}{16.00 \text{ g O}} = 0.432 \text{ mol O}$$

smallest whole-number ratio of atoms:

$$\frac{0.44 \text{ mol H}}{0.432} : \frac{0.432 \text{ mol O}}{0.432} = 1 \text{ mol H} : 1 \text{ mol O}$$

The empirical formula is therefore HO.

$$x = \frac{\text{molecular formula mass}}{\text{empirical formula mass}}$$

empirical formula mass of HO = 1.01 amu + 16.00 amu = 17.01 amu

$$x = \frac{34.00 \text{ amu}}{17.01 \text{ amu}} = 2$$

molecular formula: $H_x O_x = H_2 O_2$

ATE, Additional Sample Problems, p. 249

N-1. Given: empirical formula: OCNCl
molar mass = 232.41 g/mol

Unknown: molecular formula

$$x = \frac{\text{molar mass}}{\text{empirical molar mass}}$$

$$1 \text{ mol O} \times \frac{16.00 \text{ g O}}{\text{mol O}} = 16.00 \text{ g O}$$

$$1 \text{ mol C} \times \frac{12.01 \text{ g C}}{\text{mol C}} = 12.01 \text{ g C}$$

$$1 \text{ mol N} \times \frac{14.01 \text{ g N}}{\text{mol N}} = 14.01 \text{ g N}$$

$$1 \text{ mol Cl} \times \frac{35.45 \text{ g Cl}}{\text{mol Cl}} = 35.45 \text{ g Cl}$$

empirical molar mass = 77.47 g/mol

$$x = \frac{232.41 \text{ g/mol}}{77.47 \text{ g/mol}} = 3$$

molecular formula: $O_x C_x N_x Cl_x = O_3 C_3 N_3 Cl_3$

N-2. Given: empirical formula: NH_2
molecular formula mass = 32.06 amu

Unknown: molecular formula

$$x = \frac{\text{molecular formula mass}}{\text{empirical formula mass}}$$

empirical formula mass of NH_2 = 14.01 amu + (2 × 1.01 amu) = 16.03 amu

$$x = \frac{32.06 \text{ amu}}{16.03 \text{ amu}} = 2$$

molecular formula: $N_x H_{2x} = N_2 H_4$

1. Given: percentage composition: 36.48% Na, 25.41% S, and 38.11% O

Unknown: empirical formula

mass composition in 100.00 g sample: 36.48 g Na, 25.41 g S, 38.11 g O

composition in moles:

$$36.48 \text{ g Na} \times \frac{1 \text{ mol Na}}{22.99 \text{ g Na}} = 1.587 \text{ mol Na}$$

$$25.41 \text{ g S} \times \frac{1 \text{ mol S}}{32.07 \text{ g S}} = 0.7923 \text{ mol S}$$

$$38.11 \text{ g O} \times \frac{1 \text{ mol O}}{16.00 \text{ g O}} = 2.382 \text{ mol O}$$

smallest whole-number ratio of atoms:

$$\frac{1.587 \text{ mol Na}}{0.7923} : \frac{0.7923 \text{ mol S}}{0.7923} : \frac{2.382 \text{ mol O}}{0.7923}$$

$$= 2.003 \text{ mol Na} : 1.000 \text{ mol S} : 3.006 \text{ mol O}$$

$$= 2 \text{ mol Na} : 1 \text{ mol S} : 3 \text{ mol O}$$

The empirical formula is therefore Na_2SO_3.

2. Given: percentage composition: 53.70% Fe and 46.30% S

Unknown: empirical formula

mass composition in 100.00 g sample: 53.70 g Fe, 46.30 g S

composition in moles:

$$53.70 \text{ g Fe} \times \frac{1 \text{ mol Fe}}{55.85 \text{ Fe}} = 0.9615 \text{ mol Fe}$$

$$46.30 \text{ g S} \times \frac{1 \text{ mol S}}{32.07 \text{ g S}} = 1.444 \text{ mol S}$$

smallest whole-number ratio of atoms:

$$\frac{0.9615 \text{ mol Fe}}{0.9615} : \frac{1.444 \text{ mol S}}{0.9615} = 1.000 \text{ mol Fe} : 1.502 \text{ mol S}$$

$$= 2.000 \text{ mol Fe} : 3.004 \text{ mol S}$$

$$= 2 \text{ mol Fe} : 3 \text{ mol S}$$

The empirical formula is therefore Fe_2S_3.

3. Given: potassium mass = 1.04 g
chromium mass = 0.70 g
oxygen mass = 0.86 g

Unknown: empirical formula

composition in moles:

$$1.04 \text{ g K} \times \frac{1 \text{ mol K}}{39.10 \text{ g K}} = 0.0266 \text{ mol K}$$

$$0.70 \text{ g Cr} \times \frac{1 \text{ mol Cr}}{52.00 \text{ g Cr}} = 0.013 \text{ mol Cr}$$

$$0.86 \text{ g O} \times \frac{1 \text{ mol O}}{16.00 \text{ g O}} = 0.054 \text{ mol O}$$

smallest whole-number ratio of atoms:

$$\frac{0.0266 \text{ mol K}}{0.013} : \frac{0.013 \text{ mol Cr}}{0.013} : \frac{0.054 \text{ mol O}}{0.013}$$

$$= 2.0 \text{ mol K} : 1 \text{ mol Cr} : 4.2 \text{ mol O}$$

$$= 2 \text{ mol K} : 1 \text{ mol Cr} : 4 \text{ mol O}$$

The empirical formula is therefore K_2CrO_4.

4. Given: molecular formula
mass = 108.0 amu
nitrogen mass = 4.04 g
oxygen mass = 11.46 g

Unknown: molecular formula

composition in moles:

$$4.04 \text{ g N} \times \frac{1 \text{ mol N}}{14.01 \text{ g N}} = 0.288 \text{ mol N}$$

$$11.46 \text{ g O} \times \frac{1 \text{ mol O}}{16.00 \text{ g O}} = 0.7162 \text{ mol O}$$

smallest whole-number ratio of atoms:

$$\frac{0.288 \text{ mol N}}{0.288} : \frac{0.7162 \text{ mol O}}{0.288} = 1.00 \text{ mol N} : 2.49 \text{ mol O}$$

$$= 2.00 \text{ mol N} : 4.98 \text{ mol O}$$

$$= 2 \text{ mol N} : 5 \text{ mol O}$$

The empirical formula is therefore N_2O_5.

$$x = \frac{\text{molecular formula mass}}{\text{empirical formula mass}}$$

empirical formula mass of $N_2O_5 = (2 \times 14.01 \text{ amu}) + (5 \times 16.00 \text{ amu})$
$$= 108.02 \text{ amu}$$

$$x = \frac{108.0 \text{ amu}}{108.02 \text{ amu}} = 1$$

molecular formula: $N_{2x}O_{5x} = N_2O_5$

---

5. Given: $Na_xCl_yO_z$ is 25.42% Na; 3.25 g yield 4.33×10^{22} atoms of O

Unknown: empirical formula

$$\frac{4.33 \times 10^{22} \text{ atoms}}{6.022 \times 10^{23} \text{ atoms/mol}} = 0.0719 \text{ mol O}$$

$$0.0719 \text{ mol} \times 16 \frac{\text{g}}{\text{mol}} = 1.05 \text{ g O}$$

$$\frac{1.15 \text{ g}}{3.25 \text{ g}} = 0.354 = 35.4\% \text{ O}$$

$$100 - (35.4 + 25.42) = 39.18\% \text{ Cl}$$

$$\frac{25.42}{23} = 1.11$$

$$\frac{35.4}{16} = 2.21$$

$$\frac{39.18}{35.5} = 1.1$$

$$\frac{1.11}{1.1} = 1 \text{ Na}$$

$$\frac{2.21}{1.1} = 2 \text{ O}$$

$$\frac{1.1}{1.1} = 1 \text{ Cl}$$

$NaClO_2$

28. a. Given: $C_6H_{12}O_6$

Unknown: the formula mass of the given compound

$6 \text{ C atoms} \times \dfrac{12.01 \text{ amu}}{\text{C atom}} = 72.06 \text{ amu}$

$12 \text{ H atoms} \times \dfrac{1.01 \text{ amu}}{\text{H atom}} = 12.12 \text{ amu}$

$6 \text{ O atoms} \times \dfrac{16.00 \text{ amu}}{\text{O atom}} = 96.00 \text{ amu}$

formula mass of $C_6H_{12}O_6$ = 180.18 amu

b. Given: $Ca(CH_3COO)_2$

Unknown: the formula mass of the given compound

$1 \text{ Ca atom} \times \dfrac{40.08 \text{ amu}}{\text{Ca atom}} = 40.08 \text{ amu}$

$4 \text{ C atoms} \times \dfrac{12.01 \text{ amu}}{\text{C atom}} = 48.04 \text{ amu}$

$6 \text{ H atoms} \times \dfrac{1.01 \text{ amu}}{\text{H atom}} = 6.06 \text{ amu}$

$4 \text{ O atoms} \times \dfrac{16.00 \text{ amu}}{\text{O atom}} = 64.00 \text{ amu}$

formula mass of $Ca(CH_3COO)_2$ = 158.18 amu

c. Given: NH_4^+

Unknown: the formula mass of the given ion

$1 \text{ N atom} \times \dfrac{14.01 \text{ amu}}{\text{N atom}} = 14.01 \text{ amu}$

$4 \text{ H atoms} \times \dfrac{1.01 \text{ amu}}{\text{H atom}} = 4.04 \text{ amu}$

formula mass of NH_4^+ = 18.05 amu

d. Given: ClO_3^-

Unknown: the formula mass of the given ion

$1 \text{ Cl atom} \times \dfrac{35.45 \text{ amu}}{\text{Cl atom}} = 35.45 \text{ amu}$

$3 \text{ O atoms} \times \dfrac{16.00 \text{ amu}}{\text{O atom}} = 48.00 \text{ amu}$

formula mass of ClO_3^- = 83.45 amu

30. a. Given: KNO_3

Unknown: the molar mass of the given compound

$1 \text{ mol K} \times \dfrac{39.10 \text{ g K}}{\text{mol K}} = 39.10 \text{ g K}$

$1 \text{ mol N} \times \dfrac{14.01 \text{ g N}}{\text{mol N}} = 14.01 \text{ g N}$

$3 \text{ mol O} \times \dfrac{16.00 \text{ g O}}{\text{mol O}} = 48.00 \text{ g O}$

molar mass of KNO_3 = 101.11 g/mol

b. Given: Na_2SO_4

Unknown: the molar mass of the given compound

$2 \text{ mol Na} \times \dfrac{22.99 \text{ g Na}}{\text{mol Na}} = 45.98 \text{ g Na}$

$1 \text{ mol S} \times \dfrac{32.07 \text{ g S}}{\text{mol S}} = 32.07 \text{ g S}$

$4 \text{ mol O} \times \dfrac{16.00 \text{ g O}}{\text{mol O}} = 64.00 \text{ g O}$

molar mass of Na_2SO_4 = 142.05 g/mol

c. Given: $Ca(OH)_2$

Unknown: the molar mass of the given compound

$1 \text{ mol Ca} \times \dfrac{40.08 \text{ g Ca}}{\text{mol Ca}} = 40.08 \text{ g Ca}$

$2 \text{ mol O} \times \dfrac{16.00 \text{ g O}}{\text{mol O}} = 32.00 \text{ g O}$

$2 \text{ mol H} \times \dfrac{1.01 \text{ g H}}{\text{mol H}} = 2.02 \text{ g H}$

molar mass of $Ca(OH)_2$ = 74.10 g/mol

d. Given: $(NH_4)_2SO_3$

Unknown: the molar mass of the given compound

$2 \text{ mol N} \times \dfrac{14.01 \text{ g N}}{\text{mol N}} = 28.02 \text{ g N}$

$8 \text{ mol H} \times \dfrac{1.01 \text{ g H}}{\text{mol H}} = 8.08 \text{ g H}$

$1 \text{ mol S} \times \dfrac{32.07 \text{ g S}}{\text{mol S}} = 32.07 \text{ g S}$

$3 \text{ mol O} \times \dfrac{16.00 \text{ g O}}{\text{mol O}} = 48.00 \text{ g O}$

molar mass of $(NH_4)_2SO_3$ = 116.17 g/mol

e. Given: $Ca_3(PO_4)_2$

Unknown: the molar mass of the given compound

$3 \text{ mol Ca} \times \dfrac{40.08 \text{ g Ca}}{\text{mol Ca}} = 120.24 \text{ g Ca}$

$2 \text{ mol P} \times \dfrac{30.97 \text{ g P}}{\text{mol P}} = 61.94 \text{ g P}$

$8 \text{ mol O} \times \dfrac{16.00 \text{ g O}}{\text{mol O}} = 128.0 \text{ g O}$

molar mass of $Ca_3(PO_4)_2$ = 310.18 g/mol

f. Given: $Al_2(CrO_4)_3$

Unknown: the molar mass of the given compound

$2 \text{ mol Al} \times \dfrac{26.98 \text{ g Al}}{\text{mol Al}} = 53.96 \text{ g Al}$

$3 \text{ mol Cr} \times \dfrac{52.00 \text{ g Cr}}{\text{mol Cr}} = 156.0 \text{ g Cr}$

$12 \text{ mol O} \times \dfrac{16.00 \text{ g O}}{\text{mol O}} = 192.0 \text{ g O}$

molar mass of $Al_2(CrO_4)_3$ = 401.96 g/mol

31. a. Given: 4.50 g H_2O

Unknown: number of moles H_2O

$2 \text{ mol H} \times \dfrac{1.01 \text{ g H}}{\text{mol H}} = 2.02 \text{ g H}$

$1 \text{ mol O} \times \dfrac{16.00 \text{ g O}}{\text{mol O}} = 16.00 \text{ g O}$

molar mass of H_2O = 18.02 g/mol

$\text{mol } H_2O = \dfrac{4.50 \text{ g}}{18.02 \text{ g/mol}} = 0.250 \text{ mol}$

b. Given: 471.6 g
$Ba(OH)_2$

Unknown: number of moles $Ba(OH)_2$

$1 \text{ mol Ba} \times \dfrac{137.33 \text{ g Ba}}{\text{mol Ba}} = 137.33 \text{ g Ba}$

$2 \text{ mol O} \times \dfrac{16.00 \text{ g O}}{\text{mol O}} = 32.00 \text{ g O}$

$2 \text{ mol H} \times \dfrac{1.01 \text{ g H}}{\text{mol H}} = 2.02 \text{ g H}$

molar mass of $Ba(OH)_2$ = 171.35 g/mol

$\text{mol } Ba(OH)_2 = \dfrac{471.6 \text{ g}}{171.35 \text{ g/mol}} = 2.752 \text{ mol}$

c. Given: 129.68 g
$Fe_3(PO_4)_2$

Unknown: number of moles $Fe_3(PO_4)_2$

$3 \text{ mol Fe} \times \dfrac{55.85 \text{ g Fe}}{\text{mol Fe}} = 167.6 \text{ g Fe}$

$2 \text{ mol P} \times \dfrac{30.97 \text{ g P}}{\text{mol P}} = 61.94 \text{ g P}$

$8 \text{ mol O} \times \dfrac{16.00 \text{ g O}}{\text{mol O}} = 128.0 \text{ g O}$

molar mass of $Fe_3(PO_4)_2$ = 357.5 g/mol

$\text{mol } Fe_3(PO_4)_2 = \dfrac{129.68 \text{ g}}{357.5 \text{ g/mol}} = 0.3627 \text{ mol}$

32. a. Given: NaCl

Unknown: percentage composition of given compound

$1 \text{ mol Na} \times \dfrac{22.99 \text{ g Na}}{\text{mol Na}} = 22.99 \text{ g Na}$

$1 \text{ mol Cl} \times \dfrac{35.45 \text{ g Cl}}{\text{mol Cl}} = 35.45 \text{ g Cl}$

molar mass of NaCl = 58.44 g

$\dfrac{22.99 \text{ g Na}}{58.44 \text{ g NaCl}} \times 100 = 39.34\% \text{ Na}$

$\dfrac{35.45 \text{ g Cl}}{58.44 \text{ g NaCl}} \times 100 = 60.66\% \text{ Cl}$

b. Given: $AgNO_3$

Unknown: percentage composition of given compound

$1 \text{ mol Ag} \times \dfrac{107.87 \text{ g Ag}}{\text{mol Ag}} = 107.87 \text{ g Ag}$

$1 \text{ mol N} \times \dfrac{14.01 \text{ g N}}{\text{mol N}} = 14.01 \text{ g N}$

$3 \text{ mol O} \times \dfrac{16.00 \text{ g O}}{\text{mol O}} = 48.00 \text{ g O}$

molar mass of $AgNO_3$ = 169.88 g

$\dfrac{107.87 \text{ g Ag}}{169.88 \text{ g AgNo}_3} \times 100 = 63.50\% \text{ Ag}$

$\dfrac{14.01 \text{ g N}}{169.88 \text{ g AgNo}_3} \times 100 = 8.25\% \text{ N}$

$\dfrac{48.00 \text{ g O}}{169.88 \text{ g AgNO}_3} \times 100 = 28.26\% \text{ O}$

c. Given: $Mg(OH)_2$

Unknown: percentage composition of given compound

$$1 \text{ mol Mg} \times \frac{24.30 \text{ g Mg}}{\text{mol Mg}} = 24.30 \text{ g Mg}$$

$$2 \text{ mol O} \times \frac{16.00 \text{ g O}}{\text{mol O}} = 32.00 \text{ g O}$$

$$2 \text{ mol H} \times \frac{1.01 \text{ g H}}{\text{mol H}} = 2.02 \text{ g H}$$

molar mass of $Mg(OH)_2 = 58.32$ g

$$\frac{24.30 \text{ g Mg}}{58.32 \text{ g Mg(OH)}_2} \times 100 = 41.67\% \text{ Mg}$$

$$\frac{32.00 \text{ g O}}{58.32 \text{ g Mg(OH)}_2} \times 100 = 54.87\% \text{ O}$$

$$\frac{2.02 \text{ g H}}{58.32 \text{ g Mg(OH)}_2} \times 100 = 3.46\% \text{ H}$$

---

33. Given: $CuSO_4 \cdot 5H_2O$

Unknown: mass percentage of H_2O in given compound

$$\text{mass } H_2O = 5 \text{ mol } H_2O \times \frac{18.02 \text{ g } H_2O}{\text{mol } H_2O} = 90.10 \text{ g } H_2O$$

$$1 \text{ mol Cu} \times \frac{63.55 \text{ g Cu}}{\text{mol Cu}} = 63.55 \text{ g Cu}$$

$$1 \text{ mol S} \times \frac{32.07 \text{ g S}}{\text{mol S}} = 32.07 \text{ g S}$$

$$4 \text{ mol O} \times \frac{16.00 \text{ g O}}{\text{mol O}} = 64.00 \text{ g O}$$

molar mass of $CuSO_4 \cdot 5H_2O = 249.72$ g

mass percentage of H_2O in $CuSO_4 \cdot 5H_2O =$

$$\frac{90.10 \text{ g } H_2O}{249.72 \text{ CuSO}_4 \cdot 5H_2O} \times 100 = 36.08\% \text{ } H_2O$$

---

36. Given: percentage composition: 63.50% Ag, 8.25% N, and 28.25% O

Unknown: empirical formula

mass composition in 100.00 g sample: 63.50 g Ag, 8.25 g N, 28.25 g O

composition in moles:

$$63.50 \text{ g Ag} \times \frac{1 \text{ mol Ag}}{107.87 \text{ g Ag}} = 0.5887 \text{ mol Ag}$$

$$8.25 \text{ g N} \times \frac{1 \text{ mol N}}{14.01 \text{ g N}} = 0.589 \text{ mol N}$$

$$28.25 \text{ g O} \times \frac{1 \text{ mol O}}{16.00 \text{ g O}} = 1.766 \text{ mol O}$$

smallest whole-number ratio of atoms:

$$\frac{0.5887 \text{ mol Ag}}{0.5887} : \frac{0.589 \text{ mol N}}{0.5887} : \frac{1.766 \text{ mol O}}{0.5887}$$

$= 1 \text{ mol Ag} : 1 \text{ mol N} : 3 \text{ mol O}$

The empirical formula is therefore $AgNO_3$.

37. Given: percentage composition: 52.11% C, 13.14% H, and 34.75% O

Unknown: empirical formula

mass composition in 100.00 g sample: 52.11 g C, 13.14 g H, 34.75 g O

composition in moles:

$$52.11 \text{ g C} \times \frac{1 \text{ mol C}}{12.01 \text{ g C}} = 4.339 \text{ mol C}$$

$$13.14 \text{ g H} \times \frac{1 \text{ mol H}}{1.01 \text{ g H}} = 13.0 \text{ mol H}$$

$$34.75 \text{ g O} \times \frac{1 \text{ mol O}}{16.00 \text{ g O}} = 2.172 \text{ mol O}$$

smallest whole-number ratio of atoms:

$$\frac{4.339 \text{ mol C}}{2.172} : \frac{13.0 \text{ mol H}}{2.172} : \frac{2.172 \text{ mol O}}{2.172}$$

$$= 2 \text{ mol C} : 6 \text{ mol H} : 1 \text{ mol O}$$

The empirical formula is therefore C_2H_6O.

---

38. Given: empirical formula: CH_2O
molar mass = 120.12 g/mol

Unknown: molecular formula

$$x = \frac{\text{molar mass}}{\text{empirical molar mass}}$$

$$1 \text{ mol C} \times \frac{12.01 \text{ g C}}{\text{mol C}} = 12.01 \text{ g C}$$

$$2 \text{ mol H} \times \frac{1.01 \text{ g H}}{\text{mol H}} = 2.02 \text{ g H}$$

$$1 \text{ mol O} \times \frac{16.00 \text{ g O}}{\text{mol O}} = 16.00 \text{ g O}$$

empirical molar mass = 30.03 g/mol

$$x = \frac{120.12 \text{ g/mol}}{30.03 \text{ g/mol}} = 4.000 \rightarrow 4$$

molecular formula: $C_xH_{2x}O_x = C_4H_8O_4$

---

39. Given: molecular formula mass = 42.08 amu
percentage composition: 85.64% C and 14.36% H

Unknown: molecular formula

$$x = \frac{\text{molecular formula mass}}{\text{empirical formula mass}}$$

mass composition in 100.00 g sample: 85.64 g C, 14.36 g H

composition in moles:

$$85.64 \text{ g C} \times \frac{1 \text{ mol C}}{12.01 \text{ g C}} = 7.131 \text{ mol C}$$

$$14.36 \text{ g H} \times \frac{1 \text{ mol H}}{1.01 \text{ g H}} = 14.2 \text{ mol H}$$

smallest whole-number ratio of atoms:

$$\frac{7.131 \text{ mol C}}{7.131} : \frac{14.2 \text{ mol H}}{7.131} = 1 \text{ mol C} : 2 \text{ mol H}$$

The empirical formula is therefore CH_2.

empirical formula mass = 12.01 amu + 2 × 1.01 amu
= 12.01 amu + 2.02 amu = 14.03 amu

$$x = \frac{42.08 \text{ amu}}{14.03 \text{ amu}} = 3$$

molecular formula: $C_xH_{2x} = C_3H_6$

40. Given: percentage composition: 37.51% C, 4.20% H, and 58.29% O

Unknown: empirical formula

mass composition in 100.00 g sample: 37.51 g C, 4.20 g H, 58.29 g O

composition in moles:

$$37.51 \text{ g C} \times \frac{1 \text{ mol C}}{12.01 \text{ g C}} = 3.123 \text{ mol C}$$

$$4.20 \text{ g H} \times \frac{1 \text{ mol H}}{1.01 \text{ g H}} = 4.16 \text{ mol H}$$

$$58.29 \text{ g O} \times \frac{1 \text{ mol O}}{16.00 \text{ g O}} = 3.643 \text{ mol O}$$

smallest whole-number ratio of atoms:

$$\frac{3.123 \text{ mol C}}{3.123} : \frac{4.16 \text{ mol H}}{3.123} : \frac{3.643 \text{ mol O}}{3.123}$$

$$= 1.000 \text{ mol C} : 1.33 \text{ mol H} : 1.167 \text{ mol O}$$

$$= 6.000 \text{ mol C} : 7.98 \text{ mol H} : 7.002 \text{ mol O}$$

$$= 6 \text{ mol C} : 8 \text{ mol H} : 7 \text{ mol O}$$

The empirical formula is therefore $C_6H_8O_7$.

---

42. a. Given: 1.000 mol NaCl

Unknown: mass of NaCl

$$1 \text{ mol Na} \times \frac{22.99 \text{ g Na}}{\text{mol Na}} = 22.99 \text{ g Na}$$

$$1 \text{ mol Cl} \times \frac{35.45 \text{ g Cl}}{\text{mol Cl}} = 35.45 \text{ g Cl}$$

molar mass of NaCl = 58.44 g/mol

$$\text{mass NaCl} = \frac{58.44 \text{ g NaCl}}{\text{mol NaCl}} \times 1.000 \text{ mol NaCl} = 58.44 \text{ g}$$

b. Given: 2.000 mol H_2O

Unknown: mass of H_2O

molar mass of H_2O = 18.02 g/mol

$$\text{mass } H_2O = \frac{18.02 \text{ g } H_2O}{\text{mol } H_2O} \times 2.000 \text{ mol } H_2O$$

$$\text{mass } H_2O = 36.04 \text{ g}$$

c. Given: 3.500 mol $Ca(OH)_2$

Unknown: mass of $Ca(OH)_2$

$$1 \text{ mol Ca} \times \frac{40.08 \text{ g Ca}}{\text{mol Ca}} = 40.08 \text{ g Ca}$$

$$2 \text{ mol O} \times \frac{16.00 \text{ g O}}{\text{mol O}} = 32.00 \text{ g O}$$

$$2 \text{ mol H} \times \frac{1.01 \text{ g H}}{\text{mol H}} = 2.02 \text{ g H}$$

molar mass of $Ca(OH)_2$ = 74.10 g/mol

$$\text{mass } Ca(OH)_2 = \frac{74.10 \text{ g } Ca(OH)_2}{\text{mol } Ca(OH)_2} \times 3.500 \text{ mol } Ca(OH)_2 = 259.4 \text{ g}$$

d. Given: 0.625 mol
$Ba(NO_3)_2$
Unknown: mass of
sample in
grams

$$1 \text{ mol Ba} \times \frac{137.33 \text{ g Ba}}{\text{mol Ba}} = 137.33 \text{ g Ba}$$

$$2 \text{ mol N} \times \frac{14.01 \text{ g N}}{\text{mol N}} = 28.02 \text{ g N}$$

$$6 \text{ mol O} \times \frac{16.00 \text{ g O}}{\text{mol O}} = 96.00 \text{ g O}$$

molar mass of $Ba(NO_3)_2$ = 261.35 g/mol

$$\text{mass } Ba(NO_3)_2 = \frac{261.35 \text{ g } Ba(NO_3)_2}{\text{mol } Ba(NO_3)_2} \times 0.625 \text{ mol } Ba(NO_3)_2 = 163 \text{ g}$$

---

43. a. Given: XeF_4
Unknown: the formula
mass and
molar mass
of the given
compound

$$1 \text{ Xe atom} \times \frac{131.29 \text{ amu}}{\text{Xe atom}} = 131.29 \text{ amu}$$

$$4 \text{ F atoms} \times \frac{19.00 \text{ amu}}{\text{F atom}} = 76.00 \text{ amu}$$

formula mass of XeF_4 = 207.29 amu

$$\text{molar mass of } XeF_4 = 207.29 \text{ amu} \times \frac{1 \text{ g/mol}}{1 \text{ amu}} = 207.29 \text{ g/mol}$$

b. Given: $C_{12}H_{24}O_6$
Unknown: the formula
mass and
molar mass
of the given
compound

$$12 \text{ C atoms} \times \frac{12.01 \text{ amu}}{\text{C atom}} = 144.12 \text{ amu}$$

$$24 \text{ H atoms} \times \frac{1.01 \text{ amu}}{\text{H atom}} = 24.24 \text{ amu}$$

$$6 \text{ O atoms} \times \frac{16.00 \text{ amu}}{\text{O atom}} = 96.00 \text{ amu}$$

formula mass of $C_{12}H_{24}O_6$ = 264.36 amu

$$\text{molar mass of } C_{12}H_{24}O_6 = 264.36 \text{ amu} \times \frac{1 \text{ g/mol}}{1 \text{ amu}} = 264.36 \text{ g/mol}$$

c. Given: Hg_2I_2
Unknown: the formula
mass and
molar mass
of the given
compound

$$2 \text{ Hg atoms} \times \frac{200.59 \text{ amu}}{\text{Hg atom}} = 401.18 \text{ amu}$$

$$2 \text{ I atoms} \times \frac{126.90 \text{ amu}}{\text{I atom}} = 253.80 \text{ amu}$$

formula mass of Hg_2I_2 = 654.98 amu

$$\text{molar mass of } Hg_2I_2 = 654.98 \text{ amu} \times \frac{1 \text{ g/mol}}{1 \text{ amu}} = 654.98 \text{ g/mol}$$

d. Given: CuCN
Unknown: the formula
mass and
molar mass
of the given
compound

$$1 \text{ Cu atom} \times \frac{63.55 \text{ amu}}{\text{Cu atom}} = 63.55 \text{ amu}$$

$$1 \text{ C atom} \times \frac{12.01 \text{ amu}}{\text{C atom}} = 12.01 \text{ amu}$$

$$1 \text{ N atom} \times \frac{14.01 \text{ amu}}{\text{N atom}} = 14.01 \text{ amu}$$

formula mass of CuCN = 89.57 amu

$$\text{molar mass of CuCN} = 89.57 \text{ amu} \times \frac{1 \text{ g/mol}}{1 \text{ amu}} = 89.57 \text{ g/mol}$$

45. Given: $Fe(CHO_2)_3 \cdot H_2O$

Unknown: mass percentage of H_2O

1 mol $Fe(CHO_2)_3 \cdot H_2O$ contains 1 mol H_2O. H_2O has a molar mass of 18.02 g/mol.

1 mol $Fe(CHO_2)_3 \cdot H_2O$ contains 1 mol Fe, 3 mol C, 3 mol H, and 6 mol O in the iron (III) formate molecule proper.

$$1 \text{ mol Fe} \times \frac{55.85 \text{ g Fe}}{\text{mol Fe}} = 55.85 \text{ g Fe}$$

$$3 \text{ mol C} \times \frac{12.01 \text{ g C}}{\text{mol C}} = 36.03 \text{ g C}$$

$$3 \text{ mol H} \times \frac{1.01 \text{ H}}{\text{mol H}} = 3.03 \text{ g H}$$

$$6 \text{ mol O} \times \frac{16.00 \text{ g O}}{\text{mol O}} = 96.00 \text{ g O}$$

molar mass of $Fe(CHO_2)_3 \cdot H_2O$ = 208.93 g

mass percentage of H_2O in $Fe(CHO_2)_3 \cdot H_2O$

$$= \frac{18.02 \text{ g } H_2O}{208.93 \text{ g } Fe(CHO_2)_3 \cdot H_2O} \times 100 = 8.62\% \, H_2O$$

---

46. a. Given: HNO_2

Unknown: oxidation numbers for each atom in the given acid

According to rule 4, O has an oxidation number of –2. H is the least electronegative atom in the molecule, so according to rule 5, H has an oxidation number of +1.

$$\overset{+1}{H}\overset{}{N}\overset{-2}{O_2}$$

total oxidation number of oxygen atoms = $-2 \times 2 = -4$

total oxidation number of hydrogen atom = +1

$$\overset{+1}{\underset{+1}{H}}\overset{}{N}\overset{-2}{\underset{-4}{O_2}}$$

balance of oxidation numbers:

$$\overset{+1}{H}\overset{}{N}\overset{-2}{O_2} \rightarrow \overset{+1}{H}\overset{+3}{N}\overset{-2}{O_2}$$

N therefore has an oxidation number of +3.

H, +1

N, +3

O, –2

b. Given: H_2SO_3

Unknown: oxidation numbers for each atom in the given acid

According to rule 4, O has an oxidation number of −2. H is the least electronegative atom in the molecule, so according to rule 5, H has an oxidation number of +1.

$$\overset{+1\ \ -2}{H_2SO_3}$$

total oxidation number of oxygen atoms = $-2 \times 3 = -6$

total oxidation number of hydrogen atoms = $+1 \times 2 = +2$

$$\underset{+2\ \ \ -6}{\overset{+1\ \ -2}{H_2SO_3}}$$

balance of oxidation numbers:

$$\underset{+2\ +4\ -6}{\overset{+1\ \ \ -2}{H_2SO_3}} \rightarrow \underset{+2\ +4\ -6}{\overset{+1\ +4\ -2}{H_2SO_3}}$$

S therefore has an oxidation number of +4.

H, +1

S, +4

O, −2

c. Given: H_2CO_3

Unknown: oxidation numbers for each atom in the given acid

According to rule 4, O has an oxidation number of −2. H has the least electronegative atom in the molecule, so according to rule 5, H has an oxidation number of +1.

$$\overset{+1\ \ -2}{H_2CO_3}$$

total oxidation number of oxygen atoms = $-2 \times 3 = -6$

total oxidation number of hydrogen atoms = $+1 \times 2 = +2$

$$\underset{+2\ \ \ -6}{\overset{+1\ \ -2}{H_2CO_3}}$$

balance of oxidation numbers:

$$\underset{+2\ +4\ -6}{\overset{+1\ \ \ -2}{H_2CO_3}} \rightarrow \underset{+2\ +4\ -6}{\overset{+1\ +4\ -2}{H_2CO_3}}$$

C therefore has an oxidation number of +4.

H, +1

C, +4

O, −2

d. Given: HI

Unknown: oxidation numbers for each atom

According to rule 8, I can be treated as an anion with an oxidation number of −1. The oxidation number of H, which has an electronegativity that is smaller than that of I, has an oxidation number of +1.

H, +1

I, −1

47. a. Given: NaClO

Unknown: percentage composition of given compound

$$1 \text{ mol Na} \times \frac{22.99 \text{ g Na}}{\text{mol Na}} = 22.99 \text{ g Na}$$

$$1 \text{ mol Cl} \times \frac{35.45 \text{ g Cl}}{\text{mol Cl}} = 35.45 \text{ g Cl}$$

$$1 \text{ mol O} \times \frac{16.00 \text{ g O}}{\text{mol O}} = 16.00 \text{ g O}$$

molar mass of NaClO = 74.44 g

$$\frac{22.99 \text{ g Na}}{74.44 \text{ g NaClO}} \times 100 = 30.88\% \text{ Na}$$

$$\frac{35.45 \text{ g Cl}}{74.44 \text{ g NaClO}} \times 100 = 47.62\% \text{ Cl}$$

$$\frac{16.00 \text{ g O}}{74.44 \text{ g NaClO}} \times 100 = 21.49\% \text{ O}$$

b. Given: H_2SO_3

Unknown: percentage composition of given compound

$$2 \text{ mol H} \times \frac{1.01 \text{ g H}}{\text{mol H}} = 2.02 \text{ g H}$$

$$1 \text{ mol S} \times \frac{32.07 \text{ g S}}{\text{mol S}} = 32.07 \text{ g S}$$

$$3 \text{ mol O} \times \frac{16.00 \text{ g O}}{\text{mol O}} = 48.00 \text{ g O}$$

molar mass of H_2SO_3 = 82.09 g

$$\frac{2.02 \text{ g H}}{82.09 \text{ g H}_2\text{SO}_3} \times 100 = 2.46\% \text{ H}$$

$$\frac{32.07 \text{ g S}}{82.09 \text{ g H}_2\text{SO}_3} \times 100 = 39.07\% \text{ S}$$

$$\frac{48.00 \text{ g O}}{82.09 \text{ g H}_2\text{SO}_3} \times 100 = 58.47\% \text{ O}$$

c. Given: C_2H_5COOH

Unknown: percentage composition of given compound

$$3 \text{ mol C} \times \frac{12.01 \text{ g C}}{\text{mol C}} = 36.03 \text{ g C}$$

$$6 \text{ mol H} \times \frac{1.01 \text{ g H}}{\text{mol H}} = 6.06 \text{ g H}$$

$$2 \text{ mol O} \times \frac{16.00 \text{ g O}}{\text{mol O}} = 32.00 \text{ g O}$$

molar mass of C_2H_5COOH = 74.09 g

$$\frac{36.03 \text{ g C}}{74.09 \text{ g C}_2\text{H}_5\text{COOH}} \times 100 = 48.63\% \text{ C}$$

$$\frac{6.06 \text{ g H}}{74.09 \text{ g C}_2\text{H}_5\text{COOH}} \times 100 = 8.18\% \text{ H}$$

$$\frac{32.00 \text{ g O}}{74.09 \text{ g C}_2\text{H}_5\text{COOH}} \times 100 = 43.19\% \text{ O}$$

d. Given: $BeCl_2$

Unknown: percentage composition of given compound

$$1 \text{ mol Be} \times \frac{9.01 \text{ g Be}}{\text{mol Be}} = 9.01 \text{ g Be}$$

$$2 \text{ mol Cl} \times \frac{35.45 \text{ g Cl}}{\text{mol Cl}} = 70.90 \text{ g Cl}$$

molar mass of $BeCl_2 = 79.91$ g

$$\frac{9.01 \text{ g Be}}{79.91 \text{ g } BeCl_2} \times 100 = 11.28\% \text{ Be}$$

$$\frac{70.90 \text{ g Cl}}{79.91 \text{ g } BeCl_2} \times 100 = 88.72\% \text{ Cl}$$

---

49. a. Given: CO_2

Unknown: the oxidation numbers for each atom in the given compound

According to rule 4, O has an oxidation number of –2.

$$\overset{-2}{C}O_2$$

total oxidation number of oxygen atoms $= -2 \times 2 = -4$

$$\overset{-2}{\underset{-4}{C O_2}}$$

balance of oxidation numbers:

$$\overset{-2}{\underset{+4\,-4}{C O_2}} \rightarrow \overset{+4\,-2}{\underset{+4\,-4}{C O_2}}$$

C therefore has an oxidation number of +4.

C, +4

O, –2

b. Given: NH_4^+

Unknown: the oxidation numbers for each atom in the given ion

According to rule 5, H has an oxidation number of +1.

$$\overset{+1}{N H_4^+}$$

total oxidation number of hydrogen atoms $= +1 \times 4 = +4$

$$\overset{+1}{\underset{+4}{N H_4^+}}$$

balance of oxidation numbers:

$$\overset{+1}{\underset{-3\,+4}{N H_4^+}} \rightarrow \overset{-3\,+1}{\underset{-3\,+4}{N H_4^+}}$$

N therefore has an oxidation number of –3.

N, –3

H, +1

c. Given: MnO_4^-

Unknown: the oxidation numbers for each atom in the given ion

According to rule 4, O has an oxidation number of –2.

$$\overset{-2}{M n O_4^-}$$

total oxidation number of oxygen atoms = $-2 \times 4 = -8$

$$\underset{-8}{\overset{-2}{M n O_4^-}}$$

balance of oxidation numbers:

$$\underset{+7\ -8}{\overset{-2}{M n O_4^-}} \rightarrow \underset{+7\ -8}{\overset{+7\ -2}{M n O_4^-}}$$

Mn therefore has an oxidation number of +7.

Mn, +7

O, –2

d. Given: $S_2O_3^{2-}$

Unknown: the oxidation numbers for each atom in the given ion

According to rule 4, O has an oxidation number of –2.

$$\overset{-2}{S_2 O_3^{2-}}$$

total oxidation number of oxygen atoms = $-2 \times 3 = -6$

$$\underset{-6}{\overset{-2}{S_2 O_3^{2-}}}$$

balance of oxidation numbers:

$$\underset{+4\ -6}{\overset{-2}{S_2 O_3^{2-}}} \rightarrow \underset{+4\ -6}{\overset{+2\ -2}{S_2 O_3^{2-}}}$$

S therefore has an oxidation number of +2.

S, +2

O, –2

e. Given: H_2O_2

Unknown: the oxidation numbers for each atom in the given compound

According to rule 4, O in peroxides has an oxidation number of –1.

$$\overset{-1}{H_2 O_2}$$

total oxidation number of oxygen atoms = $-1 \times 2 = -2$

$$\underset{-2}{\overset{-1}{H_2 O_2}}$$

balance of oxidation numbers:

$$\underset{+2\ -2}{\overset{-1}{H_2 O_2}} \rightarrow \underset{+2\ -2}{\overset{+1\ -1}{H_2 O_2}}$$

H therefore has an oxidation number of +1.

H, +1

O, –1

f. Given: P_4O_{10}

Unknown: the oxidation numbers for each atom in the given compound

According to rule 4, O has an oxidation number of –2.

$$P_4\overset{-2}{O}_{10}$$

total oxidation number of oxygen atoms = $-2 \times 10 = -20$

$$\underset{-20}{P_4\overset{-2}{O}_{10}}$$

balance of oxidation numbers:

$$\underset{+20\ -20}{P_4\overset{-2}{O}_{10}} \rightarrow \underset{+20\ -20}{\overset{+5\ -2}{P_4O_{10}}}$$

P therefore has an oxidation number of +5.

P, +5

O, –2

g. Given: OF_2

Unknown: the oxidation numbers for each atom in the given compound

F always has an oxidation number of –1, according to rule 3.

$$O\overset{-1}{F}_2$$

total oxidation number of fluorine atoms = $-1 \times 2 = -2$

$$\underset{-2}{O\overset{-1}{F}_2}$$

balance of oxidation numbers:

$$\underset{+2\ -2}{O\overset{-1}{F}_2} \rightarrow \underset{+2\ -2}{\overset{+2\ -1}{O\ F}_2}$$

O therefore has an oxidation number of +2.

O, +2

F, –1

---

50. Given: sample mass = 175.0 g

carbon mass = 56.15 g

hydrogen mass = 9.43 g

oxygen mass = 74.81 g

nitrogen mass = 13.11 g

sodium mass = 21.49 g

Unknown: empirical formula

composition in moles:

$$56.15 \text{ g C} \times \frac{1 \text{ mol C}}{12.01 \text{ g C}} = 4.675 \text{ mol C}$$

$$9.43 \text{ g H} \times \frac{1 \text{ mol H}}{1.01 \text{ g H}} = 9.34 \text{ mol H}$$

$$74.81 \text{ g O} \times \frac{1 \text{ mol O}}{16.00 \text{ g O}} = 4.676 \text{ mol O}$$

$$13.11 \text{ g N} \times \frac{1 \text{ mol N}}{14.01 \text{ g N}} = 0.9358 \text{ mol N}$$

$$21.49 \text{ g Na} \times \frac{1 \text{ mol Na}}{22.99 \text{ g Na}} = 0.9348 \text{ mol Na}$$

smallest whole-number ratio of atoms:

$$\frac{4.675 \text{ mol C}}{0.9348} : \frac{9.34 \text{ mol H}}{0.9348} : \frac{4.676 \text{ mol O}}{0.9348} : \frac{0.9358 \text{ mol N}}{0.9348} : \frac{0.9348 \text{ mol Na}}{0.9348}$$

= 5 mol C : 10 mol H : 5 mol O : 1 mol N : 1 mol Na

The empirical formula is therefore $C_5H_{10}O_5NNa$.

51. Given: sulfur trioxide

Unknown: chemical information available from formula name

sulfur $\rightarrow S \times 1 \rightarrow S$

trioxide $\rightarrow O \times 3 = O_3$

formula: SO_3

According to rule 4, O has an oxidation number of –2.

$S\overset{-2}{O}_3$

total oxidation number of oxygen atoms = $-2 \times 3 = -6$

$\underset{-6}{S\overset{-2}{O}_3}$

balance of oxidation numbers

$\underset{+6-6}{\overset{-2}{S}O_3} \rightarrow \underset{+6-6}{\overset{+6-2}{S}O_3}$

S therefore has an oxidation number of +6.

S, +6

O, –2

---

52. Given: mass of crucible = 30.02 g

mass of nickel and crucible = 31.07 g

mass of nickel oxide and crucible = 31.36 g

Unknown: masses of nickel, nickel oxide, and oxygen, and the empirical formula of nickel oxide

mass of nickel = 31.07 g – 30.02 g = 1.05 g Ni

mass of nickel oxide = 31.36 g – 30.02 g = 1.34 g nickel oxide

mass of oxygen = 1.34 g – 1.05 g = 0.29 g O

composition in moles:

$1.05 \text{ g Ni} \times \dfrac{1 \text{ mol Ni}}{58.69 \text{ g Ni}} = 0.0179 \text{ mol Ni}$

$0.29 \text{ g O} \times \dfrac{1 \text{ mol O}}{16.00 \text{ g O}} = 0.018 \text{ mol O}$

smallest whole-number ratio of atoms:

$\dfrac{0.0179 \text{ mol Ni}}{0.0179} : \dfrac{0.018 \text{ mol O}}{0.0179} = 1 \text{ mol Ni} : 1 \text{ mol O}$

The empirical formula is therefore NiO.

Math Tutor, p. 256

---

1. Given: Na_2CO_3

Unknown: percent composition

molar mass of Na_2CO_3 is 105.8 g

$2 \text{ mol of Na} \times 22.9 \dfrac{g}{mol} = 45.8 \text{ g of Na}$

$1 \text{ mol of C} \times 12 \dfrac{g}{mol} = 12 \text{ g of C}$

$3 \text{ mol of O} \times 16 \dfrac{g}{mol} = 48 \text{ g of O}$

$\dfrac{45.8 \text{ g Na}}{105.8 \text{ g Na}_2\text{CO}_3} \times 100 = 43.38\% \text{ Na}$

$\dfrac{12 \text{ g C}}{105.8 \text{ g Na}_2\text{CO}_3} \times 100 = 11.33\% \text{ C}$

$\dfrac{48 \text{ g O}}{105.8 \text{ g Na}_2\text{CO}_3} \times 100 = 45.29\% \text{ O}$

2. Given: $Zn(IO_3)_2$

Unknown: percent iodine

molar mass of $Zn(IO_3)_2$ is 415.2 g

$$2 \text{ mol of I} \times 126.9 \, \frac{g}{mol} = 253.8 \text{ g of I}$$

$$\frac{253.8 \text{ g I}}{415.2 \text{ g Zn(IO}_3)_2} \times 100 = 61.1\% \text{ I}$$

Standardized Test Prep, p. 257

7. Given: H_2SO_4

Unknown: percent composition

molar mass of H_2SO_4 is 98.09 g

$$2 \text{ mol of H} \times 1.008 \, \frac{g}{mol} = 2.016 \text{ g of H}$$

$$1 \text{ mol of S} \times 32.07 \, \frac{g}{mol} = 32.07 \text{ g of S}$$

$$4 \text{ mol of O} \times 16 \, \frac{g}{mol} = 64.00 \text{ g of O}$$

$$\frac{2.016 \text{ g H}}{98.099 \text{ H}_2SO_4} \times 100 = 2.1\% \text{ H}$$

$$\frac{32.07 \text{ g S}}{98.099 \text{ H}_2SO_4} \times 100 = 32.7\% \text{ S}$$

$$\frac{64 \text{ g O}}{98.099 \text{ H}_2SO_4} \times 100 = 65.2\% \text{ C}$$

8. Given: CH_4O, CO_2, H_2O, Na_2CO_3

Unknown: the one with the highest percentage oxygen

CH_4O molar mass is 32 g

$$1 \text{ mol} \times \frac{16 \text{ g O}}{mol} = 16 \text{ g of O}$$

$$\frac{16 \text{ g O}}{32 \text{ g CH}_4O} \times 100 = 50\% \text{ O}$$

CO_2 molar mass is 44 g

$$2 \text{ mol} \times \frac{16 \text{ g O}}{mol} = 32 \text{ g O}$$

$$\frac{32 \text{ g O}}{44 \text{ g CO}_2} \times 100 = 72.7\% \text{ O}$$

H_2O molar mass is 18 g

$$1 \text{ mol} \times \frac{16 \text{ g O}}{mol} = 16 \text{ g O}$$

$$\frac{16 \text{ g O}}{18 \text{ g H}_2O} \times 100 = 88.9\% \text{ O}$$

Na_2CO_3 molar mass is 106 g

$$3 \text{ mol} \times \frac{16 \text{ g O}}{mol} = 48 \text{ g O}$$

$$\frac{48 \text{ g O}}{106 \text{ g Na}_2CO_3} \times 100 = 45.2\% \text{ O}$$

9. Given: a compound is 1.2% H, 42.0% Cl, 56.8% O

Unknown: the empirical formula

Assume 100 g of compound. Then there are 1.2 g H, 42 g Cl, 56.8 g O

and $1.2 \text{ g} \times \dfrac{1 \text{ mol}}{1 \text{ g}} = 1.2$ mol of H

$42 \text{ g} \times \dfrac{1 \text{ mol}}{35.5 \text{ g}} = 1.18$ mol of Cl

$56.8 \text{ g} \times \dfrac{1 \text{ mol}}{16 \text{ g}} = 3.55$ mol of O

$\dfrac{1.2 \text{ mol}}{1.18 \text{ mol}} = 1$

$\dfrac{1.18 \text{ mol}}{1.18 \text{ mol}} = 1$

$\dfrac{3.55 \text{ mol}}{1.18 \text{ mol}} = 3$

$HClO_3$

---

11. Given: a selenium oxide is 28.8% oxygen

Unknown: the empirical (molecular) formula and name

Assume 100 g of compound. Then there are 28.8 g of oxygen and $(100.0 - 28.8) = 71.2$ g of selenium

$28.8 \text{ g} \times \dfrac{1 \text{ mol}}{16 \text{ g}} = 1.8$ mol O

$71.2 \text{ g} \times \dfrac{1 \text{ mol}}{78.96 \text{ g}} = 0.902$ mol Se

$\dfrac{1.8 \text{ mol}}{0.902 \text{ mol}} = 1.99$

$\dfrac{0.902 \text{ mol}}{0.902 \text{ mol}} = 1$

SeO_2; selenium dioxide

CHAPTER 9

Stoichiometry

ATE, Additional Sample Problems, p. 305

A-1. Given: amount of Li = 2 mol

Unknown: amount of Li_2O in moles

balanced equation:

$$4Li + O_2 \rightarrow 2Li_2O$$

mole ratio from balanced equation $= \dfrac{2 \text{ mol } Li_2O}{4 \text{ mol Li}}$

$$\text{mol } Li_2O = 2 \text{ mol Li} \times \dfrac{2 \text{ mol } Li_2O}{4 \text{ mol Li}} = 1 \text{ mol } Li_2O$$

A-2. Given: amount of H_2O_2 = 5 mol

Unknown: amount of O_2 in moles

balanced equation:

$$2H_2O_2 \rightarrow 2H_2O + O_2$$

mole ratio from balanced equation $= \dfrac{1 \text{ mol } O_2}{2 \text{ mol } H_2O_2}$

$$\text{mol } O_2 = 5 \text{ mol } H_2O_2 \times \dfrac{1 \text{ mol } O_2}{2 \text{ mol } H_2O_2} = 2.5 \text{ mol } O_2$$

Practice, p. 306

1. Given: amount of H_2 = 6 mol

Unknown: amount of NH_3 in moles

balanced equation:

$$3H_2 + N_2 \rightarrow 2NH_3$$

mole ratio from balanced equation $= \dfrac{2 \text{ mol } NH_3}{3 \text{ mol } H_2}$

$$\text{mol } NH_3 = 6 \text{ mol } H_2 \times \dfrac{2 \text{ mol } NH_3}{3 \text{ mol } H_2} = 4 \text{ mol } NH_3$$

2. Given: amount of O_2 = 15 mol

Unknown: amount of $KClO_3$ in moles

balanced equation:

$$2KClO_3 \rightarrow 2KCl + 3O_2$$

mole ratio from balanced equation $= \dfrac{2 \text{ mol } KClO_3}{3 \text{ mol } O_2}$

$$\text{mol } KClO_3 = 15 \text{ mol } O_2 \times \dfrac{2 \text{ mol } KClO_3}{3 \text{ mol } O_2} = 10. \text{ mol } KClO_3$$

ATE, Additional Sample Problems, p. 307

B-1. Given: amount of NaN_3 = 0.500 mol; balanced equation

Unknown: mass of N in grams

mole ratio from balanced equation $= \dfrac{3 \text{ mol } N_2}{2 \text{ mol } NaN_3}$

molar mass of $N_2 = 2 \times \dfrac{14.01 \text{ g N}}{\text{mol N}} = 28.02 \text{ g/mol}$

$$\text{mass } N_2 = 0.500 \text{ mol } NaN_3 \times \dfrac{3 \text{ mol } N_2}{2 \text{ mol } NaN_3} \times \dfrac{28.02 \text{ g } N_2}{\text{mol } N_2} = 21.0 \text{ g } N_2$$

B-2. Given: amount of C = 2.00 mol; balanced equation

Unknown: mass of SiC in grams

mole ratio from balanced equation $= \dfrac{1 \text{ mol SiC}}{3 \text{ mol C}}$

molar mass of SiC $= 1 \times \dfrac{28.09 \text{ g Si}}{\text{mol Si}} + 1 \times \dfrac{12.01 \text{ g C}}{\text{mol C}} = 40.10 \text{ g/mol}$

mass SiC $= 2.00 \text{ mol C} \times \dfrac{1 \text{ mol SiC}}{3 \text{ mol C}} \times \dfrac{40.10 \text{ g SiC}}{\text{mol SiC}} = 26.7 \text{ g SiC}$

C-1. Given: amount of CH_4 = 1.00 mol; balanced equation

Unknown: mass of C in grams

mole ratio from balanced equation $= \dfrac{2 \text{ mol C}}{1 \text{ mol CH}_4}$

molar mass of C = 12.01 g/mol

mass C $= 1.00 \text{ mol CH}_4 \times \dfrac{2 \text{ mol C}}{1 \text{ mol CH}_4} \times \dfrac{12.01 \text{ g C}}{\text{mol C}} = 24.0 \text{ g C}$

C-2. Given: mass of O_2 = 1200. g; balanced equation

Unknown: mass of SO_2 in grams

mole ratio from balanced equation $= \dfrac{2 \text{ mol SO}_2}{1 \text{ mol O}_2}$

molar mass of $SO_2 = 1 \times \dfrac{32.07 \text{ g S}}{\text{mol S}} + 2 \times \dfrac{16.00 \text{ g O}}{\text{mol O}}$

$= 32.07 \text{ g/mol} + 32.00 \text{ g/mol} = 64.07 \text{ g/mol}$

molar mass of $O_2 = 2 \times \dfrac{16.00 \text{ g O}}{\text{mol O}} = 32.00 \text{ g/mol}$

mass $SO_2 = 1200. \text{ g O}_2 \times \dfrac{\text{mol O}_2}{32.00 \text{ g O}_2} \times \dfrac{2 \text{ mol SO}_2}{1 \text{ mol O}_2} \times \dfrac{64.07 \text{ g SO}_2}{\text{mol SO}_2}$

$= 4805 \text{ g SO}_2$

Practice, p. 308

1. Given: amount of Mg = 2.00 mol

Unknown: mass of MgO in grams

balanced equation:

$2Mg(s) + O_2(g) \rightarrow 2MgO(s)$

mole ratio from balanced equation $= \dfrac{2 \text{ mol MgO}}{2 \text{ mol Mg}}$

molar mass of MgO $= 1 \times \dfrac{24.30 \text{ g Mg}}{\text{mol Mg}} + 1 \times \dfrac{16.00 \text{ g O}}{\text{mol O}} = 40.30 \text{ g/mol}$

mass MgO $= 2.00 \text{ mol Mg} \times \dfrac{2 \text{ mol MgO}}{2 \text{ mol Mg}} \times \dfrac{40.30 \text{ g MgO}}{\text{mol MgO}} = 80.6 \text{ g MgO}$

---

2. Given: amount of CO_2 = 10 mol; balanced equation

Unknown: mass of $C_6H_{12}O_6$

mole ratio from balanced equation $= \dfrac{1 \text{ mol C}_6\text{H}_{12}\text{O}_6}{6 \text{ mol CO}_2}$

molar mass of $C_6H_{12}O_6 = 6 \times \dfrac{12.01 \text{ g C}}{\text{mol C}} + 12 \times \dfrac{1.01 \text{ g H}}{\text{mol H}} + 6 \times \dfrac{16.00 \text{ g O}}{\text{mol O}}$

$= 72.06 \text{ g/mol} + 12.1 \text{ g/mol} + 96.00 \text{ g/mol}$

$= 180.2 \text{ g/mol}$

mass $C_6H_{12}O_6 = 10 \text{ mol CO}_2 \times \dfrac{1 \text{ mol C}_6\text{H}_{12}\text{O}_6}{6 \text{ mol CO}_2} \times \dfrac{180.2 \text{ g C}_6\text{H}_{12}\text{O}_6}{\text{mol C}_6\text{H}_{12}\text{O}_6}$

$= 300 \text{ g C}_6\text{H}_{12}\text{O}_6$

Practice, p. 309

1. Given: mass of O_2 = 125 g

Unknown: amount of HgO in moles

balanced equation:

$2HgO \rightarrow 2Hg + O_2$

mole ratio from balanced equation $= \dfrac{2 \text{ mol HgO}}{1 \text{ mol } O_2}$

molar mass of $O_2 = 2 \times \dfrac{16.00 \text{ g O}}{\text{mol O}} = 32.00 \text{ g/mol}$

amount HgO $= 125 \text{ g } O_2 \times \dfrac{1 \text{ mol } O_2}{32.00 \text{ g } O_2} \times \dfrac{2 \text{ mol HgO}}{1 \text{ mol } O_2} = 7.81 \text{ mol HgO}$

---

2. Given: mass of O_2 = 125 g

Unknown: amount of Hg in moles

balanced equation:

$2HgO \rightarrow 2Hg + O_2$

mole ratio from balanced equation $= \dfrac{2 \text{ mol Hg}}{1 \text{ mol } O_2}$

molar mass of $O_2 = 32.00 \text{ g/mol}$

amount Hg $= 125 \text{ g } O_2 \times \dfrac{1 \text{ mol } O_2}{32.00 \text{ g } O_2} \times \dfrac{2 \text{ mol Hg}}{1 \text{ mol } O_2} = 7.81 \text{ mol Hg}$

ATE, Additional Sample Problems, p. 309

D-1a. Given: mass of NaCl = 250 g; balanced equation

Unknown: amount of Cl_2 in moles

mole ratio from balanced equation $= \dfrac{1 \text{ mol } Cl_2}{2 \text{ mol NaCl}}$

molar mass of NaCl $= 1 \times \dfrac{22.99 \text{ g Na}}{\text{mol Na}} + 1 \times \dfrac{35.45 \text{ g Cl}}{\text{mol Cl}} = 58.44 \text{ g/mol}$

amount $Cl_2 = 250 \text{ g NaCl} \times \dfrac{1 \text{ mol NaCl}}{58.44 \text{ g NaCl}} \times \dfrac{1 \text{ mol } Cl_2}{2 \text{ mol NaCl}} = 2.14 \text{ mol } Cl_2$

b. Given: mass of NaCl = 250 g; balanced equation

Unknown: amount of H_2 in moles

mole ratio from balanced equation $= \dfrac{1 \text{ mol } H_2}{2 \text{ mol NaCl}}$

molar mass of NaCl $= 58.44 \text{ g/mol}$

amount $H_2 = 250 \text{ g NaCl} \times \dfrac{1 \text{ mol NaCl}}{58.44 \text{ g NaCl}} \times \dfrac{1 \text{ mol } H_2}{2 \text{ mol NaCl}} = 2.14 \text{ mol } H_2$

D-2a. Given: mass of $PtCl_2(NH_3)_2$ = 30.0 g; balanced equation

Unknown: amount of K_2PtCl_4 in moles

mole ratio from balanced equation = $\dfrac{1 \text{ mol } K_2PtCl_4}{1 \text{ mol } PtCl_2(NH_3)_2}$

molar mass of $PtCl_2(NH_3)_2$ = $1 \times \dfrac{195.08 \text{ g Pt}}{\text{mole Pt}} + 2 \times \dfrac{35.45 \text{ g Cl}}{\text{mol Cl}}$

$+ 2 \times \dfrac{14.01 \text{ g N}}{\text{mol N}} + 6 \times \dfrac{1.01 \text{ g H}}{\text{mol H}}$

= 195.08 g/mol + 70.90 g/mol + 28.02 g/mol + 6.06 g/mol

= 300.06 g/mol

amount K_2PtCl_4 = 30.0 g $PtCl_2(NH_3)_2 \times \dfrac{1 \text{ mol } PtCl_2(NH_3)_2}{300.06 \text{ g } PtCl_2(NH_3)_2}$

$\times \dfrac{1 \text{ mol } K_2PtCl_4}{1 \text{ mol } PtCl_2(NH_3)_2}$ = 0.100 mol K_2PtCl_4

b. Given: mass of $PtCl_2(NH_3)_2$ = 30.0 g; balanced equation

Unknown: amount of NH_3 in moles

mole ratio from balanced equation = $\dfrac{2 \text{ mol } NH_3}{1 \text{ mol } PtCl_2(NH_3)_2}$

molar mass of $PtCl_2(NH_3)_2$ = 300.06 g/mol

amount NH_3 = 30.0 g $PtCl_2(NH_3)_2 \times \dfrac{1 \text{ mol } PtCl_2(NH_3)_2}{300.06 \text{ g } PtCl_2(NH_3)_2}$

$\times \dfrac{2 \text{ mol } NH_3}{1 \text{ mol } PtCl_2(NH_3)_2}$ = 0.200 mol NH_3

Practice, p. 311

1a. Given: mass of N_2O = 33.0 g; balanced equation

Unknown: mass of NH_4NO_3 in grams

mole ratio from balanced equation = $\dfrac{1 \text{ mol } NH_4NO_3}{1 \text{ mol } N_2O}$

molar mass of NH_4NO_3 = $2 \times \dfrac{14.01 \text{ g N}}{\text{mol N}} + 4 \times \dfrac{1.01 \text{ g H}}{\text{mol H}} + 3 \times \dfrac{16.00 \text{ g O}}{\text{mol O}}$

= 28.02 g/mol + 4.04 g/mol + 48.00 g/mol

= 80.05 g/mol

molar mass of N_2O = $2 \times \dfrac{14.01 \text{ g N}}{\text{mol N}} + 1 \times \dfrac{16.00 \text{ g O}}{\text{mol O}}$

= 28.02 g/mol + 16.00 g/mol = 44.02 g/mol

mass NH_4NO_3 = 33.0 g $N_2O \times \dfrac{1 \text{ mol } N_2O}{44.02 \text{ g } N_2O} \times \dfrac{1 \text{ mol } NH_4NO_3}{1 \text{ mol } N_2O}$

$\times \dfrac{80.05 \text{ g } NH_4NO_3}{\text{mol } NH_4NO_3}$ = 60.0 g NH_4NO_3

b. Given: mass of N_2O =
33.0 g; balanced
equation

Unknown: mass of H_2O
in grams

mole ratio from balanced equation = $\dfrac{2 \text{ mol } H_2O}{1 \text{ mol } N_2O}$

molar mass of N_2O = 44.02 g/mol

molar mass of H_2O = 18.02 g/mol

mass H_2O = 33.0 g $N_2O \times \dfrac{1 \text{ mol } N_2O}{44.02 \text{ g } N_2O} \times \dfrac{2 \text{ mol } H_2O}{1 \text{ mol } N_2O} \times \dfrac{18.02 \text{ g } H_2O}{\text{mol } H_2O}$

= 27.0 g H_2O

---

2. Given: mass of Cu =
100. g

Unknown: mass of Ag

balanced equation:

$Cu + 2AgNO_3 \rightarrow 2Ag + Cu(NO_3)_2$

mole ratio from balanced equation = $\dfrac{2 \text{ mol Ag}}{1 \text{ mol Cu}}$

molar mass of Ag = 107.87 g/mol

molar mass of Cu = 63.55 g/mol

mass Ag = 100. g Cu $\times \dfrac{1 \text{ mol Cu}}{63.55 \text{ g Cu}} \times \dfrac{2 \text{ mol Ag}}{1 \text{ mol Cu}} \times \dfrac{107.87 \text{ g Ag}}{\text{mol Ag}}$ = 339 g Ag

---

3. Given: mass of Al_2O_3
= 5.0 kg

Unknown: mass of Al

balanced equation:

$2Al_2O_3 \rightarrow 4Al + 3O_2$

mole ratio from balanced equation = $\dfrac{4 \text{ mol Al}}{2 \text{ mol } Al_2O_3}$

molar mass of Al = 26.98 g/mol

molar mass of Al_2O_3 = $2 \times \dfrac{26.98 \text{ g Al}}{\text{mol Al}} + 3 \times \dfrac{16.00 \text{ g O}}{\text{mol O}}$

= 53.96 g/mol + 48.00 g/mol = 101.96 g/mol

mass Al = 5.0 kg $Al_2O_3 \times \dfrac{1000 \text{ g}}{\text{kg}} \times \dfrac{1 \text{ mol } Al_2O_3}{101.96 \text{ g } Al_2O_3} \times \dfrac{4 \text{ mol Al}}{2 \text{ mol } Al_2O_3}$

$\times \dfrac{26.98 \text{ g Al}}{\text{mol Al}} = 2.6 \times 10^3$ g Al = 2.6 kg Al

E-1a. Given: mass of Na_2O_2 = 50.0 g

Unknown: mass of O_2 in grams

balanced equation:

$$2Na_2O_2(s) + 2H_2O(l) \rightarrow 4NaOH(aq) + O_2(g)$$

mole ratio from balanced equation $= \dfrac{1 \text{ mol } O_2}{2 \text{ mol } Na_2O_2}$

molar mass of $Na_2O_2 = 2 \times \dfrac{22.99 \text{ g Na}}{\text{mol Na}} + 2 \times \dfrac{16.00 \text{ g O}}{\text{mol O}}$

$$= 45.98 \text{ g/mol} + 32.00 \text{ g/mol} = 77.98 \text{ g/mol}$$

molar mass of $O_2 = 2 \times \dfrac{16.00 \text{ g O}}{\text{mol O}} = 32.00 \text{ g/mol}$

mass $O_2 = 50.0 \text{ g } Na_2O_2 \times \dfrac{1 \text{ mol } Na_2O_2}{77.98 \text{ g } Na_2O_2} \times \dfrac{1 \text{ mol } O_2}{2 \text{ mol } Na_2O_2} \times \dfrac{32.00 \text{ g } O_2}{\text{mol } O_2}$

$$= 10.3 \text{ g } O_2$$

b. Given: mass of Na_2O_2 = 50.0 g

Unknown: mass of H_2O in grams

balanced equation:

$$2Na_2O_2(s) + 2H_2O(l) \rightarrow 4NaOH(aq) + O_2(g)$$

mole ratio from balanced equation $= \dfrac{2 \text{ mol } H_2O}{2 \text{ mol } Na_2O_2}$

molar mass of $Na_2O_2 = 77.98 \text{ g/mol}$

molar mass of $H_2O = 18.02 \text{ g/mol}$

mass $H_2O = 50.0 \text{ g } Na_2O_2 \times \dfrac{1 \text{ mol } Na_2O_2}{77.98 \text{ g } Na_2O_2} \times \dfrac{2 \text{ mol } H_2O}{2 \text{ mol } Na_2O_2} \times \dfrac{18.02 \text{ g } H_2O}{\text{mol } H_2O}$

$$= 11.6 \text{ g } H_2O$$

Section Review, p. 311

1a. Given: amount of NH_3 = 4 mol

Unknown: amounts of O_2, N_2, and H_2O in moles

balanced equation:

$$4NH_3 + 3O_2 \rightarrow 2N_2 + 6H_2O$$

mole ratios from balanced equation $= \dfrac{3 \text{ mol } O_2}{4 \text{ mol } NH_3}, \dfrac{2 \text{ mol } N_2}{4 \text{ mol } NH_3}, \dfrac{6 \text{ mol } H_2O}{4 \text{ mol } NH_3}$

mol $O_2 = 4 \text{ mol } NH_3 \times \dfrac{3 \text{ mol } O_2}{4 \text{ mol } NH_3} = 3 \text{ mol } O_2$

mol $N_2 = 4 \text{ mol } NH_3 \times \dfrac{2 \text{ mol } N_2}{4 \text{ mol } NH_3} = 2 \text{ mol } N_2$

mol $H_2O = 4 \text{ mol } NH_3 \times \dfrac{6 \text{ mol } H_2O}{4 \text{ mol } NH_3} = 6 \text{ mol } H_2O$

b. Given: amount of N_2 = 4 mol

Unknown: amounts of NH_3, O_2, and H_2O in moles

mole ratios from balanced equation $= \dfrac{4 \text{ mol } NH_3}{2 \text{ mol } N_2}, \dfrac{3 \text{ mol } O_2}{2 \text{ mol } N_2}, \dfrac{6 \text{ mol } H_2O}{2 \text{ mol } N_2}$

$\text{mol } NH_3 = 4 \text{ mol } N_2 \times \dfrac{4 \text{ mol } NH_3}{2 \text{ mol } N_2} = 8 \text{ mol } NH_3$

$\text{mol } O_2 = 4 \text{ mol } N_2 \times \dfrac{3 \text{ mol } O_2}{2 \text{ mol } N_2} = 6 \text{ mol } O_2$

$\text{mol } H_2O = 4 \text{ mol } N_2 \times \dfrac{6 \text{ mol } H_2O}{2 \text{ mol } N_2} = 12 \text{ mol } H_2O$

c. Given: amount of O_2 = 4.5 mol

Unknown: amounts of NH_3, N_2, and H_2O in moles

mole ratios from balanced equation $= \dfrac{4 \text{ mol } NH_3}{3 \text{ mol } O_2}, \dfrac{2 \text{ mol } NH_3}{3 \text{ mol } O_2}, \dfrac{6 \text{ mol } H_2O}{3 \text{ mol } O_2}$

$\text{mol } NH_3 = 4.5 \text{ mol } O_2 \times \dfrac{4 \text{ mol } NH_3}{3 \text{ mol } O_2} = 6.0 \text{ mol } NH_3$

$\text{mol } N_2 = 4.5 \text{ mol } O_2 \times \dfrac{2 \text{ mol } N_2}{3 \text{ mol } O_2} = 3.0 \text{ mol } N_2$

$\text{mol } H_2O = 4.5 \text{ mol } O_2 \times \dfrac{6 \text{ mol } H_2O}{3 \text{ mol } O_2} = 9.0 \text{ mol } H_2O$

2a. Given: amount of Mg = 2.50 mol

Unknown: mass of HCl

balanced equation:

$Mg(s) + 2HCl(aq) \rightarrow MgCl_2(aq) + H_2(g)$

mole ratio from balanced equation $= \dfrac{2 \text{ mol } HCl}{1 \text{ mol } Mg}$

molar mass of $HCl = 1 \times \dfrac{1.01 \text{ g H}}{\text{mol H}} + 1 \times \dfrac{35.45 \text{ g HCl}}{\text{mol HCl}} = 36.46 \text{ g/mol}$

$\text{mass } HCl = 2.50 \text{ mol } Mg \times \dfrac{2 \text{ mol } HCl}{1 \text{ mol } Mg} \times \dfrac{36.46 \text{ g HCl}}{\text{mol HCl}} = 182 \text{ g HCl}$

b. Given: amount of Mg = 2.50 mol

Unknown: masses of $MgCl_2$ and H_2

balanced equation:

$Mg(s) + 2HCl(aq) \rightarrow MgCl_2(aq) + H_2(g)$

mole ratios from balanced equation $= \dfrac{1 \text{ mol } MgCl_2}{1 \text{ mol } Mg}, \dfrac{1 \text{ mol } H_2}{1 \text{ mol } Mg}$

molar mass of $MgCl_2 = 1 \times \dfrac{24.30 \text{ g Mg}}{\text{mol Mg}} + 2 \times \dfrac{35.45 \text{ g Cl}}{\text{mol Cl}} = 95.20 \text{ g/mol}$

$\text{mass } MgCl_2 = 2.50 \text{ mol } Mg \times \dfrac{1 \text{ mol } MgCl_2}{1 \text{ mol } Mg} \times \dfrac{95.20 \text{ g } MgCl_2}{\text{mol } MgCl_2}$

$= 238 \text{ g } MgCl_2$

molar mass of $H_2 = 2 \times \dfrac{1.01 \text{ g H}}{\text{mol H}} = 2.02 \text{ g/mol}$

$\text{mass } H_2 = 2.50 \text{ mol } Mg \times \dfrac{1 \text{ mol } H_2}{1 \text{ mol } Mg} \times \dfrac{2.02 \text{ g } H_2}{\text{mol } H_2} = 5.05 \text{ g } H_2$

3a. Given: mass of $CaC_2 = $ 32.0 g; balanced equation

Unknown: amount of H_2O in moles

mole ratio from balanced equation $= \dfrac{2 \text{ mol } H_2O}{1 \text{ mol } CaC_2}$

molar mass of $CaC_2 = 1 \times \dfrac{40.08 \text{ g Ca}}{\text{mol Ca}} + 2 \times \dfrac{12.01 \text{ g C}}{\text{mol C}}$

$= 40.08 \text{ g/mol} + 24.02 \text{ g/mol} = 64.10 \text{ g/mol}$

amount $H_2O = 32 \text{ g } CaC_2 \times \dfrac{1 \text{ mol } CaC_2}{64.10 \text{ g } CaC_2} \times \dfrac{2 \text{ mol } H_2O}{1 \text{ mol } CaC_2} = 0.998 \text{ mol } H_2O$

b. Given: mass of CaC_2 = 32.0 g

Unknown: amounts of C_2H_2 and $Ca(OH)_2$ in moles

mole ratios from balanced equation $= \dfrac{1 \text{ mol } C_2H_2}{1 \text{ mol } CaC_2}, \dfrac{1 \text{ mol } Ca(OH)_2}{1 \text{ mol } CaC_2}$

molar mass of $CaC_2 = 64.10 \text{ g/mol}$

amount $C_2H_2 = 32.0 \text{ g } CaC_2 \times \dfrac{1 \text{ mol } CaC_2}{64.10 \text{ g } CaC_2} \times \dfrac{1 \text{ mol } C_2H_2}{1 \text{ mol } CaC_2}$

$= 0.499 \text{ mol } C_2H_2$

amount $Ca(OH)_2 = 32.0 \text{ g } CaC_2 \times \dfrac{1 \text{ mol } CaC_2}{64.10 \text{ g } CaC_2} \times \dfrac{1 \text{ mol } Ca(OH)_2}{1 \text{ mol } CaC_2}$

$= 0.499 \text{ mol } Ca(OH)_2$

4. Given: mass of $AgNO_3 = $ 75.0 g

Unknown: mass of AgCl

balanced equation:

$NaCl + AgNO_3 \rightarrow AgCl + NaNO_3$

mole ratio from balanced equation $= \dfrac{1 \text{ mol AgCl}}{1 \text{ mol } AgNO_3}$

molar mass of $AgNO_3 = 1 \times \dfrac{107.87 \text{ g Ag}}{\text{mol Ag}} + 1 \times \dfrac{14.01 \text{ g N}}{\text{mol N}} + 3 \times \dfrac{16.00 \text{ g O}}{\text{mol O}}$

$= 107.87 \text{ g/mol} + 14.01 \text{ g/mol} + 48.00 \text{ g/mol}$

$= 169.88 \text{ g/mol}$

molar mass of $AgCl = 1 \times \dfrac{107.87 \text{ g Ag}}{\text{mol Ag}} + 1 \times \dfrac{35.45 \text{ g Cl}}{\text{mol Cl}} = 143.32 \text{ g/mol}$

mass $AgCl = 75.0 \text{ g } AgNO_3 \times \dfrac{1 \text{ mol } AgNO_3}{169.88 \text{ g } AgNO_3} \times \dfrac{1 \text{ mol AgCl}}{1 \text{ mol } AgNO_3}$

$\times \dfrac{143.32 \text{ g AgCl}}{\text{mol AgCl}} = 63.3 \text{ g AgCl}$

Practice, p. 313

1a. Given: amount of N_2H_4 = 1.750 mol; balanced equation amount of H_2O_2 = 0.500 mol

Unknown: limiting reactant

mole ratio of reactants $= \dfrac{2 \text{ mol } H_2O_2}{1 \text{ mol } N_2H_4}$

amount H_2O_2 required $= 0.750 \text{ mol } N_2H_4 \times \dfrac{2 \text{ mol } H_2O_2}{1 \text{ mol } N_2H_4} = 1.50 \text{ mol } H_2O_2$

Because there is only 0.500 mol H_2O_2 available, the limiting reactant is H_2O_2.

b. Given: amount of N_2H_4
= 0.750 mol
amount of H_2O_2
= 0.500 mol
(limiting
reactant)

Unknown: remaining
excess
reactant
in moles

amount N_2H_4 reacting $= \dfrac{1 \text{ mol } N_2H_4}{2 \text{ mol } H_2O_2} \times 0.500 \text{ mol } H_2O_2 = 0.250 \text{ mol } N_2H_4$

remaining excess reactant = 0.750 mol N_2H_4 – 0.250 mol N_2H_4
= 0.500 mol N_2H_4

c. Given: limiting reactant amount =
0.500 mol H_2O_2
mole ratios:
$\dfrac{1 \text{ mol } N_2}{2 \text{ mol } H_2O_2},$
$\dfrac{4 \text{ mol } H_2O}{2 \text{ mol } H_2O_2}$

Unknown: amounts of
N_2 and
H_2O in
moles

amount $N_2 = \dfrac{1 \text{ mol } N_2}{2 \text{ mol } H_2O_2} \times 0.500 \text{ mol } H_2O_2 = 0.250 \text{ mol } N_2$

amount $H_2O = \dfrac{4 \text{ mol } H_2O}{2 \text{ mol } H_2O_2} \times 0.500 \text{ mol } H_2O_2 = 1.00 \text{ mol } H_2O$

ATE, Additional Sample Problems, p. 313

F-1a. Given: amount of CO =
500. mol
amount of H_2 =
750. mol
balanced
equation

Unknown: limiting
reactant

mole ratio of reactants $= \dfrac{2 \text{ mol } H_2}{1 \text{ mol } CO}$

amount H_2 required = 500. mol CO $\times \dfrac{2 \text{ mol } H_2}{1 \text{ mol } CO} = 1.00 \times 10^3 \text{ mol } H_2$

Because there are only 750. mol H_2 available, the limiting reactant is H_2.

b. Given: amount of CO
= 500. mol
amount of H_2 =
750. mol (limit-
ing reactant)

Unknown: remaining
excess
reactant
in moles

amount CO reacting $= \dfrac{1 \text{ mol } CO}{2 \text{ mol } H_2} \times 750. \text{ mol } H_2 = 375 \text{ mol } CO$

remaining excess reactant = 500. mol CO – 375 mol CO = 125 mol CO

c. Given: limiting reactant amount =
750.0 mol H_2
mole ratio:
$\dfrac{1 \text{ mol } CH_3OH}{2 \text{ mol } H_2}$

Unknown: amount of
CH_3OH in
moles

amount $CH_3OH = \dfrac{1 \text{ mol } CH_3OH}{2 \text{ mol } H_2} \times 750. \text{ mol } H_2 = 375 \text{ mol } CH_3OH$

G-1a. Given: mass of $C_7H_6O_3$ = 20.0 g, mass of $C_4H_6O_3$ = 20.0 g, balanced equation

Unknown: limiting reactant and moles of excess reactant needed to complete reaction

$$\text{molar mass of } C_7H_6O_3 = 7 \times \frac{12.01 \text{ g C}}{\text{mol C}} + 6 \times \frac{1.01 \text{ g H}}{\text{mol H}} + 3 \times \frac{16.00 \text{ g O}}{\text{mol O}}$$

$$= 138.13 \text{ g/mol}$$

$$\text{amount } C_7H_6O_3 = \frac{20.0 \text{ g}}{138.13 \text{ g/mol}} = 0.145 \text{ mol } C_7H_6O_3$$

$$\text{molar mass of } C_4H_6O_3 = 4 \times \frac{12.01 \text{ g C}}{\text{mol C}} + 6 \times \frac{1.01 \text{ g H}}{\text{mol H}} + 3 \times \frac{16.00 \text{ g O}}{\text{mol O}}$$

$$= 102.10 \text{ g/mol}$$

$$\text{amount } C_4H_6O_3 = \frac{20.0 \text{ g}}{102.10 \text{ g/mol}} = 0.196 \text{ mol } C_4H_6O_3$$

$$\text{mole ratio of reactants} = \frac{1 \text{ mol } C_4H_6O_3}{2 \text{ mol } C_7H_6O_3}$$

$$\text{amount } C_4H_6O_3 \text{ required} = 0.145 \text{ mol } C_7H_6O_3 \times \frac{1 \text{ mol } C_4H_6O_3}{2 \text{ mol } C_7H_6O_3}$$

$$= 0.0725 \text{ mol } C_4H_6O_3$$

Because only 0.0725 mol $C_4H_6O_3$ is needed to react with all of the 0.145 mol $C_7H_6O_3$, the limiting reactant is $C_7H_6O_3$.

amount of excess reactant used = mol $C_4H_6O_3$ required = 0.0725 mol $C_4H_6O_3$

b. Given: limiting reactant amount = 0.145 mol $C_7H_6O_3$

mole ratio:
$$\frac{2 \text{ mol } C_9H_8O_4}{2 \text{ mol } C_7H_6O_3}$$

Unknown: mass of $C_9H_8O_4$ in grams

$$\text{molar mass of } C_9H_8O_5 = 9 \times \frac{12.01 \text{ g C}}{\text{mol C}} + 8 \times \frac{1.01 \text{ g H}}{\text{mol H}} + 4 \times \frac{16.00 \text{ g O}}{\text{mol O}}$$

$$= 180.2 \text{ g/mol}$$

$$\text{mass } C_9H_8O_4 = 0.145 \text{ mol } C_7H_6O_3 \times \frac{2 \text{ mol } C_9H_8O_4}{2 \text{ mol } C_7H_6O_3} \times \frac{180.2 \text{ g } C_9H_8O_4}{\text{mol } C_9H_8O_4}$$

$$= 26.1 \text{ g } C_9H_8O_4$$

Practice, p. 315

1a. Given: amount of Zn = 2.00 mol
amount of S_8 = 1.00 mol;
balanced equation

Unknown: limiting reactant

$$\text{mole ratio of reactants} = \frac{1 \text{ mol } S_8}{8 \text{ mol Zn}}$$

$$\text{amount } S_8 \text{ required} = 2.00 \text{ mol Zn} \times \frac{1 \text{ mol } S_8}{1 \text{ mol Zn}} = 0.250 \text{ mol } S_8$$

Because only 0.250 mol S_8 is needed to react with 2.00 mol Zn, the limiting reactant is Zn.

b. Given: amount of S_8
= 1.00 mol
amount of S_8 reacting with Zn =
0.250 mol S_8

Unknown: amount of reactant in excess in moles

remaining excess reactant = 1.00 mol S_8 − 0.250 mol S_8 = 0.75 mol S_8

c. Given: limiting reactant amount
= 2.00 mol Zn
mole ratio:

$$\frac{8 \text{ mol ZnS}}{8 \text{ mol Zn}}$$

Unknown: amount of ZnS in moles

amount ZnS = 2.00 mol Zn $\times \dfrac{8 \text{ mol ZnS}}{8 \text{ mol Zn}}$ = 2.00 mol ZnS

2a. Given: amount of C =
2.40 mol
amount of H_2O =
3.10 mol

Unknown: limiting reactant

balanced equation:

$$C(s) + H_2O(g) \rightarrow H_2(g) + CO(g)$$

mole ratio of reactants = $\dfrac{1 \text{ mol } H_2O}{1 \text{ mol C}}$

amount H_2O required = 2.40 mol C $\times \dfrac{1 \text{ mol } H_2O}{1 \text{ mol C}}$ = 2.40 mol H_2O

Because only 2.40 mol H_2O are needed to react with 2.40 mol C, the limiting reactant is C.

b. Given: limiting reactant amount =
2.40 mol C
mole ratios:

$$\frac{1 \text{ mol } H_2}{1 \text{ mol C}},$$
$$\frac{1 \text{ mol CO}}{1 \text{ mol C}}$$

Unknown: amounts of H_2 and CO in moles

amount H_2 = 2.40 mol C $\times \dfrac{1 \text{ mol } H_2}{1 \text{ mol C}}$ = 2.40 mol H_2

amount CO = 2.40 mol C $\times \dfrac{1 \text{ mol CO}}{1 \text{ mol C}}$ = 2.40 mol CO

c. Given: amount of H_2
= 2.40 mol
amount of CO
= 2.40 mol
Unknown: masses of H_2 and CO in grams

molar mass of H_2 = 2 $\times \dfrac{1.01 \text{ g H}}{\text{mol H}}$ = 2.02 g/mol

mass H_2 = 2.40 mol $H_2 \times \dfrac{2.02 \text{ g } H_2}{\text{mol } H_2}$ = 4.85 g H_2

molar mass of CO = 1 $\times \dfrac{12.01 \text{ g CO}}{\text{mol CO}}$ + 1 $\times \dfrac{16.00 \text{ g O}}{\text{mol O}}$

= 12.01 g/mol + 16.00 g/mol = 28.01 g/mol

mass CO = 2.40 mol CO $\times \dfrac{28.01 \text{ g CO}}{\text{mol CO}}$ = 67.2 g CO

1. Given: mass of CO = 75.0 g, balanced equation, actual yield of CH_3OH = 68.4 g

Unknown: percent yield of CH_3OH

$$\text{mole ratio from balanced equation} = \frac{1 \text{ mol } CH_3OH}{1 \text{ mol } CO}$$

$$\text{molar mass of } CH_3OH = 1 \times \frac{12.01 \text{ g C}}{\text{mol C}} + 4 \times \frac{1.01 \text{ g H}}{\text{mol H}} + 1 \times \frac{16.00 \text{ g O}}{\text{mol O}}$$

$$= 32.05 \text{ g/mol}$$

$$\text{molar mass of CO} = 1 \times \frac{12.01 \text{ g C}}{\text{mol C}} + 1 \times \frac{16.00 \text{ g O}}{\text{mol O}} = 28.01 \text{ g/mol}$$

$$\text{mass } CH_3OH \text{(theoretical)} = 75.0 \text{ g CO} \times \frac{1 \text{ mol CO}}{28.01 \text{ g CO}} \times \frac{1 \text{ mol } CH_3OH}{1 \text{ mol CO}}$$

$$\times \frac{32.05 \text{ g } CH_3OH}{\text{mol } CH_3OH} = 85.8 \text{ g } CH_3OH$$

$$\text{percent yield of } CH_3OH = \frac{68.4 \text{ g } CH_3OH}{85.8 \text{ g } CH_3OH} \times 100 = 79.7\%$$

2. Given: mass of Al = 1.85 g percent yield of Cu = 56.6%

Unknown: mass of Cu (actual yield)

balanced equation:

$$2Al(s) + 3CuSO_4(aq) \rightarrow Al_2(SO_4)_3(aq) + 3Cu(s)$$

$$\text{mole ratio from balanced equation} = \frac{3 \text{ mol Cu}}{2 \text{ mol Al}}$$

$$\text{mass Cu (theoretical)} = 1.85 \text{ g Al} \times \frac{\text{mol Al}}{26.98 \text{ g. Al}} \times \frac{3 \text{ mol Cu}}{2 \text{ mol Al}} \times \frac{63.55 \text{ g Cu}}{\text{mol Cu}}$$

$$= 6.54 \text{ g Cu}$$

$$\text{mass Cu (actual)} = \frac{56.6 \times 6.54 \text{ g Cu}}{100} = 3.70 \text{ g Cu}$$

ATE, Additional Sample Problem, p. 318

H-1. Given: percent yield of SO_2 = 86.78% mass of ZnS = 4897 g balanced equation

Unknown: mass of SO_2 (actual yield)

$$\text{mole ratio from balanced equation} = \frac{2 \text{ mol } SO_2}{2 \text{ mol ZnS}}$$

$$\text{molar mass of } SO_2 = 1 \times \frac{32.07 \text{ g S}}{\text{mol S}} + 2 \times \frac{16.00 \text{ g O}}{\text{mol O}} = 64.07 \text{ g/mol}$$

$$\text{molar mass of ZnS} = 1 \times \frac{65.39 \text{ g Zn}}{\text{mol Zn}} + 1 \times \frac{32.07 \text{ g S}}{\text{mol S}} = 97.46 \text{ g/mol}$$

$$\text{mass } SO_2 \text{ (theoretical)} = 4897 \text{ g ZnS} \times \frac{1 \text{ mol ZnS}}{97.46 \text{ g ZnS}} \times \frac{2 \text{ mol } SO_2}{2 \text{ mol ZnS}}$$

$$\times \frac{64.07 \text{ g } SO_2}{\text{mol } SO_2} = 3219 \text{ g } SO_2$$

$$\text{mass } SO_2 \text{ (actual)} = \frac{86.78}{100} \times 3219 \text{ g } SO_2 = 2794 \text{ g } SO_2$$

1a. Given: amount of CS_2
= 1.00 mol,
amount of O_2
= 1.00 mol,
balanced
equation

Unknown: limiting
reactant

mole ratio of reactants = $\dfrac{3\ \text{mol}\ O_2}{1\ \text{mol}\ CS_2}$

amount O_2 required = 1.00 mol $CS_2 \times \dfrac{3\ \text{mol}\ O_2}{1\ \text{mol}\ CS_2} = 3.00$ mol O_2

Because there is only 1.00 mol O_2 available, the limiting reactant is O_2.

b. Given: amount of CS_2
= 1.00 mol
amount of O_2 =
1.00 mol (limit-
ing reactant)

Unknown: remaining
excess
reactant
in moles

amount CS_2 reacting = $\dfrac{1\ \text{mol}\ CS_2}{3\ \text{mol}\ O_2} \times 1.00$ mol $O_2 = 0.333$ mol CS_2

remaining excess reactant = 1.00 mol CS_2 − 0.333 mol CS_2 = 0.667 mol CS_2

c. Given: limiting reactant amount =
1.00 mol O_2
mole ratios:
$\dfrac{1\ \text{mol}\ CO_2}{3\ \text{mol}\ O_2}$,
$\dfrac{2\ \text{mol}\ SO_2}{3\ \text{mol}\ O_2}$

Unknown: amounts of
CO_2 and
SO_2 in
moles

amount CO_2 = $\dfrac{1\ \text{mol}\ CO_2}{3\ \text{mol}\ O_2} \times 1.00$ mol $O_2 = 0.333$ mol CO_2

amount SO_2 = $\dfrac{2\ \text{mol}\ SO_2}{3\ \text{mol}\ O_2} \times 1.00$ mol $O_2 = 0.667$ mol SO_2

2a. Given: mass of Mg
= 16.2 g
mass of H_2O
= 12.0 g

Unknown: limiting
reactant

balanced equation:

$2Mg(s) + 4H_2O(g) \rightarrow 2Mg(OH)_2(s) + 2H_2(g)$

mole ratio of reactants = $\dfrac{4\ \text{mol}\ H_2O}{2\ \text{mol}\ Mg}$

amount H_2O = 12.0 g $H_2O \times \dfrac{1\ \text{mol}\ H_2O}{18.02\ \text{g}\ H_2O} = 0.666$ mol H_2O

amount Mg = 16.2 g Mg $\times \dfrac{1\ \text{mol}\ Mg}{24.30\ \text{g}\ Mg} = 0.667$ mol Mg

amount H_2O required = 0.667 mol Mg $\times \dfrac{4\ \text{mol}\ H_2O}{2\ \text{mol}\ Mg} = 1.33$ mol H_2O

Because there is only 0.666 mol H_2O available, the limiting reactant is H_2O.

b. Given: amount of Mg
= 0.667 mol
amount of H_2O
= 0.666 mol
(limiting
reactant)

Unknown: remaining
excess
reactant in
moles

$$\text{amount Mg reacting} = \frac{2 \text{ mol Mg}}{4 \text{ mol } H_2O} \times 0.666 \text{ mol } H_2O = 0.333 \text{ mol Mg}$$

$$\text{remaining excess reactant} = 0.667 \text{ mol Mg} - 0.333 \text{ mol Mg} = 0.334 \text{ mol Mg}$$

c. Given: limiting reactant amount =
0.666 mol H_2O
mole ratios:
$\dfrac{2 \text{ mol Mg(OH)}_2}{4 \text{ mol } H_2O}$,
$\dfrac{2 \text{ mol } H_2}{4 \text{ mol } H_2O}$

Unknown: masses of
$Mg(OH)_2$
and H_2 in
grams

$$\text{molar mass of Mg(OH)}_2 = 1 \times \frac{24.30 \text{ g Mg}}{\text{mol Mg}} + 2 \times \frac{16.00 \text{ g O}}{\text{mol O}}$$

$$+ 2 \times \frac{1.01 \text{ g H}}{\text{mol H}} = 58.32 \text{ g/mol}$$

$$\text{molar mass of } H_2 = 2 \times \frac{1.01 \text{ g H}}{\text{mol H}} = 2.02 \text{ g/mol}$$

$$\text{mass Mg(OH)}_2 = 0.666 \text{ mol } H_2O \times \frac{2 \text{ mol Mg(OH)}_2}{4 \text{ mol } H_2O} \times \frac{58.32 \text{ g Mg(OH)}_2}{\text{mol Mg(OH)}_2}$$

$$= 19.4 \text{ g Mg(OH)}_2$$

$$\text{mass } H_2 = 0.666 \text{ mol } H_2O \times \frac{2 \text{ mol } H_2}{4 \text{ mol } H_2O} \times \frac{2.02 \text{ g } H_2}{\text{mol } H_2} = 0.673 \text{ g } H_2$$

3. Given: mass of $CaCO_3$ =
2.00×10^3 g,
actual yield of
CaO = 1.05×10^3 g,
balanced reaction

Unknown: percent yield
of CaO

$$\text{mole ratio from balanced equation} = \frac{1 \text{ mol CaO}}{1 \text{ mol CaCO}_3}$$

$$\text{molar mass of CaCO}_3 = 1 \times \frac{40.08 \text{ g Ca}}{\text{mol Ca}} + 1 \times \frac{12.01 \text{ g C}}{\text{mol C}} + 3 \times \frac{16.00 \text{ g O}}{\text{mol O}}$$

$$= 100.09 \text{ g/mol}$$

$$\text{molar mass of CaO} = 1 \times \frac{40.08 \text{ g Ca}}{\text{mol Ca}} + 1 \times \frac{16.00 \text{ g O}}{\text{mol O}} = 56.08 \text{ g/mol}$$

$$\text{mass CaO (theoretical)} = (2.00 \times 10^3 \text{ g CaCO}_3) \times \frac{1 \text{ mol CaCO}_3}{100.09 \text{ g CaCO}_3}$$

$$\times \frac{1 \text{ mol CaO}}{1 \text{ mol CaCO}_3} \times \frac{56.08 \text{ g CaO}}{\text{mol CaO}}$$

$$= 1.12 \times 10^3 \text{ g CaO}$$

$$\text{percent yield of CaO} = \frac{1.05 \times 10^3 \text{ g CaO}}{1.12 \times 10^3 \text{ g CaO}} \times 100 = 93.7\%$$

Chapter Review

5a. Given: amount of H_2O
= 5.0 mol;
balanced
equation

Unknown: amount of H_2
in moles

$$\text{mole ratio from balanced equation} = \frac{2 \text{ mol } H_2}{2 \text{ mol } H_2O}$$

$$\text{amount } H_2 = 5.0 \text{ mol } H_2O \times \frac{2 \text{ mol } H_2}{2 \text{ mol } H_2O} = 5.0 \text{ mol } H_2$$

b. Given: amount of H_2O
= 5.0 mol

Unknown: amount of
O_2 in moles

mole ratio from balanced equation $= \dfrac{1 \text{ mol } O_2}{2 \text{ mol } H_2O}$

amount O_2 = 5.0 mol $H_2O \times \dfrac{1 \text{ mol } O_2}{2 \text{ mol } H_2O}$ = 2.5 mol O_2

6a. Given: amount of C_2H_6
= 4.50 mol

Unknown: amount of O_2
in moles

balanced equation:

$2C_2H_6 + 7O_2 \rightarrow 4CO_2 + 6H_2O$

mole ratio from balanced equation $= \dfrac{7 \text{ mol } O_2}{2 \text{ mol } C_2H_6}$

amount O_2 = 4.50 mol $C_2H_6 \times \dfrac{7 \text{ mol } O_2}{2 \text{ mol } C_2H_6}$ = 15.8 mol O_2

b. Given: amount of C_2H_6
= 4.50 mol

Unknown: amounts of
CO_2 and H_2O
in moles

mole ratios from balanced equation $= \dfrac{4 \text{ mol } CO_2}{2 \text{ mol } C_2H_6}, \dfrac{6 \text{ mol } H_2O}{2 \text{ mol } C_2H_6}$

amount CO_2 = 4.50 mol $C_2H_6 \times \dfrac{4 \text{ mol } CO_2}{2 \text{ mol } C_2H_6}$ = 9.00 mol CO_2

amount H_2O = 4.50 mol $C_2H_6 \times \dfrac{6 \text{ mol } H_2O}{2 \text{ mol } C_2H_6}$ = 13.5 mol H_2O

---

7. Given: amount of NaCl
= 25.0 mol

Unknown: masses of Na
and Cl

balanced equation:

$2Na + Cl_2 \rightarrow 2NaCl$

mole ratios from balanced equation $= \dfrac{2 \text{ mol Na}}{2 \text{ mol NaCl}}, \dfrac{1 \text{ mol } Cl_2}{2 \text{ mol NaCl}}$

mass Na = 25.0 mol NaCl $\times \dfrac{2 \text{ mol Na}}{2 \text{ mol NaCl}} \times \dfrac{22.99 \text{ g Na}}{\text{mol Na}}$ = 575 g Na

mass Cl_2 = 25.0 mol NaCl $\times \dfrac{1 \text{ mol } Cl_2}{2 \text{ mol NaCl}} \times \dfrac{70.90 \text{ g } Cl_2}{\text{mol } Cl_2}$ = 886 g Cl_2

---

8. Given: mass of Fe_2O_3 =
4.00 kg

Unknown: amount of
CO in moles

balanced equation:

$2Fe_2O_3(s) + 6CO(g) \rightarrow 4Fe(s) + 6CO_2(g)$

mole ratio from balanced equation $= \dfrac{6 \text{ mol CO}}{2 \text{ mol } Fe_2O_3}$

molar mass of $Fe_2O_3 = 2 \times \dfrac{55.85 \text{ g Fe}}{\text{mol Fe}} + 3 \times \dfrac{16.00 \text{ g O}}{\text{mol O}}$ = 159.7 g/mol

amount CO = 4.00 kg $Fe_2O_3 \times \dfrac{1000 \text{ g}}{\text{kg}} \times \dfrac{1 \text{ mol } Fe_2O_3}{159.7 \text{ g } Fe_2O_3} \times \dfrac{6 \text{ mol CO}}{2 \text{ mol } Fe_2O_3}$

= 75.1 mol CO

8b. Given: mass of Fe_2O_3 = 4.00 kg

Unknown: amounts of Fe and CO_2 in moles

mole ratios from balanced equation $= \dfrac{4 \text{ mol Fe}}{2 \text{ mol Fe}_2O_3}, \dfrac{6 \text{ mol CO}_2}{2 \text{ mol Fe}_2O_3}$

molar mass of Fe_2O_3 = 159.7 g/mol

amount Fe = 4.00 kg $Fe_2O_3 \times \dfrac{1000 \text{ g}}{\text{kg}} \times \dfrac{1 \text{ mol Fe}_2O_3}{159.7 \text{ g Fe}_2O_3} \times \dfrac{4 \text{ mol Fe}}{2 \text{ mol Fe}_2O_3}$

$= 50.1 \text{ mol Fe}$

amount CO_2 = 4.00 kg $Fe_2O_3 \times \dfrac{1000 \text{ g}}{\text{kg}} \times \dfrac{1 \text{ mol Fe}_2O_3}{159.7 \text{ g Fe}_2O_3} \times \dfrac{6 \text{ mol CO}_2}{2 \text{ mol Fe}_2O_3}$

$= 75.1 \text{ mol CO}_2$

---

9. Given: mass of CH_3OH = 100.0 kg

Unknown: masses of CO and H_2

balanced equation:

$CO(g) + 2H_2(g) = CH_3OH$

mole ratios from balanced equation $= \dfrac{1 \text{ mol CO}}{1 \text{ mol CH}_3OH}, \dfrac{2 \text{ mol H}_2}{1 \text{ mol CH}_3OH}$

molar mass of $CH_3OH = 1 \times \dfrac{12.01 \text{ g C}}{\text{mol C}} + 4 \times \dfrac{1.01 \text{ g H}}{\text{mol H}} + 1 \times \dfrac{16.00 \text{ g O}}{\text{mol O}}$

$= 32.05 \text{ g/mol}$

molar mass of CO $= 1 \times \dfrac{12.01 \text{ g C}}{\text{mol C}} + 1 \times \dfrac{16.00 \text{ g O}}{\text{mol O}} = 28.01 \text{ g/mol}$

mass CO = 100.0 kg $CH_3OH \times \dfrac{1000 \text{ g}}{\text{kg}} \times \dfrac{1 \text{ mol CH}_3OH}{32.05 \text{ g CH}_3OH} \times \dfrac{1 \text{ mol CO}}{1 \text{ mol CH}_3OH}$

$\times \dfrac{28.01 \text{ g CO}}{\text{mol CO}} = 8.739 \times 10^4 \text{ g CO}$

molar mass of $H_2 = 2 \times \dfrac{1.01 \text{ g H}}{\text{mol H}} = 2.02 \text{ g/mol}$

mass H_2 = 100.0 kg $H_2 \times \dfrac{1000 \text{ g}}{\text{kg}} \times \dfrac{1 \text{ mol CH}_3OH}{32.05 \text{ g CH}_3OH} \times \dfrac{2 \text{ mol H}_2}{1 \text{ mol CH}_3OH}$

$\times \dfrac{2.02 \text{ g H}_2}{\text{mol H}_2} = 1.260 \times 10^4 \text{ g H}_2$

10a. Given: mass of O_2 = 384 g

Unknown: mass of NO_2

balanced equation:

$2NO(g) + O_2(g) \rightarrow 2NO_2(g)$

mole ratio from balanced equation $= \dfrac{2 \text{ mol NO}_2}{1 \text{ mol O}_2}$

molar mass $O_2 = 2 \times \dfrac{16.00 \text{ g O}}{\text{mol O}} = 32.00 \text{ g/mol}$

molar mass of $NO_2 = 1 \times \dfrac{14.01 \text{ g N}}{\text{mol N}} + 2 \times \dfrac{16.00 \text{ g O}}{\text{mol O}} = 46.01 \text{ g/mol}$

mass NO_2 = 384 g $O_2 \times \dfrac{1 \text{ mol O}_2}{32.00 \text{ g O}_2} \times \dfrac{2 \text{ mol NO}_2}{1 \text{ mol O}_2} \times \dfrac{46.01 \text{ g NO}_2}{\text{mol NO}_2}$

$= 1.10 \times 10^3 \text{ g NO}_2$

b. Given: mass of O_2 = 384 g

Unknown: mass of NO in grams

mole ratio from balanced equation = $\dfrac{2 \text{ mol NO}}{1 \text{ mol } O_2}$

molar mass of NO = $1 \times \dfrac{14.01 \text{ g N}}{\text{mol N}} + 1 \times \dfrac{16.00 \text{ g O}}{\text{mol O}}$ = 30.01 g/mol

molar mass of O_2 = 32.00 g/mol

mass NO = 384 g $\times \dfrac{1 \text{ mol } O_2}{32.00 \text{ g } O_2} \times \dfrac{2 \text{ mol NO}}{1 \text{ mol } O_2} \times \dfrac{30.01 \text{ g NO}}{\text{mol NO}}$ = 720. g NO

11a. Given: mass of CO_2 = 925.0 g

Unknown: amount of NaOH in moles

balanced equation:

$2NaOH + CO_2 \rightarrow Na_2CO_3 + H_2O$

mole ratio from balanced equation = $\dfrac{2 \text{ mol NaOH}}{1 \text{ mol } CO_2}$

molar mass of CO_2 = $1 \times \dfrac{12.01 \text{ g C}}{\text{mol C}} + 2 \times \dfrac{16.00 \text{ g O}}{\text{mol O}}$ = 44.01 g/mol

amount NaOH = 925.0 g $CO_2 \times \dfrac{1 \text{ mol } CO_2}{44.01 \text{ g } CO_2} \times \dfrac{2 \text{ mol NaOH}}{1 \text{ mol } CO_2}$

= 42.04 mol NaOH

b. Given: mass of CO_2 = 925.0 g

Unknown: amounts of Na_2CO_3 and H_2O in moles

mole ratios from balanced equation = $\dfrac{1 \text{ mol } Na_2CO_3}{1 \text{ mol } CO_2}, \dfrac{1 \text{ mol } H_2O}{1 \text{ mol } CO_2}$

molar mass of CO_2 = 44.01 g/mol

amount Na_2CO_3 = 925.0 g $CO_2 \times \dfrac{1 \text{ mol } CO_2}{44.01 \text{ g } CO_2} \times \dfrac{1 \text{ mol } Na_2CO_3}{1 \text{ mol } CO_2}$

= 21.02 mol Na_2CO_3

amount H_2O = 925.0 g $CO_2 \times \dfrac{1 \text{ mol } CO_2}{44.01 \text{ g } CO_2} \times \dfrac{1 \text{ mol } H_2O}{1 \text{ mol } CO_2}$ = 21.02 mol H_2O

12a. Given: amount of $AgNO_3$ = 4.50 mol

Unknown: mass of NaBr

balanced equation:

$AgNO_3 + NaBr \rightarrow AgBr + NaNO_3$

mole ratio from balanced equation = $\dfrac{1 \text{ mol NaBr}}{1 \text{ mol } AgNO_3}$

molar mass of NaBr = $1 \times \dfrac{22.99 \text{ g Na}}{\text{mol Na}} + 1 \times \dfrac{79.90 \text{ g Br}}{\text{mol Br}}$ = 102.89 g/mol

mass NaBr = 4.50 mol $AgNO_3 \times \dfrac{1 \text{ mol NaBr}}{1 \text{ mol } AgNO_3} \times \dfrac{102.89 \text{ g NaBr}}{\text{mol NaBr}}$

= 463 g NaBr

b. Given: amount of $AgNO_3$ = 4.50 mol

Unknown: mass of AgBr

mole ratio from balanced equation = $\dfrac{1 \text{ mol AgBr}}{1 \text{ mol } AgNo_3}$

molar mass of AgBr = $1 \times \dfrac{107.87 \text{ g Ag}}{\text{mol Ag}} + 1 \times \dfrac{79.90 \text{ g Br}}{\text{mol Br}}$ = 187.77 g/mol

mass AgBr = 4.50 mol $AgNO_3 \times \dfrac{1 \text{ mol AgBr}}{1 \text{ mol } AgNO_3} \times \dfrac{187.77 \text{ g AgBr}}{\text{mol AgBr}}$

= 845 g AgBr

13a. Given: mass of H_2SO_4 = 150.0 g

Unknown: amount of $NaHCO_3$ in moles

balanced equation:

$$2NaHCO_3 + H_2SO_4 \rightarrow 2CO_2 + Na_2SO_4 + 2H_2O$$

$$\text{mole ratio from balanced equation} = \frac{2 \text{ mol } NaHCO_3}{1 \text{ mol } H_2SO_4}$$

$$\text{molar mass of } H_2SO_4 = 2 \times \frac{1.01 \text{ g H}}{\text{mol H}} + 1 \times \frac{32.07 \text{ g S}}{\text{mol S}} + 4 \times \frac{16.00 \text{ g O}}{\text{mol O}}$$

$$= 98.09 \text{ g/mol}$$

$$\text{amount } NaHCO_3 = 150.0 \text{ g } H_2SO_4 \times \frac{1 \text{ mol } H_2SO_4}{98.09 \text{ g } H_2SO_4} \times \frac{2 \text{ mol } NaHCO_3}{1 \text{ mol } H_2SO_4}$$

$$= 3.058 \text{ mol } NaHCO_3$$

b. Given: mass of H_2SO_4 = 150.0 g

Unknown: amounts of CO_2, Na_2SO_4, and H_2O in moles

$$\text{mole ratios from balanced equation} = \frac{2 \text{ mol } CO_2}{1 \text{ mol } H_2SO_4}, \frac{1 \text{ mol } Na_2SO_4}{1 \text{ mol } H_2SO_4},$$
$$\frac{2 \text{ mol } H_2O}{1 \text{ mol } H_2SO_4}$$

$$\text{molar mass of } H_2SO_4 = 98.09 \text{ g/mol}$$

$$\text{amount } CO_2 = 150.0 \text{ g } H_2SO_4 \times \frac{1 \text{ mol } H_2SO_4}{98.09 \text{ g } H_2SO_4} \times \frac{2 \text{ mol } CO_2}{1 \text{ mol } H_2SO_4}$$

$$= 3.058 \text{ mol } CO_2$$

$$\text{amount } Na_2SO_4 = 150.0 \text{ g } H_2SO_4 \times \frac{1 \text{ mol } H_2SO_4}{98.09 \text{ g } H_2SO_4} \times \frac{1 \text{ mol } Na_2SO_4}{1 \text{ mol } H_2SO_4}$$

$$= 1.529 \text{ mol } Na_2SO_4$$

$$\text{amount } H_2O = 150.0 \text{ g } H_2SO_4 \times \frac{1 \text{ mol } H_2SO_4}{98.09 \text{ g } H_2SO_4} \times \frac{2 \text{ mol } H_2O}{1 \text{ mol } H_2SO_4}$$

$$= 3.058 \text{ mol } H_2O$$

14b. Given: amount of NaOH = 0.75 mol

Unknown: mass of H_2SO_4

$$\text{mole ratio from balanced equation} = \frac{1 \text{ mol } H_2SO_4}{2 \text{ mol NaOH}}$$

$$\text{molar mass of } H_2SO_4 = 2 \times \frac{1.01 \text{ g H}}{\text{mol H}} + 1 \times \frac{32.07 \text{ g S}}{\text{mol S}} + 4 \times \frac{16.00 \text{ g O}}{\text{mol O}}$$

$$= 98.09 \text{ g/mol}$$

$$\text{mass } H_2SO_4 = 0.75 \text{ mol NaOH} \times \frac{1 \text{ mol } H_2SO_4}{2 \text{ mol NaOH}} \times \frac{98.09 \text{ g } H_2SO_4}{\text{mol } H_2SO_4}$$

$$= 37 \text{ g } H_2SO_4$$

c. Given: amount of NaOH
= 0.75 mol

Unknown: masses of
Na_2SO_4 and
H_2O

mole ratios from balanced equations = $\dfrac{1 \text{ mol } Na_2SO_4}{2 \text{ mol } NaOH}, \dfrac{2 \text{ mol } H_2O}{2 \text{ mol } NaOH}$

molar mass of $Na_2SO_4 = 2 \times \dfrac{22.99 \text{ g Na}}{\text{mol Na}} + 1 \times \dfrac{32.07 \text{ g S}}{\text{mol S}} + 4 \times \dfrac{16.00 \text{ g O}}{\text{mol O}}$

$= 142.05 \text{ g/mol}$

mass $Na_2SO_4 = 0.75 \text{ mol NaOH} \times \dfrac{1 \text{ mol } Na_2SO_4}{2 \text{ mol NaOH}} \times \dfrac{142.05 \text{ g } Na_2SO_4}{\text{mol } Na_2SO_4}$

$= 53 \text{ g } Na_2SO_4$

molar mass of $H_2O = 18.02 \text{ g/mol}$

mass $H_2O = 0.75 \text{ mol NaOH} \times \dfrac{2 \text{ mol } H_2O}{2 \text{ mol NaOH}} \times \dfrac{18.02 \text{ g } H_2O}{\text{mol } H_2O} = 14 \text{ g } H_2O$

15a. Given: mass of Ag
= 2.25 g

Unknown: amount of
$Cu(NO_3)_2$
in moles

balanced equation:

$Cu + 2AgNO_3 \rightarrow 2Ag + Cu(NO_3)_2$

mole ratio from balanced equation = $\dfrac{1 \text{ mol } Cu(NO_3)_2}{2 \text{ mol Ag}}$

molar mass of Ag = 107.87 g/mol

amount $Cu(NO_3)_2 = 2.25 \text{ g Ag} \times \dfrac{1 \text{ mol Ag}}{107.87 \text{ g Ag}} \times \dfrac{1 \text{ mol } Cu(NO_3)_2}{2 \text{ mol Ag}}$

$= 0.0104 \text{ mol } Cu(NO_3)_2$

b. Given: mass of Ag =
2.25 g

Unknown: amounts of
Cu and
$AgNO_3$ in
moles

mole ratios from balanced equation = $\dfrac{1 \text{ mol Cu}}{2 \text{ mol Ag}}, \dfrac{2 \text{ mol } AgNO_3}{2 \text{ mol Ag}}$

molar mass of Ag = 107.87 g/mol

amount Cu = $2.25 \text{ g Ag} \times \dfrac{1 \text{ mol Ag}}{107.87 \text{ g Ag}} \times \dfrac{1 \text{ mol Cu}}{2 \text{ mol Ag}} = 0.0104 \text{ mol Cu}$

amount $AgNO_3 = 2.25 \text{ g Ag} \times \dfrac{1 \text{ mol Ag}}{107.87 \text{ g Ag}} \times \dfrac{2 \text{ mol } AgNO_3}{2 \text{ mol Ag}}$

$= 0.0209 \text{ mol } AgNO_3$

16a. Given: amount of
$C_7H_6O_3 =$
75.0 mol

Unknown: mass of
$C_9H_8O_4$
in kg

balanced equation:

$C_7H_6O_3(s) + C_4H_6O_3(l) \rightarrow C_9H_8O_4(s) + HC_2H_3O_2(l)$

mole ratio from balanced equation = $\dfrac{1 \text{ mol } C_9H_8O_4}{1 \text{ mol } C_7H_6O_3}$

molar mass of $C_9H_8O_4 = 9 \times \dfrac{12.01 \text{ g C}}{\text{mol C}} + 8 \times \dfrac{1.01 \text{ g H}}{\text{mol H}} + 4 \times \dfrac{16.00 \text{ g O}}{\text{mol O}}$

$= 180.2 \text{ g/mol}$

mass $C_9H_8O_4 = 75.0 \text{ mol } C_7H_6O_3 \times \dfrac{1 \text{ mol } C_9H_8O_4}{1 \text{ mol } C_7H_6O_3} \times \dfrac{180.2 \text{ g } C_9H_8O_4}{\text{mol } C_9H_8O_4}$

$\times \dfrac{1 \text{ kg}}{1000 \text{ g}} = 13.5 \text{ kg } C_9H_8O_4$

16b. Given: amount of $C_7H_6O_3$ = 75.0 mol

Unknown: mass of $C_4H_6O_3$ in kg

mole ratio from balanced equation = $\dfrac{1 \text{ mol } C_4H_6O_3}{1 \text{ mol } C_7H_6O_3}$

molar mass of $C_4H_6O_3 = 4 \times \dfrac{12.01 \text{ g C}}{\text{mol C}} + 6 \times \dfrac{1.01 \text{ g H}}{\text{mol H}} + 3 \times \dfrac{16.00 \text{ g O}}{\text{mol O}}$

$= 102.10 \text{ g/mol}$

mass $C_4H_6O_3 = 75.0 \text{ mol } C_7H_6O_3 \times \dfrac{1 \text{ mol } C_4H_6O_3}{1 \text{ mol } C_7H_6O_3} \times \dfrac{102.10 \text{ g } C_4H_6O_3}{\text{mol } C_4H_6O_3}$

$\times \dfrac{1 \text{ kg}}{1000 \text{ g}} = 7.66 \text{ kg } C_4H_6O_3$

c. Given: amount of $C_7H_6O_3$ = 75.0 mol; density of $HC_2H_3O_2$ = 1.05 g/cm^3

Unknown: volume of $HC_2H_3O_2$ in liters

mole ratio from balanced equation = $\dfrac{1 \text{ mol } HC_2H_3O_2}{1 \text{ mol } C_7H_6O_3}$

molar mass of $HC_2H_3O_2 = 4 \times \dfrac{1.01 \text{ g H}}{\text{mol H}} + 2 \times \dfrac{12.01 \text{ g C}}{\text{mol C}} + 2 \times \dfrac{16.00 \text{ g O}}{\text{mol O}}$

$= 60.06 \text{ g/mol}$

$V\ HC_2H_3O_2 = 75.0 \text{ mol } C_7H_6O_3 \times \dfrac{1 \text{ mol } HC_2H_3O_2}{1 \text{ mol } C_7H_6O_3} \times \dfrac{60.06 \text{ g } HC_2H_3O_2}{\text{mol } HC_2H_3O_2}$

$\times \dfrac{1 \text{ cm}^3\ HC_2H_3O_2}{1.05 \text{ g } HC_2H_3O_2} \times \dfrac{1 \text{ L}}{1000 \text{ cm}^3} = 4.29 \text{ L } HC_2H_3O_2$

22a. Given: amount of HCl = 2.0 mol, amount of NaOH = 2.5 mol, balanced equation

Unknown: limiting reactant

mole ratio of reactants = $\dfrac{1 \text{ mol NaOH}}{1 \text{ mol HCl}}$

amount NaOH required = $2.0 \text{ mol HCl} \times \dfrac{1 \text{ mol NaOH}}{1 \text{ mol HCl}} = 2.0 \text{ mol NaOH}$

Because only 2.0 mol NaOH are needed to react with 2.0 mol HCl, the limiting reactant is HCl.

b. Given: amount of Zn = 2.5 mol, amount of HCl = 6.0 mol, balanced equation

Unknown: limiting reactant

balanced equation:

$Zn + 2HCl \rightarrow ZnCl_2 + H_2$

mole ratio of reactants = $\dfrac{2 \text{ mol HCl}}{1 \text{ mol Zn}}$

amount HCl required = $2.5 \text{ mol Zn} \times \dfrac{2 \text{ mol HCl}}{1 \text{ mol Zn}} = 5.0 \text{ mol HCl}$

Because only 5.0 mol HCl are needed to react with 2.5 mol Zn, the limiting reactant is Zn.

c. Given: amount of $Fe(OH)_3$ = 4.0 mol, amount of H_2SO_4 = 6.5 mol, balanced equation

Unknown: limiting reactant

mole ratio of reactants = $\dfrac{3 \text{ mol } H_2SO_4}{2 \text{ mol } Fe(OH)_3}$

amount H_2SO_4 required = $4.0 \text{ mol } Fe(OH)_3 \times \dfrac{3 \text{ mol } H_2SO_4}{2 \text{ mol } Fe(OH)_3}$

$= 6.0 \text{ mol } H_2SO_4$

Because only 6.0 mol H_2SO_4 are needed to react with 4.0 mol $Fe(OH)_3$, the limiting reactant is $Fe(OH)_3$.

23a. Given: amount of HCl = 2.0 mol (limiting reactant); amount of NaOH = 2.5 mol

Unknown: remaining excess reactant in moles

From problem **22.a**, 2.0 mol NaOH react with 2.0 mol HCl.

remaining excess reactant = 2.5 mol NaOH − 2.0 mol NaOH
= 0.5 mol NaOH

b. Given: amount of Zn = 2.5 mol (limiting reactant); amount of HCl = 6.0 mol

Unknown: remaining excess reactant in moles

From problem **22.b**, 5.0 mol HCl react with 2.5 mol Zn.

remaining excess reactant = 6.0 mol HCl − 5.0 mol HCl = 1.0 mol HCl

c. Given: amount of $Fe(OH)_3$ = 4.0 mol (limiting reactant); amount of H_2SO_4 = 6.5 mol

Unknown: remaining excess reactant in moles

From problem **22.c**, 6.0 mol H_2SO_4 react with 4.0 mol $Fe(OH)_3$.

remaining excess reactant = 6.5 mol H_2SO_4 − 6.0 mol H_2SO_4
= 0.5 mol H_2SO_4

24a. Given: limiting reactant amount = 2.0 mol HCl; mole ratios: $\dfrac{1 \text{ mol NaCl}}{1 \text{ mol HCl}}$, $\dfrac{1 \text{ mol } H_2O}{1 \text{ mol HCl}}$

Unknown: amounts of NaCl and H_2O in moles

$$\text{amount NaCl} = 2.0 \text{ mol HCl} \times \frac{1 \text{ mol NaCl}}{1 \text{ mol HCl}} = 2.0 \text{ mol NaCl}$$

$$\text{amount } H_2O = 2.0 \text{ mol HCl} \times \frac{1 \text{ mol } H_2O}{1 \text{ mol HCl}} = 2.0 \text{ mol } H_2O$$

b. Given: limiting reactant amount = 2.5 mol Zn; mole ratios: $\dfrac{1 \text{ mol } ZnCl_2}{1 \text{ mol Zn}}$, $\dfrac{1 \text{ mol } H_2}{1 \text{ mol Zn}}$

Unknown: amounts of $ZnCl_2$ and H_2 in moles

$$\text{amount } ZnCl_2 = 2.5 \text{ mol Zn} \times \frac{1 \text{ mol } ZnCl_2}{1 \text{ mol Zn}} = 2.5 \text{ mol } ZnCl_2$$

$$\text{amount } H_2 = 2.5 \text{ mol Zn} \times \frac{1 \text{ mol } H_2}{1 \text{ mol Zn}} = 2.5 \text{ mol } H_2$$

c. Given: limiting reactant amount = 4.0 mol $Fe(OH)_3$

mole ratios:

$$\frac{1 \text{ mol } Fe_2(SO_4)_3}{2 \text{ mol } Fe(OH)_3},$$

$$\frac{6 \text{ mol } H_2O}{2 \text{ mol } Fe(OH)_3}$$

Unknown: amounts of H_2O and $Fe_2(SO_4)_3$ in moles

$$\text{amount } Fe_2(SO_4)_3 = 4.0 \text{ mol } Fe(OH)_3 \times \frac{1 \text{ mol } Fe_2(SO_4)_3}{2 \text{ mol } Fe(OH)_3}$$

$$= 2.0 \text{ mol } Fe_2(SO_4)_3$$

$$\text{amount } H_2O = 4.0 \text{ mol } Fe(OH)_3 \times \frac{6 \text{ mol } H_2O}{2 \text{ mol } Fe(OH)_3} = 12 \text{ mol } H_2O$$

25a. Given: amount of Cu = 2.50 mol, amount of $AgNO_3$ = 5.50 mol

Unknown: limiting reactant

balanced equation:

$$Cu + 2AgNO_3 \rightarrow Cu(NO_3)_2 + 2Ag$$

$$\text{mole ratio of reactants} = \frac{2 \text{ mol } AgNO_3}{1 \text{ mol } Cu}$$

$$\text{amount } AgNO_3 \text{ required} = 2.50 \text{ mol } Cu \times \frac{2 \text{ mol } AgNO_3}{1 \text{ mol } Cu} = 5.00 \text{ mol } AgNO_3$$

Because only 5.00 mol $AgNO_3$ are needed to react with 2.50 mol Cu, the limiting reactant is Cu.

b. Unknown: remaining excess reactant in moles

5.00 mol $AgNO_3$ reacts with 2.50 mol Cu

$$\text{remaining excess reactant} = 5.50 \text{ mol } AgNO_3 - 5.00 \text{ mol } AgNO_3$$

$$= 0.50 \text{ mol } AgNO_3$$

c. Given: limiting reactant amount = 2.50 mol Cu,

mole ratios:

$$\frac{1 \text{ mol } Cu(NO_3)_2}{1 \text{ mol } Cu},$$

$$\frac{2 \text{ mol } Ag}{1 \text{ mol } Cu}$$

Unknown: amounts of $Cu(NO_3)_2$ and Ag in moles

$$\text{amount } Cu(NO_3)_2 = 2.50 \text{ mol } Cu \times \frac{1 \text{ mol } Cu(NO_3)_2}{1 \text{ mol } Cu} = 2.50 \text{ mol } Cu(NO_3)_2$$

$$\text{amount } Ag = 2.50 \text{ mol } Cu \times \frac{2 \text{ mol } Ag}{1 \text{ mol } Cu} = 5.00 \text{ mol } Ag$$

d. Given: amount of $Cu(NO_3)_2$ = 2.50 mol, amount of Ag = 5.00 mol

Unknown: masses of $Cu(NO_3)_2$ and Ag

$$\text{molar mass of } Cu(NO_3)_2 = 1 \times \frac{63.55 \text{ g Cu}}{\text{mol Cu}} + 2 \times \frac{14.01 \text{ g N}}{\text{mol N}} + 6 \times \frac{16.00 \text{ g O}}{\text{mol O}}$$

$$= 187.57 \text{ g/mol}$$

$$\text{mass } Cu(NO_3)_2 = 2.50 \text{ mol } Cu(NO_3)_2 \times \frac{187.57 \text{ g } Cu(NO_3)_2}{\text{mol } Cu(NO_3)_2}$$

$$= 469 \text{ g } Cu(NO_3)_2$$

molar mass of Ag = 107.87 g/mol

$$\text{mass } Ag = 5.00 \text{ mol } Ag \times \frac{107.87 \text{ g Ag}}{\text{mol Ag}} = 539 \text{ g Ag}$$

26a. Given: mass of H_2SO_4
= 30.0 g
mass of $Al(OH)_3$
= 25.0 g

Unknown: limiting
reactant

balanced equation:

$$3H_2SO_4 + 2Al(OH)_3 \rightarrow Al_2(SO_4)_3 + 6H_2O$$

$$\text{mole ratio of reactants} = \frac{2 \text{ mol Al(OH)}_3}{3 \text{ mol H}_2SO_4}$$

$$\text{molar mass of H}_2SO_4 = 2 \times \frac{1.01 \text{ g H}}{\text{mol H}} + 1 \times \frac{32.07 \text{ g S}}{\text{mol S}} + 4 \times \frac{16.00 \text{ g O}}{\text{mol O}}$$

$$= 98.09 \text{ g/mol}$$

$$\text{amount H}_2SO_4 = 30.0 \text{ g H}_2SO_4 \times \frac{1 \text{ mol H}_2SO_4}{98.09 \text{ g H}_2SO_4} = 0.306 \text{ mol H}_2SO_4$$

$$\text{molar mass of Al(OH)}_3 = 1 \times \frac{26.98 \text{ g Al}}{\text{mol Al}} + 3 \times \frac{16.00 \text{ g O}}{\text{mol O}} + 3 \times \frac{1.01 \text{ g H}}{\text{mol H}}$$

$$= 78.01 \text{ g/mol}$$

$$\text{amount Al(OH)}_3 = 25.0 \text{ g Al(OH)}_3 \times \frac{1 \text{ mol Al(OH)}_3}{78.01 \text{ g Al(OH)}_3} = 0.320 \text{ mol Al(OH)}_3$$

$$\text{amount Al(OH)}_3 \text{ required} = 0.306 \text{ mol H}_2SO_4 \times \frac{2 \text{ mol Al(OH)}_3}{3 \text{ mol H}_2SO_4}$$

$$= 0.204 \text{ mol Al(OH)}_3$$

Because only 0.204 mol $Al(OH)_3$ is needed to react with 0.306 mol H_2SO_4, the limiting reactant is H_2SO_4.

b. Given: amount of
H_2SO_4 =
0.306 mol (limit-
ing reactant)
amount of
$Al(OH)_3$ =
0.320 mol

Unknown: remaining
excess
reactant
in grams

molar mass of $Al(OH)_3$ = 78.01 g/mol

0.204 mol $Al(OH)_3$ reacts with 0.306 mol H_2SO_4

remaining excess reactant = 0.320 mol − 0.204 mol

$$= 0.116 \text{ mol Al(OH)}_3$$

$$\text{mass Al(OH)}_3 \text{ remaining} = 0.116 \text{ mol Al(OH)}_3 \times \frac{78.01 \text{ g Al(OH)}_3}{\text{mol Al(O)}_3}$$

$$= 9.05 \text{ g Al(OH)}_3$$

c. Given: limiting reactant
amount = 0.306
mol H_2SO_4;
mole ratios:
$\dfrac{1 \text{ mol Al}_2(SO_4)_3}{3 \text{ mol H}_2SO_4}$,
$\dfrac{6 \text{ mol H}_2O}{3 \text{ mol H}_2SO_4}$

Unknown: masses of
$Al_2(SO_4)_3$
and H_2O

$$\text{molar mass of Al}_2(SO_4)_3 = 2 \times \frac{26.98 \text{ g Al}}{\text{mol Al}} + 3 \times \frac{32.07 \text{ g S}}{\text{mol S}}$$

$$+ 12 \times \frac{16.00 \text{ g O}}{\text{mol O}} = 342.2 \text{ g/mol}$$

$$\text{mass Al}_2(SO_4)_3 = 0.306 \text{ mol H}_2SO_4 \times \frac{1 \text{ mol Al}_2(SO_4)_3}{3 \text{ mol H}_2SO_4} \times \frac{342.2 \text{ g Al}_2(SO_4)_3}{\text{mol Al}_2(SO_4)_3}$$

$$= 34.9 \text{ g Al}_2(SO_4)_3$$

molar mass of H_2O = 18.02 g/mol

$$\text{mass H}_2O = 0.306 \text{ mol H}_2SO_4 \times \frac{6 \text{ mol H}_2O}{3 \text{ mol H}_2SO_4} \times \frac{18.02 \text{ g H}_2O}{\text{mol H}_2O}$$

$$= 11.0 \text{ g H}_2O$$

27a. Given: mass of N_2H_4 = 1200. kg, mass of $(CH_3)_2N_2H_2$ = 1000. kg, mass of N_2O_4 = 4500. kg, balanced equation

Unknown: limiting reactant (reactant first used up)

mole ratios of reactants = $\dfrac{1 \text{ mol } (CH_3)_2N_2H_2}{2 \text{ mol } N_2H_4}, \dfrac{3 \text{ mol } N_2O_4}{2 \text{ mol } N_2H_4}$

molar mass of $N_2H_4 = 2 \times \dfrac{14.01 \text{ g N}}{\text{mol N}} + 4 \times \dfrac{1.01 \text{ g H}}{\text{mol H}} = 32.06 \text{ g/mol}$

molar mass of $(CH_3)_2N_2H_2 = 2 \times \dfrac{12.01 \text{ g C}}{\text{mol C}} + 8 \times \dfrac{1.01 \text{ g H}}{\text{mol H}}$

$+ 2 \times \dfrac{14.01 \text{ g N}}{\text{mol N}} = 60.12 \text{ g/mol}$

molar mass of $N_2O_4 = 2 \times \dfrac{14.01 \text{ g N}}{\text{mol N}} + 4 \times \dfrac{16.00 \text{ g O}}{\text{mol O}} = 92.02 \text{ g/mol}$

amount $N_2H_4 = 1200. \text{ kg } N_2H_4 \times \dfrac{1000 \text{ g}}{\text{kg}} \times \dfrac{1 \text{ mol } N_2H_4}{32.06 \text{ g } N_2H_4}$

$= 3.743 \times 10^4 \text{ mol } N_2H_4$

amount $(CH_3)_2N_2H_2 = 1000. \text{ kg } (CH_3)_2N_2H_2 \times \dfrac{1000 \text{ g}}{\text{kg}}$

$\times \dfrac{1 \text{ mol } (CH_3)_2N_2H_2}{60.12 \text{ g } (CH_3)_2N_2H_2} = 1.663 \times 10^4 \text{ mol } (CH_3)_2N_2H_2$

amount $N_2O_4 = 4500. \text{ kg } N_2O_4 \times \dfrac{1000 \text{ g}}{\text{kg}} \times \dfrac{1 \text{ mol } N_2O_4}{92.02 \text{ g } N_2O_4}$

$= 4.890 \times 10^4 \text{ mol } N_2O_4$

amount $(CH_3)_2N_2H_2$ required $= (3.743 \times 10^4 \text{ mol } N_2H_4)$

$\times \dfrac{1 \text{ mol } (CH_3)_2N_2H_2}{2 \text{ mol } N_2H_4} = 1.872 \times 10^4 \text{ mol } (CH_3)_2N_2H_2$

amount N_2O_4 required $= (3.743 \times 10^4 \text{ mol } N_2H_4) \times \dfrac{3 \text{ mol } N_2O_4}{2 \text{ mol } N_2H_4}$

$= 5.614 \times 10^4 \text{ mol } N_2O_4$

Both $(CH_3)_2N_2H_2$ and N_2O_4 are used up before all of the N_2H_4 is used up. To determine which is the limiting reactant, use the mole ratio:

$\dfrac{1 \text{ mol } (CH_3)_2N_2H_2}{3 \text{ mol } N_2O_4}$

amount $(CH_3)_2N_2H_2$ required $= (4.890 \times 10^4 \text{ mol } N_2O_4) \times \dfrac{1 \text{ mol } (CH_3)_2N_2H_2}{3 \text{ mol } N_2O_4}$

$= 1.630 \times 10^4 \text{ mol } (CH_3)_2N_2H_2$

There is an excess of $(CH_3)_2N_2H_2$ for the reaction, so the reactant that is used first is N_2O_4.

b. Given: limiting reactant amount = 4.890 × 10⁴ mol N_2O_4, mole ratio:
$$\frac{8 \text{ mol } H_2O}{3 \text{ mol } N_2O_4}$$

Unknown: mass of H_2O in kilograms

molar mass of H_2O = 18.02 g/mol

mass H_2O = (4.890 × 10⁴ mol N_2O_4) × $\dfrac{8 \text{ mol } H_2O}{3 \text{ mol } N_2O_4}$ × $\dfrac{18.02 \text{ g } H_2O}{\text{mol } H_2O}$

× $\dfrac{1 \text{ kg}}{1000 \text{ g}}$ = 2.350 × 10³ kg H_2O

28a. Given: theoretical yield = 20.0 g
actual yield = 15.0 g

Unknown: percent yield

percent yield = $\dfrac{15.0 \text{ g}}{20.0 \text{ g}}$ × 100 = 75.0%

b. Given: theoretical yield = 1.0 g
percent yield = 90.0%

Unknown: actual yield

percent yield = $\dfrac{\text{actual yield}}{\text{theoretical yield}}$ × 100

actual yield = $\dfrac{\text{percent yield} \times \text{theoretical yield}}{100}$ = $\dfrac{90.0 \times 1.0 \text{ g}}{100}$

actual yield = 0.90 g

c. Given: theoretical yield = 5.00 g
actual yield = 4.75 g

Unknown: percent yield

percent yield = $\dfrac{4.75 \text{ g}}{5.00 \text{ g}}$ × 100 = 95.0%

d. Given: theoretical yield = 3.45 g
percent yield = 48.0%

Unknown: actual yield

percent yield = $\dfrac{\text{actual yield}}{\text{theoretical yield}}$ × 100

actual yield = $\dfrac{\text{percent yield} \times \text{theoretical yield}}{100}$ = $\dfrac{48.0 \times 3.45 \text{ g}}{100}$

actual yield = 1.66 g

---

29. Given: percent yield = 83.2%
mass of PCl_3 = 73.7 g
balanced equation

Unknown: mass of PCl_5 (actual yield)

mole ratio from balanced equation = $\dfrac{1 \text{ mol } PCl_5}{1 \text{ mol } PCl_3}$

molar mass of PCl_5 = 1 × $\dfrac{30.97 \text{ g P}}{\text{mol P}}$ + 5 × $\dfrac{35.45 \text{ g Cl}}{\text{mol Cl}}$ = 208.2 g/mol

molar mass of PCl_3 = 1 × $\dfrac{30.97 \text{ g P}}{\text{mol P}}$ + 3 × $\dfrac{35.45 \text{ g Cl}}{\text{mol Cl}}$ = 137.3 g/mol

mass PCl_5 (theoretical) = 73.7 g PCl_3 × $\dfrac{1 \text{ mol } PCl_3}{137.3 \text{ g } PCl_3}$ × $\dfrac{1 \text{ mol } PCl_5}{1 \text{ mol } PCl_3}$

× $\dfrac{208.2 \text{ g } PCl_5}{\text{mol } PCl_5}$ = 112 g PCl_5

mass PCl_5 (actual) = $\dfrac{\text{percent yield} \times \text{g } PCl_5 \text{ (theoretical)}}{100}$

= $\dfrac{83.2 \times 112 \text{ g } PCl_5}{100}$ = 93.2 g PCl_5

30. Given: mass of NH_3 = 5.00 kg
percent yield for each step = 94.0%
balanced equation

Unknown: mass of HNO_3 (actual yield)

mole ratio of HNO_3 to NH_3 = $\dfrac{2 \text{ mol HNO}_3}{3 \text{ mol NO}_2} \times \dfrac{2 \text{ mol NO}_2}{2 \text{ mol NO}} \times \dfrac{4 \text{ mol NO}}{4 \text{ mol NH}_3}$

$= \dfrac{2 \text{ mol HNO}_3}{3 \text{ mol NH}_3}$

molar mass of HNO_3 = $1 \times \dfrac{1.01 \text{ g H}}{\text{mol H}} + 1 \times \dfrac{14.01 \text{ g N}}{\text{mol N}} + 3 \times \dfrac{16.00 \text{ g O}}{\text{mol O}}$

$= 63.02 \text{ g/mol}$

molar mass of NH_3 = $1 \times \dfrac{14.01 \text{ g N}}{\text{mol N}} + 3 \times \dfrac{1.01 \text{ g H}}{\text{mol H}} = 17.04 \text{ g/mol}$

mass HNO_3 (theoretical) = $5.00 \text{ kg NH}_3 \times \dfrac{1000 \text{ g}}{\text{kg}} \times \dfrac{1 \text{ mol NH}_3}{17.04 \text{ g NH}_3}$

$\times \dfrac{2 \text{ mol HNO}_3}{3 \text{ mol NH}_3} \times \dfrac{63.02 \text{ g HNO}_3}{\text{mol HNO}_3} = 1.23 \times 10^4 \text{ g HNO}_3$

The total percent yield equals the product of the percent yields for each step.

total percent yield = $94.0 \times 94.0 \times 94.0 = (94.0)^3$

mass HNO_3 (actual) = $\dfrac{\text{total percent yield} \times \text{g HNO}_3 \text{ (theoretical)}}{(100)^3}$

$= (0.94)^3 \times (1.23 \times 10^4 \text{ g HNO}_3) = 1.02 \times 10^4 \text{ g HNO}_3$

---

31. Given: mass of Mg = 185.0 g
mass of $MgCl_2$ = 1000. g

Unknown: percent yield

balanced equation:

$MgCl_2 \rightarrow Mg + Cl_2$

mole ratio from balanced equation = $\dfrac{1 \text{ mol Mg}}{1 \text{ mol MgCl}_2}$

molar mass of Mg = 24.30 g/mol

molar mass of $MgCl_2$ = $1 \times \dfrac{24.30 \text{ g Mg}}{\text{mol Mg}} + 2 \times \dfrac{35.45 \text{ g Cl}}{\text{mol Cl}} = 95.20 \text{ g/mol}$

mass Mg (theoretical) = $1000. \text{ g MgCl}_2 \times \dfrac{1 \text{ mol MgCl}_2}{95.20 \text{ g MgCl}_2} \times \dfrac{1 \text{ mol Mg}}{1 \text{ mol MgCl}_2}$

$\times \dfrac{24.30 \text{ g Mg}}{\text{mol Mg}} = 255.3 \text{ g Mg}$

percent yield = $\dfrac{\text{g Mg (actual)}}{\text{g Mg (theoretical)}} \times 100 = \dfrac{185.0 \text{ g Mg}}{255.3 \text{ g Mg}} \times 100$

percent yield = 72.46%

32. Given: volume of CO_2 = 0.750 L

density of CO_2 = 1.20 g/L

mass of $NaHCO_3$ in baking powder = 168 g/kg

balanced equation

Unknown: mass of baking powder

mass of CO_2 = $\dfrac{1.20 \text{ g } CO_2}{\text{L } CO_2} \times 0.750 \text{ L } CO_2 = 0.900 \text{ g } CO_2$

mole ratio from balanced equation = $\dfrac{2 \text{ mol } NaHCO_3}{2 \text{ mol } CO_2}$

molar mass of $NaHCO_3$ = $1 \times \dfrac{22.99 \text{ g Na}}{\text{mol Na}} + 1 \times \dfrac{1.01 \text{ g H}}{\text{mol H}} + 1 \times \dfrac{12.01 \text{ g C}}{\text{mol C}}$

$+\, 3 \times \dfrac{16.00 \text{ g O}}{\text{mol O}} = 84.01 \text{ g/mol}$

molar mass of CO_2 = $1 \times \dfrac{12.01 \text{ g C}}{\text{mol C}} + 2 \times \dfrac{16.00 \text{ g O}}{\text{mol O}} = 44.01 \text{ g/mol}$

mass of baking powder = $0.900 \text{ g } CO_2 \times \dfrac{1 \text{ mol } CO_2}{44.01 \text{ g } CO_2} \times \dfrac{2 \text{ mol } NaHCO_3}{2 \text{ mol } CO_2}$

$\times \dfrac{84.01 \text{ g } NaHCO_3}{\text{mol } NaHCO_3} \times \dfrac{1 \text{ kg baking powder}}{168 \text{ g } NaHCO_3}$

$= 0.0102 \text{ kg baking powder} = 10.2 \text{ g baking powder}$

---

33. Given: percent yield = 85.0%

mass of C = 1250 g

balanced equation

Unknown: mass of CH_4 (actual yield)

mole ratio from balanced equation = $\dfrac{1 \text{ mol } CH_4}{2 \text{ mol C}}$

molar mass of C = 12.01 g/mol

molar mass of CH_4 = $1 \times \dfrac{12.01 \text{ g C}}{\text{mol C}} + 4 \times \dfrac{1.01 \text{ g H}}{\text{mol H}} = 16.05 \text{ g/mol}$

mass CH_4 (theoretical) = $1250 \text{ g C} \times \dfrac{1 \text{ mol C}}{12.01 \text{ g C}} \times \dfrac{1 \text{ mol } CH_4}{2 \text{ mol C}}$

$\times \dfrac{16.05 \text{ g } CH_4}{\text{mol } CH_4} = 835 \text{ g } CH_4$

mass CH_4 (actual) = $\dfrac{\text{percent yield} \times \text{g } CH_4 \text{ (theoretical)}}{100}$

$= \dfrac{85.0 \times 835 \text{ g } CH_4}{100} = 710. \text{ g } CH_4$

---

34. Given: percent yield = 95%

mass of C = 2750 g

Unknown: mass of CH_4 (actual yield)

From problem **33**, the mole ratio = $\dfrac{1 \text{ mol } CH_4}{2 \text{ mol C}}$, the molar mass of

C = 12.01 g/mol, and the molar mass of CH_4 = 16.05 g/mol.

mass CH_4 (theoretical) = $2750 \text{ g C} \times \dfrac{1 \text{ mol C}}{12.01 \text{ g C}} \times \dfrac{1 \text{ mol } CH_4}{2 \text{ mol C}}$

$\times \dfrac{16.05 \text{ g } CH_4}{\text{mol } CH_4} = 1840 \text{ g } CH_4$

mass CH_4 (actual) = $\dfrac{\text{percent yield} \times \text{g } CH_4 \text{ (theoretical)}}{100}$

$= \dfrac{95 \times 1840 \text{ g } CH_4}{100} = 1750 \text{ g } CH_4$

35. Given: mass of $CaSO_4 \cdot 2H_2O$ = 2.00 kg
density of water vapor = 0.574 g/L

Unknown: volume of water vapor in liters

balanced equation:

$$2CaSO_4 \cdot 2H_2O \rightarrow 2CaSO_4 \cdot \frac{1}{2}H_2O + 3H_2O$$

mole ratio from balanced equation = $\dfrac{3 \text{ mol } H_2O}{2 \text{ mol } CaSO_4 \cdot 2 \, H_2O}$

molar mass of $CaSO_4 \cdot 2 \, H_2O$ = $1 \times \dfrac{40.08 \text{ g Ca}}{\text{mol Ca}} + 1 \times \dfrac{32.07 \text{ g S}}{\text{mol S}}$

$+ 4 \times \dfrac{1.01 \text{ g H}}{\text{mol H}} + 6 \times \dfrac{16.00 \text{ g O}}{\text{mol O}} = 172.19 \text{ g/mol}$

molar mass of H_2O = 18.02 g/mol

mass $CaSO_4 \cdot 2H_2O$ = $2.00 \text{ kg} \times \dfrac{1000 \text{ g}}{\text{kg}}$

$= 2.00 \times 10^3 \text{ g } CaSO_4 \cdot 2H_2O$

mass H_2O = $(2.00 \times 10^3 \text{ g } CaSO_4 \cdot 2H_2O) \times \dfrac{1 \text{ mol } CaSO_4 \cdot 2H_2O}{172.19 \text{ g } CaSO_4 \cdot 2H_2O}$

$\times \dfrac{3 \text{ mol } H_2O}{2 \text{ mol } CaSO_4 \cdot 2H_2O} \times \dfrac{18.02 \text{ g } H_2O}{\text{mol } H_2O} = 314.0 \text{ g } H_2O$

$V \, H_2O = \dfrac{314.0 \text{ g } H_2O}{\left(\dfrac{0.574 \text{ g } H_2O}{L \, H_2O}\right)} = 547 \text{ L water vapor}$

---

36. Given: mass of ZnO = 2.00 g
balanced equation

Unknown: mass of Au

mole ratio of Au to ZnO = $\dfrac{2 \text{ mol Zn}}{2 \text{ mol ZnO}} \times \dfrac{2 \text{ mol Au}}{3 \text{ mol Zn}} = \dfrac{2 \text{ mol Au}}{3 \text{ mol ZnO}}$

molar mass of ZnO = $1 \times \dfrac{65.39 \text{ g Zn}}{\text{mol Zn}} + 1 \times \dfrac{16.00 \text{ g O}}{\text{mol O}} = 81.39 \text{ g/mol}$

molar mass of Au = 196.97 g/mol

mass Au = $2.00 \text{ g ZnO} \times \dfrac{1 \text{ mol ZnO}}{81.39 \text{ g ZnO}} \times \dfrac{2 \text{ mol Au}}{3 \text{ mol ZnO}} \times \dfrac{196.97 \text{ g Au}}{\text{mol Au}} = 3.23 \text{ g Au}$

41a. Given: mass of Fe = 3.65×10^3 kg, balanced equation

Unknown: minimum mass of C

mole ratio from balanced equation = $\dfrac{1 \text{ mol C}}{3 \text{ mol Fe}}$

molar mass of Fe = 55.85 g/mol

molar mass of C = 12.01 g/mol

mass C = $(3.65 \times 10^3 \text{ kg Fe}) \times \dfrac{1000 \text{ g}}{\text{kg}} \times \dfrac{1 \text{ mol Fe}}{55.85 \text{ g Fe}} \times \dfrac{1 \text{ mol C}}{3 \text{ mol Fe}}$

$\times \dfrac{12.01 \text{ g C}}{\text{mol C}} \times \dfrac{1 \text{ kg}}{1000 \text{ g}} = 262 \text{ kg C}$

b. Given: mass of Fe = 3.65×10^3 kg

Unknown: mass of Fe_3C

mole ratio from balanced equation $= \dfrac{1 \text{ mol Fe}_3C}{3 \text{ mol Fe}}$

molar mass of $Fe_3C = 3 \times \dfrac{55.85 \text{ g Fe}}{\text{mol Fe}} + 1 \times \dfrac{12.01 \text{ g C}}{\text{mol C}} = 179.6$ g/mol

molar mass of Fe = 55.85 g/mol

mass $Fe_3C = (3.65 \times 10^3 \text{ kg Fe}) \times \dfrac{1000 \text{ g}}{\text{kg}} \times \dfrac{1 \text{ mol Fe}}{55.85 \text{ g Fe}} \times \dfrac{1 \text{ mol Fe}_3C}{3 \text{ mol Fe}}$

$\times \dfrac{179.6 \text{ g Fe}_3C}{\text{mol Fe}_3C} \times \dfrac{1 \text{ kg}}{1000 \text{ g}} = 3.91 \times 10^3$ kg Fe_3C

42a. Given: mass of Al = 30.0 g

Unknown: mass of Al_2O_3

mole ratio from balanced equation $= \dfrac{2 \text{ mol Al}_2O_3}{4 \text{ mol Al}}$

molar mass of Al = 26.98 g/mol

molar mass of $Al_2O_3 = 2 \times \dfrac{26.98 \text{ g Al}}{\text{mol Al}} + 3 \times \dfrac{16.00 \text{ g O}}{\text{mol O}} = 101.96$ g/mol

mass $Al_2O_3 = 30.0 \text{ g Al} \times \dfrac{1 \text{ mol Al}}{26.98 \text{ g Al}} \times \dfrac{2 \text{ mol Al}_2O_3}{4 \text{ mol Al}} \times \dfrac{101.96 \text{ g Al}_2O_3}{\text{mol Al}_2O_3}$

$= 56.7$ g Al_2O_3

43a. Given: mass of MgO = 154.6 g, balanced equation

Unknown: mass of CO_2

mole ratio from balanced equation $= \dfrac{1 \text{ mol CO}_2}{1 \text{ mol MgO}}$

molar mass of MgO $= 1 \times \dfrac{24.30 \text{ g Mg}}{\text{mol Mg}} + 1 \times \dfrac{16.00 \text{ g O}}{\text{mol O}} = 40.30$ g/mol

molar mass of $CO_2 = 1 \times \dfrac{12.01 \text{ g C}}{\text{mol C}} + 2 \times \dfrac{16.00 \text{ g O}}{\text{mol O}} = 44.01$ g/mol

mass $CO_2 = 154.6 \text{ g MgO} \times \dfrac{1 \text{ mol MgO}}{40.30 \text{ g MgO}} \times \dfrac{1 \text{ mol CO}_2}{1 \text{ mol MgO}} \times \dfrac{44.01 \text{ g CO}_2}{\text{mol CO}_2}$

$= 168.8$ g CO_2

b. Given: mass of MgO = 154.6 g

Unknown: mass of $MgCO_3$

mole ratio from balanced equation $= \dfrac{1 \text{ mol MgCO}_3}{1 \text{ mol MgO}}$

molar mass of $MgCO_3 = 1 \times \dfrac{24.30 \text{ g Mg}}{\text{mol Mg}} + 1 \times \dfrac{12.01 \text{ g C}}{\text{mol C}} + 3 \times \dfrac{16.00 \text{ g O}}{\text{mol O}}$

$= 84.31$ g/mol

molar mass of MgO = 40.30 g/mol

mass $MgCO_3 = 154.6 \text{ g MgO} \times \dfrac{1 \text{ mol MgO}}{40.30 \text{ g MgO}} \times \dfrac{1 \text{ mol MgCO}_3}{1 \text{ mol MgO}}$

$\times \dfrac{84.31 \text{ g MgCO}_3}{\text{mol MgCO}_3} = 323.4$ g $MgCO_3$

c. Given: mass of P_4O_{10} = 45.7 g, balanced equation

Unknown: mass of $Ca_3(PO_4)_2$

$$\text{mole ratio from balanced equation} = \frac{2 \text{ mol } Ca_3(PO_4)_2}{1 \text{ mol } P_4O_{10}}$$

$$\text{molar mass of } P_4O_{10} = 4 \times \frac{30.97 \text{ g P}}{\text{mol P}} + 10 \times \frac{16.00 \text{ g O}}{\text{mol O}} = 283.9 \text{ g/mol}$$

$$\text{molar mass of } Ca_3(PO_4)_2 = 3 \times \frac{40.08 \text{ g Ca}}{\text{mol Ca}} + 2 \times \frac{30.97 \text{ g P}}{\text{mol P}}$$

$$+ 8 \times \frac{16.00 \text{ g O}}{\text{mol O}} = 310.1 \text{ g/mol}$$

$$\text{mass } Ca_3(PO_4)_2 = 45.7 \text{ g } P_4O_{10} \times \frac{1 \text{ mol } P_4O_{10}}{283.9 \text{ g } P_4O_{10}} \times \frac{2 \text{ mol } Ca_3(PO_4)_2}{1 \text{ mol } P_4O_{10}}$$

$$\times \frac{310.1 \text{ g } Ca_3(PO_4)_2}{\text{mol } Ca_3(PO_4)_2} = 99.9 \text{ g } Ca_3(PO_4)_2$$

Math Tutor, p. 324

1. Given: 12.24 mol O_2

Unknown: Amount of SO_3 formed, mol

$$2 SO_2(g) + O_2(l) \rightarrow 2SO_3(g)$$

$$12.24 \text{ mol } O_2 \times \frac{2 \text{ mol } SO_3}{1 \text{ mol } O_2} = 24.48 \text{ mol } SO_3$$

2. Given: 78.50 g $KClO_3$

Unknown: mass of O_2 produced

$$2 KClO_3 \rightarrow 2 KCl + 3O_2$$

$$78.50 \text{ g } KClO_3 \times \frac{1 \text{ mol } KClO_3}{122.55 \text{ g } KClO_3} \times \frac{3 \text{ mol } O_2}{2 \text{ mol } KClO_3} \times \frac{32.00 \text{ g } O_2}{\text{mol } O_2} = 30.75 \text{ g}$$

Standardized Test Prep, 325

13. Given: $C_6H_6 + Br_2 \rightarrow C_6H_5Br + HBr$

40.0 g C_6H_6

95.0 g Br_2

65.0 g C_6H_5Br produced

a. Unknown: the limiting reactant

a. $40.0 \text{ g } C_6H_6 \times \dfrac{1 \text{ mol } C_6H_6}{78.12 \text{ g } C_6H_6} \times \dfrac{1 \text{ mol } Br_2}{1 \text{ mol } C_6H_6} \times \dfrac{159.80 \text{ g } Br_2}{1 \text{ mol } Br_2} = 81.82 \text{ g } Br_2$

81.8 g Br_2 < 95.0 g Br_2 available; C_6H_6 is limiting

b. Unknown: the theoretical yield of C_6H_5Br

b. $40.0 \text{ g } C_6H_6 \times \dfrac{1 \text{ mol } C_6H_6}{78.12 \text{ g } C_6H_6} \times \dfrac{1 \text{ mol } C_6H_5Br}{1 \text{ mol } C_6H_6} \times \dfrac{157.01 \text{ g } C_6H_5Br}{\text{mol } C_6H_5Br}$

$= 80.4 \text{ g } C_6H_5Br$ theoretical yield

c. Unknown: the reactant in excess, and the amount remaining

c. Br_2 is in excess. 95.0 g Br_2 – 81.8 g Br_2 reacted = = 13.2 g Br_2 remaining

d. Unknown: the percentage yield

d. $\dfrac{65.0 \text{ g } C_6H_5Br}{80.4 \text{ g } C_6H_5Br} \times 100\% = 80.8\%$ yield

CHAPTER 10

States of Matter

Practice, p. 352

1. Given: mass of H_2O (l) =
506 g
molar enthalpy of
fusion of ice =
6.009 kJ/mol
molar mass H_2O
= 18.02 g

Unknown: energy re-
leased when
water freezes

$$(506 \text{ g } H_2O)\left(\frac{1 \text{ mol } H_2O}{18.02 \text{ g } H_2O}\right) = 28.1 \text{ mol } H_2O$$

$$(28.1 \text{ mol } H_2O)(6.009 \text{ kJ/mol}) = 169 \text{ kJ}$$

2. Given: energy released
on condensation
of steam = 4.97 ×
10^5 kJ
molar mass of
H_2O = 18.02 g
molar enthalpy of
vaporization =
40.79 kJ/mol

Unknown: mass of steam
required

$$m = (4.97 \times 10^5 \text{ kJ})\left(\frac{1 \text{ mol } H_2O}{40.79 \text{ kJ}}\right)\left(\frac{18.02 \text{ g}}{\text{mol } H_2O}\right)$$

$$= 2.19 \times 10^5 \text{ g}$$

ATE, Additional Sample Problems, p. 352

A-1. Given: energy absorbed
on boiling =
5.23×10^4 kJ
molar mass of
H_2O = 18.02 g
molar enthalpy of
vaporization =
40.79 kJ/mol

Unknown: mass of liquid
water re-
quired

$$m = (5.23 \times 10^4 \text{ kJ})\left(\frac{1 \text{ mol } H_2O}{40.79 \text{ kJ}}\right)\left(\frac{18.02 \text{ g}}{\text{mol } H_2O}\right)$$

$$= 2.31 \times 10^4 \text{ g}$$

A-2. Given: mass of $H_2O(s)$ =
16.3 g
enthalpy of
fusion of
ice = 6.009 kJ/mol
molar mass of
H_2O = 18.02 g

Unknown: energy ab-
sorbed when
ice melts

$$m = (16.3 \text{ g } H_2O)\left(\frac{1 \text{ mol } H_2O}{18.02 \text{ g } H_2O}\right)\left(\frac{6.009 \text{ kJ}}{\text{mol}}\right)$$

$$= 5.44 \text{ kJ}$$

A-3. Given: mass of H_2O (g) = 783 g

enthalpy of vaporization = 40.79 kJ/mol

molar mass H_2O = 18.02 g

Unknown: energy released when steam condenses

$$m = (783 \text{ g } H_2O)\left(\frac{1 \text{ mol } H_2O}{18.02 \text{ g } H_2O}\right)(40.79 \text{ kJ/mol})$$

$$= 1.77 \times 10^3 \text{ kJ}$$

Review Problems

19. a. Given: molar enthalpy of vaporization for H_2O = 40.79 kJ/mol

molar mass of H_2O = 18.02 g

Unknown: enthalpy of vaporization in joules per gram

$$(40.79 \text{ kJ/mol})\left(\frac{\text{mol } H_2O}{18.02 \text{ g}}\right)\left(\frac{1000 \text{ J}}{\text{kJ}}\right) = 2264 \text{ J/g}$$

b. Given: enthalpy of fusion of H_2O = 6.009 kJ/mol

Unknown: enthalpy of fusion in joules per gram

$$(6.009 \text{ kJ/mol})\left(\frac{\text{mol } H_2O}{18.02 \text{ g}}\right)\left(\frac{1000 \text{ J}}{\text{kJ}}\right) = 333.5 \text{ J/g}$$

20. Given: mass of substance = 0.433 mol

energy absorbed when substance is vaporized = 36.5 kJ

Unknown: molar enthalpy of vaporization

$$\frac{36.5 \text{ kJ}}{0.433 \text{ mol}} = 84.3 \text{ kJ/mol}$$

21. Given: molar mass of substance = 259.0 g/mol

mass of substance = 71.8 g

energy absorbed by substance when it melts = 4.307 kJ

a. Unknown: moles in the sample

$$(71.8 \text{ g})\left(\frac{\text{mol}}{259.0 \text{ g}}\right) = 0.277 \text{ mol}$$

b. Unknown: molar enthalpy of fusion

$$\frac{4.307 \text{ kJ}}{0.277 \text{ mol}} = 15.5 \text{ kJ/mol}$$

22. a. Given: molar enthalpy of fusion of substance = 3.811 kJ/mol energy released when substance freezes = 83.2 kJ

Unknown: moles of substance

$$(83.2 \text{ kJ})\left(\frac{\text{mol}}{3.811 \text{ kJ}}\right) = 21.8 \text{ mol}$$

b. Given: mass of sample = 5519 g

Unknown: molar mass of substance

$$\frac{5519 \text{ g}}{21.8 \text{ mol}} = 253 \text{ g/mol}$$

---

25. Given: volume of ice = 5.00 cm^3 at 0°C volume of liquid water = 5.00 cm^3 at 0°C

Unknown: **a.** which substance contains more molecules

b. number of molecules more

c. ratio of molecules in both samples

a. $D = \dfrac{m}{V}$

$m = DV$

Density of ice at 0°C = 0.917 g/cm^3

Density of water at 0°C = 1.0 g/cm^3

mass of ice = (0.917 g/cm^3)(5.00 cm^3) = 4.6 g

moles of ice = (4.6 g)$\left(\dfrac{\text{mol}}{18.02 \text{ g}}\right)$ = 0.255 mol

$(0.255 \text{ mol})\left(\dfrac{6.022 \times 10^{23} \text{ molecules}}{\text{mol}}\right) = 1.53 \times 10^{23}$ molecules of ice

mass of liquid water = (1.0 g/cm^3)(5.00 cm^3)

$= 5.0$ g

moles of water = (5.0 g)$\left(\dfrac{\text{mol}}{18.02 \text{ g}}\right)$ = 0.277 mol

$(0.277 \text{ mol})\left(\dfrac{6.022 \times 10^{23} \text{ molecules}}{\text{mol}}\right) = 1.67 \times 10^{23}$ molecules

Liquid water contains more molecules.

b. $1.617 \times 10^{23} - 1.53 \times 10^{23} = 1.4 \times 10^{22}$ more molecules

c. Ratio $= \dfrac{1.67 \times 10^{23}}{1.53 \times 10^{23}} = \dfrac{1.09}{1.00}$

26. a. Given: T of steam =
100.°C = 373 K
P of steam =
1.00 atm
enthalpy of
fusion of ice =
6.009 kJ/mol

Unknown: volume and
mass of steam
that would
release the
same amount
of energy as
the liquid
water during
freezing

Liquid water:

$$(100. \text{ cm}^3)\left(\frac{1.00 \text{ g}}{\text{cm}^3}\right)\left(\frac{1 \text{ mol}}{18.02 \text{ g}}\right)(6.009 \text{ kJ/mol})$$

= 33.3 kJ = energy released when water is frozen

Steam:

molar enthalpy of vaporization = 40.79 kJ/mol

$$(33.3 \text{ kJ})\left(\frac{1 \text{ mol}}{40.79 \text{ kJ}}\right) = 0.816 \text{ mol}$$

$$V = \frac{nRT}{P} = \frac{(0.816 \text{ mol})\left(0.0821 \dfrac{\text{L} \bullet \text{atm}}{\text{mol} \bullet \text{K}}\right)(373 \text{ K})}{1.00 \text{ atm}}$$

$$= 25.0 \text{ L} = \text{volume of steam}$$

$$(0.816 \text{ mol})\left(\frac{18.02 \text{ g}}{\text{mol}}\right) = 14.7 \text{ g} = \text{mass of steam}$$

b. Unknown: relative volumes and
masses of
steam and
liquid water
required to
release same
amount of
energy

Volumes:

Steam = 25 L

Liquid water = $(100 \text{ cm}^2)\left(\dfrac{\text{mL}}{\text{cm}^3}\right)\left(\dfrac{\text{L}}{1000 \text{ mL}}\right)$

$\qquad\qquad\quad = 0.1 \text{ L}$

Masses:

Steam: 14.7 g

Liquid water: $(100. \text{ cm}^3)\left(\dfrac{1.00 \text{ g}}{\text{cm}^3}\right) = 100 \text{ g}$

A larger volume of steam is required than water; a smaller mass of steam
is required than water.

---

27. Given: mass of substance
= 3.21 mol
energy absorbed
on vaporization =
28.4 kJ

Unknown: molar en-
thalpy of
vaporization

$$\frac{28.4 \text{ kJ}}{3.21 \text{ mol}} = 8.85 \text{ kJ/mol}$$

---

28. Given: molar enthalpy of
fusion of water =
6.009 kJ/mol

Unknown: energy re-
quired to melt
7.95×10^5 g
ice

$$(7.95 \times 10^5 \text{ g})\left(\frac{1 \text{ mol}}{18.02 \text{ g}}\right)\left(\frac{6.009 \text{ kJ}}{\text{mol}}\right) = 2.65 \times 10^5 \text{ kJ}$$

---

29. Given: molar enthalpy of
vaporization of
substance =
31.6 kJ/mol

Unknown: amount of
substance
requiring
57.0 kJ to
vaporize

$$\frac{57.0 \text{ kJ}}{31.6 \text{ kJ/mol}} = 1.80 \text{ mol}$$

30. Given: enthalpy of vaporization of water = 40.79 kJ/mol

Unknown: grams of water vaporized by 0.545 kJ

$$\left(\frac{0.545\ kJ}{40.79\ kJ/mol}\right)\left(\frac{18.02\ g}{mol}\right) = 0.241\ g$$

---

31. Given: mass of liquid = 13.3 g

molar mass = 82.9 g/mol

enthalpy of fusion = 4.60 kJ/mol

Unknown: energy released by freezing 13.3 g

$$(13.3\ g)\left(\frac{mol}{82.9\ g}\right)\left(\frac{4.60\ kJ}{mol}\right) = 0.738\ kJ$$

---

32. Given: $T = 100.°C = 373\ K$

$P = 760.$ torr

enthalpy of fusion of ice = 6.009 kJ/mol

Unknown: volume and mass of steam that would release same amount of energy during condensation as 65.5 cm^3 liquid water would release during freezing

Liquid water:

$$(65.5\ cm^3)\left(\frac{1.00\ g}{cm^3}\right)\left(\frac{1\ mol}{18.02\ g}\right)\left(\frac{6.009\ kJ}{mol}\right)$$

$= 21.8\ kJ =$ energy released during freezing

Steam:

molar heat of vaporization = 40.79 kJ/mol

$$(21.8\ kJ)\left(\frac{1\ mol}{40.79\ kJ}\right) = 0.5344\ mol$$

$$V = \frac{nRT}{P} = \frac{(0.5344\ mol)\left(\dfrac{0.0821\ L\bullet atm}{mol\bullet K}\right)(373\ K)}{1.00\ atm}$$

$= 16.4\ L =$ volume of steam

$$(0.5344\ mol)\left(\frac{18.02\ g}{mol}\right) = 9.63\ g =$$ mass of steam

Math Tutor, p. 358

1. Given: 1.940 mol Ag

22.60 kJ

Unknown: ΔH_f for Ag

$$\Delta H_f = \frac{22.60\ kJ}{1.940\ mol} = 11.65\ kJ/mol$$

---

2. Given: $\Delta H_f =$ 11.54 kJ/mol for $C_2H_4O_2$

6.47 mol $C_2H_4O_2$

Unknown: amount of energy absorbed

energy = 11.54 kJ/mol × 6.47 mol = 74.7 kJ

9. Given: 15.0 g substance
120 g/mol = molar
mass of substance
60.0 J

$\Delta H_f = 60.0 \text{ J} \times \dfrac{1 \text{ kJ}}{1000 \text{ J}} \times \dfrac{1}{15.0 \text{ g}} \times \dfrac{120 \text{ g}}{1 \text{ mol}} = 0.48 \text{ kJ} \backslash \text{mol}$

Unknown: ΔH_f of the
substance

CHAPTER 11

Gases

Practice, p. 365

1. Given: $P = 1.75$ atm

    a. $1.75 \text{ atm} \times \dfrac{101.325 \text{ kPa}}{\text{atm}} = 177$ kPa

    b. $1.75 \text{ atm} \times \dfrac{760 \text{ mm Hg}}{\text{atm}} = 1330$ mm Hg

2. Given: $P = 72.7$ atm

    Unknown: P in Pa

$72.7 \text{ atm} \times \dfrac{101.325 \text{ kPa}}{1 \text{ atm}} \times \dfrac{1000 \text{ Pa}}{1 \text{ kPa}} = 7.37 \times 10^6$ Pa

ATE, Additional Sample Problem, p. 365

A-1. Given: $P = 745.8$ mm Hg

    a. $745.8 \text{ mm} \times \dfrac{1 \text{ atm}}{760 \text{ mm}} = 0.9813$ atm

    b. $0.9813 \text{ atm} \times \dfrac{760 \text{ torr}}{1 \text{ atm}} = 745.8$ torr

    c. $0.9813 \text{ atm} \times \dfrac{101.325 \text{ kPa}}{\text{atm}} = 99.43$ kPa

Additional Example Problem, p. 366

1. Given: Volume abundance in air of:
$N_2 = 78.08\%$
$O_2 = 20.95\%$
$Ar = 0.934\%$, and
$CO_2 = 0.035\%$

Unknown: Partial pressures of each gas at $P_{total} = 760.$ mm

$N_2 = 760 \text{ mm Hg} \times 0.7808 = 593.4$ mm Hg

$O_2 = 760 \text{ mm Hg} \times 0.2095 = 159.2$ mm Hg

$Ar = 760 \text{ mm Hg} \times 0.00934 = 7.10$ mm Hg

$CO_2 = 760 \text{ mm Hg} \times 0.00035 = 0.27$ mm Hg

Practice, p. 367

1. Given: $T = 20.0°C$

    $P_{H_2} = 742.5$ torr

    P_{H_2O} at 20°C $= 17.5$ torr

    Unknown: P_T

$P_T = P_{H_2} + P_{H_2O} = 742.5 + 17.5 = 760.0$ torr

ATE, Additional Sample Problem, p. 367

B-1. Given: $T = 27.0°C$

    $P_T = 743.3$ mm Hg

    Unknown: P_{Ne}

$P_T = P_{Ne} + P_{H_2O}$

P_{H_2O} at 27.0°C $= 26.7$ mm Hg (from Appendix A-8)

$P_{Ne} = P_T - P_{H_2O} = 743.3 - 26.7 = 716.6$ mm Hg

Section Review, p. 367

4. a. Given: $P = 151.98$ kPa

$$151.98 \text{ kPa} \times \frac{1 \text{ atm}}{101.325 \text{ kPa}} = 1.4999 \text{ atm}$$

b. Given: $P = 456$ torr

$$456 \text{ torr} \times \frac{1 \text{ atm}}{760 \text{ torr}} = 0.600 \text{ atm}$$

5. Given: $T = 23.0°C$

$P_T = P_{atm}$
$\quad = 785$ mm Hg

Unknown: P_{N_2}

$P_T = P_{N_2} + P_{H_2O}$

P_{H_2O} at 23°C = 21.1 mm Hg (from Appendix A-8)

$P_{N_2} = P_T - P_{H_2O} = 785 - 21 = 764$ mm Hg

Practice, p. 370

1. Given: $V_1 = 500$ mL He

$P_1 = 1$ atm

$P_2 = 0.5$ atm

Unknown: V_2

$P_1 V_1 = P_2 V_2$

$$V_2 = \frac{P_1 V_1}{P_2} = \frac{(1 \text{ atm})(500 \text{ mL He})}{0.5 \text{ atm}} = 1000 \text{ mL He}$$

ATE, Additional Sample Problems, p. 370

C-1. Given: $V_1 = 450$ mL

$P_1 = 1$

$P_2 = 15$

Unknown: V_2

$P_1 V_1 = P_2 V_2$

$$P_2 = \frac{P_1 V_1}{P_2} = \frac{(1)(450 \text{ mL})}{15} = 30.0 \text{ mL}$$

C-2. Given: $V_1 =$ of helium = 125 mL

$P_1 = 0.974$ atm

$P_2 = 1.000$ atm

Unknown: V_2

$P_1 V_1 = P_2 V_2$

$$V_2 = \frac{P_1 V_1}{P_2} = \frac{(0.974 \text{ atm})(125 \text{ mL})}{1.000 \text{ atm}} = 122 \text{ mL He}$$

Practice, p. 372

1. Given: $V_1 = 752$ mL

$T_1 = 25.0$ °C
$\quad = 298$ K

$T_2 = 100$ °C
$\quad = 373$ K

Unknown: V_2

$$\frac{V_1}{T_1} = \frac{V_2}{T_2}$$

$$V_2 = \frac{V_1 T_2}{T_1} = \frac{752 \text{ mL} \times 373 \text{ K}}{298 \text{ K}} = 941 \text{ mL}$$

2. Given: $V_1 = 375$ mL

$T_1 = 0.0°C$
$\quad = 273$ K

$V_2 = 500$ mL

Unknown: T_2

$$\frac{V_1}{T_1} = \frac{V_2}{T_2}$$

$$T_2 = \frac{T_1 V_2}{V_1} = \frac{(273 \text{ K})(500 \text{ mL})}{375 \text{ mL}} = 364 \text{ K}$$

$364 \text{ K} - 273 = 91°C$

ATE, Additional Sample Problem, p. 372

D-1. Given: $V_1 = 5.5$ L

$T_1 = 25°C$
$= 298$ K

$T_2 = 100°C$
$= 373$ K

Unknown: V_2

$$\frac{V_1}{T_1} = \frac{V_2}{T_2}$$

$$V_2 = \frac{V_1 T_2}{T_1} = \frac{(5.5\ L)(373\ K)}{298\ K} = 6.9\ L$$

ATE, Additional Sample Problem, p. 373

E-1. Given: $T_1 = 20°C$
$= 293$ K

$P_1 = 1.0$ atm

$T_2 = 500°C$
$= 773$ K

Unknown: P_2

$$\frac{P_1}{T_1} = \frac{P_2}{T_2}$$

$$P_2 = \frac{P_1 T_2}{T_1} = \frac{(1.0\ atm)(773\ K)}{293\ K} = 2.6\ atm$$

Practice, p. 374

1. Given: $T_1 = 120°C$
$= 393$ K

$P_1 = 1.07$ atm

$T_2 = 205°C$
$= 478$ K

Unknown: P_2

$$\frac{P_1}{T_1} = \frac{P_2}{T_2}$$

$$P_2 = \frac{P_1 T_2}{T_1} = \frac{(1.07\ atm)(478\ K)}{393\ K} = 1.30\ atm$$

2. Given: $T_1 = 122°C$
$= 395$ K

$T_2 = 205°C$
$= 478$ K

$P_1 = 1.07$ atm

Unknown: P_2

$$P_2 = \frac{P_1 T_2}{T_1} = \frac{1.07\ atm \times 478\ K}{395\ K} = 1.29\ atm$$

3. Given: $P_1 = 1.20$ atm

$T_1 = 22°C = 295$ K

$P_2 = 2.00$ atm

Unknown: T_2

$$\frac{P_1}{T_1} = \frac{P_2}{T_2}$$

$$T_2 = \frac{T_1 P_2}{P_1} = \frac{(295\ K)(2.00\ atm)}{1.20\ atm} = 492\ K$$

$$492\ K - 273 = 219°C$$

Practice, p. 375

1. Given: $V_1 = 27.5$ mL

$T_1 = 22.0°C$
$= 295$ K

$P_1 = 0.974$ atm

$T_2 = 15.0°C$
$= 288$ K

$P_2 = 0.993$ atm

Unknown: V_2

$$\frac{P_1 V_1}{T_1} = \frac{P_2 V_2}{T_2}$$

$$V_2 = \frac{P_1 V_1 T_2}{P_2 T_1} = \frac{(0.974\ atm)(27.5\ mL)(288\ K)}{(0.993\ atm)(295\ K)} = 26.3\ mL$$

2. Given: $V_1 = 700$ mL

$T_1 = 0°C = 273$ K

$P_1 = 1.00$ atm

$V_2 = 200$ mL

$T_2 = 30.0°C$
$= 303$ K

Unknown: P_2 (in Pa)

$$\frac{P_1V_1}{T_1} = \frac{P_2V_2}{T_2}$$

$$P_2 = \frac{P_1V_1T_2}{T_1V_2} = \frac{(1.00 \text{ atm})(700 \text{ mL})(303 \text{ K})}{(273 \text{ K})(200 \text{ mL})} \times \frac{101.325 \text{ kPa}}{\text{atm}} = 394 \text{ kPa}$$

$$= 3.94 \times 10^5 \text{ Pa}$$

ATE, Additional Sample Problems, p. 375

F-1. Given: $T_1 = 27.0°C$
$= 300$ K

$P_1 = 0.200$ atm

$V_1 = 80.0$ mL

$T_2 = 0°C = 273$ K

$P_2 = 1.00$ atm

Unknown: V_2

$$\frac{P_1V_1}{T_1} = \frac{P_2V_2}{T_2}$$

$$V_2 = \frac{P_1V_1T_2}{P_2T_1} = \frac{(0.200 \text{ atm})(80.0 \text{ mL})(273 \text{ K})}{(1.00 \text{ atm})(300 \text{ K})} = 14.6 \text{ mL}$$

F-2. Given: $V_1 = 75$ mL

$T_1 = 0°C = 273$ K

$P_1 = 1.00$ atm

$T_2 = 17°C = 290$ K

$P_2 = 0.97$ atm

Unknown: V_2

$$\frac{P_1V_1}{T_1} = \frac{P_2V_2}{T_2}$$

$$V_2 = \frac{P_1V_1T_2}{P_2T_1} = \frac{(1.00 \text{ atm})(75 \text{ mL})(290 \text{ K})}{(0.97 \text{ atm})(273 \text{ K})} = 82 \text{ mL}$$

Section Review, p. 375

2. Given: $V_1 = 200.0$ mL

$P_1 = 0.960$ atm

$V_2 = 50.0$ mL

Unknown: P_2

$$P_1V_1 = P_2V_2$$

$$P_2 = \frac{P_1V_1}{V_2} = \frac{(0.960 \text{ atm})(200.0 \text{ mL})}{50.0 \text{ mL}} = 3.84 \text{ atm}$$

3. Given: $V_1 = 1.55$ L

$T_1 = 27.0°C$
$= 300.$ K

$T_2 = -100.0°C$
$= 173.$ K

(Pressure is
constant)

Unknown: V_2

$$\frac{V_1}{T_1} = \frac{V_2}{T_2}$$

$$V_2 = \frac{V_1T_2}{T_1} = \frac{1.55 \text{ L} \times 173 \text{ K}}{300 \text{ K}} = 0.894 \text{ atm}$$

4. Given: $V_1 = 2.0 \text{ m}^3$

$T_1 = 100.0 \text{ K}$

$P_1 = 100.0 \text{ kPa}$

$T_2 = 400.0 \text{ K}$

$P_2 = 200.0 \text{ kPa}$

Unknown: V_2

$$\frac{P_1V_1}{T_1} = \frac{P_2V_2}{T_2}$$

$$V_2 = \frac{P_1V_1T_2}{T_1P_2} = \frac{100.0 \text{ kPa} \times 2.0 \text{ m}^3 \times 400.0 \text{ K}}{100.0 \text{ K} \times 200.0 \text{ kPa}}$$

$$V_2 = 4.0 \text{ m}^3$$

Additional Example Problems, p. 380

1. a. Given: $3O_2(g) \rightarrow$ $2O_3(g)$, 24 O_2 molecules

Unknown: number of O_3 molecules

$$24 \text{ molecules O}_2 \times \frac{2 \text{ mol O}_3}{3 \text{ mol O}_2} = 16 \text{ molecules O}_3$$

b. Given: 12 L O_2

Unknown: L O_3

$$12 \text{ L O}_2 \times \frac{2 \text{ mol O}_3}{3 \text{ mol O}_2} = 8 \text{ L O}_3$$

2. Given: $2 \text{ Cl}_2(g) + 7 \text{ O}_2(g)$ $\rightarrow 2 \text{ Cl}_2\text{O}_7$

$$35 \text{ L O}_2 \times \frac{2 \text{ mol Cl}_2}{7 \text{ mol O}_2} = 10. \text{ L Cl}_2$$

Practice, p. 381

1. Given: $n = 7.08 \text{ mol N}_2$ at STP

Unknown: V of N_2 at STP

$$V = 7.08 \text{ mol N}_2 \times \frac{22.4 \text{ L}}{\text{mol}} = 159 \text{ L N}_2$$

2. Given: $V = 14.1 \text{ L H}_2$ at STP

Unknown: n: number of moles of H_2 at STP

$$n = \frac{V \text{ H}_2}{22.4 \text{ L/mol}} = \frac{14.1 \text{ L}}{22.4 \text{ L/mol}} = 0.629 \text{ mol H}_2$$

ATE, Additional Sample Problem, p. 381

G-1. Given: $n = 0.0580 \text{ mol}$ NO at STP

Unknown: V of NO at STP

$$V \text{ of NO} = 0.0580 \text{ mol NO} \times \frac{22.4 \text{ L}}{\text{mol}} = 1.30 \text{ L}$$

Practice, p. 382

1. Given: $V = 4.55$ L O_2 $2H_2(g) + O_2(g) \rightarrow 2H_2O(g)$

     Unknown: V of H_2 gas

$$V = (4.55 \text{ L } O_2)\left(\frac{2 \text{ L } H_2}{1 \text{ L } O_2}\right) = 9.10 \text{ L } H_2$$

2. Given: V of CO = 0.626 L $2O_2 + 4CO \rightarrow 4CO_2$

     Unknown: V of O_2 gas

$$V = (0.626 \text{ L CO})\left(\frac{2 \text{ L } O_2}{4 \text{ L CO}}\right) = 0.313 \text{ L } O_2$$

3. Given: $V = 708$ L NO_2 $3NO_2(g) + H_2O(l) \rightarrow 2HNO_3(l) + NO(g)$

     Unknown: V of NO gas produced

$$V = (708 \text{ L } NO_2)\left(\frac{1 \text{ L NO}}{3 \text{ L } NO_2}\right) = 236 \text{ L NO}$$

ATE, Additional Sample Problem, p. 382

H-1. Given: $V = 3.14$ L XeF_6 $Xe(g) + 3F_2(g) \rightarrow XeF_6(g)$

     Unknown: V of Xe V of F

$$V \text{ of Xe} = (3.14 \text{ L } XeF_6)\left(\frac{1 \text{ L Xe}}{1 \text{ L } XeF_6}\right) = 3.14 \text{ L Xe}$$

$$V \text{ of F} = (3.14 \text{ L } XeF_6)\frac{(3 \text{ L } F_2)}{(1 \text{ L } XeF_6)} = 9.42 \text{ L } F_2$$

Practice, p. 385

1. Given: $n = 0.325$ mol H_2

     $V = 4.08$ L

     $T = 35°C = 308$ K

$$P = nRT/V = \frac{(0.325 \text{ mol})\left(\dfrac{0.0821 \text{ L} \cdot \text{atm}}{\text{mol} \cdot \text{K}}\right)(308 \text{ K})}{4.08 \text{ L}} = 2.01 \text{ atm}$$

     Unknown: P in atm

2. Given: $V = 8.77$ L

     $n = 1.45$ mol

     $T = 20°C = 293$ K

$$P = nRT/V = \frac{(1.45 \text{ mol})\left(\dfrac{0.0821 \text{ L} \cdot \text{atm}}{\text{mol} \cdot \text{K}}\right)(293 \text{ K})}{8.77 \text{ L}} = 3.98 \text{ atm}$$

     Unknown: P in atm

Section Review, p. 385

2. Given: $n = 0.0035$ mol CH_4 at STP

$$V = (0.0035 \text{ mol})\left(\frac{22.4 \text{ L}}{\text{mol}}\right)\left(\frac{1000 \text{ mL}}{\text{L}}\right) = 78 \text{ mL } CH_4$$

     Unknown: V of CH_4 in mL at STP

5. Given: $V = 4.44$ L

$T = 22.55°C$
$= 295.55$ K

15.4 g O_2

Unknown: P

$PV = nRT$

$P = \dfrac{nRT}{V} = \dfrac{15.4 \text{ g } O_2 \times 0.0821 \dfrac{\text{L} \cdot \text{atm}}{\text{mol} \cdot \text{k}} \times 295.55 \text{ K}}{\left(\dfrac{32.00 \text{ g } O_2}{1 \text{ mol } O_2}\right) \times 4.44 \text{ L}}$

$P = 2.63$ atm

---

6. Given: $V = 22.9$ L

$n = 14.0$ mol

$T = 12°C = 285$ K

Unknown: P in atm

$PV = nRT$

$P = \dfrac{nRT}{V} = \dfrac{14.0 \text{ mol} \times 0.0821 \dfrac{\text{L} \cdot \text{atm}}{\text{mol} \cdot \text{k}} \times 285 \text{ K}}{22.9 \text{ L}}$

$P = 14.3$ atm

---

7. Given: $2N_2O$ (g) $\rightarrow$
$2N_2$ (g) $+ O_2$ (g)

2.22 L N_2O

Unknown: Volume N_2
and O_2,
density of
mixed prod-
ucts at STP

2.22 L $N_2O \times \dfrac{2 \text{ mol } N_2}{2 \text{ mol } N_2O} = 2.22$ L N_2

2.22 L $N_2O \times \dfrac{1 \text{ mol } O_2}{2 \text{ mol } N_2O} = 1.11$ L O_2

At STP, 1 mol = 22.4 L

For N_2, density $= \dfrac{28.02 \text{ g}}{1 \text{ mol}} \times \dfrac{1 \text{ mol}}{22.4 \text{ L}} = 1.25$ g/L

For O_2, density $= \dfrac{32.00 \text{ g}}{1 \text{ mol}} \times \dfrac{1 \text{ mol}}{22.4 \text{ L}} = 1.43$ g/L

density of mixed products $= \dfrac{2}{3} \times 1.25$ g/L $+ \dfrac{1}{3} \times 1.43$ g/L

density $= 1.31$ g/L

ATE, Additional Sample Problem, p. 385

I-1. Given: $V = 2.07$ L He

$n = 2.88$ mol

$T = 22°C =$
295 K

Unknown: P of He in atm

$P = \dfrac{nRT}{V}$

$= \dfrac{(2.88 \text{ mol})\left(\dfrac{0.0821 \text{ L} \cdot \text{atm}}{\text{mol} \cdot \text{K}}\right)(295 \text{ K})}{2.07 \text{ L}} = 33.7$ atm He

Additional Example Problems, p. 386

1. Given: $V_{O_2} = 420$ m/s at 25°C (298 K)

Unknown: V_{He} at 298 K

$$\frac{V_{He}}{V_{O_2}} = \sqrt{\frac{M_{O_2}}{M_{He}}}$$

$$V_{He} = \sqrt{\frac{M_{O_2}}{M_{He}}}\, V_{O_2} = \sqrt{\frac{32.00\ \text{amu}}{4.00\ \text{amu}}} \times 420\ \text{m/s} = 1200\ \text{m/s}$$

2. Given: $V_{H_2} = 1.81 \times 10^3$ m/s

$V_X = 312$ m/s

Unknown: molar mass of X, M_X

$$\frac{V_{H_2}^2}{V_X^2} = \frac{M_X}{M_{H_2}}$$

$$M_X = \frac{V_{H_2}^2 \times M_{H_2}}{V_X^2} = \frac{(1.84 \times 10^3\ \text{m/s})^2\, (2.02\ \text{g/mol})}{(312\ \text{m/s})^2}$$

$$M_X = 70.3\ \text{g/mol}$$

Practice, p. 388

1. Given: identities of 2 gases, CO_2 and HCl

Unknown: relative rates of effusion

$$\frac{\text{rate of effusion of } CO_2}{\text{rate of effusion of HCl}} = \frac{\sqrt{M_{HCl}}}{\sqrt{M_{CO_2}}} = \frac{\sqrt{36.5\ \text{g/mol}}}{\sqrt{44\ \text{g/mol}}} = 0.9$$

2. Given: H_2 rate of effusion = 9 times that of unknown gas

Unknown: M of unknown gas (X)

$$\frac{\text{rate of effusion of } H_2}{\text{rate of effusion of X}} = \frac{\sqrt{M_X}}{\sqrt{M_{H_2}}}$$

$$\sqrt{M_X} = \left(\frac{\text{rate of effusion of } H_2}{\text{rate of effusion of X}}\right)\left(\sqrt{M_{H_2}}\right)$$

$$= \left(\frac{9}{1}\right)\left(\sqrt{2\ \text{g/mol}}\right) = 12.7$$

$$M_X \approx 160\ \text{g/mol}$$

3. Given: rate of effusion of Ne = 400 m/s

Unknown: rate of effusion of butane, C_4H_{10}, at same temperature

$$\frac{\text{rate of effusion of neon}}{\text{rate of effusion of butane}} = \frac{\sqrt{M_{C_4H_{10}}}}{\sqrt{M_{Ne}}}$$

$$\text{rate of effusion of butane} = (\text{rate of effusion of neon})\left(\frac{\sqrt{M_{Ne}}}{\sqrt{M_{C_4H_{10}}}}\right)$$

$$= (400\ \text{m/s})\left(\frac{\sqrt{20\ \text{g/mol}}}{\sqrt{58\ \text{g/mol}}}\right) = 235\ \text{m/s}$$

ATE, Additional Sample Problem, p. 388

J-1. Given: N_2 rate of effusion = 1.7 times that of other gas

Unknown: (1) M of other gas (X)
(2) identity of other gas

$$\frac{\text{rate of effusion of } N_2}{\text{rate of effusion of X}} = \frac{\sqrt{M_X}}{\sqrt{M_{N_2}}}$$

$$\sqrt{M_X} = \left(\frac{\text{rate of effusion of } N_2}{\text{rate of effusion of X}}\right)\left(\sqrt{M_{N_2}}\right)$$

$$= \left(\frac{1.7}{1}\right)\left(\sqrt{28\ \text{g/mol}}\right) = 8.995$$

(1) $M_X = 81$ g/mol

(2) Krypton (average atomic mass of Kr = 83.8)

3. Given: rate of effusion of a gas = 1.6 times that of CO_2

Unknown: M of unknown gas (X)

$$\frac{\text{rate of effusion of X}}{\text{rate of effusion of CO}_2} = \frac{\sqrt{M_{CO_2}}}{\sqrt{M_X}}$$

$$\sqrt{M_X} = (\sqrt{M_{CO_2}})\left(\frac{\text{rate of effusion CO}_2}{\text{rate of effusion X}}\right)$$

$$= (\sqrt{44}\text{ g/mol})\left(\frac{1}{1.6}\right) = 4.14$$

$$M_X = 4.14^2 = 17\text{ g/mol}$$

4. Given:

$$\frac{\text{rate of diffusion of A}}{\text{rate of diffusion of B}} = \frac{16}{1}$$

Unknown: $\dfrac{M_B}{M_A}$

$$\frac{\sqrt{M_B}}{\sqrt{M_A}} = \frac{16}{1}$$

$$\frac{M_B}{M_A} = \frac{256}{1}$$

5. Given: $T = 25°C = 298$ K

Unknown: molecular velocities of H_2O, He, HCl, BrF, NO_2

$$\frac{\text{rate of effusion of H}_2\text{O}}{\text{rate of effusion of He}} = \frac{\sqrt{M_{He}}}{\sqrt{M_{H_2O}}}$$

(Molecular velocities of 2 different gases are inversely proportional to the square root of their molar masses.)

$M_{H_2O} = 18$ g/mol

$M_{He} = 4$ g/mol

$M_{HCl} = 36.5$ g/mol

$M_{BrF} = 98.8$ g/mol

$M_{NO_2} = 46$ g/mol

Rates of effusion: BrF < NO_2 < HCl < H_2O < He

6. Given: $V_X = \frac{1}{2}V_{O_2}$, where X is either HBr or HI

Unknown: molar mass and identity of X

$$\frac{V_{O_2}^{2}}{V_X^{2}} = \frac{V_{O_2}^{2}}{\left(\frac{1}{2}V_{O_2}\right)^2} = \frac{M_X}{M_{O_2}}$$

$M_X = 4 \times M_{O_2} = 4 \times 32.00\text{ g/mol} = 128.0\text{ g/mol}$

X is HI

7. Given: $V_2 = (1.40)(V_1)$

Unknown: P_2

$$P_2 = \frac{P_1V_1}{V_2} = \frac{(760\ mm)(1)}{1.40} = 543\ mm$$

---

8. a. Given: $P = 1.25$ atm

Unknown: P in torr

$$P = (1.25\ atm)\left(\frac{760\ torr}{atm}\right) = 950\ torr$$

b. Given: $P = 2.48 \times 10^{-3}$ atm

$$P = (2.48 \times 10^{-3}\ atm)\left(\frac{760\ torr}{atm}\right) = 1.88\ torr$$

c. Given: $P = 4.75 \times 10^4$ atm

$$P = (4.75 \times 10^4\ atm)\left(\frac{760\ torr}{atm}\right) = 3.61 \times 10^7\ torr$$

d. Given: $P = 7.60 \times 10^6$ atm

$$P = (7.60 \times 10^6\ atm)\left(\frac{760\ torr}{atm}\right) = 5.78 \times 10^9\ torr$$

---

9. a. Given: $P = 125$ mm

Unknown: P in atm

$$P = (125\ mm)\left(\frac{1\ atm}{760\ mm}\right) = 0.164\ atm$$

b. Given: $P = 3.20$ atm

Unknown: P in Pa

$$P = (3.20\ atm)\left(\frac{101.325\ kPa}{atm}\right) = 324.24\ kPa = 3.24 \times 10^5\ Pa$$

c. Given: $P = 5.38$ kPa

Unknown: P in mm Hg

$$P = (5.38\ kPa)\left(\frac{1\ atm}{101.325\ kPa}\right)\left(\frac{760\ mm\ Hg}{atm}\right) = 40.4\ mm\ Hg$$

---

10. Given: $P_{CO_2} = 0.285$ torr

$P_{N_2} = 593.525$ torr

$P_T = 1$ atm $= 760$ torr

Unknown: P_{O_2}

$$P_T = P_{CO_2} + P_{N_2} + P_{O_2}$$
$$P_{O_2} = P_T - (P_{CO_2} + P_{N_2})$$
$$= 760\ torr - (593.525 + 0.285) = 166.190\ torr$$

---

11. Given: $T = 35.0°C$

$P_T = 742.0$ torr

Unknown: P_{gas}

$$P_{H_2O}\ at\ 35°C = 42.2\ mm$$
$$P_T = P_{H_2O} + P_{gas}$$
$$P_{gas} = P_T - P_{H_2O} = 742.0 - 42.2 = 699.8\ torr$$

---

18. a. Given: $P_1 = 350.$ torr

$V_1 = 200.$ mL

$P_2 = 700.$ torr

Unknown: V_2

$$P_1V_1 = P_2V_2$$
$$V_2 = \frac{P_1V_1}{P_2} = \frac{(350\ torr)(200\ mL)}{700\ torr} = 100\ mL$$

b. Given: $V_1 = 2.4 \times 10^5$ L

$P_2 = 180$ mm Hg

$V_2 = 1.8 \times 10^3$ L

Unknown: P_1

$$P_1V_1 = P_2V_2$$
$$P_1 = \frac{P_2V_2}{V_1} = \frac{(180\ mm\ Hg)(1.8 \times 10^3\ L)}{2.4 \times 10^5\ L} = 1.4\ mm\ Hg$$

19. a. Given: $V_1 = 80.0$ mL

$T_1 = 27°C$

$\quad = 300$ K

$T_2 = 77°C$

$\quad = 350$ K

Unknown: V_2

$$\frac{V_1}{T_1} = \frac{V_2}{T_2}$$

$$V_2 = \frac{V_1 T_2}{T_1} = \frac{(80.0 \text{ mL})(350 \text{ K})}{300 \text{ K}} = 93.3 \text{ mL}$$

b. Given: $V_1 = 125$ L

$V_2 = 85.0$ L

$T_2 = 127°C$

$\quad = 400$ K

Unknown: T_1

$$\frac{V_1}{T_1} = \frac{V_2}{T_2}$$

$$T_1 = \frac{V_1 T_2}{V_2} = \frac{(125 \text{ L})(400 \text{ K})}{85.0 \text{ L}} = 588 \text{ K} = 315°C$$

c. Given: $T_1 = -33°C$

$\quad = 240$ K

$V_2 = 54.0$ mL

$T_2 = 160°C$

$\quad = 433$ K

Unknown: V_1

$$\frac{V_1}{T_1} = \frac{V_2}{T_2}$$

$$V_1 = \frac{V_2 T_1}{T_2} = \frac{(54.0 \text{ mL})(2.40 \text{ K})}{433 \text{ K}} = 29.9 \text{ mL}$$

20. Given: $V_1 = 140.0$ mL

$T_1 = 67°C = 340$ K

$V_2 = 50.0$ mL

Unknown: T_2

$$\frac{V_1}{T_1} = \frac{V_2}{T_2}$$

$$T_2 = \frac{V_2 T_1}{V_1} = \frac{(50.0 \text{ mL})(340 \text{ K})}{140.0 \text{ mL}} = 121 \text{ K} = -152°C$$

21. Given: $V_1 = 240.$ mL

$P_1 = 0.428$ atm

$P_2 = 0.724$ atm

Unknown: V_2

$$P_1 V_1 = P_2 V_2$$

$$V_2 = \frac{P_1 V_1}{P_2} = \frac{(0.428 \text{ atm})(240 \text{ mL})}{(0.724 \text{ atm})} = 142 \text{ mL}$$

22. Given: $T_1 = 47°C = 320$ K

$P_1 = 0.329$ atm

$T_2 = 77°C = 350$ K

Unknown: P_2

$$\frac{P_1}{T_1} = \frac{P_2}{T_2}$$

$$P_2 = \frac{P_1 T_2}{T_1} = \frac{(0.329 \text{ atm})(350 \text{ K})}{320 \text{ K}} = 0.360 \text{ atm}$$

23. Given: $T_1 = 47°C = 320$ K

$P_1 = 1.03$ atm

$V_1 = 2.20$ L

$T_2 = 107°C = 380$ K

$P_2 = 0.789$ atm

Unknown: V_2

$$\frac{P_1 V_1}{T_1} = \frac{P_2 V_2}{T_2}$$

$$V_2 = \frac{P_1 V_1 T_2}{P_2 T_1} = \frac{(1.03 \text{ atm})(2.20 \text{ L})(380 \text{ K})}{(0.789 \text{ atm})(320 \text{ K})} = 3.41 \text{ L}$$

24. Given: $T_1 = -73°C = 200$ K

$P_1 = 1$

$P_2 = 2$

Unknown $= T_2$

$$T_2 = \frac{P_2 T_1}{P_1} = \frac{(2)(200)}{1} = 400 \text{ K} = 127°C$$

25. Given: $V_1 = 155$ cm^3

$P_1 = 22.5$ kPa

$V_2 = 90.0$ cm^3

Unknown: P_2

$$P_1 V_1 = P_2 V_2$$

$$P_2 = \frac{P_1 V_1}{V_2} = \frac{(22.5 \text{ kPa})(155 \text{ cm}^3)}{(90.0 \text{ cm}^3)} = 38.8 \text{ kPa}$$

26. Given: $V_1 = 450.0$ mL $\qquad P_1V_1 = P_2V_2$

Unknown: V_2

a. $P_2 = 2P_1 \qquad\qquad\qquad V_2 = \dfrac{P_1V_1}{P_2} = \dfrac{(1)(450.0 \text{ mL})}{2} = 225.0$ mL

b. $P_2 = \frac{1}{4}P_1 \qquad\qquad\qquad V_2 = \dfrac{(1)(450.0 \text{ mL})}{\frac{1}{4}} = 1800$ mL

---

27. Given: $V_1 = 1.00 \times 10^6$ mL $\qquad P_1V_1 = P_2V_2,\ V_2 = \dfrac{P_1V_1}{P_2}$
$\qquad\quad P_1 = 575$ mm Hg
$\qquad\quad P_2 = 1.25$ atm

Unknown: $V_2 \qquad\qquad P_1 = (575 \text{ mm})\left(\dfrac{1 \text{ atm}}{760 \text{ mm}}\right) = 0.756$ atm

$$V_2 = \dfrac{(0.756 \text{ atm})(1.00 \times 10^6 \text{ mL})}{1.25 \text{ atm}} = 6.05 \times 10^5 \text{ mL}$$

---

28. Given: $T_1 = 27°C = 300$ K $\qquad \dfrac{P_1}{T_1} = \dfrac{P_2}{T_2}$
$\qquad\quad P_1 = 0.625$ atm
$\qquad\quad P_2 = 1.125$ atm

Unknown: $T_2 \qquad\qquad T_2 = \dfrac{P_2T_1}{P_1} = \dfrac{(1.125 \text{ atm})(300 \text{ K})}{0.625 \text{ atm}} = 540 \text{ K} = 267°C$

---

29. Given: $V_1 = 1.75$ L $\qquad\qquad \dfrac{P_1V_1}{T_1} = \dfrac{P_2V_2}{T_2}$
$\qquad\quad T_1 = -23°C = 250$ K
$\qquad\quad P_1 = 150$ kPa
$\qquad\quad V_2 = 1.30$ L $\qquad\qquad T_2 = \dfrac{P_2V_2T_1}{P_1V_1} = \dfrac{(210 \text{ kPa})(1.30 \text{ L})(250 \text{ K})}{(150 \text{ kPa})(1.75 \text{ L})} = 260 \text{ K} = -13°C$
$\qquad\quad P_2 = 210$ kPa

Unknown: T_2

---

30. Given: $P_1 = 7.75 \times 10^4$ Pa $\qquad \dfrac{P_1V_1}{T_1} = \dfrac{P_2V_2}{T_2}$
$\qquad\quad T_1 = 17°C = 290$ K
$\qquad\quad V_1 = 850.\,\text{cm}^3$
$\qquad\quad V_2 = 720.\,\text{cm}^3 \qquad T_2 = \dfrac{P_2V_2T_1}{P_1V_1} = \dfrac{(8.10 \times 10^4 \text{ Pa})(720 \text{ cm}^3)(290 \text{ K})}{(7.75 \times 10^4 \text{ Pa})(850 \text{ cm}^3)} = 257 \text{ K} = -16°C$
$\qquad\quad P_2 = 8.10 \times 10^4$ Pa

Unknown: T_2

---

31. Given: $V_1 = 250$ L $\qquad\qquad \dfrac{P_1V_1}{T_1} = \dfrac{P_2V_2}{T_2}$
$\qquad\quad T_1 = 22°C = 295$ K
$\qquad\quad P_1 = 0.974$ atm
$\qquad\quad T_2 = -52°C = 221$ K $\qquad V_2 = \dfrac{P_1V_1T_2}{P_2T_1} = \dfrac{(0.974 \text{ atm})(250 \text{ L})(221 \text{ K})}{(0.750 \text{ atm})(295 \text{ K})} = 243$ L
$\qquad\quad P_2 = 0.750$ atm

Unknown: V_2

---

32. Given: $V_1 = 250$ L $\qquad\qquad \dfrac{P_1V_1}{T_1} = \dfrac{P_2V_2}{T_2}$
$\qquad\quad T_1 = 295$ K
$\qquad\quad P_1 = 0.974$ atm
$\qquad\quad V_2 = 400$ L $\qquad\qquad T_2 = \dfrac{P_2V_2T_1}{P_1V_1} = \dfrac{(0.475 \text{ atm})(400 \text{ L})(295 \text{ K})}{(0.974 \text{ atm})(250 \text{ L})} = 230 \text{ K} = -43°C$
$\qquad\quad P_2 = 0.475$ atm

Unknown: T_2

33. Given: $V_1 = 5.05 \text{ m}^3$
$P_1 = 20.°C$
$= 293 \text{ K}$
$P_1 = 9.95 \times 10^4 \text{ Pa}$
$T_2 = 0°C = 273 \text{ K}$
$P_2 = 1.01\,325 \times 10^5 \text{ Pa}$

Unknown: V_2 in m^3 per day

$$\frac{P_1 V_1}{T_1} = \frac{P_2 V_2}{T_2}$$

$$V_2 = \frac{P_1 V_1 T_2}{P_2 T_1} = \frac{(9.95 \times 10^4 \text{ Pa})(5.05 \text{ m}^3)(273 \text{ K})}{(1.01\,325 \times 10^5 \text{ Pa})(293 \text{ K})}$$

$$= 4.62 \times 10^{-4} \text{ m}^3$$

$$\left(\frac{15 \text{ breaths}}{\text{min}}\right)\left(\frac{60 \text{ min}}{\text{hour}}\right)\left(\frac{24 \text{ hours}}{\text{day}}\right) = 21\,600 \text{ breaths/day}$$

$$\left(\frac{21\,600 \text{ breaths}}{\text{day}}\right)\left(\frac{4.62 \times 10^{-4} \text{ m}^3}{\text{breath}}\right) = 9.98 \text{ m}^3\text{/day}$$

---

40. Given: $V = 5.00 \text{ L O}_2$

$n = 1.08 \times 10^{23}$ molecules

a. Unknown: number of molecules in 5.00 L H_2

$$\left(\frac{1.08 \times 10^{23} \text{ molecules}}{5.00 \text{ L O}_2}\right)\left(\frac{1 \text{ L O}_2}{\text{L H}_2}\right)(5.00 \text{ L H}_2) = 1.08 \times 10^{23} \text{ molecules H}_2$$

b. Unknown: number of molecules in 5.00 L CO_2

$$\left(\frac{1.08 \times 10^{23} \text{ molecules}}{5.00 \text{ L O}_2}\right)\left(\frac{1 \text{ L O}_2}{\text{L CO}_2}\right)(5.00 \text{ L CO}_2) = 1.08 \times 10^{23} \text{ molecules CO}_2$$

c. Unknown: number of molecules in 10.00 L NH_3

$$\left(\frac{1.08 \times 10^{23} \text{ molecules}}{5.00 \text{ L O}_2}\right)\left(\frac{1 \text{ L O}_2}{\text{L NH}_3}\right)(10.00 \text{ L NH}_3) = 2.16 \times 10^{23} \text{ molecules NH}_3$$

---

41. a. Unknown: number of moles in 22.4 L N_2 at STP

$$V = M \times \frac{22.4 \text{ L}}{\text{mol}}$$

$$n = \frac{V}{22.4 \text{ L/mol}} = \frac{22.4 \text{ L}}{22.4 \text{ L/mol}} = 1.00 \text{ mol N}_2$$

b. Unknown: number of moles in 5.60 L Cl_2 at STP

$$n = \frac{V}{22.4 \text{ L/mol}} = \frac{5.60 \text{ L}}{22.4 \text{ L/mol}} = 0.250 \text{ mol Cl}_2$$

c. Unknown: number of moles in 0.125 L Ne at STP

$$n = \frac{V}{22.4 \text{ L/mol}} = \frac{0.125 \text{ L}}{22.4 \text{ L/mol}} = 5.58 \times 10^{-3} \text{ mol Ne}$$

d. Unknown: number of moles in 70.0 mL NH_3 at STP

$$n = \frac{V}{22.4 \text{ L/mol}} = \left(\frac{70.0 \text{ mL}}{22.4 \text{ L/mol}}\right)\left(\frac{\text{L}}{1000 \text{ mL}}\right) = 3.13 \times 10^{-3} \text{ mol NH}_3$$

42. a. Unknown: m in g of 11.2 L H_2 at STP

$$m = (11.2 \text{ L})\left(\frac{1 \text{ mol}}{22.4 \text{ L}}\right)\left(\frac{2.014 \text{ g } H_2}{\text{mol}}\right) = 1.01 \text{ g } H_2$$

b. Unknown: m in g of 2.80 L CO_2 at STP

$$m = (2.80 \text{ L})\left(\frac{1 \text{ mol}}{22.4 \text{ L}}\right)\left(\frac{44 \text{ g } CO_2}{\text{mol}}\right) = 5.50 \text{ g } CO_2$$

c. Unknown: m in g of 15.0 mL SO_2 at STP

$$m = (15.0 \text{ mL})\left(\frac{\text{L}}{1000 \text{ mL}}\right)\left(\frac{1 \text{ mol}}{22.4 \text{ L}}\right)\left(\frac{64 \text{ g } SO_2}{\text{mol}}\right) = 0.0429 \text{ g } SO_2$$

d. Unknown: m in g of 3.40 cm^3 F_2 at STP

$$m = (3.40 \text{ cm}^3)\left(\frac{\text{mL}}{\text{cm}^3}\right)\left(\frac{\text{L}}{1000 \text{ mL}}\right)\left(\frac{1 \text{ mol}}{22.4 \text{ L}}\right)\left(\frac{38 \text{ g } F_2}{\text{mol}}\right) = 5.77 \times 10^{-3} \text{ g } F_2$$

43. a. Unknown: V in L of 8.00 g O_2 at STP

$$V = (8.00 \text{ g } O_2)\left(\frac{22.4 \text{ L}}{\text{mol}}\right)\left(\frac{\text{mol}}{32 \text{ g } O_2}\right) = 5.60 \text{ L } O_2$$

b. Unknown: V in L of 3.50 g CO at STP

$$V = (3.50 \text{ g CO})\left(\frac{22.4 \text{ L}}{\text{mol}}\right)\left(\frac{\text{mol}}{28 \text{ g CO}}\right) = 2.80 \text{ L CO}$$

c. Unknown: V in L of 0.017 g H_2S at STP

$$V = (0.0170 \text{ g } H_2S)\left(\frac{22.4 \text{ L}}{\text{mol}}\right)\left(\frac{\text{mol}}{34 \text{ g } H_2S}\right) = 0.0112 \text{ L } H_2S$$

d. Unknown: V in L of 2.25 $\times$ 10^5 kg NH_3 at STP

$$V = (2.25 \times 10^5 \text{ kg})\left(\frac{1000 \text{ g}}{\text{kg}}\right)\left(\frac{22.4 \text{ L}}{\text{mol}}\right)\left(\frac{\text{mol}}{17 \text{ g } NH_3}\right) = 2.96 \times 10^8 \text{ L } NH_3$$

44. Given: $V = 75.0$ L CO_2

$$2C_2H_2 + 5O_2 \rightarrow 4CO_2 + 2H_2O$$

a. Unknown: number of L C_2H_2 required

$$(75.0 \text{ L } CO_2)\left(\frac{2 \text{ L } C_2H_2}{4 \text{ L } CO_2}\right) = 37.5 \text{ L } C_2H_2$$

b. Unknown: number of L H_2O produced

$$(75.0 \text{ L } CO_2)\left(\frac{2 \text{ L } H_2O}{4 \text{ L } CO_2}\right) = 37.5 \text{ L } H_2O$$

c. Unknown: number of L O_2 required

$$(75.0 \text{ L } CO_2)\left(\frac{5 \text{ L } O_2}{4 \text{ L } CO_2}\right) = 93.8 \text{ L } O_2$$

45. Given: $CuO(s) + H_2(g) \rightarrow$
$Cu(s) + H_2O(g)$

$V = 5.60$ L H_2 at
STP

a. Unknown: n of H_2
$$n = \frac{PV}{RT} = \frac{(1.0 \text{ atm})(5.60 \text{ L})}{\left(\dfrac{0.0821 \text{ L} \cdot \text{atm}}{\text{mol} \cdot \text{K}}\right)(273 \text{ K})} = 0.250 \text{ mol } H_2$$

b. Unknown: n of Cu
produced
$$n \text{ of Cu} = (0.250 \text{ mol } H_2)\left(\frac{1 \text{ mol Cu}}{1 \text{ mol } H_2}\right) = 0.250 \text{ mol Cu}$$

c. Unknown: number of
grams Cu
produced
$$(0.250 \text{ mol})\left(\frac{63.5 \text{ g Cu}}{\text{mol}}\right) = 15.9 \text{ g Cu}$$

---

46. Given: $P = 0.961$ atm
$V = 29.0$ L CH_4
$T = 20°C = 293$ K

$CH_4 + 2O_2 \rightarrow CO_2 + 2H_2O$

a. $V = (29.0 \text{ L } CH_4)\left(\dfrac{1 \text{ L } CO_2}{1 \text{ L } CH_4}\right) = 29.0 \text{ L } CO_2$

b. $V = (29.0 \text{ L } CH_4)\left(\dfrac{2 \text{ L } H_2O}{1 \text{ L } CH_4}\right) = 58.0 \text{ L } H_2O$ vapor

Unknown: (a) V of CO_2

(b) V of H_2O

---

47. Given: air = 20.9% O_2 by
volume.

$2C_8H_{18} + 25O_2 \rightarrow 16CO_2 + 18H_2O$

a. $V = 25.0$ L C_8H_{18}

$V = (25.0 \text{ L } C_8H_{18})\left(\dfrac{25 \text{ L } O_2}{2 \text{ L } C_8H_{18}}\right) = 312.5 \text{ L } O_2$

Unknown: V of air
needed for
combustion

$V \text{ air needed} = \left(\dfrac{100 \text{ L air}}{20.9 \text{ L } O_2}\right)(312.5 \text{ L } O_2) = 1.50 \times 10^3 \text{ L air}$

b. Unknown: (1) V CO_2
produced
(2) V H_2O
produced

(1) $V = (25.0 \text{ L } C_8H_{18})\left(\dfrac{16 \text{ L } CO_2}{2 \text{ L } C_8H_{18}}\right) = 200. \text{ L } CO_2$

(2) $V = (25.0 \text{ L } C_8H_{18})\left(\dfrac{18 \text{ L } H_2O}{2 \text{ L } C_8H_{18}}\right) = 225 \text{ L } H_2O$ vapor

---

48. Given: $V = 4.50 \times 10^2$ mL
CO

$V = 825$ mL H_2

$CO(g) + 2H_2(g) \rightarrow CH_3OH(g)$

a. Unknown: reactant
present in
excess

$(4.50 \times 10^2 \text{ mL CO})\left(\dfrac{2 \text{ mL } H_2}{1 \text{ mL CO}}\right) = 900 \text{ mL } H_2$ needed

$(825 \text{ mL } H_2)\left(\dfrac{1 \text{ mL CO}}{2 \text{ mL } H_2}\right) = 413 \text{ mL CO}$ needed

CO is present in excess. $(4.50 \times 10^2 \text{ mL} > 413 \text{ mL})$

b. Unknown: amount of
CO remain-
ing after
reaction

$450 \text{ mL} - 413 \text{ mL} = 37 \text{ mL CO}$

c. Unknown: volume of
CH_3OH
produced

$(825 \text{ mL } H_2)\left(\dfrac{1 \text{ mL } CH_3OH}{2 \text{ mL } H_2}\right) = 413 \text{ mL } CH_3OH$

49. a. Given: $V = 2.50$ L HF

$n = 1.35$ mol

$T = 320.$ K

Unknown: P in atm

$$P = \frac{nRT}{V} = \frac{(1.35 \text{ mol})\left(\dfrac{0.0821 \text{ L} \cdot \text{atm}}{\text{mol} \cdot \text{K}}\right)(320.\text{ K})}{2.50 \text{ L}} = 14.2 \text{ atm}$$

b. Given: $V = 4.75$ L NO_2

$n = 0.86$ mol

$T = 300.$ K

Unknown: P

$$P = \frac{nRT}{V} = \frac{(0.86 \text{ mol})\left(\dfrac{0.0821 \text{ L} \cdot \text{atm}}{\text{mol} \cdot \text{K}}\right)(300.\text{ K})}{4.75 \text{ L}} = 4.5 \text{ atm}$$

c. Given: $V = 7.50 \times 10^4$ mL CO_2

$n = 2.15$ mol

$T = 57°C = 330$ K

Unknown: P

$$(7.50 \times 10^4 \text{ mL})\left(\frac{\text{L}}{1000 \text{ mL}}\right) = 75 \text{ L}$$

$$P = \frac{nRT}{V} = \frac{(2.15 \text{ mol})\left(\dfrac{0.0821 \text{ L} \cdot \text{atm}}{\text{mol} \cdot \text{K}}\right)(330.\text{ K})}{75 \text{ L}} = 0.777 \text{ atm}$$

50. a. Given: $n = 2.00$ mol H_2

$T = 300.$ K

$P = 1.25$ atm

Unknown: V in L

$$V = \frac{nRT}{P} = \frac{(2.00 \text{ mol})\left(\dfrac{0.0821 \text{ L} \cdot \text{atm}}{\text{mol} \cdot \text{K}}\right)(300 \text{ K})}{1.25 \text{ atm}} = 39.4 \text{ L } H_2$$

b. Given: $n = 0.425$ mol NH_3

$T = 37°C = 310$ K

$P = 0.724$ atm

Unknown: V in L

$$V = \frac{nRT}{P} = \frac{(0.425 \text{ mol})\left(\dfrac{0.0821 \text{ L} \cdot \text{atm}}{\text{mol} \cdot \text{K}}\right)(310 \text{ K})}{0.724 \text{ atm}} = 14.9 \text{ L } NH_3$$

c. Given: $m = 4.00$ g O_2

$T = 57°C = 330$ K

$P = 0.888$ atm

Unknown: V in L

$$V = \frac{nRT}{P} = \frac{(4.00 \text{ g})\left(\dfrac{\text{mol } O_2}{32 \text{ g}}\right)\left(\dfrac{0.0821 \text{ L} \cdot \text{atm}}{\text{mol} \cdot \text{K}}\right)(330 \text{ K})}{0.888 \text{ atm}} = 3.81 \text{ L } O_2$$

51. a. Given: $V = 1.25$ L

$T = 250.$ K

$P = 1.06$ atm

Unknown: n

$$n = \frac{PV}{RT} = \frac{(1.06 \text{ atm})(1.25 \text{ L})}{\left(\dfrac{0.0821 \text{ L} \cdot \text{atm}}{\text{mol} \cdot \text{K}}\right)(250.\text{ K})} = 0.0646 \text{ mol}$$

b. Given: $V = 0.80$ L

$T = 27°C = 300$ K

$P = 0.925$ atm

Unknown: n

$$n = \frac{PV}{RT} = \frac{(0.925 \text{ atm})(0.80 \text{ L})}{\left(\dfrac{0.0821 \text{ L} \cdot \text{atm}}{\text{mol} \cdot \text{K}}\right)(300 \text{ K})} = 0.030 \text{ mol}$$

c. Given: $V = 0.750$ L

$T = 50°C = 223$ K

$P = 0.921$ atm

Unknown: n

$$n = \frac{PV}{RT} = \frac{(0.921 \text{ atm})(0.75 \text{ L})}{\left(\dfrac{0.0821 \text{ L} \cdot \text{atm}}{\text{mol} \cdot \text{K}}\right)(223 \text{ K})} = 0.0377 \text{ mol}$$

52. a. Given: $V = 5.60$ L O_2

$P = 1.75$ atm

$T = 250.$ K

Unknown: m in g

$$n = \frac{PV}{RT}$$

$$n = \frac{(1.75 \text{ atm})(5.60 \text{ L})}{\left(\dfrac{0.0821 \text{ L} \cdot \text{atm}}{\text{mol} \cdot \text{K}}\right)(250 \text{ K})} = 0.478 \text{ mol } O_2$$

$$m = (0.478 \text{ mol})\left(\frac{32 \text{ g } O_2}{\text{mol}}\right) = 15.3 \text{ g } O_2$$

b. Given: $V = 3.50$ L NH_3

$P = 0.921$ atm

$T = 27°C = 300$ K

Unknown: m

$$n = \frac{PV}{RT} = \frac{(0.921 \text{ atm})(3.50 \text{ L})}{\left(\dfrac{0.0821 \text{ L} \cdot \text{atm}}{\text{mol} \cdot \text{K}}\right)(300 \text{ K})} = 0.131 \text{ mol } NH_3$$

$$m = (0.131 \text{ mol})\left(\frac{17 \text{ g } NH_3}{\text{mol}}\right) = 2.23 \text{ g } NH_3$$

c. Given: $V = 0.125$ L SO_2

$P = 0.822$ atm

$T = -5°C = 268$ K

Unknown: m

$$n = \frac{PV}{RT} = \frac{(0.822 \text{ atm})(0.125 \text{ L})}{\left(\dfrac{0.0821 \text{ L} \cdot \text{atm}}{\text{mol} \cdot \text{K}}\right)(268 \text{ K})} = 4.67 \times 10^{-3} \text{ mol } SO_2$$

$$m = (0.0047 \text{ mol})\left(\frac{64.07 \text{ g } SO_2}{\text{mol}}\right) = 0.299 \text{ g } SO_2$$

56. a. Unknown: relative rate of effusion of H_2 and N_2

$$\frac{\text{rate of effusion of } H_2}{\text{rate of effusion of } N_2} = \frac{\sqrt{M_{N_2}}}{\sqrt{M_{H_2}}} = \frac{\sqrt{28.00 \text{ g/mol}}}{\sqrt{2.02 \text{ g/mol}}} = 3.72$$

b. Unknown: relative rate of effusion of F_2 and Cl_2

$$\frac{\text{rate of effusion of } F_2}{\text{rate of effusion of } Cl_2} = \frac{\sqrt{M_{Cl_2}}}{\sqrt{M_{F_2}}} = \frac{\sqrt{71 \text{ g/mol}}}{\sqrt{38 \text{ g/mol}}} = 1.37$$

57. Unknown: relative average velocity of H_2 and Ne

$$\frac{\text{velocity of } H_2}{\text{velocity of Ne}} = \frac{\sqrt{M_{Ne}}}{\sqrt{M_{H_2}}} = \frac{\sqrt{20.179 \text{ g/mol}}}{\sqrt{2.02 \text{ g/mol}}} = 3.16$$

58. Given: velocity of Cl_2 molecules = 324 m/s

Unknown: velocity of SO_2 molecules

$$\frac{\text{velocity of } Cl_2}{\text{velocity of } SO_2} = \frac{\sqrt{M_{SO_2}}}{\sqrt{M_{Cl_2}}}$$

$$\text{velocity of } SO_2 = (\text{velocity of } Cl_2)\left(\frac{\sqrt{M_{Cl_2}}}{\sqrt{M_{SO_2}}}\right)$$

$$= (324 \text{ m/s})\left(\frac{\sqrt{71 \text{ g/mol}}}{\sqrt{64 \text{ g/mol}}}\right) = 341 \text{ m/s}$$

59. Given: $P_T = 6.11$ atm
$\qquad P_A = 1.68$ atm
$\qquad P_B = 3.89$ atm

$\qquad$ Unknown: P_C

$P_T = P_A + P_B + P_C$

$P_C = P_T - (P_A + P_B) = 6.11 - (1.68 + 3.89) = 0.54$ atm

---

60. Given: $V_1 = 2.30$ L
$\qquad T_1 = 311$ K
$\qquad T_2 = 295$ K

$\qquad$ Unknown: V_2

$\dfrac{V_1}{T_1} = \dfrac{V_1}{T_2}$

$V_2 = \dfrac{V_1 T_2}{T_1} = \dfrac{(2.30\text{ L})(295\text{ K})}{(311\text{ K})} = 2.18$ L

---

61. Given: $V_1 = 295$ mL
$\qquad T_1 = 36°C = 309$ K
$\qquad T_2 = 55°C = 328$ K

$\qquad$ Unknown: V_2

$\dfrac{V_1}{T_1} = \dfrac{V_2}{T_2}$

$V_2 = \dfrac{V_1}{T_1} = \dfrac{(295\text{ mL})(328\text{ K})}{(309\text{ K})} = 313$ mL

---

62. Given: $V_1 = 638$ mL
$\qquad P_1 = 0.893$ atm
$\qquad T_1 = 12°C = 285$ K
$\qquad V_2 = 881$ mL
$\qquad T_2 = 18°C = 291$ K

$\qquad$ Unknown: P_2

$\dfrac{P_1 V_1}{T_1} = \dfrac{P_2 V_2}{T_2}$

$P_2 = \dfrac{P_1 V_1 T_2}{T_1 V_2} = \dfrac{(0.893\text{ atm})(638\text{ mL})(291\text{ K})}{(285\text{ K})(881\text{ mL})} = 0.660$ atm

---

63. Given: $T_1 = 84°C = 357$ K
$\qquad P_1 = 0.503$ atm
$\qquad P_2 = 1.20$ atm

$\qquad$ Unknown: T_2 in °C

$\dfrac{P_1}{T_1} = \dfrac{P_2}{T_2}$

$T_2 = \dfrac{P_2 T_1}{P_1} = \dfrac{(1.20\text{ atm})(357\text{ K})}{(0.503\text{ atm})} = 852\text{ K} = 579°C$

---

64. Given: $V_1 = 4.00$ L
$\qquad T_1 = 304$ K
$\qquad P_1 = 755$ mm
$\qquad V_2 = 4.08$ L
$\qquad P_2 = 728$ mm

$\qquad$ Unknown: T_2

$\dfrac{P_1 V_1}{T_1} = \dfrac{P_2 V_2}{T_2}$

$T_2 = \dfrac{P_2 V_2 T_1}{P_1 V_1} = \dfrac{(728\text{ mm})(4.08\text{ L})(304\text{ K})}{(755\text{ mm})(4.00\text{ L})} = 299$ K

---

65. Given: $P_1 = 4.62$ atm
$\qquad V_1 = 2.33$ L
$\qquad V_2 = 1.03$ L

$\qquad$ Unknown: P_2 (in torr)

$P_1 V_1 = P_2 V_2$

$P_2 = \dfrac{P_1 V_1}{V_2} = \dfrac{(4.62\text{ atm})(2.33\text{ L})}{1.03\text{ L}} = 10.45$ atm

$(10.45\text{ atm})\left(\dfrac{760\text{ torr}}{\text{atm}}\right) = 7940$ torr

---

66. Given: $V_2 = 2.00 \times 10^7$ L
$\qquad P_2 = 20.0$ atm
$\qquad P_1 = 1.0$ atm

$\qquad$ Unknown: V_1

$P_1 V_1 = P_2 V_2$

$V_1 = \dfrac{P_2 V_2}{P_1} = \dfrac{(20.0\text{ atm})(2.00 \times 10^7\text{ L})}{1.0\text{ atm}} = 4.00 \times 10^8$ L

67. Given: effusion rate of gas X = 0.850 times effusion rate of NO_2

Unknown: M_X

$$\frac{\text{effusion rate of X}}{\text{effusion rate of } NO_2} = \frac{\sqrt{M_{NO_2}}}{\sqrt{M_X}}$$

$$\sqrt{M_X} = \left(\frac{\text{effusion rate of } NO_2}{\text{effusion rate of X}}\right)(\sqrt{M_{NO_2}})$$

$$= \left(\frac{1.00}{0.850}\right)(\sqrt{46 \text{ g/mol}}) = 8.0 \text{ g/mol}$$

$$M_X = (8.0)^2 = 64 \text{ g/mol}$$

---

68. Given: $V = 265$ mL = 0.265 L Cl_2 at STP

Unknown: m of Cl_2

$$n = (0.265 \text{ L } Cl_2)\left(\frac{1 \text{ mol}}{22.4 \text{ L}}\right)\left(\frac{70.90 \text{ g } Cl_2}{\text{mol}}\right) = 0.839 \text{ g } Cl_2$$

---

69. Given: $n = 3.11$ mol CO_2

$P = 0.820$ atm

$T = 39°C = 312$ K

Unknown: V in L

$$PV = nRT$$

$$V = \frac{nRT}{P} = \frac{(3.11 \text{ mol } CO_2)\left(\frac{0.0821 \text{ L} \cdot \text{atm}}{\text{mol} \cdot \text{K}}\right)(312 \text{ K})}{0.820 \text{ atm}} = 97.2 \text{ L}$$

---

70. Unknown: $\dfrac{\text{effusion rate of CO}}{\text{effusion rate of } SO_3}$

$$\frac{\text{effusion rate of CO}}{\text{effusion rate of } SO_3} = \frac{\sqrt{M_{SO_3}}}{\sqrt{M_{CO}}} = \frac{\sqrt{80 \text{ g/mol}}}{\sqrt{28 \text{ g/mol}}} = 1.7$$

---

71. Given: $m = 0.993$ g

$V = 0.570$ L

$T = 281$ K

$P = 1.44$ atm

Unknown: M

$$M = \frac{mRT}{PV} = \frac{(0.993 \text{ g})\left(\frac{0.0821 \text{ L} \cdot \text{atm}}{\text{mol} \cdot \text{K}}\right)(281 \text{ K})}{(1.44 \text{ atm})(0.570 \text{ L})} = 27.9 \text{ g/mol}$$

---

72. Given: $V = 1000.$ cm^3 = 1000. mL^3 = 1 L

$T = 32°C = 305$ K

$P = (752 \text{ mm Hg})\left(\dfrac{\text{atm}}{760 \text{ mm Hg}}\right) = 0.99$ atm

Unknown: n

$$PV = nRT$$

$$n = \frac{PV}{RT} = \frac{(0.99 \text{ atm})(1 \text{ L})}{\left(\frac{0.0821 \text{ L} \cdot \text{atm}}{\text{mol} \cdot \text{K}}\right)(305 \text{ K})} = 0.0395 \text{ mol He}$$

---

73. Given: $T = 16°C = 289$ K

$P = 0.982$ atm

$M = 7.40$ g

$V = 3.96$ L

Unknown: V at STP; M

$$\frac{P_1V_1}{T_1} = \frac{P_2V_2}{T_2}$$

$$V_2 = \frac{P_1V_1T_2}{P_2T_1}$$

$$= \frac{(0.982 \text{ atm})(3.96 \text{ L})(273 \text{ K})}{(1.00 \text{ atm})(289 \text{ K})} = 3.67 \text{ L}$$

$$M = \frac{mRT}{PV} = \frac{(7.40 \text{ g})\left(\frac{0.0821 \text{ L} \cdot \text{atm}}{\text{mol} \cdot \text{K}}\right)(289 \text{ K})}{(0.982 \text{ atm})(3.96 \text{ L})} = 45.1 \text{ g/mol}$$

Math Tutor, p. 396

2. Given: $V_1 = 785$ mL
  $= 0.785$ L

  $P_1 = 0.879$ atm

  $P_2 = 0.994$ atm

Unknown: V_2

$P_1 V_1 = P_2 V_2$

$V_2 = \dfrac{P_1 V_1}{P_2} = \dfrac{0.879 \text{ atm} \times 0.785 \text{ L}}{0.994 \text{ atm}} = 694$ mL

Standardized Test Prep, p. 397

2. Given: $V_1 = 150$ mL

  $P_1 = 0.923$ atm

  $P_2 = 0.987$ atm

Unknown: V_2

$V_2 = \dfrac{P_1 V_1}{P_2} = \dfrac{0.923 \text{ atm} \times 150 \text{ mL}}{0.987 \text{ atm}} = 140$ mL

---

3. Given: $n = 0.500$ mol

  $V = 10.0$ L

  $T = 20.°C = 293$ K

Unknown: P

$PV = nRT$

$P = \dfrac{nRT}{V} = \dfrac{0.500 \text{ mol} \times 8.314 \dfrac{\text{L} \cdot \text{kPa}}{\text{mol} \cdot \text{K}} \times 293 \text{ K}}{10.0 \text{ L}}$

$P = 120$ kPa

---

4. Given: $T_1 = 100.0°C$
  $= 373$ K

  $T_2 = 300.0°C$
  $= 573$ K

  $P_1 = 3.0$ atm

Unknown: P_2

$\dfrac{P_1}{T_1} = \dfrac{P_2}{T_2}$

$P_2 = \dfrac{P_1 T_2}{T_1} = \dfrac{3.0 \text{ atm} \times 573 \text{ K}}{373 \text{ K}} = 4.6$ atm

---

5. Given: $V_X = 2V_{CH_4}$

  $M_{CH_4} = 16.05$ g/mol

Unknown: M_X

$\dfrac{V_A{}^2}{V_B{}^2} = \dfrac{M_B}{M_A}$

$M_X = \dfrac{M_{CH_4} V_{CH_4}{}^2}{(2V_{CH_4})^2} = \dfrac{16.05}{4} = 4.01 \text{ g/mol} \approx 4 \text{ g/mol}$

---

6. Given: $N_2(g) + 3H_2(g) \rightarrow 2NH_3(g)$

  Molar volume N_2
  = molar volume H_2

  3 L N_2

  3 L H_2

Unknown: L N_2 remaining
    after reaction

$3 \text{ L H}_2 \left(\dfrac{1 \text{ L N}_2}{3 \text{ L H}_2} \right) = 1 \text{ L N}_2$ reacted

3 L N_2 available – 1 L N_2 reacted = 2 L N_2 remaining

CHAPTER 12

Solutions

ATE, Additional Sample Problems, p. 420

A-1a. Given: $V = 2.00$ L
mass of solute =
14.6 g NaCl

Unknown: molarity (M)

$$(14.69 \text{ NaCl})\left(\frac{\text{mol NaCl}}{58.44 \text{ g NaCl}}\right) = 0.249 \text{ mol NaCl}$$

$$M = \frac{0.249 \text{ mol}}{2.00 \text{ L}} = 0.125 \text{ M NaCl}$$

b. Given: mass of solute =
10.0 g HCl
$V = 0.250$ L

Unknown: molarity (M)

$$(10.0 \text{ g HCl})\left(\frac{\text{mol HCl}}{36.46 \text{ g HCl}}\right) = 0.274 \text{ mol}$$

$$M = \frac{0.274 \text{ mol}}{0.250 \text{ L}} = 1.10 \text{ M HCl}$$

B-1a. Given: molarity =
0.330 M NaCl
$V = 1.25$ L

Unknown: moles NaCl

mol solute = MV

$\quad = (0.330 \text{ mol/L})(1.25 \text{ L})$

$\quad = 0.413 \text{ mol}$

b. Given: $V = 0.50$ L

molarity =
0.50 M HCl

Unknown: moles HCl

mol solute = MV

$\quad = (0.50 \text{ mol/L})(0.50 \text{ L})$

$\quad = 0.25 \text{ mol}$

Practice, p. 421

1. Given: mass of solute =
5.85 g KI
$V = 0.125$ L

Unknown: molarity (M)

$$(5.85 \text{ g KI})\left(\frac{1 \text{ mol}}{166 \text{ g}}\right) = 0.0352 \text{ mol KI}$$

$$M = \frac{0.0352 \text{ mol KI}}{0.125 \text{ L}} = 0.282 \text{ M KI}$$

2. Given: $V = 0.500$ L
molarity =
0.150 M H_2SO_4

Unknown: moles H_2SO_4

mol solute = MV

$\quad = (0.150 \text{ mol/L } H_2SO_4)(0.500 \text{ L})$

$\quad = 0.0750 \text{ mol}$

3. Given: molarity =
3.00 M NaCl
mass of NaCl =
146.3 g

Unknown: V

$$(146.3 \text{ g NaCl})\left(\frac{\text{mol NaCl}}{58.44 \text{ g}}\right) = 2.503 \text{ mol NaCl}$$

$$V = \frac{2.503 \text{ mol}}{3.00 \text{ mol/L}} = 0.834 \text{ L}$$

C-1a. Given: mass of solute = 6.25 g HCl
$V = 0.300$ L

Unknown: molarity (M)

$$M = (6.25 \text{ g HCl})\left(\frac{\text{mol HCl}}{36.46 \text{ g HCl}}\right)\left(\frac{1}{0.300 \text{ L}}\right) = 0.571 \text{ M HCl}$$

b. Given: $V = 0.250$ L
molarity = 2.30 M KI

Unknown: moles KI

$$\text{mol solute} = MV$$
$$= (2.30 \text{ mol/L})(0.250 \text{ L})$$
$$= 0.575 \text{ mol}$$

c. Given: molarity = 0.500 M HBr
mass of HBr = 32.5 g

Unknown: V

$$V = (32.5 \text{ g HBr})\left(\frac{\text{mol HBr}}{80.91 \text{ g HBr}}\right)\left(\frac{1 \text{ L}}{0.500 \text{ mol}}\right) = 0.803 \text{ L}$$

Practice, p. 424

1. Given: mass of solute = 255 g $(CH_3)_2CO$
mass of solvent = 200. g H_2O

Unknown: molality (m)

$$(255 \text{ g } (CH_3)_2CO)\left(\frac{\text{mol } (CH_3)_2CO}{58.08 \text{ g } (CH_3)_2CO}\right) = 4.39 \text{ mol}$$

$$(200. \text{ g } H_2O)\left(\frac{\text{kg}}{1000 \text{ g}}\right) = 0.20 \text{ kg}$$

$$m = \frac{4.39 \text{ mol}}{0.20 \text{ kg}} = 22.0 \text{ } m \text{ acetone}$$

2. Given: molality = 0.244 m CH_3OH
mass of solvent = 400. g H_2O

Unknown: mass of solute, CH_3OH

$$\text{mass of solute} = \left(0.244 \frac{\text{mol}}{\text{kg}}\right)(0.400 \text{ kg})\left(\frac{32 \text{ g } CH_3OH}{\text{mol } CH_3OH}\right) = 3.13 \text{ g } CH_3OH$$

Section Review, p. 424

2. Given: mass of solute = 5.00 g $C_{12}H_{22}O_{11}$
$V = 1.000$ L

Unknown: molarity (M)

$$M = (5.00 \text{ g } C_{12}H_{22}O_{11})\left(\frac{\text{mol } C_{12}H_{22}O_{11}}{342.23 \text{ g } C_{12}H_{22}O_{11}}\right)\left(\frac{1}{1.000 \text{ L}}\right) = 0.0146 \text{ } M$$

D-1. Given: mass of solvent
= 13.0 g NaCl
mass of solute =
500. g H_2O

Unknown: molality (m)

$$m = (13.0 \text{ g NaCl})\left(\frac{\text{mol NaCl}}{58.44 \text{ g}}\right)\left(\frac{1}{0.500 \text{ kg } H_2O}\right) = 0.445 \; m$$

E-1. Given: m = 1.0 NaCl
mass of solvent
= 250 g

Unknown: mass of
solute

$$\text{mol NaCl} = (m)(\text{kg solvent}) = (1.0)(0.25) = 0.25 \text{ mol}$$

$$(0.25 \text{ mol})\left(\frac{58.44 \text{ g NaCl}}{\text{mol}}\right) = 15 \text{ g NaCl}$$

Chapter Review

19a. Given: 106 g Na_2CO_3
6.00 L solution

Unknown: (1) Molar
mass of
Na_2CO_3
(2) Molarity
of Na_2CO_3
in solution

(1) molar mass = $2 \times 22.99 + 12.01 + 48 = 105.99 \cong 106$ g/mol

(2) molarity = $\dfrac{\text{mol } Na_2CO_3}{\text{L solution}} = \dfrac{106 \text{ g } Na_2CO_3}{106 \text{ g/mol} \times 6 \text{ L}} = 0.167$ M

b. Given: 14.0 g NH_4Br
150 mL solution

Unknown: molarity of
NH_4Br
solution

$$\frac{14.0 \text{ g } NH_4Br}{97.95 \text{ g/mol} \times 0.150 \text{ L solution}} = 0.953 \text{ M } NH_4Br$$

20a. Given: V = 1.00 L
molarity =
3.50 M H_2SO_4

Unknown (3): mass of
solute

amount of solute (mol) = (M)(volume)

$$= (3.50 \text{ mol/L})(1.00 \text{ L})$$

$$= 3.50 \text{ mol}$$

$$\text{mass of solute} = (3.50 \text{ mol } H_2SO_4)\left(\frac{98.05 \text{ g } H_2SO_4}{\text{mol } H_2SO_4}\right) = 343 \text{ g } H_2SO_4$$

b. Given: V = 2.50 L
molarity = 1.75
M $Ba(NO_3)_2$

Unknown: mass of
$Ba(NO_3)_2$

moles solute = (M)(volume)

$$= (1.75 \text{ mol/L})(2.50 \text{ L})$$

$$= 4.38 \text{ mol}$$

$$\text{mass of solute} = (4.38 \text{ mol } Ba(NO_3)_2)\left(\frac{261.3 \text{ g } Ba(NO_3)_2}{\text{mol } Ba(NO_3)_2}\right)$$

$$= 1140 \text{ g } Ba(NO_3)_2$$

21. Given: $V = 0.065$ L
molarity =
2.20 M NaOH

Unknown: moles NaOH

mol solute = (M)(L solution)

$= (2.20 \text{ mol/L NaOH})(0.065 \text{ L})$

$= 0.143$ mol NaOH

---

22. Given: mass of solute =
26.42 g $(NH_4)_2SO_4$
$V = 0.050$ L

a. Unknown: molar mass
$(NH_4)_2SO_4$

Atomic mass N = $14.01 \times 2 = 28.02$
Atomic mass H = $1.01 \times 8 = 8.08$
Atomic mass S = 32.07
Atomic mass O = $15.99 \times 4 = \underline{63.96}$
Total: 132.13 g

$= 132.1$ g = molar mass $(NH_4)_2SO_4$

b. Unknown: molarity
(M)

$\dfrac{26.42 \text{ g } (NH_4)_2 SO_4}{132.1 \text{ g/mol } (NH_4)_2SO_4} = 0.2000 \text{ mol } (NH_4)_2SO_4$

$M = \dfrac{0.2000 \text{ mol}}{0.05000 \text{ L}} = 4.000 \text{ M}$

---

23. Given: molarity = 1.0 M
$AgNO_3$
mass of solute =
166.88 g $AgNO_3$

b. Unknown: molar mass $AgNO_3$

Atomic mass Ag = 107.87
Atomic mass N = 14.007
Atomic mass O = $\underline{15.999 \times 3 = 47.997}$
Total: 169.9 g = molar mass $AgNO_3$

c. Unknown: mL of solution

$(169.9 \text{ g } AgNO_3)\left(\dfrac{\text{mol } AgNO_3}{169.9 \text{ g } AgNO_3}\right) = 1.0 \text{ mol } AgNO_3$

$V = \dfrac{\text{moles}}{M} = \dfrac{1.0 \text{ mol}}{1.0 \text{ mol/L}} = 1.0 \text{ L} = 1000 \text{ mL}$

24b. Given: $V = 0.750$ L
H_3PO_4
molarity =
6.00 M H_3PO_4

Unknown: mass of
products

moles of solute = (M)(volume of solution)

$= (6.00 \text{ M})(0.750 \text{ L})$

$= 4.50 \text{ mol } H_3PO_4$

$(4.50 \text{ mol } H_3PO_4)\left(\dfrac{1 \text{ mol } Ca_3(PO_4)_2}{2 \text{ mol } H_3PO_4}\right)\left(\dfrac{310.1 \text{ g } Ca_3(PO_4)_2}{\text{mol } Ca_3(PO_4)_2}\right)$

$= 698 \text{ g } Ca_3(PO_4)_2$

$(4.50 \text{ mol } H_3PO_4)\left(\dfrac{6 \text{ mol } H_2O}{2 \text{ mol } H_3PO_4}\right)\left(\dfrac{18.01 \text{ g } H_2O}{\text{mol } H_2O}\right) = 243 \text{ g } H_2O$

25. Given: 0.750 M H_3PO_4
0.150 M $Ba(OH)_2$

Volume of
$Ba(OH)_2$ solution
= 250. mL
$2H_3PO_4 +$
$3Ba(OH)_2 \rightarrow$
$Ba_3(PO_4)_2 + 6H_2O$

Unknown: volume of
H_3PO_4
solution

$0.250 \text{ L } Ba(OH)_2 \times 0.150 \text{ mol/L } Ba(OH)_2 \times$

$$\frac{2 \text{ mol } H_3PO_4}{3 \text{ mol } Ba(OH)_2} \times \frac{1}{0.750 \text{ mol/L } H_3PO_4} = 0.0333 \text{ L} = 33.3 \text{ mL}$$

---

26. Given: V $AgNO_3$ solution
= 0.0750 L
mass of solute
= 0.250 g Ag

Unknown: molarity (M) of
$AgNO_3$ if other
product is
$Cu(NO_3)_2$

$(0.250 \text{ g Ag})\left(\dfrac{\text{mol Ag}}{108 \text{ g Ag}}\right) = 2.30 \times 10^{-3} \text{ mol Ag}$

$M = \dfrac{2.3 \times 10^{-3} \text{ mol Ag}}{0.0750 \text{ L } AgNO_3} = 0.0309 \text{ M } AgNO_3$

27a. Given: molality =
4.50 m H_2SO_4
mass of solvent
= 1.00 kg H_2O

Unknown: mass of
solute

moles solute = (m)(kg solvent)

$= (4.50)(1.00) = 4.50 \text{ mol } H_2SO_4$

$(4.50 \text{ mol } H_2SO_4)\left(\dfrac{98.05 \text{ g } H_2SO_4}{\text{mol } H_2SO_4}\right) = 441 \text{ g } H_2SO_4$

b. Given: molality =
1.00 m HNO_3
mass of solvent
= 2.00 kg H_2O

Unknown: mass of
solute

moles solute = (m)(kg solvent)

$= (1.00)(2.00) = 2.00 \text{ mol } HNO_3$

$(2.00 \text{ mol } HNO_3)\left(\dfrac{62.99 \text{ g } HNO_3}{\text{mol } HNO_3}\right) = 126 \text{ g } HNO_3$

---

28. Given: mass of solute =
17.1 g $C_{12}H_{22}O_{11}$
mass of solvent =
0.275 kg H_2O

a. Unknown: molar mass
of sucrose

Atomic mass C = $12.01 \times 12 = 144.12$
Atomic mass H = $1.01 \times 22 = 22.22$
Atomic mass O = $15.99 \times 11 = \underline{175.89}$

Total: 342.23 g = 342 g = molar mass sucrose

b. Unknown: molality (m)

$(17.1 \text{ g } C_{12}H_{22}O_{11})\left(\dfrac{\text{mol } C_{12}H_{22}O_{11}}{342 \text{ g } C_{12}H_{22}O_{11}}\right) = 0.05 \text{ mol } C_{12}H_{22}O_{11}$

$m = \dfrac{0.05 \text{ mol}}{0.275 \text{ kg}} = 0.182 \ m$

29. Given: mass of solute = 75.5 g $Ca(NO_3)_2$
$m = 0.500$

Unknown: mass of solvent (H_2O) in kg

$$(75.5 \text{ g Ca(NO}_3)_2)\left(\frac{\text{mol Ca(NO}_3)_2}{164.04 \text{ g Ca(NO}_3)_2}\right) = 0.46 \text{ mol Ca(NO}_3)_2$$

$$\text{kg solvent} = \frac{0.46 \text{ mol Ca(NO}_3)_2}{0.500 \text{ } m} = 0.920 \text{ kg H}_2\text{O}$$

---

30. Given: $m = 1.75$
mass of solvent = 0.250 kg

Unknown: mass of solute (C_2H_5OH) in g

$$\text{moles solute} = (m)(\text{kg solvent})$$
$$= (1.75)(0.250) = 0.438 \text{ mol C}_2\text{H}_5\text{OH}$$

$$(0.438 \text{ mol C}_2\text{H}_5\text{OH})\left(\frac{46.07 \text{ g C}_2\text{H}_5\text{OH}}{\text{mol C}_2\text{H}_5\text{OH}}\right) = 20.2 \text{ g C}_2\text{H}_5\text{OH}$$

---

31. Given: $V = 0.450$ L
molarity = 0.250 M Na_2SO_4

a. Unknown: molar mass Na_2SO_4

Atomic mass Na = $22.99 \times 2 = 45.98$
Atomic mass S = 32.07
Atomic mass O = $15.99 \times 4 = \underline{63.96}$
Total: 142.01 = molar mass Na_2SO_4

b. Unknown: moles Na_2SO_4 needed

$$\text{mol Na}_2\text{SO}_4 = (M)(\text{volume of solution})$$
$$= (0.250 \text{ mol/L})(0.450 \text{ L}) = 0.113 \text{ mol Na}_2\text{SO}_4$$

---

32. Given: $V = 2.00$ L
mass of solute = 0.150 g $C_6H_8O_7$

a. Unknown: molar mass citric acid, $C_6H_8O_7$

Atomic mass C = $12.01 \times 6 = 72.06$
Atomic mass H = $1.01 \times 8 = 8.08$
Atomic mass O = $15.99 \times 7 = \underline{111.93}$
Total: $192.07 = 192.1$ g = molar mass $C_6H_8O_7$

b. Unknown: M (molarity of $C_6H_8O_7$)

$$M = (0.150 \text{ g C}_6\text{H}_8\text{O}_7)\left(\frac{\text{mol C}_6\text{H}_8\text{O}_7}{192 \text{ g C}_6\text{H}_8\text{O}_7}\right)\left(\frac{1}{2.00 \text{ L}}\right) = 3.90 \times 10^{-4} \text{ M C}_6\text{H}_8\text{O}_7$$

---

33. Given: $V = 0.350$ L
molarity = 2.0 M KCl

a. Unknown: molar mass of KCl

Atomic mass K = 39.1
Atomic mass Cl = 35.5
Total 74.6 g = molar mass KCl

c. Unknown: mass of solute (KCl)

$$\text{moles solute} = (M)(\text{volume of solution})$$
$$= (2.0 \text{ mol/L})(0.350 \text{ L}) = 0.70 \text{ mol KCl}$$

$$(0.70 \text{ mol KCl})\left(\frac{74.6 \text{ g KCl}}{\text{mol KCl}}\right) = 52 \text{ g KCl}$$

34. Given:
mass of Na = 10.0 g
volume of H_2O = 1.00 L
final volume of system =
1 L

a. Unknown: molar mass
NaOH

Atomic mass Na = 22.99
Atomic mass O = 15.99
Atomic mass H = 1.01
Total: 39.99 = 40.0 g = molar mass NaOH

c. Unknown: molarity of
NaOH

$$(10.0 \text{ g Na})\left(\frac{\text{mol Na}}{22.99 \text{ g Na}}\right) = 0.435 \text{ mol Na}$$

$$(0.435 \text{ mol Na})\left(\frac{1 \text{ mol NaOH}}{1 \text{ mol Na}}\right) = 0.435 \text{ mol NaOH}$$

$$M = \frac{0.435 \text{ mol}}{1.00 \text{ L}} = 0.435 \text{ M}$$

35. Given: mass of solvent =
6.5 kg $C_2H_6O_2$
mass of solute =
1500 g H_2O

a. Unknown: molar mass
$C_2H_6O_2$

Atomic mass C = 12.01 × 2 = 24.02
Atomic mass H = 1.01 × 6 = 6.06
Atomic mass O = 15.99 × 2 = 31.98
Total: 62.06 = 62.1 g = molar mass $C_2H_6O_2$

b. Unknown: molality
(m) of H_2O

$$(1500 \text{ g H}_2\text{O})\left(\frac{\text{mol H}_2\text{O}}{18 \text{ g H}_2\text{O}}\right) = 83.3 \text{ mol H}_2\text{O}$$

$$m = \frac{83.3 \text{ mol}}{6.5 \text{ kg}} = 13 \ m \text{ H}_2\text{O}$$

37. Solubility at 60°C = 106
Solubility at 20°C = 31.6
106 − 31.6 = 74.4 g

38. a. Given: 294.3 g H_2SO_4
1.000 kg H_2O

$$\frac{294.3 \text{ g H}_2\text{SO}_4}{98.09 \text{g/mol H}_2\text{SO}_4 \times 1 \text{ kg H}_2\text{O}} = 3.000 \ m$$

Unknown: identities
of solute &
solvent
molality of
solution

The solute is H_2SO_4.

The solvent is H_2O.

b. Given: 63.0 g HNO_3
0.250 kg H_2O

$$\frac{63.0 \text{ g HNO}_3}{63.02 \text{ g/mol} \times 0.250 \text{ kg H}_2\text{O}} = 4.00 \ m$$

Unknown: molality of
solution

Math Tutor, p. 430

1. Given: 0.0350 mol Na_2SO_4
50.0 mL solution

$$\frac{0.0350 \text{ mol } Na_2SO_4 \times 1000 \text{ mL}}{50.0 \text{ mL} \times 1 \text{ L}} = 0.700 \text{ M } Na_2SO_4$$

Unknown: Molarity of
solution

2. Given: 45.00 g $Cd(NO_3)_2$
400.0 mL solution

$$\frac{45.00 \text{ g } Cd(NO_3)_2 \times 1000 \text{ mL}}{236.43 \text{ g/mol} \times 400.0 \text{ mL} \times 1 \text{ L}} = 0.4758 \text{ M } Cd(NO_3)_2$$

Unknown: molarity of
solution

Standardized Test Prep, p. 431

7. Given: 2.5 L of 0.010 M
NaOH

$$(2.5 \text{ L})\left(\frac{0.010 \text{ mol NaOH}}{L}\right)(40.00 \text{ g/mol}) = 1.0 \text{ g NaOH}$$

Unknown: mass of NaOH

CHAPTER 13

Ions in Aqueous Solutions and Colligative Properties

Practice, p. 436

1a. Given: dissolution of ammonium chloride, 1 mol ammonium chloride

Unknown: Chemical equation, mol of each ion mol of total ions

$$NH_4Cl(s) \xrightarrow{H_2O} NH_4^+(aq) + Cl^-(aq)$$

1 mol NH_4^+

1 mol Cl^-

2 mol total ions

b. Given: dissolution of sodium sulfide, 1 mol sodium sulfide

Unknown: chemical equation, mol of each ion mol of total ions

$$Na_2S(s) \xrightarrow{H_2O} 2\,Na^+(aq) + S^{2-}(aq)$$

2 mol Na^+

1 mol S^{2-}

3 mol total ions

c. Given: dissolution of barium nitrate, 0.50 mol barium nitrate

Unknown: chemical equation, mol of each ion mol of total ions

$$Ba(NO_3)_2(s) \xrightarrow{H_2O} Ba^{2+}(aq) + 2NO_3^-(aq)$$

0.50 mol Ba^{2+}

1.0 mol NO_3^-

1.50 mol total ions

ATE, Additional Sample Problems, p. 436

A-1. Given: amount of solute = 1 mol $Mg(ClO_3)_2$ solvent = H_2O

Unknown: number of moles of ions produced

$$Mg(ClO_3)_2(s) \xrightarrow{H_2O} Mg^{2+}(aq) + 2\,ClO_3^-(aq)$$

1 mol Mg^{2+} + 2 mol ClO_3^- = 3 mol ions produced

A-2. Given: amount of solute
= 3.5 mol
NH_4NO_3
solvent = H_2O

Unknown: number of
moles of ions
produced

$$NH_4NO_3(s) \xrightarrow{H_2O} NH_4^+(aq) + NO_3^-(aq)$$

3.5 mol NH_4^+ + 3.5 mol NO_3^- = 7.0 mol ions produced

Section Review, p. 443

1. Given: dissolution of
0.5 mol strontium
nitrate

Unknown: Chemical
equation
moles Sr^{2+}
moles NO_3^-

$$Sr(NO_3)_2(s) \xrightarrow{H_2O} Sr^{2+}(aq) + 2NO_3^-(aq)$$

0.5 mol Sr^{2+}

1.0 mol NO_3^-

ATE, Additional Sample Problems, p. 449

C-1. Given: mass of solute =
58.0 g $C_6H_{12}O_6$
mass of solvent =
0.185 kg H_2O

Unknown: freezing point
of solution

$$\Delta t_f = K_f m$$

$$(58.0 \text{ g } C_6H_{12}O_6)\left(\frac{\text{mol } C_6H_{12}O_6}{180. \text{ g } C_6H_{12}O_6}\right) = 0.322 \text{ mol } C_6H_{12}O_6$$

$$m = \frac{\text{moles of solute}}{\text{mass of solvent (kg)}}$$

$$m = \frac{0.322 \text{ mol}}{0.185 \text{ kg}} = 1.74 \ m$$

$$\Delta t_f = (-1.86°C/m)(1.74 \ m) = -3.24°C$$

f.p. solution = f.p. solvent + Δt_f
$$= 0.000°C + (-3.24°C) = -3.24°C$$

C-2. Given: mass of solute =
39.2 g
H_2NCONH_2
mass of solvent =
0.485 kg acetic
acid

Unknowns: molality (m)
of solution,
freezing
point of
solution

$$(39.2 \text{ g } H_2NCONH_2)\left(\frac{\text{mol } H_2NCONH_2}{60.06 \text{ g } H_2NCONH_2}\right) = 0.6527 \text{ mol } H_2NCONH_2$$

$$m = \frac{\text{moles of solute}}{\text{mass of solvent (kg)}}$$

$$m = \frac{0.6527 \text{ mol}}{0.485 \text{ kg}} = 1.346 \ m$$

$$\Delta t_f = K_f m$$
$$= (-3.90°C/m)(1.346 \ m) = -5.248°C$$

f.p. solution = f.p. solvent + Δt_f

f.p. = 16.6°C + (-5.246°C) = 11.4°C

D-1. Given: f.p. of solution = −6.40°C

mass of solvent = (500. g H_2O)

Unknowns: molality (*m*) of solution of $HOCH_2CH_2OH$, mass of solute needed

f.p. solution = f.p. solvent + Δt_f

Δt_f = f.p. solution − f.p. solvent

$\quad$ = −6.40° C − 0.000° C = −6.40° C

$\Delta t_f = K_f m$

$m = \Delta t_f / K_f$

$\quad$ = (−6.40°C)/(−1.86°C/*m*) = 3.44 *m*

$m = \dfrac{\text{moles of solute}}{\text{mass of solvent (kg)}}$

moles of solute = (*m*)(mass of solvent)

$\quad$ = (3.44)(0.500) = 1.72 mol

$(1.72 \text{ mol } HOCH_2CH_2OH)\left(\dfrac{62.0 \text{ g } HOCH_2CH_2OH}{\text{mol } HOCH_2CH_2OH}\right) = 107 \text{ g } HOCH_2CH_2OH$

Practice, p. 450

1. Given: mass of solute = 10.3 g $C_6H_{12}O_6$

mass of solvent = 0.250 kg H_2O

Unknown: freezing-point depression of solution

$(10.3 \text{ g } C_6H_{12}O_6)\left(\dfrac{\text{mol } C_6H_{12}O_6}{180. \text{ g } C_6H_{12}O_6}\right) = 0.0572 \text{ mol } C_6H_{12}O_6$

$m = \dfrac{\text{moles of solute}}{\text{mass of solvent (kg)}}$

$m = \dfrac{0.0572 \text{ mol}}{0.250 \text{ kg}} = 0.22 \text{ } m$

$\Delta t_f = K_f m$

$\Delta t_f = (−1.86°C/m)(0.2288 \text{ } m) = −0.426°C$

2. Given: f.p. of solution = −0.325°C

solute = $C_6H_{12}O_6$

solvent = H_2O

Unknown: molality (*m*) of solution

f.p. solution = f.p. solvent + Δt_f

Δt_f = f.p. solution − f.p. solvent

$\quad$ = −0.325°C − 0.000°C = −0.325°C

$\Delta t_f = K_f m$

$m = \Delta t_f / K_f$

$\quad = \dfrac{(−0.325°C)}{(−1.86°C/m)} = 0.175 \text{ } m$

3. Given: amount of solute = 0.500 mol

amount of solvent 0.5000 kg ether

f.p. ether = −116.3°C

Unknown: freezing point of solution

$m = \dfrac{\text{moles of solute}}{\text{mass of solvent (kg)}}$

$m = \dfrac{0.500 \text{ mol}}{0.500 \text{ kg}} = 1.00 \text{ } m$

$\Delta t_f = K_f m$

$\Delta t_f = (−1.79°C/m)(1.00 \text{ } m) = −1.79°C$

f.p. solution = f.p. ether + Δt_f

$\quad$ = −116.3°C + (−1.79°C) = −118.1°C

4. Given: f.p. of solution =
   $-9.0°C$
   solvent = H_2O
   f.p. $H_2O = 0.0°C$

a. Unknown: freezing-point depression of solution

f.p. solution = f.p. solvent + Δt_p

Δt_p = f.p. solution – f.p. solvent

$= -9.0°C - 0.0°C = -9.0°C$

b. Unknown: molality (m) of solution

$\Delta t_f = K_f m$

$m = \Delta t_f / K_f$

$= \dfrac{(-9.0°C)}{(-1.86°C/m)} = 4.8\ m$

Practice, p. 451

1. Given: mass of solute =
   50.0 g $C_{12}H_{22}O_{11}$
   (sucrose)
   mass of solvent =
   0.500 kg H_2O

Unknown: boiling-point elevation

$(50.0\ \text{g}\ C_{12}H_{22}O_{11})\left(\dfrac{\text{mol}\ C_{12}H_{22}O_{11}}{342\ \text{g}\ C_{12}H_{22}O_{11}}\right) = 0.146\ \text{mol}\ C_{12}H_{22}O_{11}$

$m = \dfrac{\text{moles of solute}}{\text{mass of solvent (kg)}}$

$m = \dfrac{0.146\ \text{mol}}{0.500\ \text{kg}} = 0.292\ m$

$\Delta t_b = K_b m$

$\Delta t_b = (0.51°C/m)(0.292\ m) = 0.15°C$

2. Given: mass of solute =
   450.0 g $C_{12}H_{22}O_{11}$
   (sucrose)
   mass of solvent =
   0.250 kg H_2O
   b.p. $H_2O = 100.0°C$

Unknown: boiling point of solution

$(450.0\ \text{g}\ C_{12}H_{22}O_{11})\left(\dfrac{\text{mol}\ C_{12}H_{22}O_{11}}{342\ \text{g}\ C_{12}H_{22}O_{11}}\right) = 1.32\ \text{mol}\ C_{12}H_{22}O_{11}$

$m = \dfrac{\text{moles of solute}}{\text{mass of solvent (kg)}}$

$m = \dfrac{1.32\ \text{mol}}{0.250\ \text{kg}} = 5.28\ m$

$\Delta t_b = K_b m$

$\Delta t_b = (0.51°C/m)(5.28\ m) = 2.7°C$

b.p. solution = b.p. solvent + Δt_b

$= 100.0°C + 2.7°C = 102.7°C$

3. Given: boiling-point elevation = $1.02°C$
   solvent = H_2O

Unknown: molality (m) of solution

$\Delta t_b = K_b m$

$m = \Delta t_b / K_b$

$= 1.02°C/(0.51°C/m) = 2.0\ m$

4. Given: boiling point of
solution = 100.75°C
solvent = H_2O

a. Unknown: boiling-point
elevation

b.p. solution = b.p. solvent + Δt_b

Δt_b = b.p. solution − b.p. solvent

$= 100.75°C − 100.0°C = 0.75°C$

b. Unknown: molality (m) of
solution

$\Delta t_b = K_b m$

$m = \Delta t_b / K_b$

$$= \frac{0.75°C}{(0.51°C/m)} = 1.5\ m$$

ATE, Additional Sample Problems, p. 451

E-1. Given: mass of
solute = 25.0 g
$HOCH_2CH_2OC_4H_9$
(butyl cellosolve)
mass of solvent =
0.0687 kg ether

Unknown: boiling point of
solution

$$(25.0\ \text{g HOCH}_2\text{CH}_2\text{OC}_4\text{H}_9)\left(\frac{\text{mol HOCH}_2\text{CH}_2\text{OC}_4\text{H}_9}{118\ \text{g HOCH}_2\text{CH}_2\text{OC}_4\text{H}_9}\right)$$

$= 0.212\ \text{mol HOCH}_2\text{CH}_2\text{OC}_4\text{H}_9$

$$m = \frac{\text{moles of solute}}{\text{mass of solvent (kg)}}$$

$$m = \frac{0.212\ \text{mol}}{0.0687\ \text{kg}} = 3.09\ m$$

$\Delta t_b = K_b m$

$= (2.02°C/m)(4.37\ m) = 6.24°C$

b.p. solution = b.p. solvent + Δt_b

$= 34.6°C + 6.24°C = 40.8°C$

E-2. Given: mass of solvent =
1.00 kg H_2O
boiling point of so-
lution = 104.5°C
solute = CH_2OH-
$CHOHCH_2OH$
(glycerol)

Unknown: mass of solute

b.p. solution = b.p. solvent + Δt_b

Δt_b = b.p. solution − b.p. solvent

$= 104.5°C − 100.0°C = 4.5°C$

$\Delta t_b = K_b m$

$m = \Delta t_b / K_b$

$= 4.5°C/(0.51°C/M) = 8.8\ m$

$$m = \frac{\text{moles of solute}}{\text{mass of solvent (kg)}}$$

moles of solute = (m)(mass of solvent)

$= (8.8\ \text{mol/kg})(1.00\ \text{kg}) = 8.8\ \text{mol}$

$$(8.8\ \text{mol glycerol})\left(\frac{92.08\ \text{g glycerol}}{\text{mol glycerol}}\right) = 810\ \text{g glycerol}$$

Practice, p. 455

1. Given: solute = 2.0 mol $MgSO_4$
mass of solvent = 1.0 kg H_2O

Unknown: expected freezing-point depression of solution

$$m = \frac{\text{moles of solute}}{\text{mass of solvent (kg)}} = \frac{2.0 \text{ mol}}{1.0 \text{ kg}}$$

$$MgSO_4 \, (s) \rightarrow Mg^{2+}(aq) + SO_4^{2-}(aq)$$

Each formula unit of $MgSO_4$ yields two ions in solution.

$$\Delta t_f = K_f m$$

$$= \left(\frac{-1.86°C \cdot \text{kg } H_2O}{\text{mol ions}}\right)\left(\frac{2.0 \text{ mol } MgSO_4}{\text{kg } H_2O}\right)\left(\frac{2 \text{ mol ions}}{\text{mol } MgSO_4}\right)$$

$$= -7.4°C$$

2. Given: mass of solute = 150 g NaCl
mass of solvent = 1.0 kg H_2O

Unknown: expected boiling-point elevation of solution

$$(150 \text{ g NaCl})\left(\frac{\text{mol NaCl}}{58.44 \text{ g NaCl}}\right) = 2.57 \text{ mol NaCl}$$

$$m = \frac{\text{moles of solute}}{\text{mass of solvent (kg)}} = \frac{2.57 \text{ mol}}{1.0 \text{ kg}}$$

$$NaCl(s) \rightarrow Na^+(aq) + Cl^-(aq)$$

Each formula unit of NaCl yields two ions in solution.

$$\Delta t_b = K_b m$$

$$= \left(\frac{0.51°C \cdot \text{kg } H_2O}{\text{mol ions}}\right)\left(\frac{2.57 \text{ mol NaCl}}{\text{kg } H_2O}\right)\left(\frac{2 \text{ mol ions}}{\text{mol NaCl}}\right)$$

$$= 2.6°C$$

3. Given: solute = NaCl
solvent = H_2O
freezing point of solution = $-0.20°C$
freezing point of $H_2O = 0.0°C$

Unknown: molality (m)

f.p. solution = f.p. solvent + Δt_f

Δt_f = f.p. solution – f.p. solvent

$= -0.20°C - 0.0°C = -0.20°C$

$$NaCl(s) \rightarrow Na^+(aq) + Cl^-(aq)$$

Each formula unit of NaCl yields two ions in solution.

$$\Delta t_f = K_f m$$

$$m = \Delta t_f / K_f$$

$$= \left(\frac{-0.20°C \cdot \text{mol ions}}{-1.86°C}\right)\left(\frac{1 \text{ mol NaCl}}{2 \text{ mol ions}}\right) = 0.054 \text{ } m \text{ NaCl}$$

Section Review, p. 456

2. Given: amount of solute = 2 mol
amount of solvent = 1 kg
freezing point of solution = 7.8°C below its normal freezing point

Unknowns: molal freezing-point constant of unknown solvent (K_f), identity of solvent

$$m = \frac{\text{moles of solute}}{\text{mass of solvent (kg)}}$$

$$= \frac{2 \text{ mol}}{1 \text{ kg}} = 2 \text{ } m$$

$$\Delta t_f = K_f m$$

$$K_f = \Delta t_f / m$$

$$= -7.8°C/2 \text{ } m = -3.9°C/m$$

Identity of solvent: acetic acid

4. a. Given: molality (m) of solution = 0.2 m solute = KNO_3

Unknown: expected freezing-point depression

$$KNO_3(s) \rightarrow K^+(aq) + NO_3^-(aq)$$

Each formula unit of KNO_3 yields two ions in solution.

$$\Delta t_f = K_f m$$

$$= \left(\frac{-1.86°C \cdot kg\ H_2O}{mol/ions}\right)\left(\frac{0.2\ mol\ KNO_3}{kg\ H_2O}\right)\left(\frac{2\ mol/ions}{mol/KNO_3}\right)$$

$$= -0.744°C$$

Chapter Review

1. a. Given: solute = KCl

Unknown: number of moles of ions present

$$KCl(s) \xrightarrow{H_2O} K^+(aq) + Cl^-(aq)$$

Ions produced = 1 mol K^+ + 1 mol Cl^- = 2 mol

b. Given: amount of solvent = 1 L
M of solution = 1 M
solute = $Mg(NO_3)_2$

Unknown: number of moles of ions present

$$Mg(NO_3)_2 \xrightarrow{H_2O} Mg^{2+}(aq) + 2NO_3^-(aq)$$

Ions produced = 1 mol Mg^{2+} + 2 mol NO_3^- = 3 mol

9. Given: dissolution of KI, $NaNO_3$, $MgCl_2$ and Na_2SO_4 in water, 1 mol of each compound

Unknown: mol of each ion, mol of total ions

$$KI(s) \xrightarrow{H_2O} K^+(aq) + I^-(aq)$$

1 mol K^+

1 mol I^-

2 mol total ions

$$NaNO_3(s) \xrightarrow{H_2O} Na^+(aq) + 2NO_3^-(aq)$$

1 mol Na^+

1 mol NO_3^-

2 mol total ions

$$MgCl_2(s) \xrightarrow{H_2O} Mg^{2+}(aq) + 2Cl^-(aq)$$

1 mol Mg^{2+}

2 mol Cl^-

3 mol total ions

$$Na_2SO_4(s) \xrightarrow{H_2O} 2Na^+(aq) + SO_4^{2-}(aq)$$

2 mol Na^+

1 mol SO_4^{2-}

3 mol total ions

10. a. Given: amount of solute = 0.50 mol $Sr(NO_3)_2$ solvent = H_2O

Unknown: total number of moles of solute ions formed

$$Sr(NO_3)_2(s) \xrightarrow{H_2O} Sr^{2+}(aq) + 2NO_3^-(aq)$$

Ions produced: $0.5 \text{ mol } Sr(NO_3)_2 \times \dfrac{1 \text{ mol } Sr^{2+}}{1 \text{ mol } Sr(NO_3)_2} = 0.5 \text{ mol } Sr^{2+}$

$0.5 \text{ mol } Sr(NO_3)_2 \times \dfrac{2 \text{ mol } NO_3^-}{1 \text{ mol } Sr(NO_3)_2} = 1.00 \text{ mol } NO_3^-$

$0.50 \text{ mol } Sr^{2+} + 1.00 \text{ mol } NO_3^- = 1.50 \text{ mol ions}$

b. Given: amount of solute = 0.50 mol Na_3PO_4

Unknown: total number of moles of solute ions formed

$$Na_3PO_4(s) \xrightarrow{H_2O} 3Na^+(aq) + PO_4^{3-}(aq)$$

Ions produced: $0.5 \text{ mol } Na_3PO_4 \times \dfrac{3 \text{ mol } Na^+}{1 \text{ mol } Na_3PO_4} = 1.5 \text{ mol } Na^+$

$0.5 \text{ mol } Na_3PO_4 \times \dfrac{1 \text{ mol } PO_4^{3-}}{1 \text{ mol } Na_3PO_4} = 0.5 \text{ mol } PO_4^{3-}$

$1.50 \text{ mol } Na^+ + 0.50 \text{ mol } PO_4^{3-} = 2.00 \text{ mol ions}$

---

13. Given: mass of $CuCl_2$ = 13.45 g

Unknown: maximum amount of precipitate formed

$$(13.45 \text{ g } CuCl_2)\left(\dfrac{\text{mol } CuCl_2}{134.45 \text{ g } CuCl_2}\right) = 0.10004 \text{ mol } CuCl_2$$

$$0.10004 \text{ mol } CuCl_2 \times \dfrac{1 \text{ mol } PbCl_2}{1 \text{ mol } CuCl_2} = 0.10004 \text{ mol } PbCl_2$$

$$(0.10004 \text{ mol } PbCl_2)\left(\dfrac{278.11 \text{ g } PbCl_2}{\text{mol } PbCl_2}\right) = 27.82 \text{ g } PbCl_2$$

---

19. a. Given: molality = 1.50 m $C_{12}H_{22}O_{11}$ (sucrose) solvent = H_2O

Unknown: freezing-point depression

$\Delta t_f = K_f m$
$= (-1.86°C/m)(1.50 \ m) = -2.79°C$

b. Given: mass of solute = 171 g $C_{12}H_{22}O_{11}$ (sucrose) mass of solvent = 1.00 kg H_2O

Unknown: freezing-point depression

$$(171 \text{ g sucrose})\left(\dfrac{\text{mol sucrose}}{342 \text{ g sucrose}}\right) = 0.500 \text{ mol sucrose}$$

$$m = \dfrac{\text{moles of solute}}{\text{mass of solvent (kg)}}$$

$$m = \dfrac{0.500 \text{ mol}}{1.00 \text{ kg}} = 0.5 \ m$$

$\Delta t_f = K_f m$

$\Delta t_f = (-1.86°C/m)(0.500 \ m) = -0.93°C$

c. Given: mass of solute = 77.0 g $C_{12}H_{22}O_{11}$ (sucrose) mass of solvent = 0.400 kg H_2O

Unknown: freezing-point depression

$$(77.0 \text{ g sucrose})\left(\dfrac{\text{mol sucrose}}{342 \text{ g sucrose}}\right) = 0.225 \text{ mol sucrose}$$

$$m = \dfrac{\text{moles of solute}}{\text{mass of solvent (kg)}}$$

$$m = \dfrac{0.225 \text{ mol}}{0.400 \text{ kg}} = 0.563 \ m$$

$\Delta t_f = K_f m$

$\Delta t_f = (-1.86°C/m)(0.563 \ m) = -1.05°C$

20. Given: solvent = H_2O;
solute =
nonelectrolyte

$\Delta t_f = K_f m$

$m = \Delta t_f / K_f$

a. freezing-point
depression = $-0.93°C$

a. $m = (-0.930°C)/(-1.86°C/m) = 0.500\ m$

b. freezing-point
depression = $-3.72°C$

b. $m = (-3.72°C)/(-1.86°C/m) = 2.00\ m$

c. freezing-point
depression = $-8.37°C$

c. $m = (-8.37°C)/(-1.86°C/m) = 4.50\ m$

Unknown: molality (m) of
each solution

---

21. Given: mass of solute =
20.0 g $C_6H_{12}O_6$
(glucose)
mass of solvent =
0.250 kg H_2O

a. Unknown: freezing-
point
depression
of solvent

$\Delta t_f = K_f m$

$(20.0\text{ g glucose})\left(\dfrac{\text{mol glucose}}{180\text{ g glucose}}\right) = 0.111\text{ mol glucose}$

$m = \dfrac{\text{moles of solute}}{\text{mass of solvent (kg)}}$

$m = \dfrac{0.111\text{ mol}}{0.250\text{ kg}} = 0.444\ m$

$\Delta t_f = K_f m$

$\Delta t_f = (-1.86°C/m)(0.444\ m) = -0.826°C$

b. Unknown: freezing
point of
solution

f.p. solution = f.p. solvent + Δt_f
$= 0.000°C + (-0.826°C) = -0.826°C$

---

22. Given: solute = $C_2H_4(OH)_2$
(antifreeze)
mass of solvent =
0.500 kg H_2O
freezing point of
solution = $-20.0°C$

Unknown: mass of solute
in g

f.p. solution = f.p. solvent + Δt_f

$\Delta t_f = $ f.p. solution $-$ f.p. solvent
$= -20.0°C - 0.000°C = -20.0°C$

$\Delta t_f = K_f m$

$m = \Delta t_f / K_f$
$= (-20.0°C)/(-1.86°C/m) = 10.8\ m$

$m = \dfrac{\text{moles of solute}}{\text{mass of solvent (kg)}}$

moles of solute = (m)(mass of solvent)
$= (10.8\text{ mol/kg})(0.500\text{ kg}) = 5.40\text{ mol}$

$(5.40\text{ mol }C_2H_4(OH)_2)\left(\dfrac{62.06\text{ g }C_2H_4(OH)_2}{\text{mol }C_2H_4(OH)_2}\right) = 334\text{ g }C_2H_4(OH)_2$

23. Given: freezing point C_6H_6 (benzene) = 5.45°C

mass of solute = 7.24 g $C_2Cl_4H_2$

mass of solvent = 0.115 kg benzene

specific gravity benzene = 0.879

freezing point of solution = 3.55°C

Unknown: molal freezing-point constant (K_f) for benzene

$$(7.24 \text{ g } C_2Cl_4H_2)\left(\frac{\text{mol } C_2Cl_4H_2}{168 \text{ g } C_2Cl_4H_2}\right) = 0.0431 \text{ mol } C_2Cl_4H_2$$

$$m = \frac{\text{moles of solute}}{\text{mass of solvent (kg)}}$$

$$m = \frac{0.0431 \text{ mol}}{0.115 \text{ kg}} = 0.375 \ m$$

f.p. solution = f.p. solvent + Δt_f

Δt_f = f.p. solution – f.p. solvent

$\quad = 3.55°C - 5.45°C = -1.90°C$

$\Delta t_f = K_f m$

$K_f = \Delta t_f / m$

$\quad = (-1.90°C)/(0.375 \ m)$

$\quad = -5.07°C/m$

---

24. Given: mass of solute = 1.500 g

molar mass of solute = 125.0 g

mass of solvent = 0.03500 kg camphor

Unknown: freezing point of solution

$$(1.500 \text{ g solute})\left(\frac{\text{mol solute}}{125.0 \text{ g solute}}\right) = 0.01200 \text{ mol solute}$$

$$m = \frac{\text{moles of solute}}{\text{mass of solvent (kg)}}$$

$$m = \frac{0.01200 \text{ mol}}{0.03500 \text{ kg}} = 0.3429 \ m$$

$\Delta t_f = K_f m$

$\Delta t_f = (-39.7°C/m)(0.3429 \ m)$

$\quad = -13.6°C$

f.p. solution = f.p. solvent + Δt_f

$\quad\quad = 178.8°C + (-13.6°C)$

$\quad\quad = 165.2°C$

---

25. a. Given: molality = 2.5 m $C_6H_{12}O_6$ (glucose)

solvent = H_2O

Unknown: boiling-point elevation of H_2O

$\Delta t_b = K_b m$

$\quad = (0.51°C/m)(2.5 \ m) = 1.3°C$

b. Given: mass of solute = 3.20 g $C_6H_{12}O_6$ (glucose)

mass of solvent = 1.00 kg H_2O

Unknown: boiling-point elevation of H_2O

$$(3.20 \text{ g glucose})\left(\frac{\text{mol glucose}}{180. \text{ g glucose}}\right) = 0.0178 \text{ mol glucose}$$

$$m = \frac{\text{moles of solute}}{\text{mass of solvent (kg)}}$$

$$m = \frac{0.0178 \text{ mol}}{1.00 \text{ kg}} = 0.0178 \ m$$

$\Delta t_b = K_b m$

$\Delta t_b = (0.51°C/m)(0.0178 \ m) = 0.0091°C$

c. Given: mass of solute = 20.0 g $C_{12}H_{22}O_{11}$ (sucrose) mass of solvent 0.500 kg H_2O

Unknown: boiling-point elevation of H_2O

$$(20.0 \text{ g sucrose})\left(\frac{\text{mol sucrose}}{342 \text{ g sucrose}}\right) = 0.0585 \text{ mol sucrose}$$

$$m = \frac{\text{moles of solute}}{\text{mass of solvent (kg)}}$$

$$m = \frac{0.585 \text{ mol}}{0.500 \text{ kg}} = 0.117 \, m$$

$$\Delta t_b = K_b m$$

$$\Delta t_b = (0.51°\text{C}/m)(0.117 \, m) = 0.060°\text{C}$$

---

26. Given: solvent = H_2O

a. boiling point of solution = 100.25°C

b. boiling point of solution = 101.53°C

c. boiling point of solution = 102.805°C

Unknown: molality (m) of each solution

$$\Delta t_b = K_b m$$

$$m = \Delta t_b / K_b$$

b.p. solution = b.p. solvent + Δt_b

$$\Delta t_b = \text{b.p. solution} - \text{b.p. solvent}$$

a. $\Delta t_b = 100.25°\text{C} - 100.00°\text{C} = 0.25°\text{C}$

$$m = \frac{0.25°\text{C}}{0.51°\text{C}/m} = 0.49 \, m$$

b. $\Delta t_b = 101.53°\text{C} - 100.00°\text{C} = 1.53°\text{C}$

$$m = \frac{1.53°\text{C}}{0.51°\text{C}/m} = 3.0 \, m$$

c. $\Delta t_b = 102.805°\text{C} - 100.000°\text{C} = 2.805°\text{C}$

$$m = \frac{2.805°\text{C}}{0.51°\text{C}/m} = 5.5 \, m$$

---

27. Given: molality = 1.00 m solvent = H_2O

a. solute = KI

b. solute = $CaCl_2$

c. solute = $Ba(NO_3)_2$

Unknown: expected freezing-point depression of solutions

$$\Delta t_f = K_f m$$

a. $KI(s) \rightarrow K^+(aq) + I^-(aq)$

Each formula unit of KI yields two ions in solution.

$$\left(\frac{-1.86°\text{C} \cdot \text{kg } H_2O}{\text{mol ions}}\right)\left(\frac{1.00 \text{ mol KI}}{\text{kg } H_2O}\right)\left(\frac{2 \text{ mol ions}}{\text{mol KI}}\right) = -3.72°\text{C}$$

b. $CaCl_2(s) \rightarrow Ca^{2+}(aq) + 2Cl^-(aq)$

Each formula unit of KI yields three ions in solution.

$$\left(\frac{-1.86°\text{C} \cdot \text{kg } H_2O}{\text{mol ions}}\right)\left(\frac{1.00 \text{ mol } CaCl_2}{\text{kg } H_2O}\right)\left(\frac{3 \text{ mol ions}}{\text{mol } CaCl_2}\right) = -5.58°\text{C}$$

c. $Ba(NO_3)_2(s) \rightarrow Ba^{2+}(aq) + 2NO_3^-(aq)$

Each formula unit $Ba(NO_3)_2$ yields three ions in solution.

$$\left(\frac{-1.86°\text{C} \cdot \text{kg } H_2O}{\text{mol ions}}\right)\left(\frac{1.00 \text{ mol } Ba(NO_3)_2}{\text{kg } H_2O}\right)\left(\frac{3 \text{ mol ions}}{\text{mol } Ba(NO_3)_2}\right) = -5.58°\text{C}$$

28. Given: molality = 0.015 m
AlCl$_3$
solvent = H$_2$O

Unknown: expected freezing-point depression of solution

$\Delta t_f = K_f m$

$AlCl_3(s) \rightarrow Al^{3+}(aq) + 3Cl^-(aq)$

Each formula unit of AlCl$_3$ yields four ions in solution.

$$\left(\frac{-1.86°C \cdot kg\ H_2O}{mol\ ions}\right)\left(\frac{0.015\ mol\ AlCl_3}{kg\ H_2O}\right)\left(\frac{4\ mol\ ions}{mol\ AlCl_3}\right) = -0.11°C$$

29. Given: mass of solute = 85.0 g NaCl
mass of solvent = 0.450 kg H$_2$O

Unknown: expected freezing point of solution

f.p. solution = f.p. solvent + Δt_f

$\Delta t_f = K_f m$

$m = \dfrac{moles\ of\ solute}{mass\ of\ solvent\ (kg)}$

$(85.0\ g\ NaCl)\left(\dfrac{mol\ NaCl}{58.44\ g\ NaCl}\right) = 1.45\ mol\ NaCl$

$NaCl(s) \rightarrow Na^+(aq) + Cl^-(aq)$

Each formula unit of NaCl yields two ions in solution.

$$\left(\frac{-1.86°C \cdot kg\ H_2O}{mol\ ions}\right)\left(\frac{1.45\ mol\ NaCl}{0.450\ kg\ H_2O}\right)\left(\frac{2\ mol\ ions}{mol\ NaCl}\right) = -12.0°C = \Delta t_f$$

f.p. solution = 0.0°C + (−12.0°C) = −12.0°C

30. Given: mass of solute = 25.0 g BaCl$_2$
mass of solvent = 0.150 kg H$_2$O

Unknown: expected boiling point of solution

b.p. solution = b.p. solvent + Δt_b

$\Delta t_b = K_b m$

$m = \dfrac{moles\ solute}{mass\ of\ solvent\ (kg)}$

$(25.0\ g\ BaCl_2)\left(\dfrac{mol\ BaCl_2}{208.23\ g\ BaCl_2}\right) = 0.120\ mol\ BaCl_2$

$BaCl_2(s) \rightarrow Ba^{2+}(aq) + 2Cl^-(aq)$

Each formula unit of BaCl$_2$ yields three ions in solution.

$$\left(\frac{0.51°C \cdot kg\ H_2O}{mol\ ions}\right)\left(\frac{0.120\ mol\ BaCl_2}{0.150\ kg\ H_2O}\right)\left(\frac{3\ mol\ ions}{mol\ BaCl_2}\right) = 1.2°C = \Delta t_b$$

b.p. solution = 100.0°C + 1.2°C = 101.2°C

31. Given: boiling-point elevation of solution = 0.65°C
solvent = H$_2$O
solute = KI

Unknown: molality (m)

$\Delta t_b = K_b m$

$KI(s) \rightarrow K^+(aq) + I^-(aq)$

Each formula unit of KI yields two ions in solution.

$m = \Delta t_b/K_b$

$$= \left(\frac{0.65°C \cdot mol\ ions}{0.51°C \cdot kg\ H_2O}\right)\left(\frac{1\ mol\ KI}{2\ mol\ ions}\right) = 0.64\ m\ KI$$

34. Given: molality = 1.00 m
  MgI_2
  solvent = H_2O
  freezing-point depression = $-4.78°C$

Unknowns: expected freezing-point depression of H_2O; reason for discrepancy between experimental and expected values

$\Delta t_f = K_f m$

$MgI_2(s) \rightarrow Mg^{2+}(aq) + 2I^-(aq)$

Each formula unit of MgI_2 yields three ions in solution.

$\left(\dfrac{-1.86°C \cdot kg\ H_2O}{mol\ ions}\right)\left(\dfrac{1.00\ mol\ MgI_2}{kg\ H_2O}\right)\left(\dfrac{3\ mol\ ions}{mol\ MgI_2}\right) = -5.58°C$

Reason for discrepancy: Because of forces of attraction between them, the ions cluster somewhat.

---

35. Given: molality = 0.01 m
  solvent = H_2O

Unknown: freezing-point depression of each solution

$\Delta t_f = K_f m$

a. Given: solute = NaI

$NaI(s) \rightarrow Na^+(aq) + I^-(aq)$

Each formula unit of NaI yields two ions in solution.

$\left(\dfrac{-1.86°C \cdot kg\ H_2O}{mol\ ions}\right)\left(\dfrac{0.01\ mol\ NaI}{kg\ H_2O}\right)\left(\dfrac{2\ mol\ ions}{mol\ NaI}\right) = -0.04°C$

b. Given: solute = $CaCl_2$

$CaCl_2(s) \rightarrow Ca^{2+}(aq) + 2Cl^-(aq)$

Each formula unit of $CaCl_2$ yields three ions in solution.

$\left(\dfrac{-1.86°C \cdot kg\ H_2O}{mol\ ions}\right)\left(\dfrac{0.01\ mol\ CaCl_2}{kg\ H_2O}\right)\left(\dfrac{3\ mol\ ions}{mol\ CaCl_2}\right) = -0.06°C$

c. Given: solute = K_3PO_4

$K_3PO_4(s) \rightarrow 3K^+(aq) + PO_4^{3-}(aq)$

Each formula unit of K_3PO_4 yields four ions in solution.

$\left(\dfrac{-1.86°C \cdot kg\ H_2O}{mol\ ions}\right)\left(\dfrac{0.01\ mol\ K_3PO_4}{kg\ H_2O}\right)\left(\dfrac{4\ mol\ ions}{mol\ K_3PO_4}\right) = -0.07°C$

d. Given: solute = $C_6H_{12}O_6$ (glucose)

$\Delta t_f = (-1.86°C/m)(0.01\ m) = -0.02°C$

order of increasing Δt_f = d($-0.02°C$), a($-0.04°C$), b($-0.06°C$), c($-0.07°C$)

---

36. Given: solute = $CaCl_2$
  solvent = H_2O
  freezing point of solution = $-2.43°C$

Unknown: molality (m)

$\Delta t_f = K_f m$

$CaCl_2(s) \rightarrow Ca^{2+}(aq) + 2Cl^-(aq)$

Each formula unit of $CaCl_2$ yields three ions in solution.

$m = \Delta t_f / K_f$

$\left(\dfrac{-2.43°C \cdot mol\ ions}{-1.86°C}\right)\left(\dfrac{1\ mol\ CaCl_2}{3\ mol/ions}\right) = 0.435\ m\ CaCl_2$

39. a. Given: solute = 0.275 mol K_2S
solvent = H_2O

Unknowns: balanced equation, total number of moles of solute ions formed

$$K_2S(s) \xrightarrow{H_2O} 2K^+(aq) + S^{2-}(aq)$$

Ions produced: $2(0.275 \text{ mol } K^+) = 0.550 \text{ mol } K^+$; $0.275 \text{ mol } S^{2-}$

$0.550 + 0.275 = 0.825$ mol solute ions formed

b. Given: solute = 0.15 mol $Al_2(SO_4)_3$

Unknowns: balanced equation, total number of moles of solute ions formed

$$Al_2(SO_4)_3(s) \xrightarrow{H_2O} 2Al^{3+}(aq) + 3SO_4^{2-}(aq)$$

Ions produced: $2(0.15 \text{ mol } Al^{3+}) = 0.30 \text{ mol } Al^{3+} + 3(0.15 \text{ mol } SO_4^{2-})$
$= 0.45 \text{ mol } SO_4^{2-}$

$0.30 + 0.45 = 0.75$ mol solute ions formed

40. Given: mass of solute = 131.2 g $AgNO_3$
mass of solvent = 2.00 kg H_2O

Unknown: expected boiling-point elevation of solution

$$(131.2 \text{ g AgNO}_3)\left(\frac{\text{mol AgNO}_3}{169.85 \text{ g AgNO}_3}\right) = 0.7724 \text{ mol AgNO}_3$$

$$m = \frac{\text{moles of solute}}{\text{mass of solvent (kg)}} = \frac{0.7724 \text{ mol}}{2.00 \text{ kg}} = 0.386 \text{ } m$$

$$\Delta t_b = K_b m$$

$$AgNO_3(s) \rightarrow Ag^+(aq) + NO_3^-(aq)$$

Each formula unit $AgNO_3$ yields two ions in solution.

$$\left(\frac{0.51°C \cdot \text{kg H}_2O}{\text{mol ions}}\right)\left(\frac{0.385 \text{ mol AgNO}_3}{\text{kg H}_2O}\right)\left(\frac{2 \text{ mol ions}}{\text{mol AgNO}_3}\right) = 0.39°C$$

42. Given: solvent = H_2O
solute = nonelectrolyte
freezing point = $-6.51°C$

Unknown: boiling point

f.p. solution = f.p. solvent + Δt_f

Δt_f = f.p. solution – f.p. solvent
$= -6.51°C - 0°C = -6.51°C$

$\Delta t_f = K_f m$

$m = \Delta t_f / K_f$

$$= \frac{-6.51°C}{-1.86°C \cdot \text{kg H}_2O/\text{mol solute}} = 3.50 \text{ } m$$

$\Delta t_b = K_b m$
$= (0.51°C/m)(3.50 \text{ } m) = 1.8°C$

Δt_b = b.p. solution – b.p. solvent

b.p. solution = Δt_b + b.p. solvent
$= 1.8°C + 100.0°C = 101.8°C$

43. Given: solute = Na_2CO_3
solvent = H_2O
amount of solute =
0.20 mol Na_2CO_3

Unknowns: **a.** balanced
equation
b. number of
moles of
each ion
produced
c. total
number
of moles
of ions

a. $Na_2CO_3(s) \xrightarrow{H_2O} 2Na^+(aq) + CO_3^{2-}(aq)$

b. $2(0.20 \text{ mol } Na^+) = 0.40 \text{ mol } Na^+$

$1(0.20 \text{ mol } CO_3^{2-}) = 0.20 \text{ mol } CO_3^{2-}$

c. $0.40 + 0.20 = 0.60$ moles of solute ions produced

---

44. Given: $K_3PO_4(aq) +$
$Pb(NO_3)_2(aq)$

Unknown: net ionic
equation

Ionic equation:

$6K^+(aq) + 2PO_4^{3-}(aq) + 3Pb^{2+}(aq) + 6NO_3^-(aq) \rightarrow 6K^+(aq) + 6NO_3^-(aq)$
$+ Pb_3(PO_4)_2(s)$

Net ionic equation:

$3Pb^{2+}(aq) + 2PO_4^{3-}(aq) \rightarrow Pb_3(PO_4)_2(s)$

---

45. Given: solvent = H_2O
mass of solute =
268 g $Al(NO_3)_3$
mass of solvent =
8.50 kg H_2O

Unknown: expected freez-
ing point of
solution

$m = \dfrac{\text{moles of solute}}{\text{mass of solvent (kg)}}$

$(268 \text{ g } Al(NO_3)_3)\left(\dfrac{\text{mol } Al(NO_3)_3}{212.9 \text{ g } Al(NO_3)_3}\right) = 1.26 \text{ mol } Al(NO_3)_3$

$Al(NO_3)_3(s) \rightarrow Al^{3+}(aq) + 3NO_3^-(aq)$

Each formula unit $Al(NO_3)_3$ yields four ions in solution.

$\Delta t_f = K_f m$

$\left(\dfrac{-1.86°C \cdot \text{kg } H_2O}{\text{mol ions}}\right)\left(\dfrac{1.26 \text{ mol } Al(NO_3)_3}{8.50 \text{ kg } H_2O}\right)\left(\dfrac{4 \text{ mol ions}}{\text{mol } Al(NO_3)_3}\right) = -1.10°C$

f.p. solution = f.p. solvent + Δt_f
$= 0.00°C + (-1.10°C) = -1.10°C$

46. a. Given: solvent = H_2O
solute = KNO_3
observed freezing point of solution = $-1.15°C$
observed freezing point of pure H_2O = $0.25°C$

Unknown: molality (m) of KNO_3

f.p. solution = f.p. solvent + Δt_f

Δt_f = f.p. solution − f.p. solvent
$= -1.15°C - 0.25°C = -1.40°C$

$\Delta t_f = K_f m$

$KNO_3(s) \rightarrow K^+(aq) + NO_3^-(aq)$

Each formula unit KNO_3 yields two ions in solution.

$m = \Delta t_f/K_f$

$= \left(\dfrac{-1.40°C \cdot \text{mol ions}}{-1.86°C}\right)\left(\dfrac{1 \text{ mol } KNO_3}{2 \text{ mol ions}}\right)$

$= 0.376\ m$

b. Given: mass of solute = 0.415 g KNO_3
volume of solution = 0.010 L
density of solution = 1.00 g/mL

Unknowns: actual molality (m) of KNO_3; percentage difference between predicted concentration and actual concentration of KNO_3

$m = \dfrac{\text{moles of solute}}{\text{mass of solvent (kg)}}$

mass of solvent = $10.00 \text{ mL} \times \dfrac{1.00 \text{ g}}{\text{mL}} = 10.0 \text{ g} \times \dfrac{\text{kg}}{1000 \text{ g}} = 0.0100 \text{ kg}$

$(0.415 \text{ g } KNO_3)\left(\dfrac{\text{mol } KNO_3}{101.02 \text{ g } KNO_3}\right) = 0.00410 \text{ mol } KNO_3$

$\dfrac{0.00410 \text{ mol}}{0.0100 \text{ kg}} = 0.410\ m\ KNO_3$

Predicted $m = 0.376\ m$

Actual $m = 0.410\ m$

$\dfrac{0.410\ m - 0.376\ m}{0.410\ m} \times 100 = 8.29\% = \text{percentage difference}$

Math Tutor, p. 462

1. Given: 28.0 g $CaCl_2$ dissolved in 295 g H_2O

Unknown: freezing point of solution

$\dfrac{28.0 \text{ g } CaCl_2 \times 1000 \text{ g} \times 3 \text{ mol ions} \times (-1.86°C/m)}{110.98 \text{ g/mol} \times 295 \text{ g } H_2O \times 1 \text{ kg} \times 1 \text{ mol } CaCl_2} = -4.77°C$

2. Given: 850 g ethylene glycol dissolved in 1100 g water

Unknown: boiling point of solution

boiling point elevation $= \dfrac{850 \text{ g } C_2H_6O_2}{62.08 \text{ g/mol} \times 1.100 \text{ kg } H_2O} \times 0.51°C/m = +6.3°C$

boiling point = $100.°C + 6.3°C = 106.3°C$

Standardized Test Prep, p. 463

8. Given: freezing point of nonelectrolyte solution = $-0.58°C$

Unknown: molality of solution

$\dfrac{-0.58°C}{-1.86°C/m} = 0.31\ m$

Chapter Review

30. Given: reactants = Zn, H_2SO_4

$$Zn(s) + H_2SO_4(aq) \rightarrow ZnSO_4(aq) + H_2(g)$$

volume of H_2SO_4 = 0.100 L

$$M = \frac{\text{amount of solute (mol)}}{\text{volume of solution (L)}}$$

molarity = 6.00 M H_2SO_4

amount of solute = (M)(volume)

$$= (6.00)(0.100) = 0.600 \text{ mol } H_2SO_4$$

a. Unknown: number of grams of $ZnSO_4$ produced

$$(0.600 \text{ mol } H_2SO_4)\left(\frac{1 \text{ mol } ZnSO_4}{1 \text{ mol } H_2SO_4}\right)\left(\frac{161.42 \text{ g } ZnSO_4}{\text{mol } ZnSO_4}\right) = 96.9 \text{ g } ZnSO_4$$

b. Unknown: number of liters of H_2 gas released at STP

$$(0.600 \text{ mol } H_2SO_4)\left(\frac{1 \text{ mol } H_2}{1 \text{ mol } H_2SO_4}\right)\left(\frac{22.4 \text{ L } H_2}{\text{mol } H_2}\right) = 13.4 \text{ L}$$

31. Given: mass of solute = 211 g $BaCO_3$

$$BaCO_3(s) + 2HNO_3(aq) \rightarrow Ba(NO_3)_2(aq) + H_2O(l) + CO_2(g)$$

solvent = HNO_3

$$(211 \text{ g } BaCO_3)\left(\frac{\text{mol } BaCO_3}{197.3 \text{ g } BaCO_3}\right)\left(\frac{1 \text{ mol } CO_2}{1 \text{ mol } BaCO_3}\right) = 1.07 \text{ mol } CO_2$$

(Assume acid is present in excess.)

$$(1.07 \text{ mol } CO_2)\left(\frac{44.0 \text{ g } CO_2}{\text{mol } CO_2}\right) = 47.1 \text{ g } CO_2$$

Unknown: mass and volume of dry CO_2 gas produced at STP

$$(1.07 \text{ mol } CO_2)\left(\frac{22.4 \text{ L } CO_2}{\text{mol } CO_2}\right) = 24.0 \text{ L } CO_2$$

32. Given: solute = $CaCO_3$

solvent = HCl

products = CO_2, $CaCl_2$, H_2O

volume CO_2 = 1.5 L

$$CaCO_3(s) + 2HCl(aq) \rightarrow CaCl_2(aq) + H_2O(l) + CO_2(g)$$

$$(1.5 \text{ L } CO_2)\left(\frac{\text{mol } CO_2}{22.4 \text{ L } CO_2}\right)\left(\frac{1 \text{ mol } CaCO_3}{1 \text{ mol } CO_2}\right) = 0.067 \text{ mol } CaCO_3$$

a. Unknown: mass of $CaCO_3$ in g

$$(0.067 \text{ mol } CaCO_3)\left(\frac{100 \text{ g } CaCO_3}{\text{mol } CaCO_3}\right) = 6.7 \text{ g } CaCO_3$$

b. Given: molarity of HCl (M) = 2.00 M HCl

$$(0.067 \text{ mol } CaCO_3)\left(\frac{2 \text{ mol HCl}}{\text{mol } CaCO_3}\right) = 0.134 \text{ mol HCl}$$

Unknown: volume of HCl used in reaction

$$\text{volume HCl} = \frac{0.13 \text{ mol}}{2.00 \text{ mol/L}} = 0.067 \text{ L}$$

---

33. Given: mass of SO_2 = 3.5×10^{11} g

$SO_2 + \frac{1}{2}O_2 \rightarrow SO_3$

$SO_3 + H_2O \rightarrow H_2SO_4$

Unknown: mass of H_2SO_4 produced in kg

$$(3.50 \times 10^{11} \text{ g } SO_2)\left(\frac{\text{mol } SO_2}{64.1 \text{ g } SO_2}\right)\left(\frac{1 \text{ mol } SO_3}{1 \text{ mol } SO_2}\right) = 5.46 \times 10^9 \text{ mol } SO_3$$

$$(5.46 \times 10^9 \text{ mol } SO_3)\left(\frac{1 \text{ mol } H_2SO_4}{1 \text{ mol } SO_3}\right)\left(\frac{98.1 \text{ g } H_2SO_4}{\text{mol } H_2SO_4}\right)\left(\frac{\text{kg}}{1000 \text{ g}}\right) =$$

$$5.36 \times 10^8 \text{ kg } H_2SO_4$$

CHAPTER 15

Acid-Base Titration and pH

Practice, p. 502

1. Given: [HCl] = 1×10^{-4} M

Unknown: [H_3O^+], [OH^-]

$$HCl(l) + H_2O(l) \rightarrow H_3O^+(aq) + Cl^-(aq)$$

$$M = \frac{\text{amount of solute (mol)}}{\text{volume of solution (L)}}$$

$$\left(\frac{1 \times 10^{-4} \text{ mol HCl}}{\text{L solution}}\right)\left(\frac{1 \text{ mol } H_3O^+}{1 \text{ mol HCl}}\right) = 1 \times 10^{-4} \text{ mol } H_3O^+/L$$

$$= 1 \times 10^{-4} \text{ M } H_3O^+$$

$$[H_3O^+][OH^+] = 1.0 \times 10^{-14} \text{ M}^2$$

$$[OH^-] = \frac{1.0 \times 10^{-14} \text{ M}^2}{1 \times 10^{-4} \text{ M}} = 1 \times 10^{-10} \text{ M}$$

2. Given: [HNO_3] = 1.0×10^{-3} M

Unknown: [H_3O^+], [OH^-]

$$HNO_3(l) + H_2O(l) \rightarrow H_3O^+(aq) + NO_3^-(aq)$$

$$\left(\frac{1.0 \times 10^{-3} \text{ mol } HNO_3}{\text{L solution}}\right)\left(\frac{1 \text{ mol } H_3O^+}{1 \text{ mol } HNO_3}\right) = 1.0 \times 10^{-3} \text{ mol } H_3O^+/L$$

$$= 1.0 \times 10^{-3} \text{ M } H_3O^+$$

$$[H_3O^+][OH^-] = 1.0 \times 10^{-14} \text{ M}^2$$

$$[OH^-] = \frac{1.0 \times 10^{-14} \text{ M}^2}{1.0 \times 10^{-3} \text{ M}} = 1.0 \times 10^{-11} \text{ M}$$

3. Given: [NaOH] = 3.0×10^{-2} M

Unknown: [H_3O^+], [OH^-]

$$NaOH(s) \xrightarrow{H_2O} Na^+(aq) + OH^-(aq)$$

$$\left(\frac{3.0 \times 10^{-2} \text{ mol NaOH}}{\text{L solution}}\right)\left(\frac{1 \text{ mol } OH^-}{1 \text{ mol NaOH}}\right) = 3.0 \times 10^{-2} \text{ mol } OH^-/L$$

$$= 3.0 \times 10^{-2} \text{ M } OH^-$$

$$[H_3O^+][OH^-] = 1.0 \times 10^{-14} \text{ M}^2$$

$$[H_3O^+] = \frac{1.0 \times 10^{-14} \text{ M}^2}{3.0 \times 10^{-2} \text{ M}} = 3.3 \times 10^{-13} \text{ M}$$

4. Given: [$Ca(OH)_2$] = 1.0×10^{-4} M

Unknown: [H_3O^+], [OH^-]

$$Ca(OH)_2(s) \xrightarrow{H_2O} Ca^{2+}(aq) + 2OH^-(aq)$$

$$\left(\frac{1.0 \times 10^{-4} \text{ mol } Ca(OH)_2}{\text{L solution}}\right)\left(\frac{2 \text{ mol } OH^-}{1 \text{ mol } Ca(OH)_2}\right) = 2.0 \times 10^{-4} \text{ M } OH^-$$

$$[H_3O^+][OH^-] = 1.0 \times 10^{-14} \text{ M}^2$$

$$[H_3O^+] = \frac{1.0 \times 10^{-14} \text{ M}^2}{2.0 \times 10^{-4} \text{ M}} = 5.0 \times 10^{-11} \text{ M}$$

A-1. Given: $[HClO_4] = 0.01$ M

Unknown: $[H_3O^+]$, $[OH^-]$

$$HClO_4(l) + H_2O(l) \rightarrow H_3O^+(aq) + ClO_4^-(aq)$$

$$\left(\frac{0.01 \text{ mol } HClO_4}{L \text{ solution}}\right)\left(\frac{1 \text{ mol } H_3O^+}{1 \text{ mol } HClO_4}\right) = \frac{0.01 \text{ mol } H_3O^+}{L}$$

$$= 0.01 \text{ M } H_3O^+ = 1 \times 10^{-2} \text{ M}$$

$$[H_3O^+][OH^-] = 1.0 \times 10^{-14} \text{ M}^2$$

$$[OH^-] = \frac{1.0 \times 10^{-14} \text{ M}^2}{0.01 \text{ M}} = 1.0 \times 10^{-12} \text{ M}$$

A-2. Given: aqueous solution of $Ba(OH)_2$
$[H_3O^+] = 1 \times 10^{-11}$ M

Unknowns: **a.** $[OH^-]$
b. $[Ba(OH)_2]$

$$[H_3O^+][OH^-] = 1.0 \times 10^{-14} \text{ M}^2$$

$$[OH^-] = \frac{1.0 \times 10^{-14} \text{ M}^2}{1 \times 10^{-11} \text{ M}} = 1 \times 10^{-3} \text{ M}$$

$$Ba(OH)_2 \xrightarrow{H_2O} Ba^{2+} + 2OH^-$$

$$\left(\frac{1 \times 10^{-3} \text{ mol } OH^-}{L}\right)\left(\frac{1 \text{ mol } Ba(OH)_2}{2 \text{ mol } OH^-}\right)$$

$$= 5 \times 10^{-4} \text{ mol/L } Ba(OH)_2 = 5 \times 10^{-4} \text{ M } Ba(OH)_2$$

Practice, p. 505

1. Given: Identity and concentrations of solutions:
a. 1×10^{-3} M HCl
b. 1.0×10^{-5} M HNO_3
c. 1×10^{-4} M NaOH
d. 1.0×10^{-2} M KOH

Unknown: pH of solutions

$$[H_3O^+][OH^-] = 1.0 \times 10^{-14} \text{ M}^2$$

a. $HCl + H_2O \rightarrow H_3O^+ + Cl^-$

$$[H_3O^+] = 1 \times 10^{-3} \text{ M}$$

$$pH = -\log [H_3O^+] = -\log (1 \times 10^{-3}) = 3.0$$

b. $HNO_3 + H_2O \rightarrow H_3O^+ + NO_3^-$

$$[H_3O^+] = 1 \times 10^{-5} \text{ M}$$

$$pH = -\log (1 \times 10^{-5}) = 5.00$$

c. $NaOH + H_2O \rightarrow Na^+ + OH^-$

$$[OH^-] = 1 \times 10^{-4} \text{ M}$$

$$[H_3O^+] = \frac{1.0 \times 10^{-14} \text{ M}^2}{1 \times 10^{-4} \text{ M}} = 1 \times 10^{-10} \text{ M}$$

$$pH = -\log (1 \times 10^{-10}) = 10.0$$

d. $KOH + H_2O \rightarrow K^+ + OH^-$

$$[OH^-] = 1.0 \times 10^{-2} \text{ M}$$

$$[H_3O^+] = \frac{1.0 \times 10^{-14} \text{ M}^2}{1.0 \times 10^{-2} \text{ M}} = 1.0 \times 10^{-12} \text{ M}$$

$$pH = -\log (1 \times 10^{-12}) = 12.00$$

B-1. Given: [HBr] = 1×10^{-4} M

Unknown: pH

$HBr + H_2O \rightarrow H_3O^+ + Br^-$

$[H_3O^+] = 1 \times 10^{-4}$ M

$pH = -\log [H_3O^+]$

$pH = -\log (1 \times 10^{-4}) = 4.0$

B-2. Given: $[Ca(OH)_2]$ = 5×10^{-4} M

Unknown: pH

$Ca(OH)_2 \xrightarrow{H_2O} Ca^{2+} + 2OH^-$

$\left(\dfrac{5 \times 10^{-4} \text{ mol } Ca(OH)_2}{L \text{ solution}} \right) \left(\dfrac{2 \text{ mol } OH^-}{1 \text{ mol } Ca(OH)_2} \right) = 1 \times 10^{-3}$ M OH^-

$[H_3O^+][OH^-] = 1.0 \times 10^{-14}$ M^2

$[H_3O^+] = \dfrac{1.0 \times 10^{-14} \text{ M}^2}{1 \times 10^{-3} \text{ M}} = 1 \times 10^{-11}$ M

$pH = -\log (1 \times 10^{-11}) = 11.0$

Practice, p. 506

1. Given: $[H_3O^+]$ = 6.7×10^{-4} M

Unknown: pH

$pH = -\log (6.7 \times 10^{-4}) = 3.17$

---

2. Given: $[H_3O^+]$ = 2.5×10^{-2} M

Unknown: pH

$pH = -\log (2.5 \times 10^{-2}) = 1.60$

---

3. Given: $[HNO_3]$ = 2.5×10^{-6} M

Unknown: pH

$HNO_3 + H_2O \rightarrow H_3O^+ + NO_3^-$

$[H_3O^+] = 2.5 \times 10^{-6}$ M

$pH = -\log [H_3O^+] = -\log (2.5 \times 10^{-6}) = 5.60$

---

4. Given: $[Sr(OH)_2]$ = 2.0×10^{-2} M

Unknown: pH

$Sr(OH)_2 \xrightarrow{H_2O} Sr^{2+} + 2OH^-$

$\left(\dfrac{2.0 \times 10^{-2} \text{ mol } Sr(OH)_2}{L \text{ solution}} \right) \left(\dfrac{2 \text{ mol } OH^-}{1 \text{ mol } Sr(OH)_2} \right) = 4.0 \times 10^{-2}$ M OH^-

$[H_3O^+][OH^-] = 1.0 \times 10^{-14}$ M^2

$[H_3O^+] = \dfrac{1.0 \times 10^{-14} \text{ M}^2}{4.0 \times 10^{-2} \text{ M}} = 2.5 \times 10^{-13}$ M

$pH = -\log [H_3O^+] = -\log (2.5 \times 10^{-13}) = 12.60$

C-1. Given: $[H_3O^+] = 6.2 \times 10^{-9}$ M

Unknown: pH

$pH = -\log [H_3O^+] = -\log (6.2 \times 10^{-9}) = 8.21$

C-2. Given: $[NaOH] = 0.00074$ M

$= 7.4 \times 10^{-4}$ M

Unknown: pH

$NaOH + H_2O \rightarrow Na^+ + OH^-$

$[OH^-] = 7.4 \times 10^{-4}$ M

$[H_3O^+][OH^-] = 1.0 \times 10^{-14}$ M^2

$[H_3O^+] = \dfrac{1.0 \times 10^{-14} \text{ M}^2}{7.4 \times 10^{-4} \text{ M}} = 1.4 \times 10^{-11}$ M

$pH = -\log [H_3O^+] = -\log (1.4 \times 10^{-11}) = 10.87$

D-1. Given: pH = 9.0

Unknown: $[H_3O^+]$, $[OH^-]$

$pH = -\log [H_3O^+]$

$\log [H_3O^+] = -pH$

$[H_3O^+] = \text{antilog} (-pH)$

$[H_3O^+] = 1 \times 10^{-pH} = 1 \times 10^{-9}$ M

$[H_3O^+][OH^-] = 1.0 \times 10^{-14}$ M^2

$[OH^-] = \dfrac{1.0 \times 10^{-14} \text{ M}^2}{1 \times 10^{-9} \text{ M}} = 1 \times 10^{-5}$ M

D-2. Given: pH = 10.0

Solution = $Sr(OH)_2$

Unknowns: **a.** $[OH^-]$

b. $[Sr(OH)_2]$

$Sr(OH)_2 \xrightarrow{H_2O} Sr^{2+} + 2OH^-$

a. $pH = -\log [H_3O^+]$

$\log [H_3O^+] = -pH$

$[H_3O^+] = \text{antilog} (-pH)$

$[H_3O^+] = 1 \times 10^{-pH} = 1 \times 10^{-10}$ M

$[H_3O^+][OH^-] = 1.0 \times 10^{-14}$ M^2

$[OH^-] = \dfrac{1.0 \times 10^{-14} \text{ M}^2}{1 \times 10^{-10} \text{ M}} = 1 \times 10^{-4}$ M

b. Molarity (M) of $Sr(OH)_2 = \dfrac{\text{mol } Sr(OH)_2}{\text{L solution}}$

$\left(\dfrac{1 \times 10^{-4} \text{ mol } OH^-}{L}\right)\left(\dfrac{1 \text{ mol } Sr(OH)_2}{2 \text{ mol } OH^-}\right) = 5 \times 10^{-5}$ M $Sr(OH)_2$

Practice, p. 508

1. Given: pH = 5.0
Unknown: $[H_3O^+]$

$pH = -\log [H_3O^+]$

$\log [H_3O^+] = -pH$

$[H_3O^+] = \text{antilog} (-pH)$

$[H_3O^+] = 1 \times 10^{-pH} = 1 \times 10^{-5}$ M

---

2. Given: pH = 12.0
Unknown: $[H_3O^+]$

$pH = -\log [H_3O^+]$

$\log [H_3O^+] = -pH$

$[H_3O^+] = \text{antilog} (-pH)$

$[H_3O^+] = 1 \times 10^{-pH} = 1 \times 10^{-12}$ M

---

3. Given: pH = 1.50
Unknown: $[H_3O^+]$, $[OH^-]$

$pH = -\log [H_3O^+]$

$\log [H_3O^+] = -pH$

$[H_3O^+] = \text{antilog} (-pH)$

$[H_3O^+] = 1 \times 10^{-pH} = 1 \times 10^{-1.50} = 3.2 \times 10^{-2}$ M

$[H_3O^+][OH^-] = 1.0 \times 10^{-14}$ M^2

$[OH^-] = \dfrac{1.0 \times 10^{-14} \text{ M}^2}{3.2 \times 10^{-2} \text{ M}} = 3.2 \times 10^{-13}$ M

---

4. Given: pH = 3.67
Unknown: $[H_3O^+]$

$pH = -\log [H_3O^+]$

$\log [H_3O^+] = -pH$

$[H_3O^+] = \text{antilog} (-pH)$

$[H_3O^+] = 1 \times 10^{-pH} = 1 \times 10^{-3.67} = 2.1 \times 10^{-4}$ M

ATE, Additional Sample Problems, p. 508

E-1. Given: pH = 0.45
Unknown: $[H_3O^+]$

$pH = -\log [H_3O^+]$

$\log [H_3O^+] = -pH$

$[H_3O^+] = \text{antilog} (-pH)$

$[H_3O^+] = 1 \times 10^{-pH} = 1 \times 10^{-0.45} = 0.35$ M

E-2. Given: pH = 8.7
Unknown: $[H_3O^+]$, $[OH^-]$

$pH = -\log [H_3O^+]$

$\log [H_3O^+] = -pH$

$[H_3O^+] = \text{antilog} (-pH)$

$[H_3O^+] = 1 \times 10^{-pH} = 1 \times 10^{-8.7} = 2 \times 10^{-9}$ M

$[H_3O^+][OH^-] = 1.0 \times 10^{-14}$ M^2

$[OH^-] = \dfrac{1.0 \times 10^{-14} \text{ M}^2}{2 \times 10^{-9} \text{ M}} = 5 \times 10^{-6}$ M

4. Given: [HCl] = 4.5×10^{-3} M

Unknown: **a.** $[H_3O^+]$
b. $[OH^-]$
c. pH

a. $HCl(l) + H_2O(l) \rightarrow H_3O^+(aq) + Cl^-(aq)$

$$\left(\frac{4.5 \times 10^{-3} \text{ mol HCl}}{\text{L solution}}\right)\left(\frac{1 \text{ mol } H_3O^+}{1 \text{ mol HCl}}\right)$$

$= 4.5 \times 10^{-3}$ mol H_3O^+/L

$= 4.5 \times 10^{-3}$ M H_3O^+

b. $[H_3O^+][OH^-] = 1.0 \times 10^{-14} \text{ M}^2$

$$[OH^-] = \frac{1.0 \times 10^{-14} \text{ M}^2}{4.5 \times 10^{-3} \text{ M}} = 2.2 \times 10^{-12} \text{ M OH}^-$$

c. pH $= -\log [H_3O^+] = -\log [4.5 \times 10^{-3}] = 2.35$

---

5. Given: pH = 8.0

Unknown: **a.** $[H_3O^+]$
b. $[OH^-]$
c. $[Ca(OH)_2]$

$Ca(OH)_2(s) \xrightarrow{H_2O} Ca^{2+}(aq) + 2OH^-(aq)$

a. pH $= -\log [H_3O^+]$

$\log [H_3O^+] = -pH$

$[H_3O^+] = $ antilog $(-pH) = 1 \times 10^{-pH} = 1 \times 10^{-8}$ M

b. $[H_3O^+][OH^-] = 1.0 \times 10^{-14} \text{ M}^2$

$$[OH^-] = \frac{1.0 \times 10^{-14} \text{ M}^2}{1 \times 10^{-8} \text{ M}} = 1 \times 10^{-6} \text{ M}$$

c. $\left(\frac{1 \times 10^{-6} \text{ mol OH}^-}{\text{L solution}}\right)\left(\frac{1 \text{ mol } Ca(OH)_2}{2 \text{ mol OH}^-}\right)$

$= 5 \times 10^{-7}$ M $Ca(OH)_2$

ATE, Additional Sample Problems, p. 520

F-1. Given: $V_{RbOH} = 25.00$ mL
$V_{HBr} = 19.22$ mL
$[HBr] = 1.017$ M

Unknown: [RbOH]

$RbOH + HBr \rightarrow RbBr + H_2O$

$\left(\frac{1.017 \text{ mol HBr}}{\text{L}}\right)(19.22 \text{ mL})\left(\frac{\text{L}}{1000 \text{ mL}}\right) = 0.01955$ mol HBr

$(0.01955 \text{ mol HBr})\left(\frac{1 \text{ mol RbOH}}{1 \text{ mol HBr}}\right)\left(\frac{1}{25.00 \text{ mL}}\right)\left(\frac{1000 \text{ mL}}{\text{L}}\right) = 0.7819 \frac{\text{mol}}{\text{L}}$ RbOH

$= 0.7819$ M RbOH

F-2. Given: $V_{Ba(OH)_2} = 29.96$ mL
$V_{HNO_3} = 16.08$ mL
$[HNO_3] = 2.303$ M

Unknown: $[Ba(OH)_2]$

$Ba(OH)_2 + 2HNO_3 \rightarrow Ba(NO_3)_2 + 2H_2O$

$\left(\frac{2.303 \text{ mol HNO}_3}{\text{L}}\right)(16.08 \text{ mL})\left(\frac{\text{L}}{1000 \text{ mL}}\right) = 0.03703$ mol HNO_3

$(0.03703 \text{ mol HNO}_3)\left(\frac{1 \text{ mol } Ba(OH)_2}{2 \text{ mol HNO}_3}\right)\left(\frac{1}{29.96 \text{ mL}}\right)\left(\frac{1000 \text{ mL}}{\text{L}}\right)$

$= 0.6180$ M $Ba(OH)_2$

F-3. Given: $[CH_3COOH] =$ 0.83 M
$V_{CH_3COOH} =$ 20.00 mL
$[NaOH] = 0.519$ M

Unknown: V_{NaOH}

$CH_3COOH + NaOH \rightarrow NaC_2H_3O_2 + H_2O$

$$\left(\frac{0.83 \text{ mol } CH_3COOH}{L}\right)(20.00 \text{ mL})\left(\frac{L}{1000 \text{ mL}}\right)$$

$= 0.0166 \text{ mol } CH_3COOH$

$$(0.0166 \text{ mol } CH_3COOH)\left(\frac{1 \text{ mol } NaOH}{1 \text{ mol } CH_3COOH}\right)$$

$= 0.0166 \text{ mol } NaOH$

$$\frac{0.0166 \text{ mol } NaOH}{\text{volume in L}} = 0.519 \text{ M}$$

$$\text{volume in L} = \frac{0.0166 \text{ mol } NaOH}{0.519 \text{ mol/L}}$$

$$= (0.032 \text{ L})\left(\frac{1000 \text{ mL}}{L}\right) = 32 \text{ mL } NaOH$$

Additional Example Problems, p. 520

1. Given: 31.15 mL of 0.688 M HCl solution

Unknown: mol of HCl

$$\frac{31.15 \text{ mL} \times 1.000 \text{ L} \times 0.688 \text{ mol/L}}{1000 \text{ mL}} = 2.14 \times 10^{-2} \text{ mol HCl}$$

2. Given: 20.0 mL of 1.39 M H_2SO_4

Unknown: mol of NaOH to neutralize

$H_2SO_4 + 2NaOH \rightarrow Na_2SO_4 + 2H_2O$

$$(20.0 \text{ mL } H_2SO_4)\left(\frac{1 \text{ L}}{1000 \text{ mL}}\right)\left(\frac{1.39 \text{ mol } H_2SO_4}{1 \text{ L}}\right)\left(\frac{2 \text{ mol } NaOH}{1 \text{ mol } H_2SO_4}\right)$$

3. Given: 2.76 M KOH solution

Unknown: mL of solution that contain 0.0825 mol

$$(0.0825 \text{ mol } KOH)\left(\frac{1 \text{ L}}{2.76 \text{ mol } KOH}\right)\left(\frac{1000 \text{ mL}}{1 \text{ L}}\right)$$

Practice, p. 521

1. Given: $[KOH] = 0.215$ M
$V_{KOH} = 15.5$ mL
$V_{CH_3COOH} =$ 21.2 mL

Unknown: $[CH_3COOH]$

$KOH + CH_3COOH \rightarrow KC_2H_3O_2 + H_2O$

$$\left(\frac{0.215 \text{ mol } KOH}{4}\right)(15.5 \text{ mL})\left(\frac{L}{1000 \text{ mL}}\right)$$

$= 0.00333 \text{ mol } KOH$

$$(0.00333 \text{ mol } KOH)\left(\frac{1 \text{ mol } CH_3COOH}{1 \text{ mol } KOH}\right)\left(\frac{1}{21.2 \text{ mL}}\right)\left(\frac{1000 \text{ mL}}{L}\right)$$

$= 0.157 \text{ mol } CH_3COOH/L = 0.157 \text{ M}$

2. Given: $V_{H_2SO_4} = 17.6$ mL
$V_{LiOH} = 27.4$ mL
[LiOH] = 0.0165 M
Unknown: [H_2SO_4]

$2LiOH + H_2SO_4 \rightarrow Li_2SO_4 + 2H_2O$

$\left(\dfrac{0.0165 \text{ mol LiOH}}{L}\right)(27.4 \text{ mL})\left(\dfrac{L}{1000 \text{ mL}}\right)$

$= 0.000452$ mol LiOH

$(0.000452 \text{ mol LiOH})\left(\dfrac{1 \text{ mol } H_2SO_4}{2 \text{ mol LiOH}}\right)\left(\dfrac{1}{17.6 \text{ mL}}\right)\left(\dfrac{1000 \text{ mL}}{L}\right)$

$= 0.0128$ M H_2SO_4

Section Review, p. 521

3. Given: [HCl] = 0.0100 M
$V_{HCl} = 20.0$ mL
$V_{NaOH} = 30.0$ mL
Unknown: [NaOH]

$HCl + NaOH \rightarrow NaCl + H_2O$

$\left(\dfrac{0.0100 \text{ mol HCl}}{L}\right)(20.0 \text{ mL})\left(\dfrac{L}{1000 \text{ mL}}\right)$

$= 0.000200$ mol HCl

$(0.000200 \text{ mol HCl})\left(\dfrac{1 \text{ mol NaOH}}{1 \text{ mol HCl}}\right)\left(\dfrac{1}{30.0 \text{ mL}}\right)\left(\dfrac{1000 \text{ mL}}{L}\right)$

$= 6.67 \times 10^{-3}$ M NaOH

4. Given: [$Ca(OH)_2$] =
0.10 M
$V_{Ca(OH)_2}$ =
20.0 mL
$V_{HCl} = 12.0$ mL
Unknown: [HCl]

$Ca(OH)_2 + 2HCl \rightarrow CaCl_2 + 2H_2O$

$\left(\dfrac{0.10 \text{ mol } Ca(OH)_2}{L}\right)(20.0 \text{ mL})\left(\dfrac{L}{1000 \text{ mL}}\right)$

$= 0.0020$ mol $Ca(OH)_2$

$(0.0020 \text{ mol } Ca(OH)_2)\left(\dfrac{2 \text{ mol HCl}}{1 \text{ mol } Ca(OH)_2}\right)\left(\dfrac{1}{12.0 \text{ mL}}\right)\left(\dfrac{1000 \text{ mL}}{L}\right) = 0.030$ M HCl

Chapter Review

6. Given: $T = 25°C$
  a. [H_3O^+] = 1.0×10^{-7} M
  b. [H_3O^+] = 1.0×10^{-10} M
  c. [OH^-] = 1.0×10^{-7} M
  d. [OH^-] = 1.0×10^{-11} M
  e. [H_3O^+] = [OH^-]
  f. pH = 3.0
  g. pH = 13.0
Unknown: if solution is acidic, basic, or neutral

a. pH = $-\log$ [H_3O^+]

$= -\log (1.0 \times 10^{-7})$ M

$= 7.0 =$ neutral

b. pH = $-\log$[H_3O^+]

$= -\log (1.0 \times 10^{-10})$ M

$= 10 =$ basic

c. pH = $-\log$[H_3O^+]

[H_3O^+][OH^-] = 1.0×10^{-14} M^2

[H_3O^+] = $\dfrac{1.0 \times 10^{-14} \text{ } M^2}{1.0 \times 10^{-7} \text{ M}}$ = 1.0×10^{-7} M

pH = $-\log (1.0 \times 10^{-7})$ M

$= 7.0 =$ neutral

d. $pH = -\log [H_3O^+]$

$$[H_3O^+][OH^-] = 1.0 \times 10^{-14} \, M^2$$

$$[H_3O^+] = \frac{1.0 \times 10^{-14} \, M^2}{1.0 \times 10^{-11} \, M} = 1.0 \times 10^{-3} \, M$$

$$pH = -\log (1.0 \times 10^{-3}) \, M$$

$$= 3.0 = \text{acidic}$$

e. $[H_3O^+][OH^-] = 1.0 \times 10^{-14} \, M^2$

$$[H_3O^+]^2 = 1.0 \times 10^{-14} \, M^{2^-}$$

$$\sqrt{[H_3O^+]^2} = \sqrt{1.0 \times 10^{-14} \, M^2}$$

$$[H_3O^+] = 1.0 \times 10^{-7} \, M$$

$$pH = -\log (1.0 \times 10^{-7}) \, M$$

$$= 7.0 = \text{neutral}$$

f. $pH = 3.0 = \text{acidic}$

g. $pH = 13.0 = \text{basic}$

---

8. Given: concentration of solution:

a. 0.030 M HCl

b. 1.0×10^{-4} M NaOH

c. 5.0×10^{-3} M HNO_3

d. 0.010 M $Ca(OH)_2$

Unknown: $[H_3O^+]$, $[OH^-]$

a. $HCl(l) + H_2O(l) \rightarrow H_3O^+(aq) + Cl^-(aq)$

$$M = \frac{\text{amount of solute (mol)}}{\text{volume of solution (L)}}$$

$$\left(\frac{0.030 \text{ mol HCl}}{\text{L solution}}\right)\left(\frac{1 \text{ mol } H_3O^+}{1 \text{ mol HCl}}\right) = 0.030 \text{ mol } H_3O^+/L$$

$$[H_3O^+] = 3.0 \times 10^{-2} \, M$$

$$[H_3O^+][OH^-] = 1.0 \times 10^{-14} \, M^2$$

$$[OH^-] = \frac{1.0 \times 10^{-14} \, M^2}{3.0 \times 10^{-2}} \, M = 3.0 \times 10^{-13} \, M$$

b. $NaOH(s) \xrightarrow{H_2O} Na^+(aq) + OH^-(aq)$

$$\left(\frac{1.0 \times 10^{-4} \text{ mol NaOH}}{\text{L solution}}\right)\left(\frac{1 \text{ mol } OH^-}{1 \text{ mol NaOH}}\right) = 1.0 \times 10^{-4} \text{ mol } OH^-/L$$

$$[OH^-] = 1.0 \times 10^{-4} \, M$$

$$[H_3O^+][OH^-] = 1.0 \times 10^{-14} \, M^2$$

$$[H_3O^+] = \frac{1.0 \times 10^{-14} \, M^2}{1.0 \times 10^{-4} \, M} = 1.0 \times 10^{-10} \, M$$

c. $HNO_3(l) + H_2O \rightarrow H_3O^+(aq) + NO_3^-(aq)$

$$\left(\frac{5.0 \times 10^{-3} \text{ mol } HNO_3}{L}\right)\left(\frac{1 \text{ mol } H_3O^+}{1 \text{ mol } HNO_3}\right) = 5.0 \times 10^{-3} \text{ mol } H_3O^+/L$$

$$[H_3O^+] = 5.0 \times 10^{-3} \, M$$

$$[H_3O^+][OH^-] = 1.0 \times 10^{-14} \, M^2$$

$$[OH^-] = \frac{1.0 \times 10^{-14} \, M^2}{5.0 \times 10^{-3} \, M} = 2.0 \times 10^{-12} \, M$$

d. $Ca(OH)_2(s) \xrightarrow{H_2O} Ca^{2+}(aq) + 2OH^-(aq)$

$$\left(\frac{0.010 \text{ mol } Ca(OH)_2}{L}\right)\left(\frac{2 \text{ mol } OH^-}{1 \text{ mol } Ca(OH)_2}\right) = 0.020 \text{ mol } OH^-/L$$

$$[OH^-] = 2.0 \times 10^{-2} \text{ M}$$

$$[H_3O^+][OH^-] = 1.0 \times 10^{-14} \text{ M}^2$$

$$[H_3O^+] = \frac{1.0 \times 10^{-14} \text{ M}^2}{2.0 \times 10^{-2} \text{ M}} = 5 \times 10^{-13} \text{ M}$$

---

9. Given: Identity and concentration of solution:

a. 1.0×10^{-2} M HCl
b. 1.0×10^{-3} M HNO$_3$
c. 1.0×10^{-5} M HI
d. 1.0×10^{-4} M HBr

Unknown: pH

a. $HCl + H_2O \rightarrow H_3O^+ + Cl^-$

$$[H_3O^+] = 1.0 \times 10^{-2} \text{ M}$$

$$pH = -\log [H_3O^+] = -\log (1.0 \times 10^{-2}) = 2.00$$

b. $HNO_3 + H_2O \rightarrow H_3O^+ + NO_3^-$

$$[H_3O^+] = 1.0 \times 10^{-3} \text{ M}$$

$$pH = -\log [H_3O^+] = -\log (1.0 \times 10^{-3}) = 3.00$$

c. $HI + H_2O \rightarrow H_3O^+ + I^-$

$$[H_3O^+] = 1.0 \times 10^{-5} \text{ M}$$

$$pH = -\log [H_3O^+] = -\log(1.0 \times 10^{-5}) = 5.00$$

d. $HBr + H_2O \rightarrow H_3O^+ + Br^-$

$$[H_3O^+] = 1.0 \times 10^{-4} \text{ M}$$

$$pH = -\log [H_3O^+] = -\log (1.0 \times 10^{-4}) = 4.00$$

---

10. Given: $[OH^-] =$

a. 1.0×10^{-6} M
b. 1.0×10^{-9} M
c. 1.0×10^{-2} M
d. 1.0×10^{-7} M

Unknown: pH

$$[H_3O^+][OH^-] = 1.0 \times 10^{-14} \text{ M}^2$$

a. $[H_3O^+] = \dfrac{1.0 \times 10^{-14} \text{ M}^2}{1.0 \times 10^{-6} \text{ M}}$

$$= 1.0 \times 10^{-8} \text{ M}$$

$$pH = -\log [H_3O^+] = -\log (1.0 \times 10^{-8}) = 8.00$$

b. $[H_3O^+] = \dfrac{1.0 \times 10^{-14} \text{ M}^2}{1.0 \times 10^{-9} \text{ M}}$

$$= 1.0 \times 10^{-5} \text{ M}$$

$$pH = -\log [H_3O^+] = -\log (1.0 \times 10^{-5}) = 5.00$$

c. $[H_3O^+] = \dfrac{1.0 \times 10^{-14} \text{ M}^2}{1.0 \times 10^{-2} \text{ M}}$

$$= 1.0 \times 10^{-12} \text{ M}$$

$$pH = -\log [H_3O^+] = -\log (1.0 \times 10^{-12}) = 12.00$$

d. $[H_3O^+] = \dfrac{1.0 \times 10^{-14} \text{ M}^2}{1.0 \times 10^{-7} \text{ M}}$

$$= 1.0 \times 10^{-7} \text{ M}$$

$$pH = -\log [H_3O^+] = -\log (1.0 \times 10^{-7}) = 7.00$$

11. Given: Identity and concentration of solution:

  a. 1.0×10^{-2} M NaOH
  b. 1.0×10^{-3} M KOH
  c. 1.0×10^{-4} M LiOH

Unknown: pH

$[H_3O^+][OH^-] = 1.0 \times 10^{-14} \text{ M}^2$

a. $\text{NaOH} \xrightarrow{H_2O} \text{Na}^+ + \text{OH}^-$

$[OH^-] = 1.0 \times 10^{-2}$ M

$[H_3O^+] = \dfrac{1.0 \times 10^{-14} \text{ M}^2}{1.0 \times 10^{-2} \text{ M}} = 1.0 \times 10^{-12}$ M

$pH = -\log [H_3O^+] = -\log (1.0 \times 10^{-12}) = 12.00$

b. $\text{KOH} \xrightarrow{H_2O} \text{K}^+ + \text{OH}^-$

$[OH^-] = 1.0 \times 10^{-3}$ M

$[H_3O^+] = \dfrac{1.0 \times 10^{-14} \text{ M}^2}{1.0 \times 10^{-3} \text{ M}} = 1.0 \times 10^{-11}$ M

$pH = -\log [H_3O^+] = -\log (1.0 \times 10^{-11}) = 11.00$

c. $\text{LiOH} \xrightarrow{H_2O} \text{Li}^+ + \text{OH}^-$

$[OH^-] = 1.0 \times 10^{-4}$ M

$[H_3O^+] = \dfrac{1.0 \times 10^{-14} \text{ M}^2}{1.0 \times 10^{-4} \text{ M}} = 1.0 \times 10^{-10}$ M

$pH = -\log [H_3O^+] = -\log (1.0 \times 10^{-10}) = 10.00$

---

12. Given: $[H_3O^+] =$
  a. 2.0×10^{-5} M
  b. 4.7×10^{-7} M
  c. 3.8×10^{-3} M

Unknown: pH

a. $pH = -\log[H_3O^+] = -\log (2.0 \times 10^{-5}) = 4.70$

b. $pH = -\log[H_3O^+] = -\log (4.7 \times 10^{-7}) = 6.33$

c. $pH = -\log [H_3O^+] = -\log (3.8 \times 10^{-3}) = 2.42$

---

13. Given: pH value:
  a. 3.0
  b. 7.00
  c. 11.0
  d. 5.0

Unknown: $[H_3O^+]$

$pH = -\log [H_3O^+]$

$\log [H_3O^+] = -pH$

$[H_3O^+] = \text{antilog} (-pH) = 1 \times 10^{-pH}$

a. $[H_3O^+] = 1 \times 10^{-3}$

b. $[H_3O^+] = 1.0 \times 10^{-7}$

c. $[H_3O^+] = 1 \times 10^{-11}$

d. $[H_3O^+] = 1 \times 10^{-5}$

14. Given: pH value:
  a. 7.00
  b. 11.00
  c. 4.00
  d. 6.00
  Unknown: $[OH^-]$

$pH = -\log[H_3O^+]$

$\log[H_3O^+] = -pH$

$[H_3O^+] = \text{antilog}(-pH) = 1 \times 10^{-pH}$

$[H_3O^+][OH^-] = 1 \times 10^{-14}$ M

a. $[H_3O^+] = 1.0 \times 10^{-7}$ M

$$[OH^-] = \frac{1.0 \times 10^{-14} \text{ M}^2}{1.0 \times 10^{-7} \text{ M}} = 1.0 \times 10^{-7} \text{ M}$$

b. $[H_3O^+] = 1.0 \times 10^{-11}$ M

$$[OH^-] = \frac{1.0 \times 10^{-14} \text{ M}^2}{1.0 \times 10^{-11} \text{ M}} = 1.0 \times 10^{-3} \text{ M}$$

c. $[H_3O^+] = 1.0 \times 10^{-4}$ M

$$[OH^-] = \frac{1.0 \times 10^{-14} \text{ M}^2}{1.0 \times 10^{-4} \text{ M}} = 1.0 \times 10^{-10} \text{ M}$$

d. $[H_3O^+] = 1.0 \times 10^{-6}$ M

$$[OH^-] = \frac{1.0 \times 10^{-14} \text{ M}^2}{1.0 \times 10^{-6} \text{ M}} = 1.0 \times 10^{-8} \text{ M}$$

---

15. Given: pH value:
  a. 4.23
  b. 7.65
  c. 9.48
  Unknown: $[H_3O^+]$

$pH = -\log[H_3O^+]$

$\log[H_3O^+] = -pH$

$[H_3O^+] = \text{antilog}(-pH)$

a. $[H_3O^+] = \text{antilog}(-4.23)$

$= 1.0 \times 10^{-4.23} = 5.9 \times 10^{-5}$ M

b. $[H_3O^+] = \text{antilog}(-7.65)$

$= 1.0 \times 10^{-7.65} = 2.2 \times 10^{-8}$ M

c. $[H_3O^+] = \text{antilog}(-9.48)$

$= 1.0 \times 10^{-9.48} = 3.3 \times 10^{-10}$ M

---

16. Given: pH = 2.70
  a. Unknown: $[H_3O^+]$

$pH = -\log[H_3O^+]$

$\log[H_3O^+] = -pH$

$[H_3O^+] = \text{antilog}(-pH)$

$[H_3O^+] = 1 \times 10^{-pH}$

$= 1 \times 10^{-2.70} = 2.0 \times 10^{-3}$ M

  b. Unknown: $[OH^-]$

$[H_3O^+][OH^-] = 1.0 \times 10^{-14}$ M^2

$$[OH^-] = \frac{1.0 \times 10^{-14} \text{ M}^2}{2.0 \times 10^{-3} \text{ M}}$$

$= 5.0 \times 10^{-12}$ M

c. Unknown: number of moles HNO_3 required to prepare 5.50 L of this solution

$$HNO_3 + H_2O \rightarrow H_3O^+ + NO_3^-$$

$$(2.0 \times 10^{-3} \text{ mol } H_3O^+)\left(\frac{1 \text{ mol } HNO_3}{1 \text{ mol } H_3O^+}\right)$$

$$= 2.0 \times 10^{-3} \text{ mol } HNO_3$$

$$\left(\frac{2.0 \times 10^{-3} \text{ mol}}{L}\right)(5.5L) = 1.1 \times 10^{-2} \text{ mol } HNO_3$$

d. Unknown: mass of 1.1×10^{-2} mol HNO_3

$$(1.1 \times 10^{-2} \text{ mol } HNO_3)\left(\frac{63 \text{ g } HNO_3}{\text{mol } HNO_3}\right) = 0.69 \text{ g } HNO_3$$

e. Given: conc. HNO_3 = 69.5% HNO_3; $D = 1.42$ g/mL

Unknown: V_{HNO_3} needed to prepare 2.0×10^{-3} M HNO_3

$$(0.69 \text{ g } HNO_3)\left(\frac{100 \text{ g concentrated } HNO_3}{69.5 \text{ g } HNO_3}\right)\left(\frac{\text{mL}}{1.42 \text{ g}}\right)$$

$$= 0.70 \text{ mL concentrated } HNO_3$$

---

24. Given: acid-base titrations:

a. NaOH with 1.0 mol HCl

b. HNO_3 with 0.75 mol KOH

c. $Ba(OH)_2$ with 0.20 mol HF

d. H_2SO_4 with 0.90 mol $Mg(OH)_2$

Unknown: Chemical equivalent in moles

a. $NaOH + HCl \rightarrow NaCl + H_2O$

$$(1.0 \text{ mol } HCl)\left(\frac{1 \text{ mol } NaOH}{1 \text{ mol } HCl}\right) = 1.0 \text{ mol } NaOH$$

b. $HNO_3 + KOH \rightarrow KNO_3 + H_2O$

$$(0.75 \text{ mol } KOH)\left(\frac{1 \text{ mol } HNO_3}{1 \text{ mol } KOH}\right) = 0.75 \text{ mol } HNO_3$$

c. $Ba(OH)_2 + 2HF \rightarrow BaF_2 + 2H_2O$

$$(0.20 \text{ mol } HF)\left(\frac{1 \text{ mol } Ba(OH)_2}{2 \text{ mol } HF}\right) = 0.10 \text{ mol } Ba(OH)_2$$

d. $3H_2SO_4 + 2Al(OH)_3 \rightarrow Al_2(SO_4)_3 + 6H_2O$

$$0.60 \text{ mol } Al(OH)_3 \times \frac{3 \text{ mol } H_2SO_4}{2 \text{ mol } Al(OH)_3} = 0.90 \text{ mol } H_2SO_4$$

---

25. Given: $[H_2SO_4]$ = 2.50×10^{-2} M
$V_{H_2SO_4}$ = 15.0 mL
V_{KOH} = 10.0 mL

Unknown: [KOH]

$$H_2SO_4 + 2KOH \rightarrow K_2SO_4 + 2H_2O$$

$$\left(\frac{2.50 \times 10^{-2} \text{ mol } H_2SO_4}{L}\right)(15.0 \text{ mL})\left(\frac{L}{1000 \text{ mL}}\right)$$

$$= 3.75 \times 10^{-4} \text{ mol } H_2SO_4$$

$$(3.75 \times 10^{-4} \text{ mol } H_2SO_4)\left(\frac{2 \text{ mol } KOH}{1 \text{ mol } H_2SO_4}\right) = 7.50 \times 10^{-4} \text{ mol } KOH$$

$$\left(\frac{7.50 \times 10^{-4} \text{ mol } KOH}{10 \text{ mL}}\right)\left(\frac{1000 \text{ mL}}{L}\right) = 7.50 \times 10^{-2} \text{ M } KOH$$

26. Given: $[Ba(OH)_2] = 1.75 \times 10^{-2}$ M
$V_{Ba(OH)_2} = 12.5$ mL
$V_{HNO_3} = 14.5$ mL
Unknown: $[HNO_3]$

$$Ba(OH)_2 + 2HNO_3 \rightarrow Ba(NO_3)_2 + 2H_2O$$

$$\left(\frac{1.75 \times 10^{-2} \text{ mol Ba(OH)}_2}{L}\right)(12.5 \text{ mL})\left(\frac{1 \text{ L}}{1000 \text{ mL}}\right)$$

$$= 2.19 \times 10^{-4} \text{ mol Ba(OH)}_2$$

$$(2.19 \times 10^{-4} \text{ mol Ba(OH)}_2)\left(\frac{2 \text{ mol HNO}_3}{1 \text{ mol Ba(OH)}_2}\right)$$

$$= 4.38 \times 10^{-4} \text{ mol HNO}_3$$

$$\left(\frac{4.38 \times 10^{-4} \text{ mol HNO}_3}{14.5 \text{ mL}}\right)\left(\frac{1000 \text{ mL}}{L}\right)$$

$$= 3.02 \times 10^{-2} \text{ M HNO}_3$$

27. Given: $[Ca(OH)_2] = 4.0 \times 10^{-4}$ M

a. Unknown: $[OH^-]$

$$Ca(OH)_2(s) \xrightarrow{H_2O} Ca^{2+}(aq) + 2OH^-(aq)$$

$$\left(\frac{4.0 \times 10^{-4} \text{ mol Ca(OH)}_2}{L}\right)\left(\frac{2 \text{ mol OH}^-}{1 \text{ mol Ca (OH)}_2}\right)$$

$$= 8.0 \times 10^{-4} \text{ M OH}^-$$

b. Unknown: $[H_3O^+]$

$$[H_3O^+][OH^-] = 1.0 \times 10^{-14} \text{ M}^2$$

$$[H_3O^+] = \frac{1.0 \times 10^{-14} \text{ M}^2}{8.0 \times 10^{-4} \text{ M}} = 1.3 \times 10^{-11} \text{ M}$$

28. Given: $[H_3O^+]$:

a. 1.0×10^{-7} M
b. 1.0×10^{-3} M
c. 1.0×10^{-12} M
d. 1.0×10^{-5} M
Unknown: pH

$$pH = -\log [H_3O^+]$$

a. $pH = -\log (1.0 \times 10^{-7}) = 7.00$

b. $pH = -\log (1.0 \times 10^{-3}) = 3.00$

c. $pH = -\log (1.0 \times 10^{-12}) = 12.00$

d. $pH = -\log (1.0 \times 10^{-5}) = 5.00$

29. Given: pH = 6.0
Unknown: $[H_3O^+]$

$$pH = -\log [H_3O^+]$$

$$\log [H_3O^+] = -pH$$

$$[H_3O^+] = \text{antilog} (-pH) = 1 \times 10^{-pH} = 1 \times 10^{-6} \text{ M}$$

30. Given: $[Ba(OH)_2] = 5.0 \times 10^{-5}$ M
Unknown: pH

$$Ba(OH)_2(s) \xrightarrow{H_2O} Ba^{2+}(aq) + 2OH^-(aq)$$

$$\left(\frac{5.0 \times 10^{-5} \text{ mol Ba(OH)}_2}{L}\right)\left(\frac{2 \text{ mol OH}^-}{1 \text{ mol Ba(OH)}_2}\right)$$

$$= 1.0 \times 10^{-4} \text{ M OH}^-$$

$$[H_3O^+][OH^-] = 1.0 \times 10^{-14} \text{ M}^2$$

$$[H_3O^+] = \frac{1.0 \times 10^{-14} \text{ M}^2}{1.0 \times 10^{-4} \text{ M}} = 1.0 \times 10^{-10} \text{ M}$$

$$pH = -\log [H_3O^+] = -\log (1.0 \times 10^{-10}) = 10.00$$

31. a. Given: $[H_3O^+] =$ 8.4×10^{-11} M

Unknown: pH

$$pH = -\log [H_3O^+] = -\log (8.4 \times 10^{-11})$$
$$= 10.08$$

b. Given: pH = 2.50

Unknown: $[H_3O^+]$

$$pH = -\log [H_3O^+]$$
$$\log [H_3O^+] = -pH$$
$$[H_3O^+] = \text{antilog} (-pH)$$
$$= 1 \times 10^{-pH}$$
$$= 1 \times 10^{-2.50}$$
$$= 3.2 \times 10^{-3} \text{ M}$$

32. a. Given: $[Mg(OH)_2] =$ 5.4×10^{-5} M

Unknown: $[OH^-]$

$$Mg(OH)_2(s) \xrightarrow{H_2O} Mg^{2+}(aq) + 2OH^-(aq)$$

$$\left(\frac{5.4 \times 10^{-5} \text{ mol Mg (OH)}_2}{L} \right)\left(\frac{2 \text{ mol OH}^-}{1 \text{ mol Mg(OH)}_2} \right)$$

$$= 1.1 \times 10^{-4} \text{ M OH}^-$$

b. Unknown: $[H_3O^+]$

$$[H_3O^+][OH^-] = 1.0 \times 10^{-14} \text{ M}^2$$

$$[H_3O^+] = \frac{1.0 \times 10^{-14} \text{ M}^2}{1.1 \times 10^{-4} \text{ M}} = 9.1 \times 10^{-11} \text{ M}$$

33. Given: pH = 8.90

a. Unknown: $[H_3O^+]$

$$pH = -\log [H_3O^+]$$
$$\log [H_3O^+] = -pH$$
$$[H_3O^+] = \text{antilog} (-pH) = 1 \times 10^{-8.90} = 1.3 \times 10^{-9} \text{ M}$$

b. Unknown: $[OH^-]$

$$[H_3O^+][OH^-] = 1.0 \times 10^{-14} \text{ M}^2$$

$$[OH^-] = \frac{1.0 \times 10^{-14} \text{ M}^2}{1.3 \times 10^{-9} \text{ M}} = 7.7 \times 10^{-6} \text{ M}$$

34. Given: $[OH^-] = 6.9 \times 10^{-10}$ M

Unknown: pH

$$pH = -\log [H_3O^+]$$
$$[H_3O^+][OH^-] = 1.0 \times 10^{-14} \text{ M}^2$$

$$[H_3O^+] = \frac{1.0 \times 10^{-14} \text{ M}^2}{6.9 \times 10^{-10} \text{ M}} = 1.4 \times 10^{-5} \text{ M}$$

$$pH = -\log (1.4 \times 10^{-5}) = 4.84$$

35. Given: $[Ba(OH)_2] =$ 3.4×10^{-3} M
$V_{Ba(OH)_2} = 25.9$ mL
$V_{HCl} = 16.6$ mL

Unknown: [HCl]

$$Ba(OH)_2 + 2HCl \rightarrow BaCl_2 + 2H_2O$$

$$\left(\frac{3.4 \times 10^{-3} \text{ mol Ba(OH)}_2}{L} \right)(25.9 \text{ mL})\left(\frac{L}{1000 \text{ mL}} \right)$$

$$= 8.8 \times 10^{-5} \text{ mol Ba(OH)}_2$$

$$(8.8 \times 10^{-5} \text{ mol Ba(OH)}_2)\left(\frac{2 \text{ mol HCl}}{1 \text{ mol Ba(OH)}_2} \right)$$

$$= 1.8 \times 10^{-4} \text{ mol HCl}$$

$$\left(\frac{1.8 \times 10^{-4} \text{ mol HCl}}{16.6 \text{ mL}} \right)\left(\frac{1000 \text{ mL}}{L} \right)$$

$$= 1.1 \times 10^{-2} \text{ M HCl}$$

36. Given: $V_{Ca(OH)_2} = 428$ mL

$V_{HNO_3} = 115$ mL

$[HNO_3] = 6.7 \times 10^{-3}$ M

Unknown: $[Ca(OH)_2]$

$$Ca(OH)_2 + 2HNO_3 \rightarrow Ca(NO_3)_2 + 2H_2O$$

$$\left(\frac{6.7 \times 10^{-3} \text{ mol HNO}_3}{L}\right)(115 \text{ mL})\left(\frac{L}{1000 \text{ mL}}\right)$$

$$= 7.705 \times 10^{-4} \text{ mol HNO}_3$$

$$(7.705 \times 10^{-4} \text{ mol HNO}_3)\left(\frac{1 \text{ mol Ca(OH)}_2}{2 \text{ mol HNO}_3}\right)$$

$$= 3.8525 \times 10^{-4} \text{ mol Ca(OH)}_2$$

$$\left(\frac{3.8525 \times 10^{-4} \text{ mol Ca(OH)}_2}{428 \text{ mL}}\right)\left(\frac{1000 \text{ mL}}{L}\right)$$

$$= 9.0 \times 10^{-4} \text{ M Ca(OH)}_2$$

37. Given: $V_{HNO_3} = 10.1$ mL

$V_{KOH} = 71.4$ mL

$[KOH] = 4.2 \times 10^{-3}$ M

Unknown: $[HNO_3]$

$$KOH + HNO_3 \rightarrow KNO_3 + H_2O$$

$$\left(\frac{4.2 \times 10^{-3} \text{ mol KOH}}{L}\right)(71.4 \text{ mL})\left(\frac{L}{1000 \text{ mL}}\right)$$

$$= 3.0 \times 10^{-4} \text{ mol KOH}$$

$$(3.0 \times 10^{-4} \text{ mol KOH})\left(\frac{1 \text{ mol HNO}_3}{1 \text{ mol KOH}}\right)$$

$$= 3.0 \times 10^{-4} \text{ mol HNO}_3$$

$$\left(\frac{3.0 \times 10^{-4} \text{ mol HNO}_3}{10.1 \text{ mL}}\right)\left(\frac{1000 \text{ mL}}{L}\right)$$

$$= 3.0 \times 10^{-2} \text{ M HNO}_3$$

Math Tutor, p. 526

1. Given: 0.00085 m HNO_3

Unknown: pH of solution

$$pH = -\log [H_3O^+] = -\log (0.00085) = 3.07$$

2. Given: pH = 9.95

Unknown: hydroxide ion concentration

$$pH + pOH = 14$$

$$pOH = 14 - 9.95 = 4.05$$

$$[OH^-] = 10^{-pOH} = 10^{-4.05} = 8.9 \times 10^{-5} \text{ M OH}^-$$

Standardized Test Prep, p. 527

2. Given: 0.0010 M HNO_3

Unknown: pH of solution

$$pH = -\log [H_3O^+] = -\log [HNO_3] = -(-3) = 3$$

7. Given: pH = 6.32

Unknown: pOH

$$pH + pOH = 14$$

$$pOH = 14 - pH = 14 - 6.32 = 7.68$$

10. Given: pH = 4.75

Unknown: $[H_3O^+]$ acidic or basic characteristic

$$pH = -\log [H_3O^+]$$

$$[H_3O^+] = \text{antilog}(-pH) = 10^{-4.75} = 1.8 \times 10^{-5} \text{ M H}_3O^+$$

12. Given: $[OH^-]$
= 1.6×10^{-11} M

Unknown: $[H_3O^+]$, pH, pOH

$[H_3O^+][OH^-] = 1 \times 10^{-14}$

$[H_3O^+] = \dfrac{1 \times 10^{-14}}{[OH^-]} = \dfrac{1 \times 10^{-14}}{1.6 \times 10^{-11}} = 6.3 \times 10^{-4}$ M

$pH = -\log [H_3O^+] = -\log (6.3 \times 10^{-4}) = 3.20$

$pOH = 14 - pH = 14 - 3.20 = 10.80$

CHAPTER 16

Reaction Energy

Practice, p. 534

1. Given: $m = 35$ g

$\Delta T = 313$ K – 293 K
$\quad = 20.$ K

$q = 48$ J

Unknown: c_p in J/(g·K)

$$c_p = \frac{q}{m \times \Delta T}$$

$$= \frac{48 \text{ J}}{(35 \text{ g})(20. \text{ K})} = 0.14 \text{ J/(g·K)}$$

---

2. Given: $q = 9.8 \times 10^5$ J

volume of $H_2O = 6.2$ L
$\quad = 6200$ g

$T_i = 291$ K

Unknown: T_f

c_p of $H_2O = 4.18$ J/(g·K)

$$c_p = \frac{q}{m \times \Delta T}$$

$$\Delta T = \frac{q}{(m)(c_p)} = \frac{9.8 \times 10^5 \text{ J}}{(6.2 \times 10^3 \text{ g})(4.18 \text{ J/(g·K)})}$$

$$= 38 \text{ K}$$

$$\Delta T = T_f - T_i$$

$$T_f = \Delta T + T_i$$

$$= 38 \text{ K} + 291 \text{ K} = 329 \text{ K}$$

ATE, Additional Sample Problems, p. 534

A-1. Given: $m = 85.0$ g

$\Delta T = 45°C - 30°C$
$\quad = 15°C = 15$ K

$q = 523$ J

a. Unknown: c_p

$$c_p = \frac{q}{m \times \Delta T}$$

$$c_p = \frac{523 \text{ J}}{(85.0 \text{ g})(15 \text{ K})} = 0.41 \text{ J/(g·K)}$$

b. Unknown: amount of energy the sample will lose if cooled to 25°C

$\Delta T = 45°C - 25°C = 20.°C = 20.$ K

$q = c_p \times m \times \Delta T$

$\quad = (0.41 \text{ J/(g·K)})(85.0 \text{ g})(20. \text{ K})$

$\quad = 7.0 \times 10^2$ J

A-2. Given: $m = 74$ g

$\Delta T = 45°C - 15°C$
$= 30.°C = 30.$ K
$q = 2000$ J

Unknown: c_p

$c_p = \dfrac{q}{m \times \Delta T}$

$= \dfrac{2000\ \text{J}}{(74\ \text{g})(30.\ \text{K})}$

$= 0.90\ \text{J/(g} \cdot \text{K)}$

Practice, p. 542

1. Given: $CH_4(g) + 2O_2 \rightarrow$
$CO_2(g) + H_2O(l)$

Unknown: $\Delta H°$ for
combustion of
CH_4

$CH_4(g) \rightarrow C(s) + 2H_2(g)$	$\Delta H_f^0 = 74.3$ kJ/mol
$C(s) + O_2(g) \rightarrow CO_2$	$\Delta H_f^0 = -393.5$ kJ/mol
$2H_2(g) + O_2(g) \rightarrow 2H_2O(l)$	$\Delta H_f^0 = 2(-285.8)$
	$= -571.6$ kJ/mol

$CH_4(g) + 2O_2(g) \rightarrow CO_2(g) + 2H_2O(l)$

$\Delta H^0 = -890.8$ kJ

2. Given: $C_{graphite}\ (s) \rightarrow$
$C_{diamond}\ (s)$
Unknown: ΔH^0

$C_{graphite}(s) + O_2(g) \rightarrow CO_2(g)$	$\Delta H_c^0 = -394$ kJ/mol
$CO_2(g) \rightarrow C_{diamond}(s) + O_2(g)$	$\Delta H_c^0 = 396$ kJ/mol
$C_{graphite}(s) \rightarrow C_{diamond}(s)$	$\Delta H^0 = 2$ kJ

ATE, Additional Sample Problem, p. 542

B-1. Given: $2N_2\ (g) + 5O_2\ (g)$
$\rightarrow 2N_2O_5\ (g)$
Unknown: ΔH

$2H_2O(l) \rightarrow 2H_2(g) + 2\left(\frac{1}{2}O_2\right)(g)$	$\Delta H_f^0 = 2(285.8) = 571.6$ kJ/mol
$(2)2HNO_3(l) \rightarrow 2N_2O_5(g) + 2H_2O(l)$	$\Delta H^0 = 2(76.6) = 153.2$ kJ/mol
$(4)\frac{1}{2}N_2(g) + (4)\frac{3}{2}O_2(g) + (4)\frac{1}{2}H_2(g)$ $\rightarrow 4HNO_3(l)$	$\Delta H_f^0 = 4(-174.1)$
	$= -696.4$ kJ/mol

$2N_2 + 5O_2 \rightarrow 2N_2O_5$	$\Delta H = 28.4$ kJ

Practice, p. 544

1. Unknown: ΔH_f of butane
(C_4H_{10})

Balanced equation:

$4C(s) + 5H_2(g) \rightarrow C_4H_{10}(g)$

$4C(s) + 4O_2(g) \rightarrow 4CO_2(g)$ $\qquad \Delta H_f^0 = 4(-393.5)$

$= -1574$ kJ

$5H_2(g) + \frac{5}{2}O_2(g) \rightarrow 5H_2O(l)$ $\qquad \Delta H_f^0 = 5(-285.8)$

$= -1429$ kJ

$4CO_2(g) + 5H_2O(l) \rightarrow C_4H_{10}(g) + \frac{13}{2}O_2(g)$ $\qquad \Delta H_c^0 = +2877.6$ kJ

$4C(s) + 5H_2(g) \rightarrow C_4H_{10}(g)$ $\qquad \Delta H_f^0 = -125.4$ kJ

2. Unknown: ΔH_c of 1 mol of N_2 to form NO_2

Balanced equation:

$$N_2(g) + 2O_2(g) \rightarrow 2NO_2(g)$$

$$\tfrac{1}{2}N_2(g) + O_2(g) \rightarrow NO_2(g) \qquad\qquad \Delta H_f^0 = 33.2 \text{ kJ}$$

$$(2)\tfrac{1}{2}N_2(g) + (2)O_2(g) \rightarrow (2)NO_2(g) \qquad \Delta H_f^0 = 2(33.2 \text{ kJ})$$

$$= 66.4 \text{ kJ}$$

---

3. Unknown: ΔH_f of SO_2 from S and O

Balanced equation:

$$S(s) + O_2(g) \rightarrow SO_2(g)$$

$$S(s) + \tfrac{3}{2}O_2(g) \rightarrow SO_3(g) \qquad\qquad \Delta H_c^0 = -395.2 \text{ kJ}$$

$$\left(\tfrac{1}{2}\right)2SO_3(g) \rightarrow \left(\tfrac{1}{2}\right)2SO_2(g) + \left(\tfrac{1}{2}\right)O_2(g) \qquad \Delta H^0 = \left(\tfrac{1}{2}\right)(+198.2) \text{ kJ}$$

$$= 99.1 \text{ kJ}$$

$$S(s) + O_2(g) \rightarrow SO_2(g) \qquad\qquad \Delta H_f = -296.1 \text{ kJ}$$

Section Review, p. 544

5. Given: $m = 75$ g
$\Delta T = 301$ K
$- 295$ K $= 6$ K

Unknown: q

c_p of iron $= 0.449$ J/(g·K)

$$c_p = \frac{q}{m \times \Delta T}$$

$$q = c_p \times m \times \Delta T$$

$$= (0.449 \text{ J/(g·K)})(75 \text{ g})(6 \text{ K})$$

$$= 2.0 \times 10^2 \text{ J}$$

ATE, Additional Example Problems, p. 549

Unknown: whether ΔS will be > 0, < 0, or $= 0$

1. $3H_2(g) + N_2(g) \rightarrow 2NH_3(g)$

$4 \text{ mol}(g) \rightarrow 2 \text{ mol}(g)$

S decreases; $\Delta S < 0$

2. $2Mg(s) + O_2(g) \rightarrow 2MgO(s)$

$3 \text{ mol} \rightarrow 2 \text{ mol}$

S decreases; $\Delta S < 0$

3. $C_6H_{12}O_6(s) + 6O_2(g) \rightarrow 6CO_2(g) + 6H_2O(g)$

$7 \text{ mol} \rightarrow 12 \text{ mol}$

S increases; $\Delta S > 0$

4. $KNO_3(s) \rightarrow K^+(aq) + NO_3^-(aq)$

$1 \text{ mol} \rightarrow 2 \text{ mol}$

S increases; $\Delta S > 0$

Practice, p. 550

1. Given: $\Delta H^0 = 31.0$ kJ/mol
$\Delta S^0 = 0.093$ kJ/mol·K

Unknown: temperature at which reaction is spontaneous

$\Delta G^0 = \Delta H^0 - T\Delta S$

Assume $\Delta G^0 < 0$ (ΔG^0 must be negative for a spontaneous reaction)

$$0 > \Delta H^0 - T\Delta S$$

$$T > \frac{\Delta H^0}{\Delta S^0}$$

$$> \frac{31.0 \text{ kJ/mol}}{0.093 \text{ kJ/mol·K}} = 333 \text{ K}$$

Temperature would need to be > 333K

ATE, Additional Sample Problem, p. 550

D-1. Given: $Cu_2S(s) + S(s) \rightarrow 2CuS(s)$
$\Delta H^0 = -26.7$ kJ/mol
$\Delta S^0 = 0.0197$ kJ/(mol·K)
$T = 298$ K

Unknown: whether reaction will be spontaneous

$\Delta G^0 = \Delta H^0 - T\Delta S^0$

$= -26.7$ kJ/mol $- (298 \text{ K})(-0.0197 \text{ kJ/(mol·K)})$

$= -26.7$ kJ/mol $- (-5.87 \text{ kJ/mol})$

$= -20.8$ kJ/mol

yes; reaction will be spontaneous (ΔG^0 is negative).

Chapter Review

7. Given: $m = 55$ g
$\Delta T = 94.6°C - 22.4°C = 72.2°C = 72.2$ K
c_p of aluminum $= 0.897$ J/(g·K)

Unknown: q

$$c_p = \frac{q}{m \times \Delta T}$$

$$q = c_p \times m \times \Delta T$$

$$= (0.897 \text{ J/(g·K)})(55 \text{ g})(72.2 \text{ K})$$

$$= 3.6 \times 10^3 \text{ J}$$

8. Given: $q = 3500$ J
$m = 28.2$ g
$T_i = 20°C = 293$ K

Unknown: T_f

c_p of iron $= 0.449$ J/(g·K)

$$c_p = \frac{q}{m \times \Delta T}$$

$$\Delta T = \frac{q}{m \times c_p} = \frac{3500 \text{ J}}{(28.2 \text{ g})(0.449 \text{ J/(g·K)})}$$

$$= 280 \text{ K}$$

$$\Delta T = T_f - T_i$$

$$T_f = \Delta T + T_i$$

$$= 280 \text{ K} + 293 \text{ K} \approx 570 \text{ K}$$

9. Given: 34.0 g NH_3
energy = 70.2 J
$T_i = 23.0°C = 296$ K
$T_f = 24.0°C = 297$ K

Unknown: c_p for NH_3

energy $= c_p m \Delta T$

$$c_p = \frac{\text{energy}}{g \cdot \Delta T} = \frac{70.2 \text{ J}}{34.0 \text{ g } NH_3 \times (297 \text{ K} - 296 \text{ K})}$$

$$c_p = 2.06 \frac{\text{J}}{g \cdot \text{K}}$$

---

10. Given: 1.0 mol In =
114.82 g In
energy = 53 J
$\Delta T = 2.0$ K

Unknown: c_p for In

$$c_p = \frac{\text{energy}}{\text{mol In} \times \Delta T} = \frac{53 \text{ J}}{114.82 \text{ g} \times 2.0 \text{ K}} = 0.23 \frac{\text{J}}{g \cdot \text{K}}$$

---

14. Given: $2Fe_2O_3(s) + 3C(s)$
$\rightarrow 4Fe(s) +$
$3CO_2(g)$
ΔH_f^0 for $Fe_2O_3 =$
-824.2 kJ/mol
ΔH_f^0 for $CO_2 =$
-393.5 kJ/mol

Unknown: ΔH_{rxn}^0

$\Delta H_{rxn}^0 = \Sigma \Delta H_f^0$, products $- \Sigma \Delta H_f^0$, reactants

$\Delta H_{rxn}^0 = 3$ mol $CO_2 \times (-393.5$ kJ/mol$)$

-2 mol $Fe_2O_3 \times (-824.2$ kJ/mol$)$

$\Delta H_{rxn}^0 = 467.9$ kJ

$$\frac{467.9 \text{ kJ}}{4 \text{ mol Fe}} = 117.6 \text{ kJ/mol Fe}$$

---

15. Unknown: ΔH

a. Given: $CaCO_3(s) \rightarrow CaO(s) + CO_2(g)$

$CaCO_3(s) \rightarrow Ca(s) + C(s) + \frac{3}{2}O_2(g)$	$\Delta H = 1207.6$ kJ/mol
$Ca(s) + \frac{1}{2}O_2(g) \rightarrow CaO(s)$	$\Delta H = -634.9$ kJ/mol
$C(s) + O_2(g) \rightarrow CO_2(g)$	$\Delta H = -393.5$ kJ/mol
$CaCO_3(s) \rightarrow CaO(s) + CO_2(g)$	$\Delta H = 179.2$ kJ/mol

$\Delta H = $ [sum of ΔH_f of products] $-$ [sum of ΔH_f of reactants]

$\Delta H = [\Delta H_f^0 \text{ CaO} + \Delta H_f \text{ CO}_2] - [\Delta H_f^0 \text{ CaCO}_3]$

$= [(-634.9 \text{ kJ/mol}) + (-393.51 \text{ kJ/mol})] - (-1207.6 \text{ kJ/mol})$

$= 179.2$ kJ/mol

b. Given: $Ca(OH)_2(s) \rightarrow CaO(s) + H_2O(g)$

$Ca(OH)_2(s) \rightarrow Ca(s) + O_2(g) + H_2(g)$	$\Delta H = 983.2$ kJ/mol
$Ca(s) + \frac{1}{2}O_2(g) \rightarrow CaO(s)$	$\Delta H = -634.9$ kJ/mol
$H_2(g) + \frac{1}{2}O_2(g) \rightarrow H_2O(g)$	$\Delta H = -241.8$ kJ/mol
$Ca(OH)_2(s) \rightarrow CaO(s) + H_2O(g)$	$\Delta H = 106.5$ kJ/mol

$\Delta H = [\Delta H_f^0 \text{ CaO} + \Delta H_f^0 \text{ H}_2O] - [\Delta H_f^0 \text{ Ca(OH)}_2]$

$= [(-634.9 \text{ kJ/mol}) + (-241.8 \text{ kJ/mol})] - (-983.2 \text{ kJ/mol})$

$= 106.5$ kJ/mol

c. Given: $Fe_2O_3(s) + 3CO(g) \rightarrow 2Fe(s) + 3CO_2(g)$

$$Fe_2O_3(s) \rightarrow 2Fe(s) + \tfrac{3}{2}O_2(g) \qquad \qquad \Delta H = 825.5 \text{ kJ/mol}$$

$$3CO(g) \rightarrow 3C(s) + \tfrac{3}{2}O_2(g) \qquad \qquad \Delta H = 3(110.5) = 331.5 \text{ kJ/mol}$$

$$3C(s) + 3O_2(g) \rightarrow 3CO_2(g) \qquad \qquad \Delta H = 3(-393.5) = -1180.5 \text{ kJ/mol}$$

$$Fe_2O_3(s) + 3CO(g) \rightarrow 2Fe(s) + 3CO_2(g) \quad \Delta H = -23.5 \text{ kJ/mol}$$

$$\Delta H = [2\Delta H_f^0 \text{ Fe} + 3\Delta H_f^0 \text{ CO}_2] - [\Delta H_f^0 \text{ Fe}_2O_3 + 3\Delta H_f^0 \text{ CO}]$$

$$= [0 + 3(-393.5 \text{ kJ/mol})] - [(-825.5 \text{ kJ/mol}) + 3(110.5 \text{ kJ/mol})]$$

$$= -23.5 \text{ kJ/mol}$$

---

16. Given: 1 mol glucose, $C_6H_{12}O_6$

$\Delta H_f^0 = -1263$ kJ/mol

Unknown: ΔH_{rxn}

$$C_6H_{12}O_6(s) + 6O_2(g) \rightarrow 6CO_2(g) + 6H_2O(l)$$

$$\Delta H_{rxn} = \Sigma \Delta H_f^0 \text{, products} - \Sigma \Delta H_f^0 \text{, reactants}$$

$$\Delta H_{rxn} = 6 \text{ mol} (-393.5 \text{ kJ/mol}) + 6 \text{ mol} (-285.8 \text{ kJ/mol}) - (1 \text{ mol})(-1263 \text{ kJ/mol})$$

$$\Delta H_{rxn} = -2813 \text{ kJ}$$

---

17. Unknown: ΔH

a. Reaction: $C_2H_6(g) + \tfrac{7}{2}O_2(g) \rightarrow 2CO_2(g) + 3H_2O(l)$

$$C_2H_6(g) \rightarrow 2C(s) + 3H_2(g) \qquad \qquad \Delta H = 83.8 \text{ kJ/mol}$$

$$2C(s) + 2O_2(g) \rightarrow 2CO_2(g) \qquad \qquad \Delta H = 2(-393.5 \text{ kJ/mol})$$
$$= -787 \text{ kJ/mol}$$

$$3H_2(g) + \tfrac{3}{2}O_2(g) \rightarrow 3H_2O(l) \qquad \qquad \Delta H = 3(-285.8 \text{ kJ/mol})$$
$$= -857.4 \text{ kJ/mol}$$

$$C_2H_6(g) + \tfrac{7}{2}O_2(g) \rightarrow 2CO_2(g) + 3H_2O(l) \qquad \Delta H = -1560.6 \text{ kJ/mol}$$

$$\Delta H = [2\Delta H_f^0 \text{ CO}_2 + 3\Delta H_f^0 \text{ H}_2O] - [\Delta H_f^0 \text{ C}_2H_6 + \tfrac{7}{2}\Delta H_f^0 \text{ O}_2]$$

$$= [2(-393.5 \text{ kJ/mol}) + 3(-285.8 \text{ kJ/mol})] - [(-83.8 \text{ kJ/mol}) + 0]$$

$$= -1560.6 \text{ kJ/mol}$$

b. Reaction: $C_6H_6(l) + \tfrac{15}{2}O_2(g) \rightarrow 6CO_2(g) + 3H_2O(l)$

$$C_6H_6(l) \rightarrow 6C(s) + 3H_2(g) \qquad \qquad \Delta H = -49.080 \text{ kJ/mol}$$

$$6 C(s) + 6O_2(g) \rightarrow 6CO_2(g) \qquad \qquad \Delta H = 6(-393.5 \text{ kJ/mol})$$
$$= -2361 \text{ kJ/mol}$$

$$3H_2(g) + \tfrac{3}{2}O_2(g) \rightarrow 3H_2O(l) \qquad \qquad \Delta H = 3(-285.8 \text{ kJ/mol})$$
$$= -857.4 \text{ kJ/mol}$$

$$C_6H_6(l) + \tfrac{15}{2}O_2(g) \rightarrow 6CO_2(g) + 3H_2O(l) \qquad \Delta H = -3267.5 \text{ kJ/mol}$$

$$\Delta H = [6\Delta H_f^0 \text{ CO}_2 + 3\Delta H_f^0 \text{ H}_2O] - [\Delta H_f^0 \text{ C}_6H_6 + \tfrac{15}{2}\Delta H_f^0 \text{ O}_2]$$

$$= [6(-393.5 \text{ kJ/mol}) + 3(-285.8 \text{ kJ/mol})] - [(+49.08 \text{ kJ/mol} - 0)]$$

$$= -3267.5 \text{ kJ/mol}$$

18. Given: ΔH_f^0 of $C_2H_5OH =$
   -277.0 kJ/mol

 Unknown: ΔH_c^0 of
   C_2H_5OH

Balanced equation:

$C_2H_5OH(l) + 3O_2(g) \rightarrow 2CO_2(g) + 3H_2O(l)$

$C_2H_5OH \rightarrow 2C + 3H_2 + \frac{1}{2}O_2$	$\Delta H = 277.0$ kJ/mol
$2C + 2O_2 \rightarrow 2CO_2$	$\Delta H = 2(-393.5$ kJ/mol$) = -787.0$ kJ/mol
$3H_2 + \frac{3}{2}O_2 \rightarrow 3H_2O$	$\Delta H = 3(-285.8$ kJ/mol$) = -857.4$ kJ/mol

$\overline{C_2H_5OH + 3O_2 \rightarrow 2CO_2 + 3H_2O \quad\quad \Delta H = -1367.4 \text{ kJ/mol}}$

23. Given: $\Delta H = -356$ kJ
   $\Delta S = -36$ J/K
   $T = 25°C = 298K$

 Unknown: ΔG &
   spontaneity

$\Delta G = \Delta H - T\Delta S$

$\Delta G = -356 \text{ kJ} - (-36 \text{ J/K}) \times \dfrac{1 \text{ kJ}}{1000 \text{ J}} \times 298 \text{ K}$

$\Delta G = -345$ kJ

The reaction is spontaneous because ΔG is negative.

24. Given: $\Delta H = 98$ kJ
   $\Delta S = 292$ J/K
   $T = 25°C = 298$ K

 Unknown: ΔG, spontaneity, and effect
   of increased
   temperature

$\Delta G = \Delta H - T\Delta S$

$\Delta G = 98 - \left(298 \text{ K} \times 292 \text{ J/K} \times \dfrac{1 \text{ kJ}}{1000 \text{ J}} \right)$

$\Delta G = 11$ kJ; reaction is not spontaneous.

If $\Delta G = 0$ then $\Delta H = T\Delta S$ and $T = \dfrac{\Delta H}{\Delta S}$

$T = \dfrac{98 \text{ J}}{0.292 \text{ J/K}} = 336 \text{ K} = 63°C$, above which the reaction will be spontaneous.

25. Given: $\Delta H = -76$ kJ
   $\Delta S = -117$ J/K
   $T = 298.15$ K

 Unknown: spontaneity

$\Delta G = \Delta H - T\Delta S$

$\Delta G = -76 \text{ kJ} - (-117 \text{ J/K} \times \dfrac{1 \text{ kJ}}{1000 \text{ kJ}} \times 298.15 \text{ K})$

$\Delta G = -41$ kJ

The reaction is spontaneous.

26. Given: $\Delta H = 11$ kJ
   $\Delta S = 41$ J/K
   $T = 298.15$ K

 Unknown: ΔG and
   spontaneity

$\Delta G = \Delta H - T\Delta S$

$\Delta G = 11 \text{ kJ} - \left(41 \text{ J/K} \times 298.15 \text{ K} \times \dfrac{1 \text{ kJ}}{1000 \text{ J}} \right)$

$\Delta G = -1.2$ kJ

The reaction is spontaneous.

27. Unknown: ΔG; whether
  reaction will
  occur sponta-
  neously

 a. Given: $\Delta H = +125$ kJ/mol

   $T = 293$ K

   $\Delta S = 0.0350$ kJ/(mol $\cdot$ K)

   $\Delta G = \Delta H - T\Delta S$

    $= (125 \text{ kJ/mol}) - (293 \text{ K})(0.0350 \text{ kJ/(mol} \cdot \text{K)})$

    $= +115$ kJ/mol; not spontaneous

 b. Given: $\Delta H = -85.2$ kJ/mol

   $T = 127°C = 400.$ K

   $\Delta S = 0.125$ kJ/(mol $\cdot$ K)

   $\Delta G = \Delta H - T\Delta S$

    $= (-85.2 \text{ kJ/mol}) - (400. \text{ K})(0.125 \text{ kJ/(mol} \cdot \text{K)})$

    $= -135$ kJ/mol; spontaneous

c. Given: $\Delta H = -275$ kJ/mol

$$T = 773 \text{ K}$$

$$\Delta S = 0.450 \text{ kJ/(mol} \cdot \text{K)}$$

$$\Delta G = \Delta H - T\Delta S$$

$$= (-275 \text{ kJ/mol}) - (773 \text{ K})(0.450 \text{ kJ/(mol} \cdot \text{K)})$$

$$= -623 \text{ kJ/mol; spontaneous}$$

---

28. Given: $C(s) + O_2(g) \rightarrow$ $CO_2(g) + 393.51$ kJ
$\Delta S^0 = 0.003\ 00$ kJ/(mol$\cdot$K)
$T = 298.15$ K

Unknown: ΔG^0; whether reaction will occur spontaneously

$\Delta G = \Delta H - T\Delta S$

$\Delta H = -393.51$ kJ/mol

$\Delta G = (-393.51 \text{ kJ/mol}) - (298.15 \text{ K})(0.003\ 00 \text{ kJ/(mol} \cdot \text{K)})$

$\quad = -394.40$ kJ/mol; spontaneous

---

29. Given: Temperature = 300 K
$\Delta H = -74.8$ kJ/mol
$\Delta S = -0.809$ kJ/(mol$\cdot$K)

Unknown: if reaction will occur spontaneously

$\Delta G = \Delta H - T\Delta S$

$\quad = (-74.8 \text{ kJ/mol}) - (300 \text{ K})(-0.0809 \text{ kJ/(mol} \cdot \text{K)})$

$\quad = -50.53$ kJ/mol

yes; it will occur spontaneously

---

32. Given: ΔH_f^0 for $SO_2 =$ -296.8 kJ/mol

Unknown: ΔH_f^0 for 30.0 g SO_2

$(30.0 \text{ g SO}_2)\left(\dfrac{\text{mol SO}_2}{64.1 \text{ g SO}_2}\right) = 0.468 \text{ mol SO}_2$

$(0.468 \text{ mol SO}_2)(296.8 \text{ kJ/mol}) = 139 \text{ kJ}$

---

33. Given: $T = 298.15$ K
$Fe_2O_3 + 2Al(s) \rightarrow$ $2Fe(s) + Al_2O_3(s)$
$\Delta H^0 = -851.5$ kJ
$\Delta S^0 = -0.0385$ kJ/K

Unknown: ΔG at 448 K

$\Delta G = \Delta H - T\Delta S$

$\quad = (-851.5 \text{ kJ}) - (448 \text{ K})(-0.0385 \text{ kJ/K})$

$\quad = -834.3$ kJ

---

35. Given: $4FeO(s) + O_2(g) \rightarrow$ $2Fe_2O_3(s)$

$(4)\text{FeO} \rightarrow (4)\text{Fe} + (4)\text{O}$

$(2)2\text{Fe} + (2)\frac{3}{2}O_2 \rightarrow (2)Fe_2O_3$

$4\text{FeO} + O_2 \rightarrow 2Fe_2O_3$

$\Delta H = 4(272.0 \text{ kJ/mol})$

$\quad = 1088.0$ kJ/mol

$\Delta H = 2(-824.2 \text{ kJ/mol})$

$\quad = -1648.4$ kJ/mol

$\Delta H = -560.4$ kJ/mol

38. Given: $S_8(s) + 8O_2(s) \rightarrow$
$8SO_2(g)$ $\Delta S =$
89 J/K
$2SO_2(s) + O_2(s) \rightarrow$
$2SO_3(g)$ $\Delta S =$
-188 J/K

$S_8(s) + 8O(s) \rightarrow 8SO_2(g)$ 89 J/K

$+ 8SO_2(s) + 4O_2(s) \rightarrow 8SO_3(g)$ $+4 \times (-188$ J/K$)$

$S_8(g) + 12O_2(s) \rightarrow 8SO_3(g)$ $= -663$ J/K

Unknown: ΔS for $12O_2(s)$
$\rightarrow 8SO_3(g)$

Math Tutor, p. 556

1. Given: $S(s) + O_2(g) \rightarrow$
$SO_2(g)$
$\Delta H_f^0 = -296.8$ kJ;
$SO_2(g) + \frac{1}{2} O_2(g)$
$\rightarrow SO_3(g)$
$\Delta H_f^0 = -99.2$ kJ

$S(s) + O_2(g) \rightarrow SO_2(g)$ $\Delta H^0 = -296.8$ kJ

$+ SO_2(g) + \frac{1}{2} O_2(g) \rightarrow SO_3(g)$ $\Delta H^0 = -99.2$ kJ

$= S(s) + \frac{3}{2} O_2(g) \rightarrow SO_3(g)$ $\Delta H^0 = -396.0$ kJ

Unknown: ΔH for $S(s) +$
$\frac{3}{2} O_2(g) \rightarrow$
$SO_3(g)$

2. Given: $Zn(s) + \frac{1}{2} O_2(g) \rightarrow$
$ZnO(s)$
$\Delta H_f^0 =$
-348.0 kJ/mol;
$Zn(s) + S(s) \rightarrow$
$ZnS(s)$
$\Delta H_f^0 = -203.0$ kJ;
$S(s) + O_2(g) \rightarrow$
$SO_2(g)$
$\Delta H_f^0 = -296.8$ kJ/mol

$ZnS(s) \rightarrow Zn(s) + S(s)$ $\Delta H^0 = +203.0$ kJ

$+ Zn(s) + \frac{1}{2} O_2(g) \rightarrow ZnO(s)$ $\Delta H^0 = -348.0$ kJ

$+ S(s) + O_2(g) \rightarrow SO_2(g)$ $\Delta H^0 = -296.8$ kJ

$= ZnS(s) + \frac{3}{2} O_2(g) \rightarrow ZnO(s) + SO_2(g)$ $= -441.8$ kJ

Unknown: ΔH^0 for $ZnS(s)$
$+ \frac{3}{2} O_2(g) \rightarrow$
$ZnO(s) + SO_2(g)$

Standardized Test Prep, p. 557

2. Given: $C(s) + 2H_2(g) \rightarrow$
$CH_4(g)$;
$C(s) + O_2(g) \rightarrow$
$CO_2(g)$
$\Delta H = -394$ kJ;
$H_2(g) + \frac{1}{2} O_2(g) \rightarrow$
$H_2O(\ell)$
$\Delta H = -286$ kJ;
$CH_4(g) + 2O_2(g)$
$\rightarrow CO_2(g) +$
$2H_2O(\ell)$
$\Delta H = -891$ kJ

$C(s) + O_2(g) \rightarrow CO_2(g)$ -394 kJ

$+ 2H_2(g) + O_2(g) \rightarrow 2H_2O(\ell)$ $2(-286)$ kJ

$+ CO_2(g) + 2H_2O(\ell) \rightarrow CH_4(g) + 2O_2(g)$ $+ 891$ kJ

$= C(s) + 2H_2(g) \rightarrow CH_4(g)$ $= -75$ kJ

Unknown: ΔH for $C(s) +$
$2H_2(g) \rightarrow$
$CH_4(g)$

CHAPTER 17

Reaction Kinetics

ATE, Additional Sample Problem, p. 566

A-1. Unknown: $\Delta E_{forward}$
$\Delta E_{reverse}$
E_a'

$\Delta E_{forward}$ = energy of products – energy of reactants

$= 30 \text{ kJ/mol} - 0 \text{ kJ/mol} = +30 \text{ kJ/mol}$

$\Delta E_{reverse}$ = energy of reactants – energy of products

$= 0 - 30 \text{ kJ/mol} = -30 \text{ kJ/mol}$

E_a' = energy of activated complex – energy of products

$= 40 \text{ kJ/mol} - 30 \text{ kJ/mol}$

$= 10 \text{ kJ/mol}$

Practice, p. 567

1.a. Unknown: $\Delta E_{forward}$
$\Delta E_{reverse}$
E_a
E_a'

$\Delta E_{forward}$ = energy of products – energy of reactants

$= -150 \text{ kJ/mol} - 0 = -150 \text{ kJ/mol}$

$\Delta E_{reverse}$ = energy of reactants – energy of products

$= 0 - (-150 \text{ kJ/mol}) = +150 \text{ kJ/mol}$

E_a = energy of activated complex – energy of reactants

$= 100 \text{ kJ/mol} - 0 = 100 \text{ kJ/mol}$

E_a' = energy of activated complex – energy of products

$= 100 \text{ kJ/mol} - (-150 \text{ kJ/mol}) = +250 \text{ kJ/mol}$

2.b. (see diagram in 2.a.)

Given: $E_{reactants}$ =
0 kJ/mol
E_a = 125 kJ/mol
E_a' = 86 kJ/mol

Unknown: $\Delta E_{forward}$
$\Delta E_{reverse}$

$E_{activated\ complex} = E_a - E_{reactants} = 125 \text{ kJ/mol} - 0 = +125 \text{ kJ/mol}$

$E_{products} = E_{activated\ complex} - E_a' = 125 \text{ kJ/mol} - 86 \text{ kJ/mol} = +39 \text{ kJ/mol}$

$\Delta E_{forward} = E_{products} - E_{reactants} = +39 \text{ kJ/mol} - 0 \text{ kJ/mol} = +39 \text{ kJ/mol}$

$\Delta E_{reverse} = E_{reactants} - E_{products} = 0 - 39 \text{ kJ/mol} = -39 \text{ kJ/mol}$

Practice, p. 574

1. Given: $3A \rightarrow C$
$[A]_1 = 0.2 \text{ M}$
$[A]_2 = 0.4 \text{ M}$
$rate_1 = 1.0 \text{ m/s}$
$rate_2 = 4.0 \text{ m/s}$

Unknown: rate law for
reaction

$rate = k[A]^n$

$\text{concentration ratio} = \dfrac{[A]_2}{[A]_1} = \dfrac{0.4 \text{ M}}{0.2 \text{ M}} = 2$

$\text{rate ratio} = \dfrac{rate_2}{rate_1} = \dfrac{4.0 \text{ m/s}}{1.0 \text{ m/s}} = 4$

when [A] doubles, the rate quadruples, or increases by a factor of 4, or 2^2.

rate low $= k[A]^2$

2. Given: rate law $= k[X]^3$
$[X]_2 = 3[X]_1$
Unknown: factor of rate increase

$$\text{rate}_2 = \frac{\text{rate}_1\,(3[X]_1)^3}{[X]_1^{\,3}} = 27 \times \text{rate}_1$$

The rate increases by a factor of 27.

Additional Sample Problems, p. 574

B-1. Given: $2Mn_2O_7(aq) \rightarrow$
$4Mn(s) = 7O_2(g)$
$[Mn_2O_7]_1 =$
7.5×10^{-5} M
$[Mn_2O_7]_2 =$
1.5×10^{-4} M
$\text{rate}_1 =$
1.2×10^{-4} m/s
$\text{rate}_2 =$
4.8×10^{-4} m/s

Unknown: rate law for reaction

$\text{rate} = k[Mn_2O_7]^n$

$$\text{concentration ratio} = \frac{[Mn_2O_7]_2}{[Mn_2O_7]_1} = \frac{1.5 \times 10^{-4}\ \text{M}}{7.5 \times 10^{-5}\ \text{M}} = 2$$

$$\text{rate ratio} = \frac{\text{rate}_2}{\text{rate}_1} = \frac{4.8 \times 10^{-4}}{1.2 \times 10^{-4}} = 4$$

when $[Mn_2O_7]$ changes by a factor of 2, rate changes by a factor of 4, or 2^2

rate law $= k[Mn_2O_7]^2$

B-2. Given: $A + B \rightarrow C$
$[A]_1 = 0.100$ M
$[A]_2 = 0.200$ M
$\text{rate}_1 =$
4.0×10^{-5} m/s
$\text{rate}_2 =$
16.0×10^{-5} m/s

Unknowns: rate law
rate constant

$\text{rate} = k[A]^n$

$$\text{concentration ratio} = \frac{[A]_2}{[A]_1} = \frac{0.200\ \text{M}}{0.100\ \text{M}} = 2$$

$$\text{rate ratio} = \frac{\text{rate}_2}{\text{rate}_1} = \frac{16.0 \times 10^{-5}\ \text{m/s}}{4.0 \times 10^{-5}\ \text{m/s}} = 4$$

when $[A]$ changes by a factor of 2, rate changes by a factor of 4, or 2^2.

rate law $= k[A]^2$

$$\text{rate constant} = \frac{\text{rate}}{[A]^2} = \frac{16 \times 10^{-5}\ \text{m/s}}{(0.200\ \text{M})^2} = \frac{4.0 \times 10^{-3}\ \text{L}}{\text{mol} \cdot \text{s}}$$

Additional Sample Problems, p. 575

C-1. Given: $\text{rate}_1 =$
1.3×10^{-4} m/s;
$[CH_3NC]_1 =$
0.040 M;
$[CH_3NC]_2 =$
0.025 M;
$CH_3NC \rightarrow$
CH_3CN
is first order

Unknown: rate_2

$$\text{rate}_2 = \text{rate}_1 \frac{[CH_3NC]_2^{\,1}}{[CH_3NC]_1^{\,1}} = 1.3 \times 10^{-4} \times \frac{0.025\ \text{M}}{0.040\ \text{M}}$$

$$\text{rate}_2 = 8.1 \times 10^{-5}\ \text{M/s}$$

Chapter Review

6. Unknown: $\Delta E_{forward}$, $\Delta E_{reverse}$, E_a, E_a'

$\Delta E_{forward}$ = energy of products – energy of reactants

$\Delta E_{reverse}$ = energy of reactants – energy of products

E_a = energy of activated complex – energy of reactants

E_a' = energy of activated complex – energy of products

a. $\Delta E_{forward}$ = +60 kJ/mol – (–20 kJ/mol) = +80 kJ/mol

$\Delta E_{reverse}$ = –20 kJ/mol – 60 kJ/mol = –80 kJ/mol

E_a = 80 kJ/mol – (–20 kJ/mol) = 100 kJ/mol

E_a' = 80 kJ/mol – 60 kJ/mol = 20 kJ/mol

b. $\Delta E_{forward}$ = –40 kJ/mol – 0 kJ/mol = –40 kJ/mol

$\Delta E_{reverse}$ = 0 kJ/mol – (–40 kJ/mol) = +40 kJ/mol

E_a = 20 kJ/mol – 0 kJ/mol = 20 kJ/mol

E_a' = 20 kJ/mol – (–40 kJ/mol) = 60 kJ/mol

c. $\Delta E_{forward}$ = 10 kJ/mol – 0 kJ/mol = +10 kJ/mol

$\Delta E_{reverse}$ = 0 kJ/mol – 10 kJ/mol = –10 kJ/mol

E_a = 70 kJ/mol – 0 kJ/mol = 70 kJ/mol

E_a' = 70 kJ/mol – 10 kJ/mol = 60 kJ/mol

7. a. Given: $\Delta E_{forward}$ = –10 kJ/mol

E_a' = 40 kJ/mol

Unknown: $\Delta E_{reverse}$, E_a

$\Delta E_{reverse}$ = energy of reactants – energy of products

= 0 kJ/mol – (–10 kJ/mol) = +10 kJ/mol

E_a = energy of activated complex – energy of reactants

= 30 kJ/mol – 0 kJ/mol = 30 kJ/mol

b. Given: $\Delta E_{forward}$ = –95 kJ/mol

E_a = 20 kJ/mol

Unknown: $\Delta E_{reverse}$, E_a'

$\Delta E_{reverse}$ = energy of reactants – energy of products

= 0 – (–95 kJ/mol) = +95 kJ/mol

E_a' = energy of activated complex – energy of products

= 20 kJ/mol – (–95 kJ/mol) = +115 kJ/mol

c. Given: $\Delta E_{reverse}$ = –40 kJ/mol

E_a' = 30 kJ/mol

Unknown: $\Delta E_{forward}$, E_a

$\Delta E_{forward}$ = energy of products – energy of reactants

= 40 kJ/mol – 0 = +40 kJ/mol

E_a = energy of activated complex – energy of reactants

= 70 kJ/mol – 0 = +70 kJ/mol

10.a. Given: Step 1: $B_2 + B_2 \rightarrow E_3 + D$, slow

Step 2: $E_3 + A \rightarrow B_2 + C_2$, fast

Unknown: balanced equation, rate law

$A + B_2 \rightarrow C_2 + D$

$R = k[B_2]^2$ (from the 2 molecules of B_2 in the rate-determining step)

11. Given: $2A + B \rightarrow A_2B$

Unknown: (a) rate law, (b) effect of doubling the concentration of either reactant on reaction rate

a. $R = k[A]^2[B]$

b. If [A] is doubled; the rate will increase fourfold: $R = k[2A]^2[B]$

If [B] is doubled, the rate will double: $R = k[A]^2[2B]$

---

12. Given: $A + 2B \rightarrow C$
(See data table, p. 549 for experimental data.)

a. Unknown: rate law

$R = k[A][B]^2$

b. Unknown: value of k (specific rate constant)

$R = k[A][B]^2$

$k = \dfrac{R}{[A][B]^2}$

$= \dfrac{2.0 \times 10^{-4} \text{ M/min}}{(0.20 \text{ M})(0.20 \text{ M})^2} = 2.5 \times 10^{-2} \text{ min M}^{-2}$

c. Unknown: initial rate that C is formed at, if initial concentrations of A and B = 0.30 M

$R = k[A][B]^2$

$= (2.5 \times 10^{-2} \text{ min}^{-1} \text{ M}^{-2})(0.30 \text{ M})(0.30 \text{ M})^2$

$= 6.8 \times 10^{-4} \text{ M/min}$

13a. Given: $\Delta E = +30 \text{ kJ/mol}$
$E_a' = 20 \text{ kJ/mol}$
energy of reactants = 0

Unknown: E_a

E_a = energy of activated complex − energy of reactants

$= 50 \text{ kJ/mol} - 0 = +50 \text{ kJ/mol}$

b. Given: $\Delta E = -30 \text{ kJ/mol}$
$E_a = 20 \text{ kJ/mol}$

Unknown: E_a'

E_a' = energy of activated complex − energy of products

$= 20 \text{ kJ/mol} - (-30 \text{ kJ/mol}) = +50 \text{ kJ/mol}$

---

14. Given: $R = k[A][B]^2$

a. Unknown: effect on R if [A] is cut in half

$R = k\frac{1}{2}[A][B]^2$

R is reduced by $\frac{1}{2}$.

b. Unknown: effect on R if [B] is tripled

$R = k[A][3B]^2$

R is increased by a factor of 9. (3^2)

c. Unknown: effect on R if [A] is doubled, but [B] is cut in half

$R = k[2A]\frac{1}{2}[B]^2$

R is reduced by $\frac{1}{2}$. $\left((2)\left(\frac{1}{2}\right)^2 = (2)\left(\frac{1}{4}\right) = \frac{1}{2}\right)$

1. Given: $O_2(g) + 2NO(g) \rightarrow$
$2NO_2(g)$

$[O_2]_1 =$
1.20×10^{-5} M

$[O_2]_2 =$
2.40×10^{-2} M

$[O_3]_3 =$
1.20×10^{-2} M

$[NO]_1 =$
1.40×10^{-2} M

$[NO]_2 =$
1.40×10^{-2} M

$[NO]_3 =$
2.80×10^{-2} M

$rate_1 =$
$3.30 \times 10^{-3} \frac{mol}{L \cdot s}$

$rate_2 =$
$6.60 \times 10^{-3} \frac{mol}{L \cdot s}$

$rate_3 =$
$1.32 \times 10^{-2} \frac{mol}{L \cdot s}$

Unknown: rate law for
reaction

O_2 concentration ratio $= \dfrac{[O_2]_2}{[O_2]_1} = \dfrac{2.40 \times 10^{-2} \text{ M}}{1.20 \times 10^{-2} \text{ M}} = 2$

O_2 rate ratio $= \dfrac{rate_2}{rate_1} = \dfrac{6.60 \times 10^{-3} \text{ m/s}}{3.30 \times 10^{-3} \text{ m/s}} = 2$

when $[O_2]$ doubles, rate increases by a factor of 2^1, so the reaction is 1st order in O_2

NO concentration ratio $= \dfrac{[NO]_3}{[NO]_2} = \dfrac{2.80 \times 10^{-3} \text{ M}}{1.40 \times 10^{-3} \text{ M}} = 2$

NO rate ratio $= \dfrac{rate_3}{rate_1} = \dfrac{1.32 \times 10^{-2}}{6.60 \times 10^{-3}} = 4$

when $[NO]$ doubles, rate increases by a factor of 4, or 2^2, so the reaction is 2nd order in NO.

rate law $= k[O_2][NO]^2$

2. Given: $2H_2(g) + C_2H_2(g)$
$\rightarrow C_2H_6(g)$

$[H_2]_1 = 0.20$ M

$[H_2]_2 = 0.40$ M

$[H_2]_3 = 0.20$ M

$[C_2H_2]_1 = 0.20$ M

$[C_2H_2]_2 = 0.20$ M

$[C_2H_2]_3 = 0.40$ M

$rate_1 =$
$1.5 \times 10^{-4} \frac{M}{min}$

$rate_2 =$
$3.0 \times 10^{-4} \frac{M}{min}$

$rate_3 =$
$1.5 \times 10^{-4} \frac{M}{min}$

Unknown: rate law for
reaction

H_2 concentration ratio $= \dfrac{[H_2]_2}{[H_2]_1} = \dfrac{0.40 \text{ M}}{0.20 \text{ M}} = 2$

H_2 rate ratio $= \dfrac{3.0 \times 10^{-4} \text{ M/min}}{1.5 \times 10^{-4} \text{ M/min}} = 2$

When $[H_2]$ doubles, the rate doubles, or increases by 2^1, so the reaction is first order in H_2.

C_2H_2 concentration ratio $= \dfrac{[C_2H_2]_3}{[C_2H_2]_1} = \dfrac{0.40 \text{ M}}{0.20 \text{ M}} = 2$

C_2H_2 rate ratio $= \dfrac{1.5 \times 10^{-4} \text{ M/min}}{1.5 \times 10^{-4} \text{ M/min}} = 1$

When $[C_2H_2]$ doubles, rate increases by a factor of $2^0 = 1$. That is, rate remains constant, so the reaction is zero order in C_2H_2.

rate law $= k[H_2]^1[C_2H_2]^0 = k[H_2]$

ATE, Additional Sample Problems, p. 594

A-1. Given: $[PCl_3] = 6.4 \times 10^{-3}$ mol/L

$[Cl_2] = 2.5 \times 10^{-2}$ mol/L

$[PCl_5] = 4.0 \times 10^{-3}$ mol/L

$PCl_5(g) \rightleftharpoons PCl_3(g) + C_2(g)$

Unknown: K

$$K = \frac{[PCl_3][Cl_2]}{[PCl_5]}$$

$$= \frac{(6.4 \times 10^{-3} \text{ mol/L})(2.5 \times 10^{-2} \text{ mol/L})}{(4.0 \times 10^{-3} \text{ mol/L})}$$

$$= 4.0 \times 10^{-2}$$

A-2. Given: volume = 2.0 L

$[H_2] = 0.36$ mol

$[Br_2] = 0.11$ mol

$[HBr] = 37$ mol

$H_2(g) + Br_2(g) \rightleftharpoons 2HBr(g)$

Unknown: K

$$K = \frac{[HBr]^2}{[H_2][Br_2]}$$

$$= \frac{(37 \text{ mol/2 L})^2}{(0.36 \text{ mol/2 L})(0.11 \text{ mol/2 L})}$$

$$= 3.5 \times 10^4$$

Practice, p. 595

1. Given: $[N_2] = 0.602$ mol/L

$[H_2] = 0.420$ mol/L

$[NH_3] = 0.113$ mol/L

$N_2(g) + 3H_2(g) \rightleftharpoons 2NH_3(g)$

Unknown: K

$$K = \frac{[NH_3]^2}{[N_2][H_2]^3}$$

$$= \frac{(0.113 \text{ mol/L})^2}{(0.602 \text{ mol/L})(0.420 \text{ mol/L})^3}$$

$$= 0.286$$

2. Given: $AB_2C = 0.084$ mol

$B_2 = 0.035$ mol

$AC = 0.059$ mol

volume = 5.00 L

$AB_2C(g) \rightleftharpoons B_2(g) + AC(g)$

Unknown: K

$$K = \frac{[B_2][AC]}{[AB_2C]}$$

$$= \frac{(0.035 \text{ mol/5 L})(0.059 \text{ mol/5 L})}{(0.084 \text{ mol/5 L})}$$

$$= 4.9 \times 10^{-3}$$

3. Given: $[SO_2] = 1.50$ mol/L $2SO_2(g) + O_2(g) \rightleftharpoons 2SO_3(g)$

$\qquad[O_2] = 1.25$ mol/L

$\qquad[SO_3] = 3.50$ mol/L $K = \dfrac{[SO_3]^2}{[SO_2]^2[O_2]}$

Unknown: K

$$= \dfrac{(3.50 \text{ mol/L})^2}{(1.50 \text{ mol/L})^2(1.25 \text{ mol/L})}$$

$$= 4.36$$

Section Review, p. 595

7. Given: $[HCl] =$
0.0625 mol/L

$[H_2] =$
0.0045 mol/L

$[Cl_2] =$
0.0045 mol/L

$H_2(g) + Cl_2(g) \rightleftharpoons$
$2HCl(g)$

Unknown: K

$$K = \dfrac{[HCl]^2}{[H_2][Cl_2]}$$

$$= \dfrac{(0.0625 \text{ mol/L})^2}{(0.0045 \text{ mol/L})(0.0045 \text{ mol/L})}$$

$$= 190$$

8. Given: $[H_2] =$
1.83×10^{-3} mol/L

$[I_2] =$
3.13×10^{-3} mol/L

$[HI] =$
1.77×10^{-2} mol/L

$H_2(g) + I_2(g) \rightleftharpoons$
$2HI(g)$

Unknown: K

$$K = \dfrac{[HI]^2}{[H_2][I_2]}$$

$$= \dfrac{(1.77 \times 10^{-2} \text{ mol/L})^2}{(1.83 \times 10^{-3} \text{ mol/L})(3.13 \times 10^{-3} \text{ mol/L})}$$

$$= 54.7$$

9. Given: $[H_2] =$
4.79×10^{-4} mol/L

$[I_2] =$
4.79×10^{-4} mol/L

$K = 54.3$

$H_2(g) + I_2(g) \rightleftharpoons$
$2HI(g)$

Unknown: $[HI]$

$$K = \dfrac{[HI]^2}{[H_2][I_2]}$$

$$[HI] = \sqrt{[H_2][I_2]K}$$

$$= \sqrt{(4.79 \times 10^{-4} \text{ mol/L})(4.79 \times 10^{-4} \text{ mol/L})(54.3)}$$

$$= 3.53 \times 10^{-3}$$

10. Given: $2HI(g) \rightleftharpoons H_2(g) + I_2(g)$

$K = \dfrac{[I_2][H_2]}{[HI]^2}$

Unknown: Value of K

For Experiment 1,

$$K = \frac{(0.4953 \times 10^{-3})(0.4953 \times 10^{-3})}{(3.655 \times 10^{-3})^2} = 1.836 \times 10^{-2}$$

The equilibrium constant for the reverse reaction is the reciprocal of the rate constant for the forward reaction.

Practice, p. 616

1. Given: solubility of $PbCl_2 = 1.0$ g/ 100. g H_2O

$$\text{solubility} = \left(\frac{1.0 \text{ g } PbCl_2}{100 \text{ g } H_2O}\right)\left(\frac{1 \text{ g } H_2O}{1 \text{ mL}}\right)\left(\frac{1000 \text{ mL}}{L}\right)\left(\frac{1 \text{ mol } PbCl_2}{278 \text{ g } PbCl_2}\right)$$

$$= 3.6 \times 10^{-2} \text{ mol/L } PbCl_2$$

Unknown: K_{sp}

$PbCl_2(s) \rightleftharpoons Pb^{2+}(aq) + 2Cl^-(aq)$

$[Pb^{2+}] = 3.6 \times 10^{-2}$

$[Cl^-] = 2(3.6 \times 10^{-2}) = 7.2 \times 10^{-2}$

$K_{sp} = [Pb^{2+}][Cl^-]^2$

$K_{sp} = (3.6 \times 10^{-2})(7.2 \times 10^{-2})^2$

$= 1.9 \times 10^{-4}$

2. Given: solubility of $Ag_2SO_4 = 5.0$ g/1.0 L H_2O

$$\text{solubility} = \left(\frac{5 \text{ g } Ag_2SO_4}{L}\right)\left(\frac{\text{mol } Ag_2SO_4}{311.77 \text{ g } Ag_2SO_4}\right)$$

$$= 0.016 \text{ mol/L } Ag_2SO_4$$

Unknown: K_{sp}

$Ag_2SO_4(s) \rightleftharpoons 2Ag^+(aq) + SO_4^{2-}(aq)$

$[Ag^+] = 2(0.016) = 0.032$

$[SO_4^-] = 0.016$

$K_{sp} = [Ag^+]^2[SO_4^-]$

$= 1.6 \times 10^{-5}$

ATE, Additional Sample Problems, p. 616

B-1. Given: solubility of SnS = 5.2×10^{-12} g/ 100 g H_2O

$$\text{solubility} = \left(\frac{5.2 \times 10^{-12} \text{ g SnS}}{100 \text{ g } H_2O}\right)\left(\frac{1 \text{ g}H_2O}{1 \text{ mL}}\right)\left(\frac{1000 \text{ mL}}{L}\right)\left(\frac{\text{mol SnS}}{150.78 \text{ g SnS}}\right)$$

$$= 3.4 \times 10^{-13} \text{ mol/L Sns}$$

Unknown: K_{sp}

$SnS(s) \rightleftharpoons Sn^2(aq) + S^{2-}(aq)$

$[Sn^{2+}] = 3.4 \times 10^{-13}$

$[S^{2-}] = 3.4 \times 10^{-13}$

$K_{sp} = [Sn^{2+}][S^{2-}]$

$= (3.4 \times 10^{-13})(3.4 \times 10^{-13})$

$= 1.2 \times 10^{-25}$

B-2. Given: solubility of $CaCO_3 = 5.3 \times 10^{-3}$ g/L H_2O

Unknown: K_{sp}

$$solubility = \left(\frac{5.3 \times 10^{-3} \text{ g } CaCO_3}{L}\right)\left(\frac{mol\ CaCO_3}{100.06 \text{ g } CaCO_3}\right)$$

$$= 5.3 \times 10^{-5} \text{ mol/L } CaCO_3$$

$$CaCO_3(s) \rightleftharpoons Ca^{2+}(aq) + CO_3^{2-}(aq)$$

$$[Ca^{2+}] = [CO_3^{2-}] = 5.3 \times 10^{-5}$$

$$K_{sp} = [Ca^{2+}][CO_3^{2-}]$$

$$= (5.3 \times 10^{-5})(5.3 \times 10^{-5})$$

$$= 2.8 \times 10^{-9}$$

Practice, p. 618

1. Given: K_{sp} of CdS $= 8.0 \times 10^{-27}$

Unknown: solubility of CdS in mol/L

$$CdS(s) \rightleftharpoons Cd^{2+}(aq) + S^{2-}(aq)$$

$$K_{sp} = [Cd^{2+}][S^{2-}]$$

$$[Cd^{2+}] = [S^{2-}] = x$$

$$K_{sp} = x^2$$

$$x^2 = 8.0 \times 10^{-27}$$

$$x = 8.9 \times 10^{-14} \text{ mol/L} = \text{solubility of CdS}$$

2. Given: K_{sp} of SrSO$_4$ = 3.2×10^{-7}

Unknown: $[Sr^{2+}]$

$$SrSO_4(s) \rightleftharpoons Sr^{2+}(aq) + SO_4^{2-}(aq)$$

$$K_{sp} = [Sr^{2+}][SO_4^{2-}]$$

$$[Sr^{2+}] = [SO_4^{2-}]$$

$$K_{sp} = x^2 = 3.2 \times 10^{-7}$$

$$x = \sqrt{3.2 \times 10^{-7}}$$

$$= 5.7 \times 10^{-4} \text{ mol/L} = [Sr^{2+}]$$

ATE, Additional Sample Problems, p. 618

C-1. Given: K_{sp} of MnS = 2.5×10^{-13}

Unknown: solubility of MnS in mol/L

$$MnS(s) \rightleftharpoons Mn^{2+}(aq) + S^{2-}(aq)$$

$$K_{sp} = [Mn^{2+}][S^{2-}]$$

$$[Mn^{2+}] = [S^{2-}]$$

$$K_{sp} = x^2$$

$$x^2 = 2.5 \times 10^{-13}$$

$$x = 5.0 \times 10^{-7} \text{ mol/L} = \text{solubility of MnS}$$

C-2. Given: K_{sp} of ZnS = 1.6×10^{-24}

Unknown: $[Zn^2]$

$$ZnS(s) \rightleftharpoons Zn^{2+}(aq) + S^{2-}(aq)$$

$$K_{sp} = [Zn^{2+}][S^{2-}]$$

$$[Zn^{2+}] = [S^{2-}]$$

$$K_{sp} = x^2 = 1.6 \times 10^{-24}$$

$$x = 1.3 \times 10^{-12} \text{ mol/L} = [Zn^{2+}]$$

D-1. Given: V NaCl = 0.02 L

$\quad$ [NaCl] = 0.034 M

$\quad$ V CuNO$_3$ = 0.15 L

$\quad$ [CuNO$_3$] = 0.083 M

Unknown: whether a precipitate forms

$NaCl + CuNO_3 \rightarrow NaNO_3 + CuCl$

$CuCl(s) \rightleftharpoons Cu^+(aq) + Cl^-(aq)$

$K_{sp} = [Cu^+][Cl^-] = 1.2 \times 10^{-6}$

$(0.15 \text{ L})\left(\dfrac{0.083 \text{ mol Cu}^+}{\text{L}}\right) = 1.2 \times 10^{-2} \text{ mol Cu}^+$

$(0.02 \text{ L})\left(\dfrac{0.034 \text{ mol Cl}^-}{\text{L}}\right) = 6.8 \times 10^{-4} \text{ mol Cl}^-$

total volume = 0.02 L + 0.15 L = 0.17 L

$\dfrac{1.2 \times 10^{-2} \text{ mol Cu}^+}{0.17 \text{ L}} = 7.0 \times 10^{-2} \text{ mol/L Cu}^+$

$\dfrac{6.8 \times 10^{-4} \text{ mol Cl}^-}{0.17 \text{ L}} = 4.0 \times 10^{-3} \text{ mol/L Cl}^-$

$[Cu^+][Cl^-] = (7.0 \times 10^{-2})(4.0 \times 10^{-3}) = 2.8 \times 10^{-4}$

$2.8 \times 10^{-4} > K_{sp}$; CuCl precipitates

D-2. Given: V Ca(NO$_3$)$_2$ = 0.1 L

$\quad$ [Ca(NO$_3$)$_2$] = 0.0014 M

$\quad$ V Na$_2$SO$_4$ = 0.2 L

$\quad$ [Na$_2$SO$_4$] = 0.000 20 M

Unknown: whether a precipitate forms

$Ca(NO_3)_2 + Na_2SO_4 \rightarrow CaSO_4 + NaNO_3$

$CaSO_4(s) \rightleftharpoons Ca^{2+}(aq) + SO_4^{2-}(aq)$

$K_{sp} = [Ca^{2+}][SO_4^{2-}] = 9.1 \times 10^{-6}$

$(0.1 \text{ L})\left(\dfrac{0.0014 \text{ mol Ca}^+}{\text{L}}\right) = 1.4 \times 10^{-4} \text{ mol Ca}^{2+}$

$(0.2 \text{ L})\left(\dfrac{0.0020 \text{ mol SO}_4^{2-}}{\text{L}}\right) = 4.0 \times 10^{-5} \text{ mol SO}_4^{2-}$

Total volume = 0.1 L + 0.2 L = 0.3 L

$\dfrac{1.4 \times 10^{-4} \text{ mol Ca}^{2+}}{0.3 \text{ L}} = 4.7 \times 10^{-4} \text{ mol/L Ca}^{2+}$

$\dfrac{4.0 \times 10^{-5} \text{ mol SO}_4^{2-}}{0.3 \text{ L}} = 1.3 \times 10^{-4} \text{ mol/L SO}_4^{2-}$

$[Ca^{2+}][SO_4^{2-}] = (4.7 \times 10^{-4})(1.3 \times 10^{-4})$

$\qquad\qquad = 6.1 \times 10^{-8}$

$6.1 \times 10^{-8} < 9.1 \times 10^{-6}$; CaSO$_4$ does not precipitate.

1. Given: $V\, AgNO_3 = 0.1$ L

    $[AgNO_3] =$ 0.0025 M

    $V\, NaBr = 0.150$ L

    $[NaBr] = 0.0020$ M

Unknown: whether a precipitate forms

$AgNO_3 + NaBr \rightarrow AgBr + NaNO_3$

$AgBr(s) \rightleftharpoons Ag^+(aq) + Br^-(aq)$

$K_{sp} = [Ag^+][Br^-] = 5.0 \times 10^{-13}$

$(0.150\text{ L})\left(\dfrac{0.0020\text{ mol Ag}^+}{\text{L}}\right) = 3.0 \times 10^{-4}\text{ mol Ag}^+$

$(0.100\text{ L})\left(\dfrac{0.0025\text{ mol Br}^-}{\text{L}}\right) = 2.5 \times 10^{-4}\text{ mol Br}^-$

Total volume = 0.150 L + 0.100 L = 0.250 L

$\dfrac{3.0 \times 10^{-4}\text{ mol Ag}^+}{0.250\text{ L}} = 1.2 \times 10^{-3}\text{ mol/L Ag}^+$

$\dfrac{2.5 \times 10^{-4}\text{ mol Br}^-}{0.250\text{ L}} = 1.0 \times 10^{-3}\text{ mol/L Br}^-$

$[Ag^+][Br^-] = (1.2 \times 10^{-3})(1.0 \times 10^{-3}) = 1.2 \times 10^{-6}$

$1.2 \times 10^{-6} > K_{sp}$; AgBr precipitates

2. Given: $V\, Pb(NO_3)_2 =$ 0.020 L

    $[Pb(NO_3)_2] =$ 0.038 M

    $V\, KCl = 0.030$ L

    $[KCl] = 0.018$ M

Unknown: whether a precipitate forms

$Pb(NO_3)_2 + 2KCl \rightarrow PbCl_2 + 2KNO_3$

$PbCl_2(s) \rightleftharpoons Pb^{2+}(aq) + 2Cl^-(aq)$

$K_{sp} = [Pb^{2+}][Cl^-]^2 = 1.6 \times 10^{-5}$

$(0.020\text{ L})\left(\dfrac{0.038\text{ mol Pb}^{2+}}{\text{L}}\right) = 7.6 \times 10^{-4}\text{ mol Pb}^{2+}$

$(0.030\text{ L})\left(\dfrac{0.018\text{ mol Cl}^-}{\text{L}}\right) = 5.4 \times 10^{-4}\text{ mol Cl}^-$

Total volume = 0.020 L + 0.030 L = 0.050 L

$\dfrac{7.6 \times 10^{-4}\text{ mol Pb}^{2+}}{0.050\text{ L}} = 1.5 \times 10^{-2}\text{ mol/L Pb}^{2+}$

$\dfrac{5.4 \times 10^{-4}\text{ mol Cl}^-}{0.050\text{ L}} = 1.1 \times 10^{-2}\text{ mol/L Cl}^-$

$[Pb^{2+}][Cl^-]^2 = (1.5 \times 10^{-2})(1.1 \times 10^{-2})^2$

$\qquad\qquad = 1.8 \times 10^{-6}$

$1.8 \times 10^{-6} < K_{sp}$; $PbCl_2$ does not precipitate.

Section Review, p. 620

5. Given: solubility of $Ag_2SO_4 = 5.40$ g/ 1.00 L H_2O

Unknown: K_{sp}

solubility $= \left(\dfrac{5.4\text{ g Ag}_2SO_4}{\text{L}}\right)\left(\dfrac{\text{mol Ag}_2SO_4}{311.75\text{ g Ag}_2SO_4}\right)$

$\qquad\qquad = 0.0173\text{ mol/L Ag}_2SO_4$

$Ag_2SO_4(s) \rightleftharpoons 2\,Ag^+(aq) + SO_4^{2-}(aq)$

$[Ag^+] = 2(0.0173) = 0.0346\text{ mol/L}$

$[SO_4^{2-}] = 0.0173\text{ mol/L}$

$K_{sp} = [Ag^+]^2[SO_4^{2-}]$

$\qquad = (0.0346)^2(0.0173)$

$\qquad = 2.07 \times 10^{-5}$

6. Given: V AgNO$_3$ = 0.02 L

$[$AgNO$_3] =$
1.00×10^{-7} M

V NaCl = 0.02 L

$[$NaCl$] =$
2.00×10^{-9} M

Unknown: whether a pre-
cipitate forms

AgNO$_3$ + NaCl → AgCl + NaNO$_3$

AgCl(s) ⇌ Ag$^+$(aq) + Cl$^-$(aq)

$K_{sp} = [$Na$^+][$Cl$^-] = 1.8 \times 10^{-10}$

$(0.02 \text{ L})\left(\dfrac{1.00 \times 10^{-7} \text{ mol Ag}^+}{\text{L}}\right) = 2.0 \times 10^{-9}$ mol Ag$^+$

$(0.02 \text{ L})\left(\dfrac{2.00 \times 10^{-9} \text{ mol Cl}^-}{\text{L}}\right) = 4.0 \times 10^{-11}$ mol Cl$^-$

Total volume = 0.02 L + 0.02 L = 0.04 L

$\dfrac{2.0 \times 10^{-9} \text{ mol Ag}^+}{0.04 \text{ L}} = 5.0 \times 10^{-8}$ mol/L Ag$^+$

$\dfrac{4.0 \times 10^{-11} \text{ mol Cl}^-}{0.04 \text{ L}} = 1.0 \times 10^{-9}$ mol/L Cl$^-$

$[$Ag$^+][$Cl$^-] = (5.0 \times 10^{-8})(1.0 \times 10^{-9})$

$= 5.0 \times 10^{-17}$

$5.0 \times 10^{-17} < K_{sp}$; AgCl does not precipitate.

---

7. Given: Solution of
0.20 M Ca(NO$_3$)$_2$,
Cr(NO$_3$)$_3$, and
La(NO$_3$)$_3$.

$[$F$^-] = 1.0 \times 10^{-4}$ M

K_{sp} for CaF$_2$ =
3.9×10^{-11}

K_{sp} for CaF$_3$ =
6.6×10^{-11}

K_{sp} for LaF$_3$ =
4.0×10^{-17}

Unknown: which metal
fluorides will
form a
precipitate

For CaF$_2$:

$[$Ca$^{2+}][$F$^-]^2 = (0.20)(1.0 \times 10^{-4})^2 = 2.0 \times 10^{-9}$

$K_{sp} < 2.0 \times 10^{-9}$, so a precipitate of CaF$_2$ will form.

For CrF$_3$:

$[$Cr$^{3+}][$F$^-]^3 = (0.20)(1.0 \times 10^{-4})^3 = 2.0 \times 10^{-13}$

$K_{sp} > 2.0 \times 10^{-13}$, so a precipitate of CrF$_3$ will not form.

For LaF$_3$:

$[$La$^{3+}][$F$^-]^3 = (0.20)(1.0 \times 10^{-4})^3 = 2.0 \times 10^{-13}$

$K_{sp} < 2.0 \times 10^{-13}$, so a precipitate of LaF$_3$ will form.

4. Unknown: K

a. Given: $[A] = 2.0$
$[B] = 3.0$
$[C] = 4.0$

$A + B \rightleftharpoons C$

$$K = \frac{[C]}{[A][B]}$$

$$= \frac{4.0}{(2.0)(3.0)} = 0.67$$

b. Given: $[D] = 1.5$
$[E] = 2.0$
$[F] = 1.8$
$[G] = 1.2$

$D + 2E \rightleftharpoons F + 3G$

$$K = \frac{[F][G]^3}{[D][E]^2} = \frac{(1.8)(1.2)^3}{(1.5)(2.0)^2} = 0.52$$

c. Given: $[N_2] = 0.45$
$[H_2] = 0.14$
$[NH_3] = 0.62$

$N_2(g) + 3H_2(g) \rightleftharpoons$
$2NH_3(g)$

$$K = \frac{[NH_3]^2}{[N_2][H_2]^3} = \frac{(0.62)^2}{(0.45)(0.14)^3} = 310$$

5. Given: $[HCl] =$
1.2×10^{-3} mol/L

$[O_2] =$
3.8×10^{-4} mol/L

$[H_2O] =$
5.8×10^{-2} mol/L

$[Cl_2] =$
5.8×10^{-2} mol/L

$4HCl(g) + O_2(g) \rightleftharpoons$
$2H_2O(g) +$
$2Cl_2(g)$

Unknown: K

$$K = \frac{[H_2O]^2[Cl_2]^2}{[HCl]^4[O_2]}$$

$$= \frac{(5.8 \times 10^{-2})^2(5.8 \times 10^{-2})^2}{(1.2 \times 10^{-3})^4(3.8 \times 10^{-4})}$$

$$= 1.4 \times 10^{10}$$

6. Given: $K = 6.59 \times 10^{-3}$

$[NH_3] =$
1.23×10^{-4} M

$[H_2] =$
2.75×10^{-2} M

$N_2(g) + 3H_2(g) \rightleftharpoons 2NH_3(g)$

Unknown: $[N_2]$

$$K = \frac{[NH_3]^2}{[N_2][H_2]^3}$$

$$[N_2] = \frac{[NH_3]^2}{K[H_2]^3}$$

$$= \frac{(1.23 \times 10^{-4} \text{ M})^2}{(6.59 \times 10^{-3} \text{ M})(2.75 \times 10^{-2} \text{ M})^3}$$

$$= 0.110$$

7. Given: $K = 40.0$

$$H_2(g) + I_2(g) \rightleftharpoons 2HI(g)$$

Unknown: K for reverse reaction

$$2HI(g) \rightleftharpoons H_2(g) - I_2(g)$$

K for forward reaction $= 40.0 = \dfrac{[HI]^2}{[H_2][I_2]}$

K for reverse reaction $= \dfrac{[H_2][I_2]}{[HI]^2} = \dfrac{1}{40.0}$

$\qquad\qquad = 0.0250$

---

28. Given: solubility of EJ $= 8.45 \times 10^{-6}$ mol/L

Unknown: K_{sp}

$$EJ \rightleftharpoons E^{2+} + J^{2-}$$

$[E^{2+}] = 8.45 \times 10^{-6} = [J^{2-}]$

$K_{sp} = [E^{2+}][J^{2-}]$

$\qquad = (8.45 \times 10^{-6})(8.45 \times 10^{-6})$

$\qquad = 7.14 \times 10^{-11}$

---

29. Unknown: K_{sp}

   a. Given: solubility of $BaSO_4 =$ 2.4×10^{-4} g/ 100. g H_2O

solubility $= \left(\dfrac{2.4 \times 10^{-4} \text{ g } BaSO_4}{100 \text{ g } H_2O}\right)\left(\dfrac{1 \text{ g } H_2O}{1 \text{ mL}}\right)\left(\dfrac{1000 \text{ mL}}{L}\right)\left(\dfrac{1 \text{ mol } BaSO_4}{233.36 \text{ g } BaSO_4}\right)$

$\qquad = 1.0 \times 10^{-5}$ mol/L $BaSO_4$

$$BaSO_4(s) \rightleftharpoons Ba^{2+}(aq) + SO_4^{2-}(aq)$$

$[Ba^{2+}] = 1.0 \times 10^{-5} = [SO_4^{2-}]$

$K_{sp} = [Ba^{2+}][SO_4^{2-}]$

$\qquad = (1.0 \times 10^{-5})(1.0 \times 10^{-5})$

$\qquad = 1.0 \times 10^{-10}$

   b. Given: solubility of $Ca(OH)_2 =$ 0.173 g/100. g H_2O

solubility $= \left(\dfrac{0.173 \text{ g } Ca(OH)_2}{100 \text{ g } H_2O}\right)\left(\dfrac{1 \text{ g } H_2O}{1 \text{ mL}}\right)\left(\dfrac{1000 \text{ mL}}{L}\right)\left(\dfrac{1 \text{ mol } Ca(OH)_2}{74.1 \text{ g } Ca(OH)_2}\right)$

$\qquad = 0.0233$ mol/L $Ca(OH)_2$

$$Ca(OH)_2(s) \rightleftharpoons Ca^{2+}(aq) + 2OH^-(aq)$$

$[Ca^{2+}] = 0.0233$

$[OH^-] = 2(0.0233) = 0.0466$

$K_{sp} = [Ca^{2+}][OH^-]^2$

$\qquad = (0.0233)(0.0466)^2$

$\qquad = 5.06 \times 10^{-5}$

---

30. Given: K_{sp} of $MN = 8.1 \times 10^{-6}$

Unknown: solubility of MN

$$MN \rightleftharpoons M^{2+} + N^{2-}$$

$K_{sp} = [M^{2+}][N^{2-}]$

$[M^{2+}] = [N^{2-}] = x$

$K_{sp} = x^2 = 8.1 \times 10^{-6}$

$x = 2.8 \times 10^{-3}$ mol/L $=$ solubility of MN

31. a. Given: K_{sp} of AgBr = 5.0×10^{-13}

Unknown: solubility of AgBr

$AgBr(s) \rightarrow Ag^+(aq) + Br^-(aq)$

$K_{sp} = [Ag^+][Br^-]$

$[Ag^+] = [Br^-] = x$

$K_{sp} = x^2 = 5.0 \times 10^{-13}$

$x = 7.1 \times 10^{-7}$ mol/L = solubility of AgBr

b. Given: K_{sp} of CoS = 4.0×10^{-21}

Unknown: solubility of CoS

$CoS(s) \rightleftharpoons Co^{2+}(aq) + S^{2-}(aq)$

$K_{sp} = [Co^{2+}][S^{2-}]$

$[Co^{2+}] = [S^{2-}] = x$

$K_{sp} = x^2 = 4.0 \times 10^{-21}$

$x = 6.3 \times 10^{-11}$ mol/L = solubility of CoS

33. Given: $T_3U_2 \rightarrow T^{2+} + U^{3-}$

solubility of T_3U_2 = 3.8×10^{-10} mol/L

Unknown: K_{sp}

$T_3U_2(s) \rightleftharpoons 3T^{2+}(aq) + 2U^{3-}(aq)$

$K_{sp} = [T^{2+}]^3[U^{3-}]^2$

$[T^{2+}] = 3(3.8 \times 10^{-10}) = 1.14 \times 10^{-9}$

$[U^{3-}] = 2(3.8 \times 10^{-10}) = 7.6 \times 10^{-10}$

$K_{sp} = (1.14 \times 10^{-9})^3(7.6 \times 10^{-10})^2$

$= (1.48 \times 10^{-27})(5.78 \times 10^{-19})$

$= 8.6 \times 10^{-46}$

34. Given: $[Ag^+] = 2.7 \times 10^{-10}$ mol/L

Unknown: $[I^-]$

$AgI(s) \rightleftharpoons Ag^+(aq) + I^-(aq)$

K_{sp} of AgI = 8.3×10^{-17}

$K_{sp} = [Ag^+][I^-]$

$[I^-] = K_{sp}/[Ag^+]$

$= 8.3 \times 10^{-17}/2.7 \times 10^{-10}$ mol/L

$= 3.1 \times 10^{-7}$ mol/L

35. Given: V Ca(NO$_3$)$_2$ = 0.35 L

$[Ca(NO_3)_2]$ = 0.0044 M

V NaOH = 0.17 L

$[NaOH]$ = 0.000 39 M

Unknown: whether a precipitate forms

$Ca(NO_3)_2 + NaOH \rightarrow Ca(OH)_2 + NaNO_3$

$Ca(OH)_2(s) \rightleftharpoons Ca^{2+}(aq) + 2OH^-(aq)$

$K_{sp} = [Ca^{2+}][OH^-]^2 = 5.5 \times 10^{-6}$

$(0.35 \text{ L})\left(\dfrac{0.0044 \text{ mol Ca}^{2+}}{\text{L}}\right) = 1.5 \times 10^{-3}$ mol Ca^{2+}

$(0.17 \text{ L})\left(\dfrac{0.0003\ 39 \text{ mol OH}^-}{\text{L}}\right) = 6.6 \times 10^{-5}$ mol OH$^-$

Total volume = 0.35 L + 0.17 L = 0.52 L

$\dfrac{1.5 \times 10^{-3} \text{ mol Ca}^{2+}}{0.52 \text{ L}} = 2.9 \times 10^{-3}$ mol/L Ca^{2+}

$\dfrac{6.6 \times 10^{-5} \text{ mol OH}^-}{0.52 \text{ L}} = 1.3 \times 10^{-4}$ mol/L OH$^-$

$[Ca^{2+}][OH^-]^2 = (2.9 \times 10^{-3})(1.3 \times 10^{-4})^2$

$= 4.9 \times 10^{-11}$

$4.9 \times 10^{-11} < K_{sp}$; Ca(OH)$_2$ does not precipitate.

36. Given: solubility of $AgNO_3 = 1.70$ g/200. mL H_2O

solubility of $NaCl = 14.5$ g/200 mL H_2O

Unknown: whether a precipitate will form

$AgNO_3 + NaCl \rightarrow AgCl + NaNO_3$

$AgCl(s) \rightleftharpoons Ag^+(aq) + Cl^-(aq)$

$K_{sp} = [Ag^+][Cl^-] = 1.8 \times 10^{-10}$

$(1.70 \text{ g } AgNO_3)\left(\dfrac{1 \text{ mol } AgNO_3}{169.85 \text{ g } AgNO_3}\right) = 0.0100 \text{ mol } AgNO_3 = 0.0100 \text{ mol } Ag^+$

$\left(\dfrac{0.0100 \text{ mol } Ag^+}{200. \text{ mL}}\right)\left(\dfrac{1000 \text{ mL}}{L}\right) = 0.0500 \text{ mol/L } Ag^+$

$(14.5 \text{ g } NaCl)\left(\dfrac{1 \text{ mol } NaCl}{58.44 \text{ g } NaCl}\right) = 0.248 \text{ mol } NaCl = 0.248 \text{ mol } Cl^-$

$\left(\dfrac{0.248 \text{ mol } Cl^-}{200. \text{ mL}}\right)\left(\dfrac{1000 \text{ mL}}{L}\right) = 1.24 \text{ mol/L } Cl^-$

$[Ag^+][Cl^-] = (0.0500)(1.24) = 6.20 \times 10^{-2}$

$6.20 \times 10^{-2} > K_{sp}$; AgCl precipitates.

---

37. Given: 2.50×10^{-2} g $Fe(NO_3)_3$

100. mL 1.0×10^{-4} NaOH solution

Unknown: will $Fe(OH)_3$ precipitate?

$Fe(OH)_3 \rightarrow Fe^{3+} + 3OH^- \qquad K_{sp} = 4.0 \times 10^{-38}$

$\dfrac{2.50 \times 10^{-2} \text{g } Fe(NO_3)_3}{0.100 \text{ L} \times 241.88 \text{ g/mol}} = [Fe^{3+}] = 1.03 \times 10^{-3} \text{ M}$

Ion product $= [Fe^{3+}][3OH^-]^3 = 2.79 \times 10^{-14}$

Since Ion product $> K_{sp}$, a precipitate of $Fe(OH)_3$ will form.

---

39. a. Given: HgS(s) forms a saturated solution

Unknown: $[Hg^{2+}]$

a. $HgS(s) \rightleftharpoons Hg^{2+}(aq) + S^{2-}(aq)$

$K_{sp} = [Hg^{2+}][S^{2-}]$

$[Hg^{2+}] = [S^{2-}] = x$

$K_{sp} = x^2 = 1.6 \times 10^{-52}$

$x = 1.3 \times 10^{-26} \text{ mol/L} = [Hg^{2+}]$

b. Given: saturated HgS solution

Unknown: Number of Hg^{2+} ions in 1000 L of HgS solution

b. $HgS \rightarrow Hg^{2+} + S^{2-} \quad K_{sp} = 1.6 \times 10^{-52}$

$K_{sp} = [Hg^{3+}][S^{2-}] = [Hg^{2+}]^2$

$[Hg^{2+}] = \sqrt{K_{sp}} = \sqrt{1.6 \times 10^{-52}} \approx 1.3 \times 10^{-26} \text{ M}$

$1.26 \times 10^{-26} \text{ mol/L} \times 1000 \text{ L} \times 6.022 \times 10^{23} \text{ ions/mol} \approx 8 \text{ ions}$

---

40. Given: $H_2(g) + CO_2(g) \rightleftharpoons H_2O(g) + CO(g)$

$[H_2] = 0.061$ mol/L

$[CO_2] = 0.16$ mol/L

$[H_2O] = 0.11$ mol/L

$[CO] = 0.14$ mol/L

Unknown: K

$K = \dfrac{[H_2O][CO]}{[H_2][CO_2]}$

$= \dfrac{(0.11 \text{ mol/L})(0.14 \text{ mol/L})}{(0.061 \text{ mol/L})(0.16 \text{ mol/L})}$

$= 1.6$

41. Given: $[Ba^{2+}] = 5.0 \times 10^{-4}$ M $\quad Ba_3(PO_4)_2(s) \rightleftharpoons 3Ba^{2+}(aq) + 2\,PO_4^{3-}(aq)$

$\qquad K_{sp} = 3.4 \times 10^{-23} \qquad K_{sp} = [Ba^{2+}]^3[PO_4^{3-}]^2$

$\qquad$ solute $= Ba_3(PO_4)_2 \qquad [PO_4^{3-}]^2 = K_{sp}/[Ba^{2+}]^3$

$\qquad$ Unknown: $[PO_4^{3-}] \qquad [PO_4^{3-}] = \sqrt{K_{sp}/[Ba^{2+}]^3}$

$$= \sqrt{3.4 \times 10^{-23}/(5.0 \times 10^{-4})^3}$$

$$= 5.2 \times 10^{-7} \text{ mol/L } PO_4^{3-}$$

---

42. Given: $K = 1.7 \times 10^{-13} \qquad K = \dfrac{[NO]^4}{[N_2O]^2[O_2]}$

$\qquad 2N_2O(g) + O_2(g) \rightleftharpoons$
$\qquad 4NO(g)$

$\qquad [N_2O] = \qquad\qquad [NO]^4 = \sqrt{K\,[N_2O]^2[O_2]}$
$\qquad 0.0035$ mol/L $\qquad [NO] = \sqrt[4]{K\,[N_2O]^2[O_2]}$

$\qquad [O_2] = \qquad\qquad\quad = \sqrt[4]{(1.7 \times 10^{-13})(0.0035)^2(0.0027)}$
$\qquad 0.0027$ mol/L $\qquad\quad = \sqrt[4]{5.6 \times 10^{-21}}$

$\qquad$ Unknown: $[NO] \qquad\quad = 8.7 \times 10^{-6}$

---

43. Given: K_{sp} of fluorapatite $\qquad Ca_5(PO_4)_3F \rightleftharpoons 5Ca^{2+} + 3PO_4^{3-} + F^-(aq)$
$\qquad (Ca_5(PO_4)_3F) =$
$\qquad 1 \times 10^{-60} \qquad\qquad K_{sp} = [Ca^{2+}]^5[PO_4^{3-}]^3[F^-]$

$\qquad\qquad\qquad\qquad\qquad$ Let $[F^-] = x$

$\qquad$ Unknown: solubility of $\qquad$ Therefore $[Ca^{2+}] = 5x$ and $[PO_4^{3-}] = 3x$
$\qquad\quad$ fluorapatite in
$\qquad\quad H_2O \qquad\qquad\qquad K_{sp} = [5x]^5[3x]^3[x]$

$\qquad\qquad\qquad\qquad\qquad K_{sp} = [3125x^5][27x^3][x] = 84375x^9$

$\qquad\qquad\qquad\qquad\qquad 1 \times 10^{-60} = 84375x^9$

$\qquad\qquad\qquad\qquad\qquad x^9 = 1.2 \times 10^{-65}$

$\qquad\qquad\qquad\qquad\qquad x = 6.1 \times 10^{-8} \text{ mol/L}$

---

44. Given: amount of $\qquad Na_2CO_3 + BaBr_2 \rightarrow NaBr + BaCO_3$
$\qquad\quad Na_2CO_3 =$
$\qquad\quad 0.96$ g/10 L $\qquad NaBr(s) \rightleftharpoons Na^+(aq) + Br^-(aq)$

$\qquad$ amount of $BaBr_2 = \qquad K_{sp} = [Na^+][Br^-]$
$\qquad\quad 0.20$ g/10 L

$\qquad K_{sp} = 2.8 \times 10^{-9} \qquad (0.96 \text{ g } Na_2CO_3)\left(\dfrac{2 \text{ mol } Na^+}{105.96 \text{ g } Na_2NO_3}\right) = 1.8 \times 10^{-2} \text{ mol } Na^+$

$\qquad$ Unknown: whether a $\qquad \dfrac{1.8 \times 10^{-2} \text{ mol } Na^+}{10 \text{ L}} = 1.8 \times 10^{-3} \text{ mol/L } Na^+$
$\qquad\quad$ precipitate
$\qquad\quad$ will form

$\qquad\qquad\qquad (0.20 \text{ g } BaBr_2)\left(\dfrac{2 \text{ mol } Br^-}{297.13 \text{ g } BaBr_2}\right) = 1.3 \times 10^{-3} \text{ mol } Br^-$

$\qquad\qquad\qquad \dfrac{1.3 \times 10^{-3} \text{ mol } Br^-}{10 \text{ L}} = 1.3 \times 10^{-4} \text{ mol/L } Br^-$

$\qquad\qquad\qquad [Na^+][Br^-] = (1.8 \times 10^{-2})(1.3 \times 10^{-4}) = 2.3 \times 10^{-6}$

$\qquad\qquad\qquad 2.3 \times 10^{-6} > K_{sp}; \text{ NaBr precipitates.}$

45. Given: $K = 5.2 \times 10^{-5}$ for NH_3

$[N_2] = 2.00$ M

$[H_2] = 0.80$ M

$N_2(g) + 3H_2(g) \rightleftharpoons 2NH_3(g)$

Unknown: number of grams of NH_3 in 10 L at equilibrium

$$K = \frac{[NH_3]^2}{[N_2][H_2]^3}$$

$$[NH_3]^2 = K[N_2][H_2]^3$$

$$[NH_3] = \sqrt{K[N_2][H_2]^3}$$

$$= \sqrt{(5.2 \times 10^{-5})(2.00 \text{ M})(0.80 \text{ M})^3}$$

$$= \sqrt{5.32 \times 10^{-5}} = 7.3 \times 10^{-3} \text{ M}$$

$$\left(\frac{7.3 \times 10^{-3} \text{ mol NH}_3}{L}\right)\left(\frac{17.04 \text{ g NH}_3}{mol}\right)$$

$$= 1.2 \times 10^{-1} \text{ g NH}_3/L = 1.2 \text{ g/10 L}$$

Math Tutor, p. 626

1a. Given: $A(ag) + 2B(ag) \rightleftharpoons AB_2(ag)$

Unknown: equilibrium constant, K

$$K = \frac{[AB_2]}{[A][B]^2}$$

b. Given: $2DE_2(g) \rightleftharpoons D_2(g) + 2E_2(g)$

Unknown: equilibrium constant, K

$$K = \frac{[D_2][E_2]^2}{[DE_2]^2}$$

2. Given: $2BrF_5(g) \rightleftharpoons Br_2(g) + 5F_2(g)$

$[BrF_5] = 0.000137$ mol/L

$[Br_2] = 0.00050$ mol/L

$[F_2] = 0.0025$ mol/L

Unknown: value of equilibrium constant, K

$$K = \frac{[F_2]^5[Br_2]}{[BrF_5]^2} = \frac{(0.0025)^5 (0.00050)}{(0.000137)^2} = 2.6 \times 10^{-9}$$

Standardized Test Prep, p. 627

4. Given: $CdCO_3 \rightleftharpoons Cd^{2+} + CO_3^{2-}$

$K_{sp} = 1.0 \times 10^{-12}$

Unknown: $[Cd^{2+}]$

$$K_{sp} = [Cd^{2+}][CO_3^{2-}] = [Cd^{2+}]^2$$

$$[Cd^{2+}] = \sqrt{K_{sp}} = \sqrt{1.0 \times 10^{-12}} = 1.0 \times 10^{-6} \text{ M}$$

CHAPTER 19

Oxidation-Reduction Reactions

Section Review, p. 635

3. Unknown: if reaction is a redox reaction

a. $2KNO_3(s) \rightarrow 2KNO_2(s) + O_2(g)$

$$\overset{+1\,+5\,-2}{2K\,N\,O_3^-} \rightarrow \overset{+1\,+3\,-2}{2K\,N\,O_2^-} + \overset{0}{O_2}$$

$$\overset{-2}{2O} \rightarrow \overset{0}{O_2} + 4e^-$$

$$\overset{+5}{2N} + 4e^- \rightarrow \overset{+3}{2N}$$

redox

b. $H_2(g) + CuO(s) \rightarrow Cu(s) + H_2O(\ell)$

$$\overset{0}{H_2} + \overset{+2\,-2}{CuO} \rightarrow \overset{0}{Cu} + \overset{+1\,-2}{H_2O}$$

$$\overset{0}{H_2} \rightarrow \overset{+1}{2H} + 2e^-$$

$$\overset{+2}{Cu} + 2e^- \rightarrow \overset{0}{Cu}$$

redox

c. $NaOH(aq) + HCl(aq) \rightarrow NaCl(aq) + H_2O(\ell)$

$$\overset{+1\,-2\,+1}{Na\,O\,H} + \overset{+1\,-1}{HCl} \rightarrow \overset{+1\,-1}{NaCl} + \overset{+1\,-2}{H_2O}$$

not redox

d. $H_2(g) + Cl_2(g) \rightarrow 2HCl(g)$

$$\overset{0}{H_2} + \overset{0}{Cl_2} \rightarrow \overset{+1\,-1}{2HCl}$$

$$\overset{0}{H_2} \rightarrow \overset{+1}{2H} + 2e^-$$

$$\overset{0}{Cl_2} + 2e^- \rightarrow \overset{-1}{2Cl}$$

redox

e. $SO_3(g) + H_2O(\ell) \rightarrow H_2SO_4(aq)$

$$\overset{+6\,-2}{S\,O_3} + \overset{+1\,-2}{H_2O} \rightarrow \overset{+1\,+6\,-2}{H_2S\,O_4}$$

not redox

Practice Problems, p. 641

1. Given: $Cu + H_2SO_4 \rightarrow CuSO_4 + SO_2 + H_2O$

Unknown: balanced equation

$$Cu \rightarrow Cu^{2+} + 2e^-$$

$$SO_4^{2-} + 4H^+ + 2e^- \rightarrow SO_2 + 2H_2O$$

$$\overline{Cu + SO_4^{2-} + 4H^+ \rightarrow Cu^{2+} + SO_2 + 2H_2O}$$

$$Cu + 2H_2SO_4 \rightarrow CuSO_4 + SO_2 + 2H_2O$$

2. Given: $HNO_3 + KI \rightarrow KNO_3 + I_2 + NO + H_2O$

Unknown: balanced equation

$$3[2I^- \rightarrow \overset{0}{I_2} + 2e^-]$$

$$2[\overset{+5}{NO_3^-} + 4H^+ + 3e^- \rightarrow \overset{+2}{NO} + 2H_2O]$$

$$\overline{2NO_3^- + 8H^+ + 6I^- \rightarrow 3I_2 + 2NO + 4H_2O}$$

$$8HNO_3 + 6KI \rightarrow 6KNO_3 + 3I_2 + 2NO + 4H_2O$$

A-1. Given: $K_2Cr_2O_7$ + C_2H_5OH + HCl → $CrCl_3$ + H_2O + CO_2 + KCl

Unknown: balanced equation

$$\overset{-2}{C_2H_5OH} + 3H_2O \rightarrow 2\overset{+4}{C}O_2 + 12H^+ + 12e^-$$

$$2[\overset{+6}{Cr_2O_7^{2-}} + 1\overset{+1}{4H^+} + 6e^- \rightarrow 2\overset{+3}{Cr}^{3+} + 7H_2O]$$

$$2Cr_2O_7^{2-} + C_2H_5OH + 3H_2O + 28H^+ \rightarrow 4Cr^{3+} + 14H_2O + 2CO_2 + 12H^+$$

$$2K_2Cr_2O_7 + C_2H_5OH + 16\ HCl \rightarrow 4CrCl_3 + 11H_2O + 2CO_2 + 4\ KCl$$

Section Review, p. 641

3. Given: Na_2SnO_2 + $Bi(OH)_3$ → Bi + Na_2SnO_3 + H_2O

Unknown: balanced equation

$$3[\overset{+2}{Na_2SnO_2} + H_2O \rightarrow \overset{+4}{Na_2SnO_3} + 2H^+ + 2e^-]$$

$$2[\overset{+3}{Bi(OH)_3} + 3H^+ + 3e^- \rightarrow \overset{0}{Bi} + 3H_2O]$$

$$3Na_2SnO_2 + 3H_2O + 2Bi(OH)_3 + 6H^+ \rightarrow 3Na_2SnO_3 + 6H^+ + 2Bi + 6H_2O$$

$$3Na_2SnO_2 + 2Bi(OH)_3 \rightarrow 2Bi + 3Na_2SnO_3 + 3H_2O$$

4. Given: $P_4 + H_2O \rightarrow PH_3 + H_3PO_4$ (unbalanced) 56 g P_4

Unknown: g PH_3 formed

Reduction: $P \rightarrow P^{3-}$

Oxidation $P \rightarrow P^{5+}$

$2P_4 \rightarrow 5P^{3-} + 3P^{5+}$ balancing charges

$2P_4 + H_2O \rightarrow 5PH_3 + 3H_3PO_4$ known species

$2P_4 + 12H_2O \rightarrow 5PH_3 + 3H_3PO_4$ balancing H + O

$$\frac{56\ g\ P_4}{123.88\ g\ P_4/mol\ P_4} \times \frac{5\ mol\ PH_3}{2\ mol\ P_4} \times \frac{34\ g\ PH_3}{mol\ PH_3} = 38\ g\ PH_3$$

Chapter Review

5. Unknown: if reaction is a redox reaction

a. $2NH_4Cl(aq)$ + $Ca(OH)_2(aq) \rightarrow$ $2NH_3(aq) + 2H_2O(\ell)$ + $CaCl_2(aq)$

Ionic equation:

$$2\overset{-3+1}{NH_4^+} + \overset{-1}{Cl^-} + \overset{+2}{Ca^{2+}} + 2\overset{-2+1}{OH^-} \rightarrow 2\overset{-3+1}{NH_3} + 2\overset{+1\ -2}{H_2O} + \overset{+2}{Ca^{2+}} + 2\overset{-1}{Cl^-}$$

nonredox

b. $2HNO_3(aq) + 3H_2S(g)$ $\rightarrow 2NO(g) + 4H_2O(\ell) +$ $3S(s)$

Ionic equation:

$$2\overset{+1}{H^+} + \overset{+5\ -2}{NO_3^-} + 3\overset{+1\ -2}{H_2S} \rightarrow 2\overset{+2\ -2}{NO} + 4\overset{+1\ -2}{H_2O} + 3\overset{0}{S}$$

$$2\overset{+5}{NO_3^-} + 6e^- \rightarrow 2\overset{+2}{NO}$$

$$3\overset{-2}{H_2S} \rightarrow 3\overset{0}{S} + 6e^-$$

redox

c. $[Be(H_2O)_4]^{2+}(aq) +$
$H_2O(\ell) \rightarrow H_3O^+(aq) +$
$[Be(H_2O)_3OH]^+(aq)$

Ionic equation:

$$\overset{+2}{[Be}\overset{+1}{(H_2}\overset{-2}{O)_4]^{2+}} + \overset{+1}{H_2}\overset{-2}{O} \rightarrow \overset{+1}{H_3}\overset{-2}{O^+} + \overset{+2}{[Be}\overset{+1}{(H_2}\overset{-2}{O)_3}\overset{-2+1}{O\,H]^+}$$

nonredox

6.

Oxidation numbers:

$$\overset{0}{Xe}, \overset{+1-1}{XeF}, \overset{+2\,-1}{XeF_2}, \overset{+4-2-1}{XeOF_2},$$

$$\overset{+6-2}{XeO_3}, \overset{+1\,+7-1}{CsXeF_8}$$

---

17. Unknown: if reaction is a
redox reaction

a. $\overset{0}{Mg}(s) + \overset{+2\,-1}{ZnCl_2}(aq) \rightarrow$
$\overset{0}{Zn}(s) + \overset{+2\,-1}{MgCl_2}(aq)$

$\overset{0}{Mg} \rightarrow Mg^{2+} + 2e^-$

$Zn^{2+} + 2e^- \rightarrow \overset{0}{Zn}$

redox

b. $\overset{0}{H_2}(g) + \overset{+2-1}{O\,F_2}(g) \rightarrow$
$\overset{+1\,-2}{H_2O}(g) + \overset{+1-1}{H\,F}(g)$

$\overset{0}{H_2} \rightarrow 2\overset{+1}{H} + 2e^-$

$\overset{+2}{O} + 4e^- \rightarrow \overset{-2}{O}$

redox

c. $2\overset{+1-1}{K\,I}(aq) + \overset{+2\,+5-2}{Pb(NO_3)_2}(aq) \rightarrow$
$\overset{+2-1}{Pb\,I_2}(s) + 2\overset{+1+5-2}{K\,NO_3}(aq)$

nonredox

d. $\overset{+2-2}{CaO}(s) + \overset{+1\,-2}{H_2O}(\ell) \rightarrow$
$\overset{+2\ \ -2+1}{Ca(O\,H)_2}(aq)$

nonredox

e. $3\overset{+2\,-1}{CuCl_2}(aq) +$
$2(\overset{-3+1}{N\,H_4})_3\overset{+5-2}{P\,O_4}(aq) \rightarrow$
$6\overset{-3+1\ -1}{N\,H_4Cl}(aq) +$
$\overset{+2\ \ +5-2}{Cu_3(P\,O_4)_2}(s)$

nonredox

f. $\overset{-4+1}{C\,H_4}(g) + 2\overset{0}{O_2}(g) \rightarrow$
$\overset{+4-2}{C\,O_2}(g) + 2\overset{+1\,-2}{H_2O}(g)$

$\overset{-4}{C} \rightarrow \overset{+4}{C} + 8e^-$

$\overset{0}{O_2} + 4e^- \rightarrow 2\overset{-2}{O}$

redox

---

18. $\overset{+5-2}{N\,O_3^-}, \overset{+4\,-2}{N_2O_4}, \overset{+1\,-2}{N_2O}, \overset{0}{N_2},$
$\overset{-2\ +1}{N_2H_4}, \overset{-3+1}{N\,H_3}$

19. a. $SbCl_5 + KI \rightarrow KCl + I_2 + SbCl_3$

$$2I^- \rightarrow I_2 + 2e^-$$
$$\underline{SbCl_5 + 2e^- \rightarrow SbCl_3 + 2Cl^-}$$
$$SbCl_5 + 2I^- \rightarrow SbCl_3 + 2Cl^- + I_2$$

$$SbCl_5 + 2KI \rightarrow 2KCl + I_2 + SbCl_3$$

b. $Ca(OH)_2 + NaOH + ClO_2 + C \rightarrow NaClO_2 + CaCO_3 + H_2O$

$$\overset{0}{C} + 6OH^- \rightarrow \overset{+4}{CO_3^{2-}} + 3H_2O + 4e^-$$
$$\underline{4[\overset{+4}{ClO_2} + 1e^- \rightarrow \overset{+3}{ClO_2^-}]}$$
$$C + 6OH^- + 4ClO_2 \rightarrow CO_3^{2-} + 3H_2O + 4ClO_2^-$$

$$Ca(OH)_2 + 4NaOH + 4ClO_2 + C \rightarrow 4NaClO_2 + CaCO_3 + 3H_2O$$

20. a. Given:
$PbO_2 + KCl \rightarrow KClO + KPb(OH)_3$

Unknown: balanced chemical equation

Oxidation: $Cl^- \rightarrow ClO^-$
$$Cl^- + H_2O \rightarrow ClO^- + 2H^+$$
$$Cl^- + H_2O \rightarrow ClO^- + 2H^+ + 2e^-$$

Reduction: $PbO_2 \rightarrow Pb(OH)_3^-$
$$PbO_2 + H_2O + H^+ \rightarrow Pb(OH)_3^-$$
$$PbO_2 + H_2O + H^+ + 2e^- \rightarrow Pb(OH)_3^-$$

Combining: $PbO_2 + 2H_2O + H^+ + 2e^- + Cl^- \rightarrow ClO^- + 2H^+ + 2e^- + Pb(OH)_3^-$
$$PbO_2 + 2H_2O + Cl^- \rightarrow ClO^- + Pb(OH)_3^- + H^+$$
$$PbO_2 + H_2O + OH^- + Cl^- \rightarrow ClO^- + Pb(OH)_3^-$$
$$PbO_2 + H_2O + KOH + KCl \rightarrow KClO + KPb(OH)_3$$

b. Given: $KMnO_4 + KIO_3 \rightarrow MnO_2 + KIO_4$ (unbalanced)

Unknown: balanced chemical equation in basic solution

Oxidation: $IO_3^- \rightarrow IO_4^-$
$$IO_3^- + 2OH^- \rightarrow IO_4^- + H_2O$$
$$IO_3^- + 2OH^- \rightarrow IO_4^- + H_2O + 2e^-$$

Reduction: $MnO_4^- \rightarrow MnO_2$
$$MnO_4^- + 2H_2O \rightarrow MnO_2 + 4OH^-$$
$$MnO_4^- + 2H_2O + 3e^- \rightarrow MnO_2 + 4OH^-$$

Combining: $2MnO_4^- + 4H_2O + 6e^- + 3IO_3^- + 6OH^- \rightarrow$
$$2MnO_2 + 8H_2O + 3IO_4^- + 3H_2O + 6e^-$$
$$2MnO_4^- + 4H_2O + 3IO_3^- \rightarrow 2MnO_2 + 2OH^- + 3IO_4^-$$
$$2KMnO_4 + H_2O + 3KIO_3 \rightarrow 2MnO_2 + 2KOH + 3KIO_4$$

c. Given: $K_2MnO_4 \rightarrow MnO_2 + KMnO_4$

Unknown: balanced chemical equation in basic solution

Oxidation: $MnO_4^{2-} \rightarrow MnO_4^-$
$$MnO_4^{2-} \rightarrow MnO_4^- + e^-$$

Reduction: $MnO_4^{2-} \rightarrow MnO_2$
$$MnO_4^{2-} + 2H_2O \rightarrow MnO_2 + 4OH^-$$
$$MnO_4^{2-} + 2H_2O + 2e^- \rightarrow MnO_2 + 4OH^-$$

Combining: $3MnO_4^{2-} + 2H_2O + 2e^- \rightarrow 2MnO_4^- + 2e^- + MnO_2 + 4OH^-$
$$3K_2MnO_4 + 2H_2O \rightarrow 2KMnO_4 + MnO_2 + 4KOH$$

21. a. Given: $MnO_4^- + Cl^- \rightarrow Mn^{2+} + HClO$

Unknown: balanced chemical equation in acidic solution

Oxidation: $Cl^- \rightarrow ClO^-$
$$Cl^- + H_2O \rightarrow ClO^- + 2H^+$$
$$Cl^- + H_2O \rightarrow ClO^- + 2H^+ + 2e^-$$

Reduction: $MnO_4^- \rightarrow Mn^{2+}$
$$MnO_4^- + 8H^+ \rightarrow Mn^{2+} + 4H_2O$$
$$MnO_4^- + 8H^+ + 5e^- \rightarrow Mn^{2+} + 4H_2O$$

Combining: $2MnO_4^- + 16H^+ + 10e^- + 5Cl^- + 5H_2O \rightarrow$
$$2Mn^{2+} + 8H_2O + 5ClO^- + 10H^+ + 10e^-$$
$$2MnO_4^- + 6H^+ + 5Cl^- \rightarrow 2Mn^{2+} + 3H_2O + 5ClO^-$$
$$2MnO_4^- + 11H^+ + 5Cl^- \rightarrow 2Mn^{2+} + 3H_2O + 5HClO$$

b. Given: $NO_3^- + I^2 \rightarrow$
$IO_3^- + NO_2$

Unknown: balanced
chemical
equation in
acidic
solution

Oxidation: $I_2 \rightarrow 2IO_3^-$
$I_2^- + 6H_2O \rightarrow 2IO_3^- + 12H^+$
$I_2^- + 6H_2O \rightarrow 2IO_3^- + 12H^+ + 10e^-$

Reduction: $NO_3^- \rightarrow NO_2$
$NO_3^- + 2H^+ \rightarrow NO_2 + H_2O$
$NO_3^- + 2H^+ + e^- \rightarrow NO_2 + H_2O$

Combining: $10NO_3^- + 20H^+ + 10e^- + I_2 + 6H_2O \rightarrow$
$10NO_2 + 10H_2O + 2IO_3^- + 12H^+ + 10e^-$
$10NO_3^- + 8H^+ + I_2 \rightarrow 10NO_2 + 4H_2O + 2IO_3^-$

c. Given: $NO_2^- \rightarrow$
$NO_2 + NO_3^-$

Unknown: balanced
chemical
equation
in acidic
solution

Oxidation: $NO_2 \rightarrow NO_3^-$
$NO_2^- + H_2O \rightarrow NO_3^- + 2H^+$
$NO_2^- + H_2O \rightarrow NO_3^- + 2H^+ + 2e^-$

Reduction: $NO_2^- \rightarrow NO$
$NO_2^- + 2H^+ \rightarrow NO + H_2O$
$NO_2^- + 2H^+ + e^- \rightarrow NO + H_2O$

Combining: $3NO_2^- + H_2O + 4H^+ + 2e^- \rightarrow 2NO + 2H_2O + NO_3^- + 2H^+ + 2e^-$
$3NO_2^- + 2H^+ \rightarrow 2NO + NO_3^- + H_2O$

Math Tutor, p. 650

1. Given: $MnO_2(s) +$
$NaClO_3(aq) \rightarrow$
$NaMnO_4 + NaCl +$
H_2O (unbalanced)

Unknown: balanced
chemical
equation in
basic solution

Oxidation: $MnO_2 \rightarrow MnO_4^-$
$MnO_2 + 4OH^- \rightarrow MnO_4^- + 2H_2O$
$MnO_2 + 4OH^- \rightarrow MnO_4^- + 2H_2O + 3e^-$

Reduction: $ClO_3^- \rightarrow Cl^-$
$ClO_3^- + 3H_2O \rightarrow Cl^- + 6OH^-$
$ClO_3^- + 3H_2O + 6e^- \rightarrow Cl^- + 6OH^-$

Combining: $2MnO_2 + 8OH^- + ClO_3 + 3H_2O + 6e^- \rightarrow$
$2MnO_4^- + 4H_2O + 6e^- + Cl^- + 6OH^-$
$2MnO_2 + 2OH^- + ClO_3^- \rightarrow 2MnO_4^- + H_2O + Cl^-$
$2MnO_2 + 2NaOH + NaClO_3 \rightarrow 2NaMnO_4 + H_2O + NaCl$

2. Given: $N_2O(g) +$
$KClO(aq) +$
$KOH(aq) \rightarrow$
$KCl(aq) +$
$KNO_2(aq) +$
$H_2O(l)$

Unknown: balanced
chemical
equation in
basic solution

Oxidation: $N_2O \rightarrow 2NO_2^-$
$N_2O + 6OH^- \rightarrow 2NO_2^- + 3H_2O$
$N_2O + 6OH^- \rightarrow 2NO_2^- + 3H_2O + 4e^-$

Reduction: $ClO^- \rightarrow Cl^-$
$ClO^- + H_2O \rightarrow Cl^- + 2OH^-$
$ClO^- + H_2O + 2e^- \rightarrow Cl^- + 2OH^-$

Combining: $N_2O + 6OH^- + 2ClO^- + 2H_2O + 4e^- \rightarrow 2NO_2^- + 3H_2O + 4e^- + 2Cl^- + 4OH^-$
$N_2O + 2OH^- + 2ClO^- \rightarrow 2NO_2^- + H_2O + 2Cl^-$
$N_2O + 2KOH + 2KClO \rightarrow 2KNO_2 + H_2O + 2KCl$

5. Given: $Cl_2 + H_2O \rightarrow HCl$ + HOCl

Unknown: oxidation states of chlorine

Oxidation: $\overset{0}{Cl_2} \rightarrow 2\overset{+1}{O\,Cl^-}$

$Cl_2 + 2H_2O \rightarrow 2OCl^- + 4H^+$

$Cl_2 + 2H_2O \rightarrow 2OCl^- + 4H^+ + 2e^-$

reduction: $\overset{0}{Cl_2} \rightarrow 2\overset{-1}{Cl^-}$

$\overset{0}{Cl_2} + 2e^- \rightarrow 2\overset{-1}{Cl^-}$

Oxidation states of chlorine are -1, 0, and $+1$

---

6. Given: $H_2O + PbO_2 + NaOH + KCl \rightarrow KClO + NaPb(OH)_3$

Unknown: type of reaction

$PbO_2 \rightarrow Pb(OH)_3^-$

$PbO_2 \rightarrow 2OH^- \rightarrow Pb(OH)_3^- + H_2O + e^-$

$Cl^- \rightarrow ClO^-$

$Cl^- + 2OH^- \rightarrow ClO^- + H_2O + 2e^-$

PbO_2 is reduced to $Pb(OH)_3^-$ and Cl^- is oxidized to OCl^-, so this is an oxidation-reduction reaction.

---

7. Given: $S_2O_3^{2-}$, $S_4O_6^{2-}$, HSO_4^- and H_2S

Unknown: increasing order of oxidation numbers

In these compounds, O always has an oxidation state of -2 and H always has an oxidation state of $+1$.

For $S_2O_3^{2-}$, 2 S atoms must equal a $+4$ oxidation state, $-(-2 \times 3 + 2)$, so each S atom has an oxidation state of $+2$.

For $S_4O_6^{2-}$, the 4 sulfur atoms must equal a $+10$ oxidation state, so the oxidation state for S is $+2.5$.

For HSO_4^-, the sulfur atom must equal an oxidation state of $-(-8 + 1 + 1)$, so the oxidation state of sulfur is $+6$.

For H_2S, sulfur has an oxidation state of $-(+1 \times 2)$, or -2

The correct arrangement of compounds is H_2S, $S_2O_3^{2-}$, $S_4O_6^{2-}$, and HSO_4^-.

---

9. Given: $YBa_2Cu_3O_7$ oxidation number for $Y = +3$

Unknown: oxidation numbers for Cu

Ba has an oxidation number of $+2$. Oxygen has an oxidation number of -2. The three Cu atoms must share a total oxidation state of $-(-2 \times 7 + 2 \times 2 + 3) = +7$. Two of the Cu atoms must have oxidation states of $+2$ and one Cu atom must be at $+3$.

---

12. Given: $ClO_2 \rightarrow KClO_3 + KClO_2$

Unknown: balanced chemical equation in basic solution

oxidation: $ClO_2 \rightarrow ClO_3^-$

$ClO_2 + 2OH^- \rightarrow ClO_3^- + H_2O$

$ClO_2 + 2OH^- \rightarrow ClO_3^- + e^- + H_2O$

ClO_2 is the oxidizing agent

reduction: $ClO_2 \rightarrow ClO_2^-$

$ClO_2 + e^- \rightarrow ClO_2^-$

ClO_2 is also the reducing agent

combining: $ClO_2 + 2OH^- + ClO_2 + e^- \rightarrow ClO_3^- + e^- + ClO_2^-$

$2ClO_2 + 2KOH \rightarrow KClO_3 + KClO_2 + H_2O$

CHAPTER 20

Electrochemistry

Practice, p. 665

1.a. Given: $Cr_2O_7{}^{2-} | Cr^{3+}$
half-cell
$Ni^{2+} | Ni$ half-cell

Unknowns: spontaneous
reaction and
$E^0{}_{cell}$ value

half-cell reactions:

$Cr_2O_7^{2-} + 14H^+ + 6e^- \rightarrow 2Cr^{3+} + 7H_2O \qquad E^0 = 1.33 \text{ V}$
$\qquad\qquad\qquad\qquad\qquad\qquad\qquad\qquad\qquad E^0 = -0.23 \text{ V}$

$Ni^{2+} + 2e^- \rightarrow Ni$
$-0.23 \text{ V} < 1.33 \text{ V}$, so Ni in Ni^{2+} is the anode and $Cr_2O_7^{2-}$ in Cr^{3+} is the cathode.

The overall reaction is:
$Cr_2O_7^{2-} + 14H^+ + 6e^- + 3Ni \rightarrow 2Cr^{3+} + 7H_2O + 3Ni^{2+} + 6e^-$
$Cr_2O_7^{2-} + 14H^+ + 3Ni \rightarrow 2Cr^{3+} + 7H_2O + 3Ni^{2+}$

The cell potential $E^0{}_{cell} = 1.33 \text{ V} - (-0.23 \text{ V}) = 1.56 \text{ V}$

b. Given: Standard
Hydrogen
Electrode (SHE)
$Fe^{2+} | Fe^{3+}$ half-cell

Unknowns: spontaneous
reaction and
$E^0{}_{cell}$ value

half-cell reactions

$2H^+(aq) + 2e^- \rightarrow H_2 \qquad\qquad E^0 = 0.00 \text{ V}$
$Fe^{3+} + e^- \rightarrow Fe^{2+} \qquad\qquad E^0 = 0.77 \text{ V}$

$0.00 \text{ V} < 0.77 \text{ V}$, so H^+ in H_2 is the anode and Fe^{3+} in Fe^{2+} is the cathode
The overall reaction is:
$2Fe^{3+} + H_2 \rightarrow 2Fe^{2+} + 2H^+(aq)$

The cell potential $E^0{}_{cell} = 0.77 \text{ V} - 0.00 \text{ V} = 0.77 \text{ V}$

Section Review, p. 665

3. Given: Na^+/Na and K^+/K
half-cells

Unknown: a. overall
electrochemical reaction
b. E^0 value

Half-reactions:

$K^+ + e^- \rightarrow K \qquad E^0 = -2.93 \text{ V}$
$Na^+ + e^- \rightarrow Na \qquad E^0 = -2.71 \text{ V}$

Anode = K (oxidation)

Cathode = Na (reduction) .

Overall reaction:

$K + Na^+ \rightarrow K^+ + Na$

$E^0{}_{anode} = -2.93 \text{ V}$
$E^0{}_{cathode} = -2.71 \text{ V}$
$E^0{}_{cell} = E^0{}_{cathode} - E^0{}_{anode}$
$\qquad = -2.71 \text{ V} - (-2.93 \text{ V}) = +0.22 \text{ V}$

4. Given: $MnO_2 | Mn^{2+}$
half-cell
$Cr^{3+} | Cr$ half-cell

Unknowns: Overall spon-
taneous reac-
tion and $E^0{}_{cell}$
value

Half-reactions:

$MnO_2 + 4H^+ + 2e^- \rightarrow Mn^{2+} + 2H_2O \qquad E^0 = +1.21 \text{ V}$
$Cr^{3+} + 3e^- \rightarrow Cr \qquad\qquad\qquad\qquad\qquad E^0 = -0.74 \text{ V}$

$-0.74 \text{ V} < +1.21 \text{ V}$, so Cr in Cr^{3+} is the cathode and MnO_2 in Mn^{2+} is the anode.

overall reaction is: $3MnO_2 + 12H^+ + 6e^- + 2Cr \rightarrow 3Mn^{2+}$
$\qquad\qquad\qquad\qquad\qquad + 6H_2O + 2Cr^{3+} + 6e^-$

overall cell potential: $E^0{}_{cell} = 1.21 \text{ V} - (-0.74 \text{ V}) = 1.95 \text{ V}$

15. a. Given: $Na^+|Na$ half-cell
$Ni^{2+}|Ni$ half-cell

$$Na^+ + e^- \rightleftarrows Na \qquad E^0 = -2.71 \text{ V}$$
$$Ni^{2+} + 2e^- \rightleftarrows Ni \qquad E^0 = -0.23 \text{ V}$$

-2.71 V < -0.23 V, so Na in Na^+ is the anode and Ni in Ni^{2+} is the cathode.

Unknown: overall spontaneous electro-chemical reaction

$$Ni^{2+} + 2e^- + 2Na \rightarrow Ni + 2Na^+ + 2e^-$$
$$Ni^{2+} + 2Na \rightarrow Ni + 2Na^+$$

b. Given: $F_2|F^-$ half-cell
$S|H_2S$ half-cell

$$F_2 + 2e^- \rightleftarrows 2F^- \qquad E^0 = +2.87 \text{ V}$$
$$S + 2H^+ + 2e^- \rightleftarrows H_2S \qquad E^0 = +0.14 \text{ V}$$

$+0.14$ V $< +2.87$ V, so S in H_2S is the anode and F_2 in F^- is the cathode.

Unknown: overall spontaneous electro-chemical reaction

$$H_2S + F_2 \rightarrow S + 2H^+ + 2F^-$$

c. Given: $Br_2|Br^-$ half-cell
$Cr^{3+}|Cr$ half-cell

$$Br_2 + 2e^- \rightleftarrows 2Br^- \qquad E^0 = +1.07 \text{ V}$$
$$Cr^{3+} + 3e^- \rightleftarrows Cr \qquad E^0 = -0.74 \text{ V}$$

-0.74 V $< +1.07$ V, so Cr in Cr^{3+} is the anode and Br_2 in Br^- is the cathode.

Unknown: Overall spontaneous electro-chemical reaction

$$3Br_2 + 2Cr + 6e^- \rightarrow 6Br^- + 6e^- + 2Cr^{3+}$$
$$3Br_2 + 2Cr \rightarrow 6Br^- + 2Cr^{3+}$$

d. Given: $MnO_4^-|Mn^{2+}$ half-cell
$Co^{2+}|Co$ half-cell

$$MnO_4^- + 8H^+ + 5e^- \rightleftarrows Mn^{2+} + 4H_2O \qquad E^0 = 1.49 \text{ V}$$
$$Co^{2+} + 2e^- \rightleftarrows Co \qquad E^0 = -0.28 \text{ V}$$

-0.28 V < 1.49 V, so MnO_4^- in Mn^{2+} is the cathode and Co in Co^{2+} is the anode.

Unknown: Overall spontaneous electro-chemical reaction

$$2MnO_4^- + 16H^+ + 10e^- + 5Co \rightarrow 2Mn^{2+} + 8H_2O + 5Co^{2+} + 10e^-$$
$$2MnO_4^- + 16H^+ + 5Co \rightarrow 2Mn^{2+} + 8H_2O + 5Co^{2+}$$

16. (see previous problem for equations)

a. -0.23 V $- (-2.71$ V$) =$ $+2.48$ V

b. 2.87 V $- (+0.14$ V$) =$ $+2.73$ V

c. 1.07 V $- (-0.74$ V$) =$ $+1.81$ V

d. 1.49 V $- (-0.28$ V$) =$ $+1.77$ V

17. Given: $I_2 + 2e^- \rightarrow 2I^-$
new $E^0 = +0.54$ V $-$
0.54 V $= 0$ V

Unknown: E^0_{cell}

a. $Br_2 + 2e^- \rightarrow 2Br^-$ $\quad E^0 = +1.07$ V

$E^0_{cell} = +1.07$ V $- (+0.54$ V$) = +0.53$ V

b. $Al^{3+} + 3e^- \rightarrow Al$ $\quad E^0 = -1.66$ V

Anode = Al
Cathode = I_2

$E^0_{cell} = -1.66$ V $- (+0.54$ V$) = -2.20$ V

c. original: $+1.07$ V $- +0.54$ V $= +0.53$ V

new: $+0.53$ V $- 0 = +0.53$ V

No change would be observed.

---

18. Given: $Ag^+ \,|\, Ag$ half-cell
$Ni^{2+} \,|\, Ni$ half-cell

Unknown: would a
reaction
spontaneously
occur?

$Ag^+ + e^- \rightleftharpoons Ag$ $\qquad E^0 = +0.80$ V
$Ni^{2+} + 2e^- \rightleftharpoons Ni$ $\qquad E^0 = -0.23$ V

-0.23 V $< +0.80$ V, so Ni in Ni^{2+} is the anode and Ag in Ag^+ is the cathode.

The spontaneous reaction would be
$2Ag^+ + Ni \rightarrow Ag + Ni^{2+}$ $\qquad E^0_{cell} = +1.03$ V

Silver metal would spontaneously deposit on the nickel surface.

---

21. Given: $CdCl_2(aq) \rightarrow$
$Cd + Cl_2$

Unknown: voltage of cell
in which this
reaction occurs

$Cd^{2+} + 2e^- \rightarrow \ Cd$ $\qquad E^0 = -0.40$ V
$Cl_2 + 2e^- \rightarrow 2Cl^-$ $\qquad E^0 = +1.36$ V

In the reaction, cadmium is reduced, so Cd in Cd^{2+} is the cathode and Cl_2 in Cl^- is the anode.

$E^0_{cell} = E^0_{cathode} - E^0_{anode} = -0.40$ V $- 1.36 = -1.76$ V

The reaction is not spontaneous.

---

22. Given: $Ni^{2+} \,|\, Ni$ half-cell
$Zn^{2+} \,|\, Zn$ half-cell

Unknown: will Ni be
plated out of
$Ni(NO_3)_2(aq)$
onto zinc?

$Ni^{2+} + 2e^- \rightleftharpoons Ni$ $\qquad E^0 = -0.23$ V
$Zn^{2+} + 2e^- \rightleftharpoons Zn$ $\qquad E^0 = -0.76$ V

In order for Ni to be plated onto a Zn object, the Zn object must be the cathode. The anode could be made of Ni. The half-reaction for the reduction of Ni is $Ni^{2+} + 2e^- \rightarrow$ Ni ($E^0 = -0.23$ V). Therefore, Ni can be plated onto the Zn cathode as long as the applied voltage is at least $+0.23$ V.

---

25. a. Given: Reactants Mg
and Sn^{2+}

Unknown: will Mg and
Sn^{2+} react
sponta-
neously?

$E^0_{cell} = -0.14$ V $- (-2.37$ V$) = +2.23$ V

The reaction will be spontaneous.

$Mg + Sn^{2+} \rightarrow Mg^{2+} + Sn$

b. Given: Reactants K
and Al^{3+}

Unknown: will K and
Al^{3+} react
sponta-
neously?

$E^0_{cell} = -1.66$ V $- (-2.93$ V$) = +1.27$ V

The reaction will be spontaneous.

$3K + Al^{3+} \rightarrow 3K^+ + Al$

c. Given: Reactants Li^+ and Zn

Unknown: will Li^+ and Zn react spontaneously?

$E^0_{cell} = -3.04 - (-0.76) = -2.28$

The reaction is not spontaneous.

d. Given: Reactants Cu and Cl_2

Unknown: will Cu and Cl_2 react spontaneously?

$E^0_{cell} = 1.36\ V - 0.34\ V = +1.02\ V$

The reaction will be spontaneous.

$Cu + Cl_2 \rightarrow Cu^{2+} + 2Cl^-$

---

28. Given: $Sn(NO_3)_2$, Al

Unknown: can a solution of $Sn(NO_3)_2$ be stored in an aluminum container?

$Sn^{2+} + 2e^- \rightleftarrows Sn$ $\qquad E^0 = -0.14\ V$
$Al^{3+} + 3e^- \rightleftarrows Al$ $\qquad E^0 = -1.66\ V$

For the reaction
$3\ Sn(NO_3)_2 + 2Al \rightarrow 2Al(NO_3)_3 + 35\ n$
$E^0_{cell} = -0.14\ V - (-1.66\ V) = +1.52\ V$

This reaction is spontaneous and the aluminum container will dissolve.

---

30. Given: $Cd^{2+} \mid Cd$ half-cell $Fe^{2+} \mid Fe$ half-cell

Unknown: Quality of battery of these half-cells

$E^0_{cell} = E_{cathode} - E_{anode} = 0.40\ V - (-0.41\ V) = 0.01\ V$

These half-cells would not make a good battery; the difference between their half-cell potentials is too small.

---

31. a. Given: $Zn(NO_3)_2$ solution, aluminum spoon

Unknown: will the Al spoon react with the $Zn(NO_3)_2$?

For the half-cells
$Al^{3+} + 3e^- \rightarrow Al$ $\qquad E^0 = -1.66\ V$
$Zn^{2+} + 2e^- \rightarrow Zn$ $\qquad E^0 = -0.76\ V$

Since $-1.66\ V < -0.76\ V$, Al in Al^{3+} is the anode and oxidation will occur there. The aluminum spoon will "dissolve" in the $Zn(NO_3)_2$ solution, releasing Al^{3+} ions.

b. Given: Zn metal strip, $Al(NO_3)_3$ solution

Unknown: will the Zn metal strip react with $Al(NO_3)_3$?

Consider the half-cell potentials in part a. If the zinc strip were to react, the overall reaction would be:

$3Zn + 2Al^{3+} \rightarrow 3Zn^{2+} + 2Al$
$E^0_{cell} = -1.66\ V\ (-0.76\ V) = -0.90\ V$

This reaction does not occur spontaneously, and the zinc strip could be used to stir the $Al(NO_3)_3$ solution.

1. Given: $Al^{3+} \mid Al$ half-cell $\qquad Al^{3+} + 3e^- \rightarrow Al \qquad\qquad E^0 = -1.66 \text{ V}$
$\qquad\quad Cu^{2+} \mid Cu^+$ half-cell $\qquad Cu^{2+} + e^- \rightarrow Cu^+ \qquad\quad E^0 = +0.16 \text{ V}$

Unknown: overall cell potential, E^0_{cell}

$-1.66 \text{ V} < +0.16$, so Al in Al^{3+} is the anode and Cu^+ in Cu^{2+} is the cathode.

$$Al + 3Cu^{2+} \rightleftharpoons Al^{3+} + 3Cu^+$$

$$E^0_{cell} = +0.16 \text{ V} - (-1.66 \text{ V}) = +1.82 \text{ V}$$

2. Given: $Pb^{2+} \mid Pb$ half-cell $\qquad Pb^{2+} + 2e^- \rightarrow Pb \qquad\qquad E^0 = -0.13 \text{ V}$
$\qquad\quad Br_2 \mid Br^-$ half-cell $\qquad Br_2 + 2e^- \rightarrow 2Br^- \qquad\quad E^0 = +1.07 \text{ V}$

Unknown: overall cell potential, E^0_{cell}

$-0.13 \text{ V} < +1.07 \text{ V}$, so Pb in Pb^{2+} is the anode and Br_2 in Br^- is the cathode.

$$E^0_{cell} = E^0_{cathode} - E^0_{anode} = 1.07 \text{ V} - (-0.13 \text{ V})$$
$$E^0_{cell} = +1.20 \text{ V}$$

Standardized Test Prep, p. 677

4. Given: $Sn \mid Sn^{2+} \parallel Cr^{3+} \mid Cr$
$\qquad\quad E^0_{cell} = -0.60 \text{ V}$

Unknown: E^0 for the half-cell $Cr^{3+} \mid Cr$

$E^0_{cell} = E_{cathode} - E_{anode}$

In the cell, Cr^{3+} is reduced, so Cr in Cr^{3+} is the cathode and Sn in Sn^{2+} is the anode.

$$E^0_{cathode} = E^0_{cell} + E^0_{anode} = -0.60 \text{ V} + (-0.14 \text{ V})$$
$$E^0_{cathode} = -0.74 \text{ V for } Cr^{3+} + 3e^- \rightarrow Cr$$

9. Given:

$$NO_3^- + 4H^+ + 3e^- \rightarrow NO + 2H_2O \quad E^0 = 0.96 \text{ V}$$
$$Au^{3+} + 3e^- \rightarrow Au \qquad\qquad\qquad\qquad E^0 = 1.50 \text{ V}$$

$0.96 \text{ V} < 1.50 \text{ V}$, so $NO_3^- \mid NO$ is the anode and Au in Au^{3+} is the cathode. Reduction takes place at the cathode, so the overall cell potential will be
$$Au^{3+} + NO + 2H_2O \rightarrow Au + NO_3^- + 4H^+ \quad E^0_{cell}$$

$$E^0_{cell} = 1.50 \text{ V} - 0.96 \text{ V} = 0.54 \text{ V}$$

Gold dissolves in the reverse reaction, with E^0_{cell} of -0.54 V, which is not spontaneous. Gold will not dissolve in 1 M HNO_3.

CHAPTER 21

Nuclear Chemistry

ATE, Additional Example Problems, p. 682

1. Given: measured atomic mass of $^{32}_{16}S$ = 31.972 070 amu

Unknown: binding energy of $^{32}_{16}S$

16 protons: $(16 \times 1.007\ 276\ \text{amu}) = 16.116\ 416$ amu

16 neutrons: $(16 \times 1.008\ 665\ \text{amu}) = 16.138\ 64$ amu

16 electrons: $(16 \times 0.000\ 5486\ \text{amu}) = \underline{0.008\ 7776\ \text{amu}}$

total combined mass: 32.263 834 amu

mass defect = 32.263 834 amu − 31.972 070 amu
= 0.291 764 amu

$$= (0.291\ 764\ \text{amu})\left(\frac{1.6605 \times 10^{-27}\ \text{kg}}{1\ \text{amu}}\right)$$

$$= 4.8447 \times 10^{-28}\ \text{kg}$$

$$E = mc^2$$

$$E = (4.8447 \times 10^{-28}\ \text{kg})(3.00 \times 10^8\ \text{m/s})^2$$

$$= 4.36 \times 10^{-11}\ \text{kg} \cdot \text{m}^2/\text{s}^2 = 4.36 \times 10^{-11}\ \text{J}$$

2. Given: measured atomic mass of $^{16}_{8}O$ = 15.994 915 amu

Unknown: binding energy for 1 mole of $^{16}_{8}O$

8 protons: $(8 \times 1.007\ 276\ \text{amu}) = 8.058\ 8208$ amu

8 neutrons: $(8 \times 1.008\ 665\ \text{amu}) = 8.069\ 32$ amu

8 electrons: $(8 \times 0.000\ 5486\ \text{amu}) = \underline{0.004\ 3888\ \text{amu}}$

total combined mass: 16.131 917 amu

mass defect = 16.131 917 amu − 15.994 915 amu = 0.137 0018 amu

$$= (0.137\ 0018\ \text{amu})\left(\frac{1.6605 \times 10^{-27}\ \text{kg}}{1\ \text{amu}}\right) = 2.2749 \times 10^{-28}\ \text{kg}$$

$$E = mc^2$$

$$E = (2.2749 \times 10^{-28}\ \text{kg})(3.00 \times 10^8\ \text{m/s})^2$$

$$= 2.047 \times 10^{-11}\ \text{kg} \cdot \text{m}^2/\text{s}^2 = 2.047 \times 10^{-11}\ \text{J}$$

binding energy/mol = $(2.047 \times 10^{-11}\ \text{J/atom})(6.022 \times 10^{-23}\ \text{atoms/mol})$
= $1.23 \times 10^{13}\ \text{J/mol}$

3. Given: measured atomic mass of $^{55}_{25}\text{Mn}$ = 54.938 047 amu

Unknown: binding energy per nucleon of a $^{55}_{25}\text{Mn}$ atom

25 protons: $(25 \times 1.007\ 276\ \text{amu}) = 25.1819\ \text{amu}$

30 neutrons: $(30 \times 1.008\ 665\ \text{amu}) = 30.259\ 95\ \text{amu}$

25 electrons: $(25 \times 0.000\ 5486\ \text{amu}) = \underline{0.0137\ 15\ \text{amu}}$

total combined mass: $55.455\ 115\ \text{amu}$

mass defect $= 55.455\ 115\ \text{amu} - 54.938\ 047\ \text{amu} = 0.517\ 068\ \text{amu}$

$$= (0.517\ 068\ \text{amu})\left(\frac{1.6605 \times 10^{-27}\ \text{kg}}{1\ \text{amu}}\right) = 8.5859 \times 10^{-28}\ \text{kg}$$

$$E = mc^2$$

$$E = (88.5859 \times 10^{-28}\ \text{kg})(3.00 \times 10^8\ \text{m/s})^2$$

$$= 7.727 \times 10^{-11}\ \text{kg} \cdot \text{m}^2/\text{s}^2 = 7.727 \times 10^{-11}\ \text{J}$$

$$\text{binding energy/nucleon} = \frac{7.727 \times 10^{-11}\ \text{J}}{55\ \text{nucleons}} = 1.41 \times 10^{-12}\ \text{J/nucleon}$$

Practice, p. 684

1. Given: $^{253}_{99}\text{Es} + {}^{4}_{2}\text{He} \rightarrow {}^{1}_{0}n + ?$

mass number: $253 + 4 - 1 = 256$

atomic number: $99 + 2 - 0 = 101$

$? = {}^{256}_{101}\text{Md}$

2. Given: $^{142}_{61}\text{Pm} + ? \rightarrow {}^{142}_{60}\text{Nd}$

mass number: $142 - 142 = 0$

atomic number: $60 - 61 = -1$

$? = {}^{0}_{-1}e$

ATE, Additional Sample Problems, p. 684

A-1. Given: $^{238}_{92}\text{U} \rightarrow ? + {}^{234}_{90}\text{Th}$

mass number: $238 - 234 = 4$

atomic number: $92 - 90 = 2$

$? = {}^{4}_{2}\text{He}$

A-2. Given: $^{37}_{18}\text{Ar} + ? \rightarrow {}^{37}_{17}\text{Cl}$

mass number: $37 - 37 = 0$

atomic number: $17 - 18 = -1$

$? = {}^{0}_{-1}e$

Section Review, p. 684

3. a. Given: $^{187}_{75}Re + ? \rightarrow$

$^{188}_{75}Re + ^{1}_{1}H$

mass number: $188 + 1 - 187 = 2$

atomic number: $75 + 1 - 75 = 1$

$? = ^{2}_{1}H$

b. $^{9}_{4}Be + ^{4}_{2}He \rightarrow ? + ^{1}_{0}n$

mass number: $9 + 4 - 1 = 12$

atomic number: $4 + 2 - 0 = 6$

$? = ^{12}_{6}C$

c. $^{22}_{11}Na + ? \rightarrow ^{22}_{10}Ne$

mass number: $22 - 22 = 0$

atomic number: $10 - 11 = -1$

$? = ^{0}_{-1}e$

Practice, p. 689

1. Given: orig. mass of
Po-210 = 2.0 mg
half-life of
Po-210 = 1388.4
days
time elapsed =
415.2 days

Unknown: mass of Po-210
remaining
after 415.2
days

number of half-lives $= (415.2 \text{ days})\left(\dfrac{1 \text{ half-life}}{138.4 \text{ days}}\right) = 3$ half-lives

mass of ^{210}Po remaining $= 2.0 \text{ mg} \times \left(\dfrac{1}{2}\right)^3 = 0.25$ mg

2. Given: half-life of
radium-226 =
1599 years

Unknown: number of
years needed
for decay of $\frac{15}{16}$
of a given
amount of
radium-226

amount remaining $= \dfrac{1}{16} = 0.0625 = \left(\dfrac{1}{2}\right)^4$; 4 half-lives

years needed for decay of $\dfrac{15}{16} = (1599 \text{ years})(4) = 6396$ years

3. Given: half-life of
radon-222 =
3.824 days

Unknown: time needed
for $\frac{1}{4}$ of a given
amount of
radon-222 to
remain

amount remaining $= \dfrac{1}{4} = 0.25 = \left(\dfrac{1}{2}\right)^2$; 2 half-lives

days needed for $\dfrac{3}{4}$ to decay $= (3.824 \text{ days})(2) = 7.648$ days

4. Given: starting mass of
Co-60 = 10.0 mg
half-life of Co-60 =
5.27 y
time elapsed =
52.7 y

number of half-lives $= (5.27 \text{ y})\left(\dfrac{1 \text{ half-life}}{52.7 \text{ y}}\right) = 10$ half-lives

mass remaining after 10 half-lives $= \left(\dfrac{1}{2}\right)^{10}(10.0 \text{ mg}) = 0.009\ 77$ mg

Unknown: mass of Co-60
remaining
after 52.7 y

---

5. Given: original mass
U-238 = 4.0 mg
mass U-238
remaining after
4.46×10^9 years
= 2.0 g

fraction of sample remaining $= \dfrac{2.0 \text{ mg}}{4.0 \text{ mg}} = \dfrac{1}{2}$

half-life = time needed for $\dfrac{1}{2}$ of sample to decay $= 4.46 \times 10^9$ years

Unknown: Half-life of
U-238

ATE , Additional Sample Problems, p. 689

1. Given: half-life of
carbon-14 =
5715 years

time needed for $\dfrac{1}{2}$ of sample to decay = 1 half-life = 5715 years

Unknown: time needed
for $\dfrac{1}{2}$ of sample
to remain

---

2. Given: original mass of
radon-222 =
4.38 µg
half-life of
radon-222 =
3.8 days

number of half-lives $= (15.2 \text{ days})\left(\dfrac{1 \text{ half-life}}{3.8 \text{ days}}\right) = 4$ half-lives

mass of radon-222 remaining $= 4.38 \text{ µg} \times \left(\dfrac{1}{2}\right)^4 = 0.274$ µg

Unknown: mass of radon-
222 remaining
after 1.52 days

---

3. Given: half-life of
uranium-238 =
4.46×10^9 years

amount remaining $= \dfrac{1}{8} = 0.125 = \left(\dfrac{1}{2}\right)^3$; 3 half-lives

time needed for decay $= (4.46 \times 10^9 \text{ years})(3) = 1.34 \times 10^{10}$ years

Unknown: time needed
for $\dfrac{7}{8}$ of sample
to decay

Section Review, p. 692

3. Given: 4 half-lives in
radioactive decay

Unknown: fraction of
sample
remaining

$\text{fraction remaining} = \left(\dfrac{1}{2}\right)^n$; $n = $ number of half-lives.

$\text{fraction remaining} = \left(\dfrac{1}{2}\right)^4 = \dfrac{1}{16}$

Chapter Review

3. Given: measured atomic
mass of $^{20}_{10}\text{Ne} = $
19.992 44 amu

Unknown: mass defect

10 protons: $(10 \times 1.007\ 276\ \text{amu}) = 10.072\ 76\ \text{amu}$

10 neutrons: $(10 \times 1.008\ 665\ \text{amu}) = 10.086\ 65\ \text{amu}$

10 electrons: $(10 \times 0.000\ 5486\ \text{amu}) = \underline{0.005\ 486\ \text{amu}}$

total combined mass: $20.164\ 896\ \text{amu}$

mass defect $= 20.164\ 896\ \text{amu} - 19.992\ 44\ \text{amu} = 0.172\ 46\ \text{amu}$

4. Given: measured atomic
mass of $^{7}_{3}\text{Li} = $
7.016 00 amu

Unknown: mass defect

3 protons: $(3 \times 1.007\ 276\ \text{amu}) = 3.021\ 828\ \text{amu}$

4 neutrons: $(4 \times 1.008\ 665\ \text{amu}) = 4.034\ 66\ \text{amu}$

3 electrons: $(3 \times 0.000\ 5486\ \text{amu}) = \underline{0.001\ 646\ \text{amu}}$

total combined mass: $7.058\ 1338\ \text{amu}$

mass defect $= 7.058\ 133\ 8\ \text{amu} - 7.016\ 00\ \text{amu} = 0.042\ 13\ \text{amu}$

5. Given: measured atomic
mass of $^{6}_{3}\text{Li} = $
6.015 amu

Unknown: nuclear bind-
ing energy

3 protons: $(3 \times 1.007\ 276\ \text{amu}) = 3.021\ 828\ \text{amu}$

3 neutrons: $(3 \times 1.008\ 665\ \text{amu}) = 3.025\ 995\ \text{amu}$

3 electrons: $(3 \times 0.000\ 5486\ \text{amu}) = \underline{0.001\ 646\ \text{amu}}$

total combined mass: $6.049\ 4688\ \text{amu}$

mass defect $= 6.049\ 469\ \text{amu} - 6.015\ \text{amu} = 0.034\ 469\ \text{amu}$

$$= (0.034\ 469\ \text{amu})\left(\frac{1.6605 \times 10^{-27}\ \text{kg}}{1\ \text{amu}}\right) = 5.7235 \times 10^{-29}\ \text{kg}$$

$E = mc^2$

$E = (5.7235 \times 10^{-29}\ \text{kg})(3.00 \times 10^8\ \text{m/s})^2$

$\quad = 5.15 \times 10^{-12}\ \text{kg·m}^2/\text{s}^2 = 5.2 \times 10^{-12}\ \text{J}$

6. Given: measured atomic mass of $^{35}_{19}K$ = 34.988 011 amu measured atomic mass of $^{23}_{11}Na$ = 22.989 757 amu

Unknown: nuclear binding energy of both nuclei; which nucleus releases more energy when formed

a. $^{35}_{19}K$

b. $^{23}_{11}Na$

a. $^{35}_{19}K$: 19 protons: $(19 \times 1.007\ 276\ amu) = 19.138\ 244\ amu$

16 neutrons: $(16 \times 1.008\ 665\ amu) = 16.138\ 64\ amu$

19 electrons: $(19 \times 1.000\ 5486\ amu) = \underline{0.010\ 4234\ amu}$

total combined mass: $35.287\ 307\ amu$

mass defect = $35.287\ 307\ amu - 34.988\ 011\ amu = 0.299\ 296\ amu$

$$= (0.299\ 296\ amu)\left(\frac{1.6605 \times 10^{-27}\ kg}{1\ amu}\right) = 4.9698 \times 10^{-28}\ kg$$

$E = mc^2$

$E = (4.9698 \times 10^{-28}\ kg)(3.00 \times 10^8\ m/s)^2$

$= 4.47 \times 10^{-11}\ kg \cdot m^2/s^2 = 4.47 \times 10^{-11}\ J$

b. $^{23}_{11}Na$: 11 protons: $(11 \times 1.007\ 276\ amu) = 11.080\ 036\ amu$

12 neutrons: $(12 \times 1.008\ 665\ amu) = 12.103\ 98\ amu$

11 electrons: $(11 \times 0.000\ 5486\ amu) = \underline{0.060\ 346\ amu}$

total combined mass: $23.190\ 051\ amu$

mass defect = $23.190\ 151\ amu - 22.989\ 767\ amu = 0.200\ 2836\ amu$

$$= (0.200\ 2836\ amu)\left(\frac{1.6605 \times 10^{-27}\ kg}{1\ amu}\right) = 3.3257 \times 10^{-28}\ kg$$

$E = mc^2$

$E = (3.3257 \times 10^{-28}\ kg)(3.00 \times 10^8\ m/s)^2$

$= 2.99 \times 10^{-11}\ kg \cdot m^2/s^2 = 2.99 \times 10^{-11}\ J$

The nucleus in part **a** ($^{35}_{19}K$) releases more energy.

---

7. a. Unknown: binding energy per nucleon for each nucleus in problem #28

$^{35}_{19}K: \dfrac{4.5 \times 10^{-11}\ J}{35\ nucleons} = 1.28 \times 10^{-12}\ J/nucleon$

$^{23}_{11}Na: \dfrac{2.99 \times 10^{-11}\ J}{23\ nucleons} = 1.30 \times 10^{-12}\ J/nucleon$

b. Unknown: which nucleus is more stable

The greater the nuclear binding energy, the greater the stability. Therefore, $^{23}_{11}Na$ is more stable.

8. Given: measured atomic mass of ^7_3Li = 7.016 00 amu

Unknown: binding energy per nucleon

3 protons: $(3 \times 1.007\ 276\ \text{amu}) = 3.021\ 828\ \text{amu}$

4 neutrons: $(4 \times 1.008\ 665\ \text{amu}) = 4.034\ 66\ \text{amu}$

3 electrons: $(3 \times 0.000\ 5486\ \text{amu}) = \underline{0.016\ 46\ \text{amu}}$

total combined mass: 7.058 1338 amu

mass defect = 7.058 1338 amu − 7.016 00 amu = 0.042 13 amu

$$= (0.042\ 13\ \text{amu})\left(\frac{1.6605 \times 10^{-27}\ \text{kg}}{\text{amu}}\right) = 6.9956 \times 10^{-29}\ \text{kg}$$

$$E = mc^2$$

$$E = (6.9956 \times 10^{-29}\ \text{kg})(3.00 \times 10^8\ \text{m/s})^2$$

$$= 6.30 \times 10^{-12}\ \text{kg}\cdot\text{m}^2/\text{s}^2 = 6.30 \times 10^{-29}\ \text{J}$$

$$\frac{6.30 \times 10^{-29}\ \text{J}}{7\ \text{nucleons}} = 9.00 \times 10^{-13}\ \text{J/nucleon}$$

---

9. Unknown: neutron-proton ratios

a. $^{12}_6\text{C}$ = 6 protons, 6 neutrons

Ratio $= \dfrac{6}{6} = 1:1$

b. ^3_1H = 1 proton, 2 neutrons

Ratio $= 2:1$

c. $^{206}_{82}\text{Pb}$ = 82 protons, 124 neutrons

Ratio $= \dfrac{124}{82} = 1.51:1$

d. $^{134}_{50}\text{Sn}$ = 50 protons, 84 neutrons

Ratio $= \dfrac{84}{50} = 1.68:1$

---

11. a. $^{43}_{19}\text{K} \rightarrow {}^{43}_{20}\text{Ca} + ?$

mass number: 43 − 43 = 0

atomic number: 19 − 20 = −1

$? = {}^{\ 0}_{-1}\beta$

b. $^{233}_{92}\text{U} \rightarrow {}^{229}_{90}\text{Th} + ?$

mass number: 233 − 229 = 4

atomic number: 92 − 90 = 2

$? = {}^4_2\text{He}$

c. $^{11}_6\text{C} + ? \rightarrow {}^{11}_5\text{B}$

mass number: 11 − 11 = 0

atomic number: 5 − 6 = 1

$? = {}^{\ 0}_{-1}e$

d. $^{13}_7\text{N} \rightarrow {}^{\ 0}_{+1}\beta + ?$

mass number: 13 − 0 = 13

atomic number: 7 − 1 = 6

$? = {}^{13}_6\text{C}$

26. Given: original mass of
Pu-239 = 100 g

$$\text{number of half-lives} = (96\ 440\ \text{years})\left(\frac{1\ \text{half-life}}{24\ 110\ \text{years}}\right) = 4\ \text{half-lives}$$

Unknown: mass of Pu-239
remaining
after 96 440
years

$$\text{mass of plutonium-239 remaining after 4 half-lives} = (100\ \text{g})\left(\frac{1}{2}\right)^4 = 6.25\ \text{g}$$

---

27. Given: half-life of
Th-227 =
18.72 days

$$\text{amount remaining} = \frac{1}{4} = \left(\frac{1}{2}\right)^2;\ 2\ \text{half-lives}$$

Unknown: length of
time for $\frac{3}{4}$ of a
given amount
to decay

$$\text{length of time for decay} = (18.72\ \text{days})(2) = 37.44\ \text{days}$$

---

28. Given: fraction of a given
amount of Pa-234
remaining $= \frac{1}{16}$
time elapsed
= 26.76 hours

$$\text{amount remaining} = \frac{1}{16} = \left(\frac{1}{2}\right)^4;\ 4\ \text{half-lives}$$

$$\text{half-life} = \frac{26.76\ \text{hours}}{4} = 6.69\ \text{hours}$$

Unknown: half-life of
Pa-234

---

29. Given: original mass of
Ra-226 = 15.0 mg
half-life of Ra-226
= 1599 years

$$\text{number of half-lives} = (6396\ \text{years})\left(\frac{1\ \text{half-life}}{1\ 599\ \text{years}}\right) = 4\ \text{half-lives}$$

Unknown: mass remain-
ing after 6396
years

$$\text{mass remaining} = 15.0\ \text{mg} \times \left(\frac{1}{2}\right)^4 = 0.938\ \text{mg}$$

---

40. a. $^{239}_{93}\text{Np} \rightarrow\ ^{0}_{-1}\beta + ?$

mass number: $239 - 0 = 239$

atomic number: $93 - (-1) = 94$

$? = ^{239}_{94}\text{Pu}$

b. $^{9}_{4}\text{Be} + ^{4}_{2}\text{He} \rightarrow ?$

mass number: $9 + 4 = 13$

atomic number: $4 + 2 = 6$

$? = ^{13}_{6}\text{C}$

c. $^{32}_{15}\text{P} + ? \rightarrow ^{33}_{15}\text{P}$

mass number: $33 - 32 = 1$

atomic number: $15 - 15 = 0$

$? = ^{1}_{0}n$

d. $^{236}_{92}\text{U} \rightarrow ^{94}_{36}\text{Kr} + ? + 3^{1}_{0}n$

mass number: $236 - 94 = 139$

atomic number: $92 - 36 - 0 = 56$

$? = ^{139}_{56}\text{Ba}$

41. Given: half-life of Ra-226
= 1599 years
original mass of
Ra-226 = 0.250 g

Unknown: mass remaining after
4797 years

number of half-lives = $(4797 \text{ years})\left(\dfrac{1 \text{ half-life}}{1599}\right)$ = 3 half-lives

mass remaining = $0.250 \text{ g} \times \left(\dfrac{1}{2}\right)^3 = 0.0313 \text{ g}$

---

43. Given: half-life of Ra-224
= 3.66 days
mass remaining
after 7.32 days =
0.0500 g

Unknown: original mass
of radium-224

number of half-lives = $(7.32 \text{ days})\left(\dfrac{1 \text{ half-life}}{3.66 \text{ days}}\right)$ = 2 half-lives

x = original mass

$(x)\left(\dfrac{1}{2}\right)^2 = 0.0500 \text{ g}$

$x = (0.0500 \text{ g})\left(\dfrac{2}{1}\right)^2 = 0.200 \text{ g}$

---

44. Unknown: neutron-proton ratios; location in relation to band of stability

a. $^{235}_{92}$U: 92 protons, 143 neutrons

Ratio = $\dfrac{143}{92}$ = 1.55 : 1 (outside)

b. $^{16}_{8}$O: 8 protons, 8 neutrons

Ratio = $\dfrac{8}{8}$ = 1 : 1 (within)

c. $^{56}_{26}$Fe: 26 protons, 30 neutrons

Ratio = $\dfrac{30}{26}$ = 1.15 : 1 (within)

d. $^{156}_{60}$Nd: 60 protons, 96 neutrons

Ratio = $\dfrac{96}{60}$ = 1.6 : 1 (outside)

---

45. Given: measured atomic
mass of $^{238}_{92}$U =
238.050 784 amu

Unknown: binding energy
per nucleon

92 protons: $(92 \times 1.007\ 276 \text{ amu}) = 92.669\ 392 \text{ amu}$

146 neutrons: $(146 \times 1.008\ 665 \text{ amu}) = 147.265\ 09 \text{ amu}$

92 electrons: $(92 \times 0.000\ 5486 \text{ amu}) = \underline{0.050\ 4712 \text{ amu}}$

total combined mass: 239.984 95 amu

mass defect = 239.984 95 amu − 238.050 784 amu = 1.933 72 amu

$= (1.933\ 72 \text{ amu})\left(\dfrac{1.6605 \times 10^{-27} \text{ kg}}{1 \text{ amu}}\right) = 3.210 \times 10^{-27} \text{ kg}$

$E = mc^2$

$E = (3.2109 \times 10^{-27} \text{ kg})(3.00 \times 10^8 \text{ m/s})^2$

$= 2.889 \times 10^{-10} \text{ kg} \cdot \text{m}^2/\text{s}^2 = 2.889 \times 10^{-10} \text{ J}$

energy per nucleon = $\dfrac{2.889 \times 10^{-10} \text{ J}}{238 \text{ nucleons}} = 1.21 \times 10^{-12} \text{ J/nucleon}$

46. Given: nuclear binding
energy of $^{56}_{26}Fe = 7.89 \times 10^{-11}$ J

Unknown: mass lost in kg

$E = mc^2$

$m = E/C^2$

$= \dfrac{7.89 \times 10^{-11} \text{ J}}{(3.00 \times 10^8 \text{ m/s})^2} = 8.77 \times 10^{-28}$ kg

---

47. Given: measured atomic
mass of deuterium
$= 2.0140$ amu

Unknown: binding energy
for 1 mole of
deuterium
atoms

deuterium $= ^2_1H$

1 proton: $(1 \times 1.007\ 276 \text{ amu}) = 1.007\ 276$ amu

1 neutron: $(1 \times 1.008\ 665 \text{ amu}) = 1.008\ 665$ amu

1 electron: $(1 \times 0.000\ 5486 \text{ amu}) = \underline{0.000\ 5486 \text{ amu}}$

total combined mass: 2.016 4896 amu

mass defect = 2.016 4896 amu − 2.0140 amu = 0.002 4896 amu

$= (0.002\ 489 \text{ amu})\left(\dfrac{1.6605 \times 10^{-27} \text{ kg}}{1 \text{ amu}}\right) = 4.1339 \times 10^{-30}$ kg

$E = mc^2$

$E = (4.1339 \times 10^{-30} \text{ kg})(3.00 \times 10^8 \text{ m/s})^2$

$= 3.72 \times 10^{-13} \text{ kg} \cdot \text{m}^2/\text{s}^2 = 3.72 \times 10^{-13}$ J

energy per mole $= (3.72 \times 10^{-13} \text{ J/atom})(6.022 \times 10^{23} \text{ atoms/mol})$
$= 2.24 \times 10^{11}$ J/mol

Math Tutor, p. 706

1. Given: 8.9×10^{-5} sample
half-life $= 28$ days
elapsed time $=$
168 days

Unknown: amount of
sample
remaining,
in grams

number of half-lives $= \dfrac{168}{28} = 6$

amount remaining $= \left(\dfrac{1}{2}\right)^6 \times 8.9 \times 10^{-5} \text{ g} = 1.4 \times 10^{-6}$ g Cr-51

---

2. Given: half-life $=$
53,000 yr
amount remaining
$= \frac{1}{256}$ of original
mass

Unknown: age of sample

$\dfrac{1}{256} = \left(\dfrac{1}{2}\right)^8$ so 8 half-lives have passed

(8 half-lives)(53 000 yr/half-life) = 420 000 yr

Standardized Test Prep, p. 707

1. Given: β-decay of element
76

Unknown: parent
element

$^{187}_{75}Re \rightarrow ^{187}_{76}Os + ^{0}_{-1}\beta$

parent element is Rhenium-187.

5. Given: $^{37}_{18}\text{Ar} + ^{\ 0}_{-1}e \rightarrow ^{37}_{17}\text{Cl}$

Unknown: Is the nuclear equation balanced?

sum of mass numbers: $37 + 0 = 37$
sum of positive charges: $18 + (-1) = 17$
The atomic number of Ar is 18 and the atomic number of Cl is 17.

The nuclear equation is correctly balanced.

---

8. Given: half-life $= 24$ days
elapsed time $= 72$ days
original sample mass $= 42.0$ g

Unknown: mass of sample remaining

$$\text{number of half-lives} = \frac{72 \text{ days}}{24 \text{ days/half-life}} = 3$$

$$\text{mass remaining} = \text{original mass} \left(\frac{1}{2}\right) \text{ number of half-lives}$$

$$\text{mass remaining} = 42.0 \text{ g} \left(\frac{1}{2}\right)^3 = 5.25 \text{ g Th-234}$$

---

9. Given: elapsed time $= 5.2$ minutes
original sample mass $= 4.0$ g Fr-210
sample mass remaining $= 1.0$ g

Unknown: length of half-life

$$\text{fraction remaining} = \frac{1.0 \text{ g}}{4.0 \text{ g}} = 0.25$$

$$0.25 = \left(\frac{1}{2}\right)^n ; n = \text{number of half-lives} = 2$$

5.2 min $= 2$ half-lives
half-life $= 2.6$ min

CHAPTER 22

Organic Chemistry

Math Tutor, p. 746

1. Given: Percent Composition
20.00% C =
20.00 g C/100.0 g compound etc.
6.71% H
46.65% N
26.64% O

Unknown: empirical formula of compound

$$\frac{20.00 \text{ g C}}{12.01 \text{ g C/mol C}} = 1.665 \text{ mol C}$$

$$\frac{6.71 \text{ g H}}{1.01 \text{ g H/mol H}} = 6.644 \text{ mol H}$$

$$\frac{46.65 \text{ g N}}{14.01 \text{ g N/mol N}} = 3.330 \text{ mol N}$$

$$\frac{26.64 \text{ g O}}{16.00 \text{ g O/mol O}} = 1.665 \text{ mol O}$$

least abundant elements are O and C

$$\frac{1.665 \text{ mol C}}{1.665 \text{ mol C}} = 1$$

$$\frac{6.644 \text{ mol H}}{1.665 \text{ mol C}} = 3.99 \approx 4$$

$$\frac{3.330 \text{ mol N}}{1.665 \text{ mol C}} = 2$$

$$\frac{1.665 \text{ mol O}}{1.665 \text{ mol C}} = 1$$

Empirical formula = $C_1H_4N_2O_1$
= CH_4N_2O

2. Given: Percent Composition
29.78% C =
29.78 g C/100.0 g compound etc.
4.17% H
66.05% Br

Unknown: empirical formula of compound

$$\frac{29.78 \text{ g C}}{12.01 \text{ g C/mol C}} = 2.480 \text{ mol C}$$

$$\frac{4.17 \text{ g H}}{1.01 \text{ g H/mol H}} = 4.129 \text{ mol H}$$

$$\frac{66.05 \text{ g Br}}{79.90 \text{ g Br/mol Br}} = 0.8267 \text{ mol Br}$$

Least abundant element is Br

$$\frac{2.480 \text{ mol C}}{0.8267 \text{ mol Br}} = 3$$

$$\frac{4.129 \text{ mol H}}{0.8267 \text{ mol Br}} = 4.995 \approx 5$$

$$\frac{0.8267 \text{ mol Br}}{0.8267 \text{ mol Br}} = 1$$

Empirical formula = $C_3H_5Br_1$
= C_3H_5Br

3. Given: Percent
Composition
40.00% C =
40.00 g C/100.0 g
compound etc.
6.71% H
53.28% O

Unknown: empirical
formula of
compound

$$\frac{40.00 \text{ g C}}{12.01 \text{ g C/mol C}} = 3.331 \text{ mol C}$$

$$\frac{6.71 \text{ g H}}{1.01 \text{ g H/mol H}} = 6.644 \text{ mol H}$$

$$\frac{53.28 \text{ g O}}{16.00 \text{ g O/mol O}} = 3.330 \text{ mol O}$$

Least abundant elements are C and O

$$\frac{3.331 \text{ mol C}}{3.331 \text{ mol C}} = 1$$

$$\frac{6.644 \text{ mol H}}{3.331 \text{ mol C}} = 1.995 \approx 2$$

$$\frac{3.330 \text{ mol O}}{3.331 \text{ mol C}} = 1$$

Empirical formula = $C_1H_2O_1$
= CH_2O

APPENDIX D
Problem Bank

1. a. Given: 5.2 cm
Unknown: length in millimeters

$$5.2 \text{ cm} \times \frac{10 \text{ mm}}{\text{cm}} = 52 \text{ mm}$$

b. Given: 0.049 kg
Unknown: mass in grams

$$0.049 \text{ kg} \times \frac{1000 \text{ g}}{\text{kg}} = 49 \text{ g}$$

c. Given: 1.60 mL
Unknown: volume in microliters

$$1.60 \text{ mL} \times \frac{1000 \text{ μL}}{\text{mL}} = 1600 \text{ μL}$$

d. Given: 0.0025 g
Unknown: mass in micrograms

$$0.0025 \text{ g} \times \frac{1\,000\,000 \text{ μg}}{\text{g}} = 2500 \text{ μg}$$

e. Given: 0.020 kg
Unknown: mass in milligrams

$$0.020 \text{ kg} \times \frac{1\,000\,000 \text{ mg}}{\text{kg}} = 20\,000 \text{ mg}$$

f. Given: 3 kL
Unknown: volume in liters

$$3 \text{ kL} \times \frac{1000 \text{ L}}{\text{kL}} = 3000 \text{ L}$$

---

2. a. Given: 150 mg
Unknown: mass in grams

$$150 \text{ mg} \times \frac{1 \text{ g}}{1000 \text{ mg}} = 0.15 \text{ g}$$

b. Given: 2500 mL
Unknown: volume in liters

$$2500 \text{ mL} \times \frac{1 \text{ L}}{1000 \text{ mL}} = 2.5 \text{ L}$$

c. Given: 0.5 g
Unknown: mass in kilograms

$$0.5 \text{ g} \times \frac{1 \text{ kg}}{1000 \text{ g}} = 0.0005 \text{ kg}$$

d. Given: 55 L
Unknown: volume in kiloliters

$$55 \text{ L} \times \frac{1 \text{ kL}}{1000 \text{ L}} = 0.055 \text{ kL}$$

e. Given: 35 mm

Unknown: length in cm

$$35 \text{ mm} \times \frac{1 \text{ cm}}{10 \text{ mm}} = 3.5 \text{ cm}$$

f. Given: 8740 m

Unknown: length in kilometers

$$8740 \text{ m} \times \frac{1 \text{ km}}{1000 \text{ m}} = 8.74 \text{ km}$$

g. Given: 209 nm

Unknown: length in millimeters

$$209 \text{ nm} \times \frac{1 \text{ mm}}{1000\,000 \text{ nm}} = 0.000\,209 \text{ mm}$$

h. Given: 500 000 µg

Unknown: mass in kilograms

$$500\,000 \text{ µg} \times \frac{1 \text{ kg}}{1000\,000\,000 \text{ µg}} = 0.0005 \text{ kg}$$

3. Given: 152 million km

Unknown: length in megameters

$$152\,000\,000 \text{ km} \times \frac{1 \text{ Mm}}{1000 \text{ km}} = 152\,000 \text{ Mm}$$

4. Given: 1.87 L in a 2.00 L bottle

Unknown: volume in milliliters needed to fill the bottle

$$2.00 \text{ L} - 1.87 \text{ L} = 0.13 \text{ L}$$

$$0.13 \text{ L} \times \frac{1000 \text{ mL}}{\text{L}} = 130 \text{ mL}$$

5. Given: a wire 150 cm long

Unknown: length in millimeters; number of 50 mm segments in the wire

$$150 \text{ cm} \times \frac{10 \text{ mm}}{\text{cm}} = 1500 \text{ mm}$$

$$1500 \text{ mm} \times \frac{1 \text{ piece}}{50 \text{ mm}} = 30 \text{ pieces}$$

6. Given: 8500 kg to fill a ladle

646 metric tons to make rails

1 metric ton = 1000 kg

Unknown: number of ladlefuls to make rails

$$646 \text{ metric tons} \times \frac{1000 \text{ kg}}{\text{metric ton}} = 646\,000 \text{ kg}$$

$$646\,000 \text{ kg} \times \frac{1 \text{ ladleful}}{8500 \text{ kg}} = 76 \text{ ladlefuls}$$

7. a. Given: 310 000 cm^3

Unknown: volume in cubic meters

$$310\,000 \text{ cm}^3 \times \frac{1 \text{ m}^3}{1\,000\,000 \text{ cm}^3} = 0.31 \text{ m}^3$$

b. Given: 6.5 m^2

Unknown: area in square centimeters

$$6.5 \text{ m}^2 \times \frac{10\ 000 \text{ cm}^2}{\text{m}^2} = 65\ 000 \text{ cm}^2$$

c. Given: 0.035 m^3

Unknown: volume in cubic centimeters

$$0.035 \text{ m}^3 \times \frac{1\ 000\ 000 \text{ cm}^3}{\text{m}^3} = 35\ 000 \text{ cm}^3$$

d. Given: 0.49 cm^2

Unknown: area in square millimeters

$$0.49 \text{ cm}^2 \times \frac{100 \text{ mm}^2}{\text{cm}^2} = 49 \text{ mm}^2$$

e. Given 1200 dm^3

Unknown: volume in cubic meters

$$1200 \text{ dm}^3 \times \frac{1 \text{ m}^3}{1000 \text{ dm}^3} = 1.2 \text{ m}^3$$

f. Given: 87.5 mm3

Unknown: volume in cubic centimeters

$$87.5 \text{ mm}^3 \times \frac{1 \text{ cm}^3}{1000 \text{ mm}^3} = 0.0875 \text{ cm}^3$$

g. Given: 250 000 cm^2

Unknown: area in square meters

$$250\ 000 \text{ cm}^2 \times \frac{1 \text{ m}^2}{10\ 000 \text{ cm}^2} = 25 \text{ m}^2$$

---

8. Given: volume of a cell = 0.0147 mm^3

Unknown: number of cells that fit into a volume of 1.0 cm^3

$$1.0 \text{ cm}^3 \times \frac{1000 \text{ mm}^3}{\text{cm}^3} = 1000.0 \text{ mm}^3$$

$$1000.00 \text{ mm}^3 \times \frac{1 \text{ cell}}{0.0147 \text{ mm}^3} = 68\ 027 \text{ cells}$$

---

9. a. Given: 12.75 Mm

Unknown: length in kilometers

$$12.75 \text{ Mm} \times \frac{1000 \text{ km}}{\text{Mm}} = 12\ 750 \text{ km}$$

b. Given: 277 cm

Unknown: length in meters

$$277 \text{ cm} \times \frac{1 \text{ m}}{100 \text{ cm}} = 2.77 \text{ m}$$

c. Given: 30 560 m^2

1 ha = 10 000 m^2

Unknown: area in hectares

$$30\ 560 \text{ m}^2 \times \frac{1 \text{ ha}}{10\ 000 \text{ m}^2} = 3.056 \text{ ha}$$

d. Given: 81.9 cm^2

Unknown: area in square meters

$$81.9 \text{ cm}^2 \times \frac{1 \text{ m}^2}{10\ 000 \text{ cm}^2} = 0.00819 \text{ m}^2$$

e. Given: 300 000 km

Unknown: length in megameters

$$300\ 000 \text{ km} \times \frac{1 \text{ Mm}}{1000 \text{ km}} = 300 \text{ Mm}$$

---

10. a. Given: 0.62 km

Unknown: length in meters

$$0.62 \text{ km} \times \frac{1000 \text{ m}}{\text{km}} = 620 \text{ m}$$

b. Given: 3857 g

Unknown: mass in milligrams

$$3857 \text{ g} \times \frac{1000 \text{ mg}}{\text{g}} = 3857\ 000 \text{ mg}$$

c. Given: 0.0036 mL

Unknown: volume in microliters

$$0.0036 \text{ mL} \times \frac{1000 \text{ μL}}{\text{mL}} = 3.6 \text{ μL}$$

d. Given: 0.342 metric tons

1 metric ton = 1000 kg

Unknown: mass in kilograms

$$0.342 \text{ metric tons} \times \frac{1000 \text{ kg}}{\text{metric ton}} = 342 \text{ kg}$$

e. Given: 68.71 kL

Unknown: volume in liters

$$68.71 \text{ kL} \times \frac{1000 \text{ L}}{\text{kL}} = 68\ 710 \text{ L}$$

---

11. a. Given: 856 mg

Unknown: mass in kilograms

$$856 \text{ mg} \times \frac{1 \text{ kg}}{1000\ 000 \text{ mg}} = 0.000\ 856 \text{ kg}$$

b. Given: 1210 000 μg

Unknown: mass in kilograms

$$1210\ 000 \text{ μg} \times \frac{1 \text{ kg}}{1000\ 000\ 000 \text{ μg}} = 0.00121 \text{ kg}$$

c. Given: 6598 μL

1 mL = 1 cm^3

Unknown: volume in cm^3

$$6598 \text{ μL} \times \frac{1 \text{ mL}}{1000 \text{ μL}} \times \frac{1 \text{ cm}^3}{\text{mL}} = 6.598 \text{ cm}^3$$

d. Given: 80 600 nm

Unknown: length in millimeters

$$80\ 600 \text{ nm} \times \frac{1 \text{ mm}}{1000\ 000 \text{ nm}} = 0.0806 \text{ mm}$$

e. Given: 10.74 cm^3

Unknown: volume in liters

$$10.74 \text{ cm}^3 \times \frac{1 \text{ mL}}{\text{cm}^3} \times \frac{1 \text{ L}}{1000 \text{ mL}} = 0.010\ 74 \text{ L}$$

---

12. a. Given: 7.93 L

Unknown: volume in cubic centimeters

$$7.93 \text{ L} \times \frac{1000 \text{ mL}}{\text{L}} \times \frac{1 \text{ cm}^3}{\text{mL}} = 7930 \text{ cm}^3$$

b. Given: 0.0059 km

Unknown: length in centimeters

$$0.0059 \text{ km} \times \frac{100\ 000 \text{ cm}}{\text{km}} = 590 \text{ cm}$$

c. Given: 4.19 L

Unknown: volume in cubic decimeters

$$4.19 \text{ L} \times \frac{1 \text{ dm}^3}{\text{L}} = 4.19 \text{ dm}^3$$

d. Given: 7.48 m^2

Unknown: area in square centimeters

$$7.48 \text{ m}^2 \times \frac{10\ 000 \text{ cm}^2}{\text{m}^2} = 74\ 800 \text{ cm}^2$$

e. Given: 0.197 m^3

Unknown: volume in liters

$$0.197 \text{ m}^3 \times \frac{1000 \text{ dm}^3}{\text{m}^3} \times \frac{1 \text{ L}}{\text{dm}^3} = 197 \text{ L}$$

---

13. Given: 0.05 mL oil used per kilometer

Unknown: volume in liters of oil used for 20 000 km

$$20\ 000 \text{ km} \times \frac{0.05 \text{ mL}}{\text{km}} \times \frac{1 \text{ L}}{1000 \text{ mL}} = 1 \text{ L}$$

---

14. Given: 370 mm^3

Unknown: volume in microliters

$$370 \text{ mm}^3 \times \frac{1 \text{ cm}^3}{1000 \text{ mm}^3} \times \frac{1 \text{ mL}}{\text{cm}^3} \times \frac{1000 \text{ μL}}{\text{mL}} = 370 \text{ μL}$$

---

15. Given: 1.5 tsp vanilla per cake
1 tsp = 5 mL

Unknown: volume of vanilla in liters for 800 cakes

$$800 \text{ cakes} \times \frac{1.5 \text{ tsp}}{\text{cake}} \times \frac{5 \text{ mL}}{\text{tsp}} \times \frac{1 \text{ L}}{1000 \text{ mL}} = 6 \text{ L}$$

16. Given: eight 300 mL glasses of water/day
1 yr = 365 days
D_{water} = 1.00 kg/L

Unknown: volume in liters of water consumed in a year mass in kilograms of this volume

$$\frac{8 \text{ glasses}}{\text{day}} \times \frac{365 \text{ days}}{\text{yr}} \times \frac{300 \text{ mL}}{\text{glass}} \times \frac{1 \text{ L}}{1000 \text{ mL}} = 876 \text{ L per year}$$

$$876 \text{ L} \times \frac{1 \text{ kg}}{\text{L}} = 876 \text{ kg}$$

17. a. Given: 465 m/s

Unknown: velocity in kilometers per hour

$$\frac{465 \text{ m}}{\text{s}} \times \frac{1 \text{ km}}{1000 \text{ m}} \times \frac{3600 \text{ s}}{\text{h}} = 1674 \text{ km/h}$$

b. Given: 465 m/s

Unknown: velocity in kilometers per day

$$\frac{1674 \text{ km}}{\text{h}} \times \frac{24 \text{ h}}{\text{day}} = 40 \text{ } 176 \text{ km/day}$$

18. Given: 130 g/student
60 students

Unknown: total mass in kilograms

$$\frac{130 \text{ g}}{\text{student}} \times 60 \text{ students} \times \frac{1 \text{ kg}}{1000 \text{ g}} = 7.8 \text{ kg}$$

19. Given: 750 mm/student
60 students

Unknown: total length in meters

$$\frac{750 \text{ mm}}{\text{student}} \times 60 \text{ students} \times \frac{1 \text{ m}}{1000 \text{ mm}} = 45 \text{ m}$$

20. a. Given: 550 µL/h

Unknown: rate in milliliters per day

$$\frac{550 \text{ µL}}{\text{h}} \times \frac{1 \text{ mL}}{1000 \text{ µL}} \times \frac{24 \text{ h}}{\text{day}} = 13.2 \text{ mL/day}$$

b. Given: 9.00 metric tons/h

Unknown: rate in kilograms per minute

$$\frac{9.00 \text{ metric tons}}{\text{h}} \times \frac{1000 \text{ kg}}{\text{metric ton}} \times \frac{1 \text{ h}}{60 \text{ min}} = 150 \text{ kg/min}$$

c. Given: 3.72 L/h

Unknown: rate in cubic centimeters per minute

$$\frac{3.72 \text{ L}}{\text{h}} \times \frac{1000 \text{ mL}}{\text{L}} \times \frac{1 \text{ cm}^3}{\text{mL}} \times \frac{1 \text{ h}}{60 \text{ min}} = 62 \text{ cm}^3/\text{min}$$

d. Given: 6.12 km/h

Unknown: rate in meters per second

$$\frac{6.12 \text{ km}}{\text{h}} \times \frac{1000 \text{ m}}{\text{km}} \times \frac{1 \text{ h}}{3600 \text{ s}} = 1.7 \text{ m/s}$$

21. a. Given: 2.97 kg/L

Unknown: rate in g/cm^3

$$\frac{2.97 \text{ kg}}{\text{L}} \times \frac{1000 \text{ g}}{\text{kg}} \times \frac{1 \text{ L}}{1000 \text{ mL}} \times \frac{1 \text{ mL}}{cm^3} = 2.97 \text{ g/cm}^3$$

b. Given: 4128 g/dm^2

Unknown: mass per area in kilograms per square centimeters

$$\frac{4128 \text{ g}}{dm^2} \times \frac{1 \text{ kg}}{1000 \text{ g}} \times \frac{1 \text{ dm}^2}{100 \text{ cm}^2} = 0.04128 \text{ kg/cm}^2$$

c. Given: 5.27 g/cm^3

Unknown: density as kilograms per cubic decimeter

$$\frac{5.27 \text{ g}}{cm^3} \times \frac{1 \text{ kg}}{1000 \text{ g}} \times \frac{1000 \text{ cm}^3}{dm^3} = 5.27 \text{ kg/dm}^3$$

d. Given: 6.91 kg/m^3

Unknown: density as milligrams per cubic millimeter

$$\frac{6.91 \text{ kg}}{m^3} \times \frac{1\,000\,000 \text{ mg}}{\text{kg}} \times \frac{1 \text{ m}^3}{1\,000\,000\,000 \text{ mm}^3} = 0.00691 \text{ mg/mm}^3$$

22. a. Given: density of 5.56 g/L

Unknown: volume in milliliters occupied by 4.17 g

$$4.17 \text{ g} \times \frac{1 \text{ L}}{5.56 \text{ g}} \times \frac{1000 \text{ mL}}{\text{L}} = 750 \text{ mL}$$

b. Given: density of 5.56 g/L

Unknown: mass in kilograms of 1 m^3

$$1 \text{ m}^3 \times \frac{1000 \text{ dm}^3}{m^3} \times \frac{1 \text{ L}}{dm^3} \times \frac{5.56 \text{ g}}{\text{L}} \times \frac{1 \text{ kg}}{1000 \text{ g}} = 5.56 \text{ kg}$$

23. Given: mass per area of 0.10 g/cm^2

Unknown: mass in kilometers per 0.125 ha

$$0.125 \text{ ha} \times \frac{10\,000 \text{ m}^2}{\text{ha}} \times \frac{10\,000 \text{ cm}^2}{m^2} \times \frac{0.10 \text{ g}}{cm^2} \times \frac{1 \text{ kg}}{1000 \text{ g}} = 1250 \text{ kg}$$

24. a. Given: length of book = 250. mm
width of book = 224 mm
thickness of book = 50.0 mm

Unknown: volume in cubic meters

$$250. \text{ mm} \times 224 \text{ mm} \times 50.0 \text{ mm} = 2\,800\,000 \text{ mm}^3 \times \frac{1 \text{ m}^3}{1\,000\,000\,000 \text{ mm}^3}$$

$$= 0.0028 \text{ m}^3$$

b. Given: length of book = 250. mm
width of book = 224 mm
thickness of book = 50.0 mm
mass of book = 2.94 kg

Unknown: density in grams per cubic centimeter

$$\frac{2.94 \text{ kg}}{0.0028 \text{ m}^3} \times \frac{1000 \text{ g}}{\text{kg}} \times \frac{1 \text{ m}^3}{1\,000\,000 \text{ cm}^3} = 1.05 \text{ g/cm}^3$$

c. Given: length of book = 250. mm
width of book = 224 mm
thickness of book = 50.0 mm

Unknown: area of front cover in square meters

$$250 \text{ mm} \times 224 \text{ mm} \times \frac{1 \text{ m}^2}{1\,000\,000 \text{ mm}^2} = 0.056 \text{ m}^2$$

---

25. a. Given: 25 drops = 1.00 mL

Unknown: volume of one drop in milliliters

$$\frac{1.00 \text{ mL}}{25 \text{ drops}} = 0.04 \text{ mL}$$

b. Given: 25 drops = 1.00 mL

Unknown: volume in milliliters of 37 drops

$$37 \text{ drops} \times \frac{0.04 \text{ mL}}{\text{drop}} = 1.48 \text{ mL}$$

c. Given: 25 drops = 1.00 mL

Unknown: number of drops in 0.68 L

$$0.68 \text{ L} \times \frac{1000 \text{ mL}}{\text{L}} \times \frac{1 \text{ drop}}{0.04 \text{ mL}} = 17\,000 \text{ drops}$$

26. a. Given: 504 700 mg
Unknown: mass in kilograms and grams

$$504\ 700 \text{ mg} \times \frac{1 \text{ kg}}{1000\ 000 \text{ mg}} = 0.5047 \text{ kg}$$

$$504\ 700 \text{ mg} \times \frac{1g}{1000 \text{ mg}} = 504.7 \text{ g}$$

b. Given: 9200 000 µg
Unknown: mass in kilograms and grams

$$9200\ 000 \text{ µg} \times \frac{1 \text{ kg}}{1000\ 000\ 000 \text{ µg}} = 0.0092 \text{ kg}$$

$$9200\ 000 \text{ µg} \times \frac{1 \text{ g}}{1000\ 000 \text{ µg}} = 9.2 \text{ kg}$$

c. Given: 122 mg
Unknown: mass in kilograms and grams

$$122 \text{ mg} \times \frac{1 \text{ kg}}{1000\ 000 \text{ mg}} = 0.000\ 122 \text{ kg}$$

$$122 \text{ mg} \times \frac{1 \text{ g}}{1000 \text{ mg}} = 0.122 \text{ g}$$

d. Given: 7195 cg
Unknown: mass in kilograms and grams

$$7195 \text{ cg} \times \frac{1 \text{ kg}}{100\ 000 \text{ cg}} = 0.07195 \text{ kg}$$

$$7195 \text{ cg} \times \frac{1 \text{ g}}{100 \text{ cg}} = 71.95 \text{ g}$$

27. a. Given: 582 cm³
Unknown: volume in liters and milliliters

$$582 \text{ cm}^3 \times \frac{1 \text{ mL}}{\text{cm}^3} \times \frac{1 \text{ L}}{1000 \text{ mL}} = 0.582 \text{ L}$$

$$582 \text{ cm}^3 \times \frac{1 \text{ mL}}{\text{cm}^3} = 582 \text{ mL}$$

b. Given: 0.0025 m³
Unknown: volume in liters and milliliters

$$0.0025 \text{ m}^3 \times \frac{1000 \text{ dm}^3}{\text{m}^3} \times \frac{1 \text{ L}}{\text{dm}^3} = 2.5 \text{ L}$$

$$0.0025 \text{ m}^3 \times \frac{1000\ 000 \text{ cm}^3}{\text{m}^3} \times \frac{1 \text{ mL}}{\text{cm}^3} = 2500 \text{ mL}$$

c. Given: 1.18 dm³
Unknown: volume in liters and milliliters

$$1.18 \text{ dm}^3 \times \frac{1 \text{ L}}{\text{dm}^3} = 1.18 \text{ L}$$

$$1.18 \text{ dm}^3 \times \frac{1 \text{ L}}{\text{dm}^3} \times \frac{1000 \text{ mL}}{\text{L}} = 1180 \text{ mL}$$

d. Given: 32 900 µL
Unknown: volume in liters and milliliters

$$32\ 900 \text{ µL} \times \frac{1 \text{ L}}{1000\ 000 \text{ µL}} = 0.0329 \text{ L}$$

$$32\ 900 \text{ µL} \times \frac{1 \text{ mL}}{1000 \text{ µL}} = 32.9 \text{ mL}$$

28. a. Given: 1.37 g/cm³
Unknown: density in grams per liter and kilograms per cubic meter

$$\frac{1.37 \text{ g}}{\text{cm}^3} \times \frac{1 \text{ cm}^3}{\text{mL}} \times \frac{1000 \text{ mL}}{\text{L}} = 1370 \text{ g/L}$$

$$\frac{1.37 \text{ g}}{\text{cm}^3} \times \frac{1 \text{ kg}}{1000 \text{ g}} \times \frac{1000\ 000 \text{ cm}^3}{\text{m}^3} = 1370 \text{ kg/m}^3$$

b. Given: 0.692 kg/dm^3

Unknown: density in grams per liter and kilograms per cubic meter

$$\frac{0.692 \text{ kg}}{\text{dm}^3} \times \frac{1000 \text{ g}}{\text{kg}} \times \frac{1 \text{ dm}^3}{\text{L}} = 692 \text{ g/L}$$

$$\frac{0.692 \text{ kg}}{\text{dm}^3} \times \frac{1000 \text{ dm}^3}{\text{m}^3} = 692 \text{ kg/m}^3$$

c. Given: 5.2 kg/L

Unknown: density in gams per liter and kilograms per cubic meter

$$\frac{5.2 \text{ kg}}{\text{L}} \times \frac{1000 \text{ g}}{\text{kg}} = 5200 \text{ g/L}$$

$$\frac{5.2 \text{ kg}}{\text{L}} \times \frac{1 \text{ L}}{\text{dm}^3} \times \frac{1000 \text{ dm}^3}{\text{m}^3} = 5200 \text{ kg/m}^3$$

d. Given: 38 000 g/m^3

Unknown: density in grams per liter and kilograms per cubic meter

$$\frac{38 \, 000 \text{ g}}{\text{m}^3} \times \frac{1 \text{ m}^3}{1000 \text{ dm}^3} \times \frac{1 \text{ dm}^3}{\text{L}} = 38 \text{ g/L}$$

$$\frac{38 \, 000 \text{ g}}{\text{m}^3} \times \frac{1 \text{ kg}}{1000 \text{ g}} = 38 \text{ kg/m}^3$$

e. Given: 5.79 mg/mm^3

Unknown: density in grams per liter and kilograms per cubic meter

$$\frac{5.79 \text{ mg}}{\text{mm}^3} \times \frac{1 \text{ g}}{1000 \text{ mg}} \times \frac{1000 \, 000 \text{ mm}^3}{\text{dm}^3} \times \frac{1 \text{ dm}^3}{\text{L}} = 5790 \text{ g/L}$$

$$\frac{5.79 \text{ mg}}{\text{mm}^3} \times \frac{1 \text{ kg}}{1000 \, 000 \text{ mg}} \times \frac{1000 \, 000 \, 000 \text{ mm}^3}{\text{m}^3} = 5790 \text{ kg/m}^3$$

f. Given: 1.1 μg/ml

Unknown: density in grams per liter and kilograms per cubic meter

$$\frac{1.1 \, \mu\text{g}}{\text{mL}} \times \frac{1 \text{ g}}{1000 \, 000 \, \mu\text{g}} \times \frac{1000 \text{ mL}}{\text{L}} = 0.0011 \text{ g/L}$$

$$\frac{1.1 \, \mu\text{g}}{\text{mL}} \times \frac{1 \text{ kg}}{1000 \, 000 \, 000 \, \mu\text{g}} \times \frac{1 \text{ mL}}{\text{cm}^3} \times \frac{1000 \, 000 \text{ cm}^3}{\text{m}^3} = 0.0011 \text{ kg/m}^3$$

29. a. Given: 648 kg/30.0 h

Unknown: rate in grams per minute

$$\frac{648 \text{ kg}}{30.0 \text{ h}} \times \frac{1000 \text{ g}}{\text{kg}} \times \frac{1 \text{ h}}{60 \text{ min}} = 360 \text{ g/min}$$

b. Given: 648 kg/30.0 h

Unknown: rate in kilograms per day

$$\frac{648.0 \text{ kg}}{30.0 \text{ h}} \times \frac{24 \text{ h}}{\text{day}} = 518.4 \text{ kg/day}$$

c. Given: 648 kg/30.0 h

Unknown: rate in milli-grams per milli-second

$$\frac{648.0 \text{ kg}}{30.0 \text{ h}} \times \frac{1000 \, 000 \text{ mg}}{\text{kg}} \times \frac{1 \text{ h}}{3600 \text{ s}} \times \frac{1 \text{ s}}{1000 \text{ ms}} = 6 \text{ mg/ms}$$

30. Given: 100 km/h

Unknown: rate in meters per second

$$\frac{100.\text{ km}}{\text{h}} \times \frac{1000\text{ m}}{\text{km}} \times \frac{1\text{ h}}{3600\text{ s}} = 27.8\text{ m/s}$$

---

31. Given: 330 kJ/min

1 cal = 4.184 J

Unknown: rate in kilocalories per hour

$$\frac{330\text{ kJ}}{\text{min}} \times \frac{60\text{ min}}{\text{h}} \times \frac{1\text{ kcal}}{4.184\text{ kJ}} = 4732\text{ kcal/h}$$

---

32. Given: 62 g/m^2

1 ha = 10 000 m^2

Unknown: mass in kilograms required for 1.0 ha

$$\frac{62\text{ g}}{\text{m}^2} \times \frac{10\,000\text{ m}^2}{\text{ha}} \times \frac{1\text{ kg}}{1000\text{ g}} \times \frac{1.0\text{ ha}}{1000\text{ g}} = 620\text{ kg}$$

---

33. Given: 3.9 mL/h

1 year = 365 days

Unknown: volume in liters per year

$$\frac{3.9\text{ mL}}{\text{h}} \times \frac{1\text{ L}}{1000\text{ mL}} \times \frac{24\text{ h}}{\text{day}} \times \frac{365\text{ days}}{\text{yr}} = 34\text{ L/yr}$$

---

34. Given: 50 μL/dose

2.0 mL/bottle

Unknown: number of doses in a bottle

$$2.0\text{ mL} \times \frac{1\text{ dose}}{50\text{ μL}} \times \frac{1000\text{ μL}}{\text{mL}} = 40\text{ doses}$$

---

35. a. Given: 640 cm^3

Unknown: number of signicant figures

2; the zero is not significant

b. Given: 200.0 mL

Unknown: number of significant figures

4; all digits are significant

c. Given: 0.5200 g

Unknown: number of significant figures

4; all digits to the right of the decimal point are significant

d. Given: 1.005 kg

Unknown: number of significant figures

4; all digits are significant

e. Given: 10 000 L

Unknown: number of significant
figures

1; the zeros are placeholders

f. Given: 20.900 cm

Unknown: number of significant
figures

5; all digits are significant

g. Given: 0.000 000 56
g/L

Unknown: number of significant
figures

2; all the zeros are placeholders

h. Given: 0.040 02
kg/m^3

Unknown: number of significant
figures

4; the two initial zeros are placeholders

i. Given: 790 001 cm^2

Unknown: number of significant
figures

6; all digits are significant

j. Given: 665.000
$kg \cdot m/s^2$

Unknown: number of significant
figures

6; all digits are significant

38. a. Given: 0.0120 m

Unknown: number of significant
figures

3; the two initial zeros are placeholders

b. Given: 100.5 mL

Unknown: number of significant
figures

4; all digits are significant

c. Given: 101 g

Unknown: number of significant figures

3; all digits are significant

d. Given: 350 cm^2

Unknown: number of significant figures

2; zero is a placeholder

e. Given: 0.97 km

Unknown: number of significant figures

2; zero is a placeholder

f. Given: 1000 kg

Unknown: number of significant figures

1; zeros are placeholders

g. Given: 180. mm

Unknown: number of significant figures

3; all digits are significant

h. Given: 0.4936 L

Unknown: number of significant figures

4; zero is a placeholder

i. Given: 0.020 700 s

Unknown: number of significant figures

5; initial zeros are placeholders

---

39. a. Given: 5 487 129 m

Unknown: value expressed to 3 significant figures

5 490 000 m; the digit following the last digit to be retained is greater than 5

b. Given: 0.013 479 265 mL

Unknown: value expressed to 6 significant figures

0.013 479 3; initial zeros are placeholders; the digit following the last digit to be retained is greater than 5

c. Given: 31 947.972 cm^2

Unknown: value expressed to 4 significant figures

31 950 cm^2; the digit following the last digit to be retained is greater than 5

d. Given: 192.6739 m^2

Unknown: value expressed to 5 significant figures

192.67 m^2; the digit following the last digit to be retained is less than 5

e. Given: 786.9164 cm

Unknown: value expressed to 2 significant figures

790 cm; the digit following the last digit to be retained is greater than 5

f. Given: 389 277 600 J

Unknown: value expressed to 6 significant figures

389 278 000 J; the digit following the last digit to be retained is greater than 5; the zeros are placeholders

g. Given: 225 834.762 cm^3

Unknown: value expressed to 7 significant figures

225 834.8 cm^3; the digit following the last to be retained is greater than 5

---

42. a. Given: dimensions of 87.59 cm × 35.1 mm

Unknown: area in cm^2

$$87.59 \text{ cm} \times 35.1 \text{ mm} \times \frac{1 \text{ cm}}{10 \text{ mm}} = 307 \text{ cm}^2$$

b. Given: dimensions of 87.59 cm × 35.1 mm

Unknown: area in mm^2

$$87.59 \text{ cm} \times \frac{10 \text{ mm}}{1 \text{ cm}} \times 35.1 \text{ mm} = 30 \, 700. \text{ mm}^2$$

c. Given: dimensions of 87.59 cm × 35.1 mm

Unknown: area in m^2

$$87.59 \text{ cm} \times \frac{1 \text{ m}}{100 \text{ cm}} \times 35.1 \text{ mm} \times \frac{1 \text{ m}}{1000 \text{ mm}} = 0.0307 \text{ m}^2$$

43. a. Given: dimensions of
900. mm ×
31.5 mm ×
6.3 cm

Unknown: volume in
cm^3

$$900. \text{ mm} \times \frac{10 \text{ cm}}{10 \text{ mm}} \times 31.5 \text{ mm} \times \frac{1 \text{ cm}}{10 \text{ mm}} \times 6.3 \text{ cm} = 1800 \text{ cm}^3$$

b. Given: dimensions of
900. mm ×
31.5 mm ×
6.3 cm

Unknown: volume in
m^3

$$900. \text{ mm} \times \frac{1 \text{ m}}{1000 \text{ mm}} \times 31.5 \text{ mm} \times \frac{1 \text{ m}}{1000 \text{ mm}} \times 6.3 \text{ cm} \times \frac{1 \text{ m}}{100 \text{ cm}}$$
$$= 0.0018 \text{ m}^3$$

c. Given: dimensions of
900. mm ×
31.5 mm ×
6.3 cm

Unknown: volume in
mm^3

$$900. \text{ mm} \times 31.5 \text{ mm} \times 6.3 \text{ cm} \times \frac{10 \text{ mm}}{1 \text{ cm}} = 1\ 800\ 000 \text{ mm}^3$$

---

44. a. Given: 0.16 kg/125 mL
Unknown: density in
kg/m^3

$$\frac{0.16 \text{ kg}}{125 \text{ mL}} \times \frac{1 \text{ mL}}{1 \text{ cm}^3} \times \frac{1\ 000\ 000 \text{ cm}^3}{1 \text{ m}^3} = 1300 \text{ kg/m}^3$$

b. Given: 0.16 kg/125 mL
Unknown: density in
g/mL

$$\frac{0.16 \text{ kg}}{125 \text{ mL}} \times \frac{1000 \text{ g}}{1 \text{ kg}} = 1.3 \text{ g/mL}$$

c. Given: 0.16 kg/125 mL
Unknown: density in
kg/dm^3

$$\frac{0.16 \text{ kg}}{125 \text{ mL}} \times \frac{1000 \text{ mL}}{1 \text{ L}} \times \frac{1 \text{ L}}{1 \text{ dm}^3} = 1.3 \text{ kg/dm}^3$$

---

45. a. Given: numbers with
4, 3, and 2
significant
figures,
respectively

Unknown: product to
2 signifi-
cant
figures

$$13.75 \text{ mm} \times 10.1 \text{ mm} \times 0.91 \text{ mm} = 130 \text{ mm}^3$$

b. Given: numbers with
3 and 2 signif-
icant figures,
respectively

Unknown: product to
2 signifi-
cant
figures

$$89.4 \text{ cm}^2 \times 4.8 \text{ cm} = 430 \text{ cm}^3$$

c. Given: numbers with 3 and 2 significant figures, respectively

Unknown: quotient to 2 significant figures

$14.9 \text{ m}^3 \div 3.0 \text{ m}^2 = 5.0 \text{ m}$

d. Given: numbers with 4, 1, and 3 significant figures, respectively

Unknown: product to 1 significant figure

$6.975 \text{ m} \times 30 \text{ m} \times 21.5 \text{ m} = 4000 \text{ m}^3$

---

48. Given: dimensions of 30.5 mm × 202 mm × 153 mm; mass empty = 0.30 kg; mass full = 1.33 kg

Unknown: density of the liquid in kg/L

$V = 30.5 \text{ mm} \times 202 \text{ mm} \times 153 \text{ mm} = 943\,000 \text{ mm}^3$

$m = 1.33 \text{ kg} - 0.30 \text{ kg} = 1.03 \text{ kg}$

$D = \dfrac{1.03 \text{ kg}}{943\,000 \text{ mm}^3} \times \dfrac{1.000\,000 \text{ mm}^3}{1 \text{ dm}^3} \times \dfrac{1 \text{ dm}^3}{1 \text{ L}} = 1.09 \text{ kg/L}$

---

49. Given: 3.3 kg/7.76 km

Unknown: mass in g/m; length with a mass of 1.0 g

$\dfrac{3.3 \text{ kg}}{7.76 \text{ km}} \times \dfrac{1000 \text{ g}}{1 \text{ kg}} \times \dfrac{1 \text{ km}}{1000 \text{ m}} = 0.43 \text{ g/m}$

$1.0 \text{ g} \times \dfrac{1 \text{ m}}{0.43 \text{ g}} = 2.3 \text{ m}$

---

50. Given: rate of 52 kg/ha; container holds 10 kg; 1 ha = 10 000 m^2

Unknown: area in m^2 covered by full container

$\dfrac{10 \text{ kg}}{1 \text{ container}} \times \dfrac{1 \text{ ha}}{52 \text{ kg}} \times \dfrac{10\,000 \text{ m}^2}{1 \text{ ha}} = 2000 \text{ m}^2$

---

51. Given: 974 550 kJ/37.0 min

Unknown: rate in kJ/min and kJ/s

$\dfrac{974\,550 \text{ kJ}}{37.0 \text{ min}} = 26\,300 \text{ kJ/min}$

$\dfrac{974\,550 \text{ kJ}}{37.0 \text{ min}} \times \dfrac{1 \text{ min}}{60 \text{ s}} = 439 \text{ kJ/s}$

---

52. a. Given: dimensions of 189 cm × 307 cm × 272 cm

Unknown: volume in cubic meters

$189 \text{ cm} \times 307 \text{ cm} \times 272 \text{ cm} \times \dfrac{1 \text{ m}^3}{1\,000\,000 \text{ cm}^3} = 15.8 \text{ m}^3$

b. Given: dimensions of 189 cm × 307 cm × 272 cm; fill time of 97 s

Unknown: rate in liters per minute

$$\frac{189 \text{ cm} \times 307 \text{ cm} \times 272 \text{ cm}}{97 \text{ s}} \times \frac{1 \text{ dm}^3}{1000 \text{ cm}^3} \times \frac{60 \text{ s}}{1 \text{ min}} \times \frac{1 \text{ L}}{1 \text{ dm}^3} = 9800 \text{ L/min}$$

c. Given: dimensions of 189 cm × 307 cm × 272 cm; fill time of 97 s

Unknown: rate in cubic meters per hour

$$\frac{189 \text{ cm} \times 307 \text{ cm} \times 272 \text{ cm}}{97 \text{ s}} \times \frac{1 \text{ m}^3}{1000\,000 \text{ cm}^3} \times \frac{3600 \text{ s}}{1 \text{ h}} = 590 \text{ m}^3/\text{h}$$

55. a. Given: lengths expressed in scientific notation

Unknown: sum expressed in scientific notation to hundredths place

$4.74 \times 10^4 \text{ km} + 7.71 \times 10^3 \text{ km} + 1.05 \times 10^3 \text{ km}$
$= 4.74 \times 10^4 \text{ km} + 0.771 \times 10^4 \text{ km} + 0.105 \times 10^4 \text{ km}$
$= 5.62 \times 10^4 \text{ km}$

b. Given: lengths expressed in scientific notation

Unknown: sum expressed in scientific notation to thousandths place

$2.75 \times 10^{-4} \text{ m} + 8.03 \times 10^{-5} \text{ m} + 2.122 \times 10^{-3} \text{ m}$
$= 0.275 \times 10^{-3} \text{ m} + 0.0803 \times 10^{-3} \text{ m} + 2.122 \times 10^{-3} \text{ m}$
$= 2.477 \times 10^{-3} \text{ m}$

c. Given: volume expressed in scientific notation

Unknown: answer expressed in scientific notation to tenths place

$4.0 \times 10^{-5} \text{ m}^3 + 6.85 \times 10^{-6} \text{ m}^3 - 1.05 \times 10^{-5} \text{ m}^3$
$= 4.0 \times 10^{-5} \text{ m}^3 + 0.685 \times 10^{-5} \text{ m}^3 - 1.05 \times 10^{-5} \text{ m}^3$
$= 3.6 \times 10^{-5} \text{ m}^3$

d. Given: masses expressed in scientific notation

Unknown: sum expressed in scientific notation to hundredths place

3.15×10^2 mg $+ 3.15 \times 10^3$ mg $+ 3.15 \times 10^4$ mg
$= 0.0315 \times 10^4$ mg $+ 0.315 \times 10^4$ mg $+ 3.15 \times 10^4$ mg
$= 3.50 \times 10^4$ mg

e. Given: number of atoms expressed in scientific notation

Unknown: sum expressed in scientific notation to hundredths place

3.01×10^{22} atoms $+ 1.19 \times 10^{23}$ atoms $+ 9.80 \times 10^{21}$ atoms
$= 0.301 \times 10^{23}$ atoms $+ 1.19 \times 10^{23}$ atoms $+ 0.0980 \times 10^{23}$ atoms
$= 1.59 \times 10^{23}$ atoms

f. Given: lengths expressed in scientific notation

Unknown: answer expressed in scientific notation to thousandths place

6.85×10^7 nm $+ 4.0229 \times 10^8$ nm $- 8.38 \times 10^6$ nm
$= 0.685 \times 10^8$ nm $+ 4.0229 \times 10^8$ nm $- 0.0838 \times 10^8$ nm
$= 4.624 \times 10^8$ nm

65. a. Given: 7.11×10^{24} molecules per 100.0 cm^3

Unknown: number of molecules per 1.09 cm^3

$$\frac{7.11 \times 10^{24} \text{ molecules}}{100.0 \text{ cm}^3} \times 1.09 \text{ cm}^3 = 7.75 \times 10^{22} \text{ molecules}$$

b. Given: 7.11×10^{24} molecules per 100.0 cm^3

Unknown: number of molecules in 2.24×10^4 cm^3

$$\frac{7.11 \times 10^{24} \text{ molecules}}{100.0 \text{ cm}^3} \times 2.24 \times 10^4 \text{ cm}^3 = 0.159 \times 10^{28} \text{ molecules}$$
$$= 1.59 \times 10^{27} \text{ molecules}$$

c. Given: 7.11×10^{24} molecules per 100.0 cm^3

Unknown: number of molecules in $9.01 \times 10^{-6} \text{ cm}^3$

$$\frac{7.11 \times 10^{24} \text{ molecules}}{100.0 \text{ cm}^3} \times 9.01 \times 10^{-6} \text{ cm}^3$$

$$= 0.641 \times 10^{18} \text{ molecules} = 6.41 \times 10^{17} \text{ molecules}$$

---

66. a. Given: 3 518 000 transistors per $9.5 \text{ mm} \times 8.2 \text{ mm}$

Unknown: area per transistor

$$\frac{9.5 \text{ mm} \times 8.2 \text{ mm}}{3\,578\,000 \text{ transistors}} = 0.000\,022 \text{ mm}^2/\text{transistor}$$

$$= 2.2 \times 10^{-5} \text{ mm}^2/\text{transistor}$$

b. Given: 2.2×10^{-5} $\text{mm}^2/$ transistor

Unknown: number of transistors on $353 \text{ mm} \times 265 \text{ mm}$

$$353 \text{ mm} \times 265 \text{ mm} \times \frac{1 \text{ transistor}}{2.2 \times 10^{-5} \text{ mm}^2} = 43\,000 \times 10^5 \text{ transistors}$$

$$= 4.3 \times 10^9 \text{ transistors}$$

---

67. Given: 0.0501 g per 1.00 L

Unknown: concentration in grams per microliter

$$\frac{0.0501 \text{ g}}{1.00 \text{ L}} \times \frac{1 \text{ L}}{1 \times 10^6 \ \mu\text{L}} = 0.0501 \times 10^{-6} \text{ g/}\mu\text{L} = 5.01 \times 10^{-8} \text{ g/}\mu\text{L}$$

---

68. Given: 5.30×10^{-10} m/Cs atom

Unknown: number of Cs atoms in 2.54 cm

$$\frac{1 \text{ Cs atom}}{5.30 \times 10^{-10} \text{ m}} \times \frac{1 \text{ m}}{10^2 \text{ cm}} \times 2.54 \text{ cm} = 4.79 \times 10^7 \text{ Cs atoms}$$

---

69. Given: $V_{\text{neutron}} = 1.4 \times 10^{-44} \text{ m}^3$
$M_{\text{neutron}} = 1{,}675 \times 10^{-24} \text{ g}$

Unknown: D_{neutron} in g/m^3
mass of 1.0 cm^3 of neutrons in kg

$$D_{\text{neutron}} = \frac{1.675 \times 10^{-24} \text{ g}}{1.4 \times 10^{-44} \text{ m}^3} = 1.2 \times 10^{20} \text{ g/m}^3$$

$$\frac{1.675 \times 10^{-24} \text{ g}}{1.4 \times 10^{-44} \text{ m}^3} \times \frac{1 \text{ kg}}{10^3 \text{ g}} \times \frac{1 \text{ m}^3}{10^6 \text{ cm}^3} \times 1.0 \text{ m}^3 = 1.2 \times 10^{11} \text{ kg}$$

---

70. Given: $1.6 \times 10^{-8} \text{ m}$ per pit

Unknown: number of pits in 0.305 m

$$0.305 \text{ m} \times \frac{1 \text{ pit}}{1.6 \times 10^{-8} \text{ m}} = 1.9 \times 10^7 \text{ pits}$$

71. a. Given: 6.022×10^{23} O_2 molecules per 22 400 mL at 0°C and standard atmospheric pressure

Unknown: number of O_2 molecules in 0.100 mL

$$\frac{6.022 \times 10^{23}\ O_2\ \text{molecules}}{22\ 400\ \text{mL}} \times 0.100\ \text{mL} = 0.000\ 026\ 9 \times 10^{23}\ O_2\ \text{molecules}$$

$$= 2.69 \times 10^{18}\ O_2\ \text{molecules}$$

b. Given: 6.022×10^{23} O_2 molecules per 22 400 mL at 0°C and standard atmospheric pressure

Unknown: number of O_2 molecules in 1.00 L

$$\frac{6.022 \times 10^{23}\ O_2\ \text{molecules}}{22\ 400\ \text{mL}} \times \frac{10^3\ \text{mL}}{1\ \text{L}} \times 1.00\ \text{L}$$

$$= 0.000\ 269 \times 10^{26}\ O_2\ \text{molecules} = 2.69 \times 10^{22}\ O_2\ \text{molecules}$$

c. Given: 6.022×10^{23} O_2 molecules per 22 400 mL at 0°C and standard atmospheric pressure

Unknown: average space in milliliters occupied by one oxygen molecule

$$\frac{22\ 400\ \text{mL}}{6.022 \times 10^{23}\ O_2\ \text{molecules}} = 3720 \times 10^{-23}\ \text{mL/}O_2\ \text{molecule}$$

$$= 3.72 \times 10^{-20}\ \text{mL/}O_2\ \text{molecule}$$

72. a. Given: $m = 5.136 \times 10^{18}$ kg; 6 500 000 000 people

Unknown: mass in kg per person

$$\frac{5.136 \times 10^{18}\ \text{kg}}{6.5 \times 10^9\ \text{people}} = 7.9 \times 10^8\ \text{kg/person}$$

b. Given: $m = 5.136 \times 10^{18}$ kg; 6 500 000 000 people

Unknown: mass in metric tons per person

$$\frac{5.136 \times 10^{18}\ \text{kg}}{6.5 \times 10^9\ \text{people}} \times \frac{1\ \text{metric ton}}{10^3\ \text{kg}} = 0.79 \times 10^6\ \text{metric ton/person}$$

$$= 7.9 \times 10^5\ \text{metric ton/person}$$

c. Given: $m = 5.136 \times 10^{18}$ kg; 9 500 000 000 people

Unknown: mass in kg per person

$$\frac{5.136 \times 10^{18} \text{ kg}}{9.5 \times 10^9 \text{ people}} = 0.54 \times 10^9 \text{ kg/person} = 5.4 \times 10^8 \text{ kg/person}$$

---

73. Given: $m_{\text{sun}} = 1.989 \times 10^{30}$ kg

$m_{\text{earth}} = 5.974 \times 10^{24}$ kg

Unknown: number of Earths to equal mass of sun

$$\frac{1.989 \times 10^{30} \text{ kg}}{5.974 \times 10^{24} \text{ kg}} = 0.3329 \times 10^6 = 3.329 \times 10^5 \text{ Earths}$$

---

74. c. Given: landfill dimensions of 2.3 km × 1.4 km × 0.15 km; 250 000 000 objects, each 0.060 m^3, per year

Unknown: how many years to fill landfill

$$\frac{2.3 \text{ km} \times 1.4 \text{ km} \times 0.15 \text{ km}}{2.5 \times 10^8 \text{ objects/yr} \times 6.0 \times 10^{-2} \text{ m}^3/\text{objects}} \times \frac{10^9 \text{ m}^3}{1 \text{ km}^3}$$

$$= 0.032 \times 10^3 \text{ yr} = 32 \text{ yr}$$

---

75. Given: 1 C = 1000 cal
intake of 2400 C per day
1 cal = 4.184 J

Unknown: intake in joules per day

$$\frac{2400 \text{ C}}{1 \text{ day}} \times \frac{1000 \text{ cal}}{1 \text{ C}} \times \frac{4.184 \text{ J}}{1 \text{ cal}} = 10\ 000\ 000 \text{ J/day} = 1.0 \times 10^7 \text{ J/day}$$

---

76. Given: $D = 0.73$ g/cm^3

$m_{\text{automobile}} = 1271$ kg

Unknown: volume in L of gasoline to raise mass of car to 1305 kg

$$\frac{1305 \text{ kg} - 1271 \text{ kg}}{0.73 \text{ g/cm}^3} \times \frac{1 \text{ L}}{10^3 \text{ mL}} \times \frac{10^3 \text{ g}}{1 \text{ kg}} \times \frac{1 \text{ mL}}{1 \text{ cm}^3} = 47 \text{ L}$$

77. Given: pool dimensions of 9.0 m × 3.5 m × 1.75 m
D_{water} = 0.997 g/cm^3
1 metric ton = 1000 kg

Unknown: mass of water in pool in metric tons

$$9.0 \text{ m} \times 3.5 \text{ m} \times 1.75 \text{ m} \times \frac{0.997 \text{ g}}{1 \text{ cm}^3} \times \frac{10^6 \text{ cm}^3}{1 \text{ m}^3} \times \frac{1 \text{ kg}}{10^3 \text{ g}} \times \frac{1 \text{ metric ton}}{10^3 \text{ kg}}$$

$$= 55 \text{ metric tons}$$

78. Given: m = 250 g; dimensions of 7.0 cm × 17.0 cm × 19.0 cm

Unknown: density in kilograms per liter

$$\frac{250 \text{ g}}{7.0 \text{ cm} \times 17.0 \text{ cm} \times 19.0 \text{ cm}} \times \frac{1 \text{ kg}}{10^3 \text{ g}} \times \frac{10 \text{ cm}^3}{1 \text{ mL}} \times \frac{10^3 \text{ mL}}{1 \text{ L}} = 0.11 \text{ kg/L}$$

79. Given: area of 18.5 m^2; mass of 1275 g; density of 2.7 g/cm^3

Unknown: thickness in millimeters

$$\frac{1275 \text{ g}}{18.5 \text{ m}^2} \times \frac{1 \text{ cm}^3}{2.7 \text{ g}} \times \frac{1 \text{ m}^3}{10^6 \text{ cm}^3} \times \frac{10^3 \text{ mm}}{1 \text{ m}} = 2.6 \times 10^{-2} \text{ mm}$$

80. Given: density of 1.17 g/cm^3; mass of 3.75 kg

Unknown: volume in liters

$$3.75 \text{ kg} \times \frac{1 \text{ cm}^3}{1.17 \text{ g}} \times \frac{10^3 \text{ g}}{1 \text{ kg}} \times \frac{1 \text{ mL}}{1 \text{ cm}^3} \times \frac{1 \text{ L}}{10^3 \text{ mL}} = 3.21 \text{ L}$$

81. Given: dimensions of 28 cm × 21 cm × 44.5 mm; mass of 2090 g

Unknown: density in g/cm^3

$$\frac{2090 \text{ g}}{28 \text{ cm} \times 21 \text{ cm} \times 44.5 \text{ mm}} \times \frac{10 \text{ mm}}{1 \text{ cm}} = 0.80 \text{ g/cm}^3$$

82. Given: mass of 6.58 g; triangle with base of 36.4 mm, height of 30.1 mm, and thickness of 0.560 mm

Unknown: density in g/cm^3

$$\frac{6.58 \text{ g}}{0.5(36.4 \text{ mm} \times 30.1 \text{ mm}) \times 0.560 \text{ mm}} \times \frac{10^3 \text{ mm}^3}{1 \text{ cm}^3} = 21.4 \text{ g/cm}^3$$

83. Given: crate dimensions of 0.40 m × 0.40 m × 0.25 m; box dimensions of 22.0 cm × 12.0 cm × 5.0 cm

Unknown: number of boxes to fill the crate

$$\frac{0.40 \text{ m} \times 0.40 \text{ m} \times 0.25 \text{ m}}{1 \text{ crate}} \times \frac{1 \text{ box}}{22.0 \text{ cm} \times 12.0 \text{ cm} \times 5.0 \text{ cm}} \times \frac{10^6 \text{ cm}^3}{1 \text{ m}^3}$$

$$= 30 \text{ boxes/crate}$$

84. a. Given: $V_{cube} = l \times l \times l$
$D = 2.27 \text{ g/cm}^3$
$m = 3.93 \text{ kg}$

Unknown: volume in liters; dimensions of the cube

$3.93 \text{ kg} \times \dfrac{1 \text{ cm}^3}{2.27 \text{ g}} \times \dfrac{10^3 \text{ g}}{1 \text{ kg}} \times \dfrac{1 \text{ mL}}{1 \text{ cm}^3} \times \dfrac{1 \text{ L}}{10^3 \text{ mL}} = 1.73 \text{ L}$

$1.73 \text{ L} \times \dfrac{1 \text{ dm}^3}{1 \text{ L}} \times \dfrac{1 \text{ m}^3}{10^3 \text{ dm}^3} = 1.73 \times 10^{-3} \text{ m}^3 = 0.00173 \text{ m}^3$

$\sqrt[3]{0.00173 \text{ m}^3} = 0.120 \text{ m}$; dimensions $= 0.120 \text{ m} \times 0.120 \text{ m} \times 0.120 \text{ m}$

b. Given: $V_{rectangle}$
$= l \times w \times h$
$D =$
1.85 g/cm^3
dimensions of
$33 \text{ mm} \times$
$21 \text{ mm} \times 7.2 \text{ mm}$

Unknown: mass in grams volume in cm^3

$V = 33 \text{ mm} \times 21 \text{ mm} \times 7.2 \text{ mm} \times \dfrac{1 \text{ cm}^3}{10^3 \text{ mm}^3} = 5.0 \text{ cm}^3$

$m = DV = \dfrac{1.85 \text{ g}}{1 \text{ cm}^3} \times 5.0 \text{ cm}^3 = 9.2 \text{ g}$

c. Given: $V_{sphere} = \frac{4}{3}\pi r^3$;
$D = 3.21 \text{ g/L}$;
diameter $=$
3.30 m

Unknown: mass in kilograms, volume in dm^3

$V = \dfrac{4}{3}\pi r^3 = \dfrac{4}{3} \times 3.14 \times \left(\dfrac{3.30 \text{ m}}{2}\right)^3 \times \dfrac{10^2 \text{ dm}^3}{1 \text{ m}^3} = 18.8 \times 10^3 \text{ dm}^3$

$= 1.88 \times 10^4 \text{ dm}^3$

$m = DV = \dfrac{3.21 \text{ g}}{1 \text{ L}} \times 1.88 \times 10^4 \text{ dm}^3 \times \dfrac{1 \text{ L}}{1 \text{ dm}^3} \times \dfrac{1 \text{ kg}}{10^3 \text{ g}} = 60.3 \text{ kg}$

d. Given: $V_{cylinder}$
$= \pi r^2 \times h$;
mass $= 497 \text{ g}$;
dimensions of
cylinder:
7.5 cm diame-
ter $\times 12 \text{ cm}$

Unknown: density in g/cm^3, volume in m^3

$V = \pi r^2 \times h = 3.14 \left(\dfrac{7.5 \text{ cm}}{2}\right)^2 \times 12 \text{ cm} \times \dfrac{1 \text{ m}^3}{10^6 \text{ cm}^3} = 5.3 \times 10^{-4} \text{ m}^3$

$D = \dfrac{m}{V} = \dfrac{497 \text{ g}}{5.3 \times 10^{-4} \text{ m}^3} \times \dfrac{1 \text{ m}^3}{10^6 \text{ cm}^3} = 0.94 \text{ g/cm}^3$

e. Given: $V_{rectangle} =$
$l \times w \times h$;
$D =$
0.92 g/cm^3;
dimensions of
$3.5 \text{ m} \times 1.2 \text{ m}$
$\times 0.65 \text{ m}$

Unknown: mass in kilograms, volume in cm^3

$V = l \times w \times h = 3.5 \text{ m} \times 1.2 \text{ m} \times 0.65 \text{ m} \times \dfrac{10^6 \text{ cm}^3}{1 \text{ m}^3} = 2.7 \times 10^6 \text{ cm}^3$

$m = DV = \dfrac{0.92 \text{ g}}{1 \text{ cm}^3} \times (2.7 \times 10^6 \text{ cm}^3) \times \dfrac{1 \text{ kg}}{10^3 \text{ g}} = 2.5 \times 10^3 \text{ kg}$

85. Given: mass of 9.65 g; initial V_{water} = 16.0 mL; final V_{water} = 19.5 mL

Unknown: Density in g/cm^3

$V = 19.5 \text{ mL} - 16.0 \text{ mL} = 3.5 \text{ mL}$

$$D = \frac{m}{V} = \frac{9.65 \text{ g}}{3.5 \text{ mL}} \times \frac{1 \text{ mL}}{1 \text{ cm}^3} = 2.8 \text{ g/cm}^3$$

---

86. a. Given: m = 50. kg; area = 3620 m^2; D = 19.3 g/cm^3

Unknown: thickness of the gold in micrometers

$$D = \frac{m}{\text{area} \times \text{thickness}}; \text{thickness} = \frac{m}{\text{area} \times D}$$

$$= \frac{50. \text{ kg}}{3620 \text{ m}^2} \times \frac{1 \text{ cm}^3}{19.3 \text{ g}} \times \frac{1 \text{ m}^2}{10^4 \text{ cm}^2} \times \frac{10^4 \text{ μm}}{\text{cm}} \times \frac{10^3 \text{ g}}{1 \text{ kg}} = 0.000 \ 72 \times 10^3 \text{ μm}$$

$$= 0.72 \text{ μm}$$

b. Given: thickness = 0.72 μm; atom radius = 1.44×10^{-10} m

Unknown: number of atoms

diameter = $2 \times$ radius = $2(1.44 \times 10^{-10} \text{ m}) = 2.88 \times 10^{-10}$ m

$$0.72 \text{ μm} \times \frac{1 \text{ atom}}{2.88 \times 10^{-10} \text{ m}} \times \frac{1 \text{ m}}{10^6 \text{ μm}} = 2.5 \times 10^3 \text{ atoms}$$

---

87. Given: fill time = 238 s; cylinder diameter = 1.2 m; cylinder height = 4.6 m

Unknown: flow rate in L/min

$$V_{cylinder} = \pi r^2 \times h = 3.14 \left(\frac{1.2 \text{ m}}{2}\right)^2 \times 4.6 \text{ m} = 5.2 \text{ m}^3$$

$$\frac{5.2 \text{ m}^3}{238 \text{ s}} \times \frac{10^3 \text{ dm}^3}{1 \text{ m}^3} \times \frac{1 \text{ L}}{1 \text{ dm}^3} \times \frac{60 \text{ s}}{1 \text{ min}} = 1300 \text{ L/min}$$

---

88. Given: 2.8 g produces 1.0 J/s; 1 cal = 4.184 J; dimensions = 4.5 cm × 3.05 cm × 15 cm; D = 19.86 g/cm^3

Unknown: calories generated per hour

$V = 4.5 \text{ cm} \times 3.05 \text{ cm} \times 15 \text{ cm} = 210 \text{ cm}^3$

$$m = DV = \frac{19.86 \text{ g}}{1 \text{ cm}^3} \times 210 \text{ cm}^3 = 4200 \text{ g}$$

$$4200 \text{ g} \times \frac{1.0 \text{ J}}{2.8 \text{ g} \cdot \text{s}} \times \frac{1 \text{ cal}}{4.184 \text{ J}} \times \frac{3600 \text{ s}}{1 \text{ h}} = 1.3 \times 10^6 \text{ cal/h}$$

---

89. Given: $m = 5.974 \times 10^{24}$ kg; sphere diameter = 1.28×10^4 km

Unknown: density in g/cm^3

$$V = \frac{4}{3}\pi r^3 = \frac{4}{3} \times 3.14 \left(\frac{1.28 \times 10^4 \text{ km}}{2}\right)^3 \times \frac{10^{15} \text{ cm}^3}{1 \text{ km}^3} = 1.10 \times 10^{27} \text{ cm}^3$$

$$D = \frac{m}{V} = \frac{5.974 \times 10^{24} \text{ kg}}{1.10 \times 10^{27} \text{ cm}^3} \times \frac{10^3 \text{g}}{1 \text{ kg}} = 5.43 \text{ g/cm}^3$$

90. Given: $D_{Mg} = 1.74$ g/cm^3
$D_{Pt} = 21.45$ g/cm^3

Unknown: volume of Mg in cm^3 with the same mass as 1.82 dm^3 of Pt

$$m_{Pt} = 1.82 \text{ dm}^3 \times \frac{21.45 \text{ g}}{1 \text{ cm}^3} \times \frac{10^3 \text{ cm}^3}{1 \text{ dm}^3} = 3.90 \times 10^4 \text{ g} = m_{Mg}$$

$$V_{Mg} = \frac{m_{Mg}}{D_{Mg}} = 3.90 \times 10^4 \text{ g} \times \frac{1 \text{ cm}^3}{1.74 \text{ g}} = 2.24 \times 10^4 \text{ cm}^3$$

---

91. Given: 66 m/roll;
5.0 cm/use

Unknown: number of uses in 24 rolls

$$\frac{66 \text{ m}}{1 \text{ roll}} \times 24 \text{ rolls} \times \frac{1 \text{ use}}{5.0 \text{ cm}} \times \frac{100 \text{ cm}}{1 \text{ m}} = 32\ 000 \text{ uses}$$

---

92. Given: 38 km/4.0 L gasoline; driven 75% of year; 86 km/day; 1 yr = 365 days

Unknown: volume of gasoline in liters per year

365 days $\times$ 0.75 = 274 days driven

274 days driven $\times \dfrac{86 \text{ km}}{1 \text{ day}} = 24\ 000$ km driven

24 000 km $\times \dfrac{4.0 \text{ L}}{38 \text{ km}} = 2500$ L

---

93. Given: fill time of 97 h; pool dimensions = 9.0 m $\times$ 3.5 m $\times$ 1.75 m

Unknown: rate of fill in L/min

$$\frac{9.0 \text{ m} \times 3.5 \text{ m} \times 1.75 \text{ m}}{97 \text{ h}} \times \frac{10^3 \text{ dm}^3}{1 \text{ m}^3} \times \frac{1 \text{ L}}{1 \text{ dm}^3} \times \frac{1 \text{ h}}{60 \text{ min}} = 9.5 \text{ L/min}$$

---

94. Given: $D_{H_2SO_4} = 1.285$ g/cm^3; 38% sulfuric acid in battery

Unknown: mass of sulfuric acid in 500. mL battery acid

$$500.\text{ mL} \times 0.38 \times \frac{1.285 \text{ g}}{1 \text{ cm}^3} \times \frac{1 \text{ cm}^3}{1 \text{ mL}} = 244 \text{ g } H_2SO_4$$

---

95. a. Given: 64.1 g of Al

Unknown: number of moles Al

$$64.1 \text{ g Al} \times \frac{1 \text{ mol Al}}{26.98 \text{ g Al}} = 2.38 \text{ mol Al}$$

b. Given: 28.1 g of Si

Unknown: number of moles Si

$$28.1 \text{ g Si} \times \frac{1 \text{ mol Si}}{28.09 \text{ g Si}} = 1.00 \text{ mol Si}$$

c. Given: 0.255 g of S

Unknown: number of moles S

$$0.255 \text{ g S} \times \frac{1 \text{ mol S}}{32.07 \text{ g S}} = 7.95 \times 10^{-3} \text{ mol S}$$

d. Given: 850.5 g of Zn
Unknown: number of moles Zn

$$850.5 \text{ g Zn} \times \frac{1 \text{ mol Zn}}{65.39 \text{ g Zn}} = 13.01 \text{ mol Zn}$$

96. a. Given: 1.22 mol Na
Unknown: mass Na

$$1.22 \text{ mol Na} \times \frac{22.99 \text{ g N}}{1 \text{ mol Na}} = 28.0 \text{ g Na}$$

b. Given: 14.5 mol Cu
Unknown: mass Cu

$$14.5 \text{ mol Cu} \times \frac{63.55 \text{ g Cu}}{1 \text{ mol Cu}} = 921 \text{ g Cu}$$

c. Given: 0.275 mol Hg
Unknown: mass Hg

$$0.275 \text{ mol Hg} \times \frac{200.59 \text{ g Hg}}{1 \text{ mol Hg}} = 55.2 \text{ g Hg}$$

d. Given: 9.37×10^{-3} mol Mg
Unknown: mass Mg

$$9.37 \times 10^{-3} \text{ mol Mg} \times \frac{24.31 \text{ g Mg}}{1 \text{ mol Mg}} = 0.228 \text{ g Mg}$$

97. a. Given: 3.01×10^{23} atoms Rb
Unknown: amount in moles

$$3.01 \times 10^{23} \text{ atoms Rb} \times \frac{1 \text{ mol}}{6.022 \times 10^{23} \text{ atoms}} = 0.500 \text{ mol Rb}$$

b. Given: 8.08×10^{22} atoms Kr
Unknown: amount in moles

$$8.08 \times 10^{22} \text{ atoms Kr} \times \frac{1 \text{ mol}}{6.022 \times 10^{23} \text{ atoms}} = 0.134 \text{ mol Kr}$$

c. Given: 5 700 000 000 atoms of Pb
Unknown: amount in moles

$$5.7 \times 10^{9} \text{ atoms Pb} \times \frac{1 \text{ mol}}{6.022 \times 10^{23} \text{ atoms}} = 9.5 \times 10^{-15} \text{ mol Pb}$$

d. Given: 2.997×10^{25} atoms of V
Unknown: amount in moles

$$2.997 \times 10^{25} \text{ atoms V} \times \frac{1 \text{ mol}}{6.022 \times 10^{23} \text{ atoms}} = 49.77 \text{ mol V}$$

98. a. Given: 1.004 mol Bi
Unknown: number of atoms

$$1.004 \text{ mol Bi} \times \frac{6.022 \times 10^{23} \text{ atoms}}{1 \text{ mol}} = 6.046 \times 10^{23} \text{ atoms Bi}$$

b. Given: 2.5 mol Mn
Unknown: number of atoms

$$2.5 \text{ mol Mn} \times \frac{6.022 \times 10^{23} \text{ atoms}}{1 \text{ mol}} = 1.5 \times 10^{24} \text{ atoms Mn}$$

c. Given: 0.000 000 2 mol He
Unknown: number of atoms

$$2 \times 10^{-7} \text{ mol He} \times \frac{6.022 \times 10^{23} \text{ atoms}}{1 \text{ mol}} = 1 \times 10^{17} \text{ atoms He}$$

d. Given: 32.6 mol Sr

Unknown: number of atoms

$$32.6 \text{ mol Sr} \times \frac{6.022 \times 10^{23} \text{ atoms}}{1 \text{ mol}} = 1.96 \times 10^{25} \text{ atoms Sr}$$

99. a. Given: 54.0 g Al

Unknown: number of of atoms Al

$$54.0 \text{ g Al} \times \frac{1 \text{ mol Al}}{26.98 \text{ g Al}} \times \frac{6.022 \times 10^{23} \text{ atoms}}{1 \text{ mol}} = 1.21 \times 10^{24} \text{ atoms Al}$$

b. Given: 69.45 g La

Unknown: number of atoms La

$$69.45 \text{ g La} \times \frac{1 \text{ mol La}}{138.91 \text{ g La}} \times \frac{6.022 \times 10^{23} \text{ atoms}}{1 \text{ mol}} = 3.011 \times 10^{23} \text{ atoms La}$$

c. Given: 0.697 g Ga

Unknown: number of atoms Ga

$$0.697 \text{ g Ga} \times \frac{1 \text{ mol Ga}}{69.72 \text{ g Ga}} \times \frac{6.022 \times 10^{23} \text{ atoms}}{1 \text{ mol}} = 6.02 \times 10^{21} \text{ atoms Ga}$$

d. Given: 0.000 000 020 g Be

Unknown: number of atoms Be

$$2.0 \times 10^{-8} \text{ g Be} \times \frac{1 \text{ mol Be}}{9.01 \text{ g Be}} \times \frac{6.022 \times 10^{23} \text{ atoms}}{1 \text{ mol}} = 1.3 \times 10^{15} \text{ atoms Be}$$

100. a. Given: 6.022×10^{24} atoms Ta

Unknown: mass Ta

$$6.022 \times 10^{24} \text{ atoms Ta} \times \frac{1 \text{ mol}}{6.022 \times 10^{23} \text{ atoms}} \times \frac{180.95 \text{ g Ta}}{1 \text{ mol Ta}} = 1810 \text{ g Ta}$$

b. Given: 3.01×10^{21} atoms Co

Unknown: mass Co

$$3.01 \times 10^{21} \text{ atoms Co} \times \frac{1 \text{ mol}}{6.022 \times 10^{23} \text{ atoms}} \times \frac{58.93 \text{ g Co}}{1 \text{ mol Co}} = 0.295 \text{ g Co}$$

c. Given: 1.506×10^{24} atoms Ar

Unknown: mass Ar

$$1.506 \times 10^{24} \text{ atoms Ar} \times \frac{1 \text{ mol}}{6.022 \times 10^{23} \text{ atoms}} \times \frac{39.95 \text{ g Ar}}{1 \text{ mol Ar}} = 99.91 \text{ g Ar}$$

d. Given: 1.20×10^{25} atoms He

Unknown: mass He

$$1.20 \times 10^{25} \text{ atoms He} \times \frac{1 \text{ mol}}{6.022 \times 10^{23} \text{ atoms}} \times \frac{4.00 \text{ g He}}{1 \text{ mol He}} = 79.7 \text{ g He}$$

101. a. Given: 3.00 g BBr_3

Unknown: number of moles BBr_3

$$\text{formula mass} = 1 \text{ atom B} \times \frac{10.81 \text{ amu}}{1 \text{ atom B}} + 3 \text{ atoms Br} \times \frac{79.90 \text{ amu}}{1 \text{ atom Br}}$$

$$= 10.81 \text{ amu} + 239.70 \text{ amu} = 250.51 \text{ amu}$$

$$3.00 \text{ g } BBr_3 \times \frac{1 \text{ mol } BBr_3}{250.51 \text{ g } BBr_3} = 0.0120 \text{ mol } BBr_3$$

b. Given: 0.472 g NaF

Unknown: number of moles NaF

$$\text{formula mass NaF} = 1 \text{ atom Na} \times \frac{22.99 \text{ amu}}{1 \text{ atom Na}} + 1 \text{ atom F} \times \frac{19.00 \text{ amu}}{1 \text{ atom F}}$$

$$= 41.99 \text{ amu}$$

$$0.472 \text{ g NaF} \times \frac{1 \text{ mol NaF}}{41.99 \text{ g NaF}} = 0.0112 \text{ mol NaF}$$

c. Given: 7.50×10^2 g CH$_3$OH

Unknown: number of moles CH$_3$OH

$$\text{formula mass CH}_3\text{OH} = 1 \text{ atom C} \times \frac{12.01 \text{ amu}}{1 \text{ atom C}} + 4 \text{ atoms H} \times \frac{1.01 \text{ amu}}{1 \text{ atom H}}$$

$$+ 1 \text{ atom O} \times \frac{16.00 \text{ amu}}{1 \text{ atom O}} = 32.05 \text{ amu}$$

$$7.50 \times 10^2 \text{ g CH}_3\text{OH} \times \frac{1 \text{ mol CH}_3\text{OH}}{32.05 \text{ g CH}_3\text{OH}} = 23.4 \text{ mol CH}_3\text{OH}$$

d. Given: 50.0 g Ca(ClO$_3$)$_2$

Unknown: number of moles Ca(ClO$_3$)$_2$

$$\text{formula mass Ca(ClO}_3)_2 = 1 \text{ atom Ca} \times \frac{40.08 \text{ amu}}{1 \text{ atom Ca}} + 2 \text{ atoms Cl}$$

$$\times \frac{35.45 \text{ amu}}{1 \text{ atom Cl}} + 6 \text{ atoms O} \times \frac{16.00 \text{ amu}}{1 \text{ atom O}}$$

$$= 206.98 \text{ amu}$$

$$50.0 \text{ g Ca(ClO}_3)_2 \times \frac{1 \text{ mol Ca(ClO}_3)_2}{206.98 \text{ g Ca(ClO}_3)_2} = 0.242 \text{ mol Ca(ClO}_3)_2$$

---

102. a. Given: 1.366 mol NH$_3$

Unknown: mass NH$_3$

$$\text{formula mass NH}_3 = 1 \text{ atom N} \times \frac{14.01 \text{ amu}}{1 \text{ atom N}} + 3 \text{ atoms H} \times \frac{1.01 \text{ amu}}{1 \text{ atom H}}$$

$$= 17.04 \text{ amu}$$

$$1.366 \text{ mol NH}_3 \times \frac{17.04 \text{ g NH}_3}{1 \text{ mol NH}_3} = 23.28 \text{ g NH}_3$$

b. Given: 0.120 mol C$_6$H$_{12}$O$_6$

Unknown: mass C$_6$H$_{12}$O$_6$

$$\text{formula mass C}_6\text{H}_{12}\text{O}_6 = 6 \text{ atoms C} \times \frac{12.01 \text{ amu}}{1 \text{ atom C}} + 12 \text{ atoms H}$$

$$\times \frac{1.01 \text{ amu}}{1 \text{ atom H}} + 6 \text{ atoms O} \times \frac{16.00 \text{ amu}}{1 \text{ atom O}}$$

$$= 180.18 \text{ amu}$$

$$0.120 \text{ mol C}_6\text{H}_{12}\text{O}_6 \times \frac{180.18 \text{ g C}_6\text{H}_{12}\text{O}_6}{1 \text{ mol C}_6\text{H}_{12}\text{O}_6} = 21.6 \text{ g C}_6\text{H}_{12}\text{O}_6$$

c. Given: 6.94 mol BaCl$_2$

Unknown: mass BaCl$_2$

$$\text{formula mass BaCl}_2 = 1 \text{ atom Ba} \times \frac{137.33 \text{ amu}}{1 \text{ atom Ba}} + 2 \text{ atoms Cl} \times \frac{35.45 \text{ amu}}{1 \text{ atom Cl}}$$

$$= 208.23 \text{ amu}$$

$$6.94 \text{ mol BaCl}_2 \times \frac{208.23 \text{ g BaCl}_2}{1 \text{ mol BaCl}_2} = 1450 \text{ g BaCl}_2$$

d. Given: 0.005 mol C$_3$H$_8$

Unknown: mass C$_3$H$_8$

$$\text{formula mass C}_3\text{H}_8 = 3 \text{ atoms C} \times \frac{12.01 \text{ amu}}{1 \text{ atom C}} + 8 \text{ atoms H} \times \frac{1.01 \text{ amu}}{1 \text{ atom H}}$$

$$= 44.11 \text{ amu}$$

$$0.005 \text{ mol C}_3\text{H}_8 \times \frac{44.11 \text{ g C}_3\text{H}_8}{1 \text{ mol C}_3\text{H}_8} = 0.2 \text{ g C}_3\text{H}_8$$

---

103. a. Given: 4.99 mol CH$_4$

Unknown: number of molecules

$$4.99 \text{ mol CH}_4 \times \frac{6.022 \times 10^{23} \text{ molecules}}{1 \text{ mol}} = 3.00 \times 10^{24} \text{ molecules CH}_4$$

b. Given: 0.005 20 mol N_2

Unknown: number of molecules

$$5.20 \times 10^{-3} \text{ mol } N_2 \times \frac{6.022 \times 10^{23} \text{ molecules}}{1 \text{ mol}} = 3.13 \times 10^{21} \text{ molecules } N_2$$

c. Given: 1.05 mol PCl_3

Unknown: number of molecules

$$1.05 \text{ mol } PCl_3 \times \frac{6.022 \times 10^{23} \text{ molecules}}{1 \text{ mol}} = 6.32 \times 10^{23} \text{ molecules } PCl_3$$

d. Given: 3.5×10^{-5} mol $C_6H_8O_6$

Unknown: number of molecules

$$3.5 \times 10^{-5} \text{ mol } C_6H_8O_6 \times \frac{6.022 \times 10^{23} \text{ molecules}}{1 \text{ mol}}$$

$$= 2.1 \times 10^{19} \text{ molecules } C_6H_8O_6$$

---

104. a. Given: 1.25 mol KBr

Unknown: number of formula units

$$1.25 \text{ mol } KBr \times \frac{6.022 \times 10^{23} \text{ formula units}}{1 \text{ mol}}$$

$$= 7.53 \times 10^{23} \text{ formula units } KBr$$

b. Given: 5.00 mol $MgCl_2$

Unknown: number of formula units

$$5.00 \text{ mol } MgCl_2 \times \frac{6.022 \times 10^{23} \text{ formula units}}{1 \text{ mol}}$$

$$= 3.01 \times 10^{24} \text{ formula units } MgCl_2$$

c. Given: 0.025 mol Na_2CO_3

Unknown: number of formula units

$$0.025 \text{ mol } Na_2CO_3 \times \frac{6.022 \times 10^{23} \text{ formula units}}{1 \text{ mol}}$$

$$= 1.5 \times 10^{22} \text{ formula units } Na_2CO_3$$

d. Given: 6.82×10^{-6} mol $Pb(NO_3)_2$

Unknown: number of formula units

$$6.82 \times 10^{-6} \text{ mol } Pb(NO_3)_2 \times \frac{6.022 \times 10^{23} \text{ formula units}}{1 \text{ mol}}$$

$$= 4.11 \times 10^{18} \text{ formula units } Pb(NO_3)_2$$

---

105. a. Given: 3.34×10^{34} formula units $Cu(OH)_2$

Unknown: amount in moles

$$3.34 \times 10^{34} \text{ formula units } Cu(OH)_2 \times \frac{1 \text{ mol}}{6.022 \times 10^{23} \text{ formula units}}$$

$$= 5.55 \times 10^{10} \text{ mol } Cu(OH)_2$$

b. Given: 1.17×10^{16} molecules of H_2S

Unknown: amount in moles

$$1.17 \times 10^{16} \text{ molecules } H_2S \times \frac{1 \text{ mol}}{6.022 \times 10^{23} \text{ molecules}} = 1.94 \times 10^{-8} \text{ mol } H_2S$$

c. Given: 5.47×10^{21} formula units of $NiSO_4$

Unknown: amount in moles

$$5.47 \times 10^{21} \text{ formula units } NiSO_4 \times \frac{1 \text{ mol}}{6.022 \times 10^{23} \text{ formula units}}$$

$$= 9.08 \times 10^{-3} \text{ mol } NiSO_4$$

d. Given: 7.66×10^{19}
molecules of
H_2O_2

Unknown: amount in
moles

7.66×10^{19} molecules $H_2O_2 \times \dfrac{1 \text{ mol}}{6.022 \times 10^{23} \text{ molecules}}$

$= 1.27 \times 10^{-4} \text{ mol } H_2O_2$

---

106. a. Given: 2.41×10^{24}
molecules H_2

Unknown: mass H_2

formula mass $H_2 = 2$ atoms $H \times \dfrac{1.01 \text{ amu}}{1 \text{ atom H}} = 2.02$ amu

2.41×10^{24} molecules $H_2 \times \dfrac{1 \text{ mol}}{6.022 \times 10^{23} \text{ molecules}} \times \dfrac{2.02 \text{ g } H_2}{1 \text{ mol } H_2}$

$= 8.08 \text{ g } H_2$

b. Given: 5.00×10^{21}
formula units
$Al(OH)_3$

Unknown: mass
$Al(OH)_3$

formula mass $Al(OH)_3 = 1$ atom $Al \times \dfrac{26.98 \text{ amu}}{1 \text{ atom Al}} + 3$ atoms O

$\times \dfrac{16.00 \text{ amu}}{1 \text{ atom O}} + 3$ atoms $H \times \dfrac{1.01 \text{ amu}}{1 \text{ atom H}} = 78.01$ amu

5.00×10^{21} formula units $Al(OH)_3 \times \dfrac{1 \text{ mol}}{6.022 \times 10^{23} \text{ formula units}}$

$\times \dfrac{78.01 \text{ g } Al(OH)_3}{1 \text{ mol } Al(OH)_3} = 0.648 \text{ g } Al(OH)_3$

c. Given: 8.25×10^{22}
molecules
BrF_5

Unknown: mass
BrF_5

formula mass $BrF_5 = 1$ atom $Br \times \dfrac{79.90 \text{ amu}}{1 \text{ atom Br}} + 5$ atoms $F \times \dfrac{19.00 \text{ amu}}{1 \text{ atom F}}$

$= 174.90$ amu

8.25×10^{22} molecules $BrF_5 \times \dfrac{1 \text{ mol}}{6.022 \times 10^{23} \text{ molecules}} \times \dfrac{174.90 \text{ g } BrF_5}{1 \text{ mol } BrF_5}$

$= 24.0 \text{ g } BrF_5$

d. Given: 1.20×10^{23}
formula units
$Na_2C_2O_4$

Unknown: mass
$Na_2C_2O_4$

formula mass $Na_2C_2O_4 = 2$ atoms $Na \times \dfrac{22.99 \text{ amu}}{1 \text{ atom Na}} + 2$ atoms C

$\times \dfrac{12.01 \text{ amu}}{1 \text{ atom C}} + 4$ atoms $O \times \dfrac{16.00 \text{ amu}}{1 \text{ atom O}} = 134$ amu

1.20×10^{23} formula units $Na_2C_2O_4 \times \dfrac{1 \text{ mol}}{6.022 \times 10^{23} \text{ formula units}}$

$\times \dfrac{134 \text{ g } Na_2C_2O_4}{1 \text{ mol } Na_2C_2O_4} = 26.7 \text{ g } Na_2C_2O_4$

---

107. a. Given: 22.9 g Na_2S

Unknown: number of
formula
units
Na_2S

formula mass $Na_2S = 2$ atoms $Na \times \dfrac{22.99 \text{ amu}}{1 \text{ atom Na}} + 1$ atom $S \times \dfrac{32.01 \text{ amu}}{1 \text{ atom S}}$

$= 77.99$ amu

$22.9 \text{ g } Na_2S \times \dfrac{1 \text{ mol } Na_2S}{77.99 \text{ g } Na_2S} \times \dfrac{6.022 \times 10^{23} \text{ formula units}}{1 \text{ mol}}$

$= 1.77 \times 10^{23}$ formula units Na_2S

b. Given: 0.272 g
Ni(NO$_3$)$_2$

Unknown: number of formula units Ni(NO$_3$)$_2$

formula mass Ni(NO$_3$)$_2$ = 1 atom Ni $\times \dfrac{58.69 \text{ amu}}{1 \text{ atom Ni}}$ + 2 atoms N

$\times \dfrac{14.01 \text{ amu}}{1 \text{ atom N}}$ + 6 atoms O $\times \dfrac{16.00 \text{ amu}}{1 \text{ atom O}}$ = 182.71 amu

0.272 g Ni(NO$_3$)$_2 \times \dfrac{1 \text{ mol Ni(NO}_3)_2}{182.71 \text{ g Ni(NO}_3)_2} \times \dfrac{6.022 \times 10^{23} \text{ formula units}}{1 \text{ mol}}$

= 8.96×10^{20} formula units Ni(NO$_3$)$_2$

c. Given: 260 mg
CH$_2$CHCN

Unknown: number of molecules CH$_2$CHCN

formula mass CH$_2$CHCN = 3 atoms C $\times \dfrac{12.01 \text{ amu}}{1 \text{ atom C}}$ + 3 atoms H

$\times \dfrac{1.01 \text{ amu}}{1 \text{ atom H}}$ + 1 atom N $\times \dfrac{14.01 \text{ amu}}{1 \text{ atom N}}$ = 53.07 amu

260 mg CH$_2$CHCN $\times \dfrac{1 \text{ mol CH}_2\text{CHCN}}{53.07 \text{ g CH}_2\text{CHCN}} \times \dfrac{1 \text{ g}}{1000 \text{ mg}}$

$\times \dfrac{6.022 \times 10^{23} \text{ molecules}}{1 \text{ mol}}$ = 3.0×10^{21} molecules CH$_2$CHCN

---

108. a. Given: 0.039 g Pd

Unknown: number of moles Pd

0.039 g Pd $\times \dfrac{1 \text{ mol Pd}}{106.42 \text{ g Pd}}$ = 3.7×10^{-4} mol Pd

b. Given: 8200 g Fe

Unknown: number of moles Fe

8200 g Fe $\times \dfrac{1 \text{ mol Fe}}{55.85 \text{ g Fe}}$ = 150 mol Fe

c. Given: 0.0073 kg Ta

Unknown: number of moles Ta

0.0073 kg Ta $\times \dfrac{1000 \text{ g}}{1 \text{ kg}} \times \dfrac{1 \text{ mol Ta}}{180.95 \text{ g Ta}}$ = 0.040 mol Ta

d. Given: 0.006 55 g Sb

Unknown: number of moles Sb

0.006 55 g Sb $\times \dfrac{1 \text{ mol Sb}}{121.76 \text{ g Sb}}$ = 5.38×10^{-5} mol Sb

e. Given: 5.64 kg Ba

Unknown: number of moles Ba

5.64 kg Ba $\times \dfrac{1 \text{ mol Ba}}{137.33 \text{ g Ba}} \times \dfrac{1000 \text{ g}}{1 \text{ kg}}$ = 41.1 mol Ba

f. Given: 3.37×10^{-6} g Mo

Unknown: number of moles Mo

3.37×10^{-6} g Mo $\times \dfrac{1 \text{ mol Mo}}{95.94 \text{ g Mo}}$ = 3.51×10^{-8} mol Mo

---

109. a. Given: 1.002 mol Cr

Unknown: mass Cr

1.002 mol Cr $\times \dfrac{52.00 \text{ g Cr}}{1 \text{ mol Cr}}$ = 52.10 g Cr

b. Given: 550 mol Al

Unknown: mass Al

550 mol Al $\times \dfrac{26.98 \text{ g Al}}{1 \text{ mol Al}}$ = 1.5×10^4 g Al

c. Given: 4.08×10^{-8} mol Ne

Unknown: mass Ne

$$4.08 \times 10^{-8} \text{ mol Ne} \times \frac{20.18 \text{ g Ne}}{1 \text{ mol Ne}} = 8.23 \times 10^{-7} \text{ g Ne}$$

d. Given: 7 mol Ti

Unknown: mass Ti

$$7 \text{ mol Ti} \times \frac{47.88 \text{ g Ti}}{1 \text{ mol Ti}} = 3 \times 10^2 \text{ g Ti}$$

e. Given: 0.0086 mol Xe

Unknown: mass Xe

$$0.0086 \text{ mol Xe} \times \frac{131.29 \text{ g Xe}}{1 \text{ mol Xe}} = 1.1 \text{ g Xe}$$

f. Given: 3.29×10^4 mol Li

Unknown: mass Li

$$3.29 \times 10^4 \text{ mol Li} \times \frac{6.94 \text{ g Li}}{1 \text{ mol Li}} = 2.28 \times 10^5 \text{ g Li}$$

---

110. a. Given: 17.0 mol Ge

Unknown: number of atoms

$$17.0 \text{ mol Ge} \times \frac{6.022 \times 10^{23} \text{ atoms}}{1 \text{ mol}} = 1.02 \times 10^{25} \text{ atoms Ge}$$

b. Given: 0.6144 mol Cu

Unknown: number of atoms

$$0.6144 \text{ mol Cu} \times \frac{6.022 \times 10^{23} \text{ atoms}}{1 \text{ mol}} = 3.700 \times 10^{23} \text{ atoms Cu}$$

c. Given: 3.02 mol Sn

Unknown: number of atoms

$$3.02 \text{ mol Sn} \times \frac{6.022 \times 10^{23} \text{ atoms}}{1 \text{ mol}} = 1.82 \times 10^{24} \text{ atoms Sn}$$

d. Given: 2.0×10^6 mol C

Unknown: number of atoms

$$2.0 \times 10^6 \text{ mol C} \times \frac{6.022 \times 10^{23} \text{ atoms}}{1 \text{ mol}} = 1.2 \times 10^{30} \text{ atoms C}$$

e. Given: 0.0019 mol Zr

Unknown: number of atoms

$$0.0019 \text{ mol Zr} \times \frac{6.022 \times 10^{23} \text{ atoms}}{1 \text{ mol}} = 1.1 \times 10^{21} \text{ atoms Zr}$$

f. Given: 3.227×10^{-10} mol K

Unknown: number of atoms

$$3.227 \times 10^{-10} \text{ mol K} \times \frac{6.022 \times 10^{23} \text{ atoms}}{1 \text{ mol}} = 1.943 \times 10^{14} \text{ atoms K}$$

---

111. a. Given: 6.022×10^{24} atoms Co

Unknown: number of moles Co

$$6.022 \times 10^{24} \text{ atoms Co} \times \frac{1 \text{ mol}}{6.022 \times 10^{23} \text{ atoms}} = 10.00 \text{ mol Co}$$

b. Given: 1.06×10^{23} atoms W

Unknown: number of moles W

$$1.06 \times 10^{23} \text{ atoms W} \times \frac{1 \text{ mol}}{6.022 \times 10^{23} \text{ atoms}} = 0.176 \text{ mol W}$$

c. Given: 3.008×10^{19} atoms Ag

Unknown: number of moles Ag

$$3.008 \times 10^{19} \text{ atoms Ag} \times \frac{1 \text{ mol}}{6.022 \times 10^{23} \text{ atoms}} = 4.995 \times 10^{-5} \text{ mol Ag}$$

d. Given: 950 000 000 atoms Pu

Unknown: number of moles Pu

$$9.5 \times 10^{8} \text{ atoms Pu} \times \frac{1 \text{ mol}}{6.022 \times 10^{23} \text{ atoms}} = 1.6 \times 10^{-15} \text{ mol Pu}$$

e. Given 4.61×10^{17} atoms Rn

Unknown: number of moles Rn

$$4.61 \times 10^{17} \text{ atoms Rn} \times \frac{1 \text{ mol}}{6.022 \times 10^{23} \text{ atoms}} = 7.66 \times 10^{-7} \text{ mol Rn}$$

f. Given: 8 trillion atoms Ce

Unknown: number of moles Ce

$$8 \times 10^{12} \text{ atoms Ce} \times \frac{1 \text{ mol}}{6.022 \times 10^{23} \text{ atoms}} = 1 \times 10^{-11} \text{ mol Ce}$$

---

112. a. Given: 0.0082 g Au

Unknown: number of atoms Au

$$0.0082 \text{ g Au} \times \frac{1 \text{ mol Au}}{196.97 \text{ g Au}} \times \frac{6.022 \times 10^{23} \text{ atoms}}{1 \text{ mol}} = 2.5 \times 10^{19} \text{ atoms Au}$$

b. Given: 812 g Mo

Unknown: number of atoms Mo

$$812 \text{ g Mo} \times \frac{1 \text{ mol Mo}}{95.94 \text{ g Mo}} \times \frac{6.022 \times 10^{23} \text{ atoms}}{1 \text{ mol}} = 5.10 \times 10^{24} \text{ atoms Mo}$$

c. Given: 2.00×10^{2} mg Am

Unknown: number of atoms Am

$$2.00 \times 10^{2} \text{ mg Am} \times \frac{1 \text{ g}}{1000 \text{ mg}} \times \frac{1 \text{ mol Am}}{243.06 \text{ g Am}} \times \frac{6.022 \times 10^{23} \text{ atoms}}{1 \text{ mol}}$$

$$= 4.96 \times 10^{20} \text{ atoms Am}$$

d. Given: 10.09 kg Ne

Unknown: number of atoms Ne

$$10.09 \text{ kg Ne} \times \frac{1000 \text{ g}}{1 \text{ kg}} \times \frac{1 \text{ mol Ne}}{20.18 \text{ g Ne}} \times \frac{6.022 \times 10^{23} \text{ atoms}}{1 \text{ mol}}$$

$$= 3.011 \times 10^{26} \text{ atoms Ne}$$

e. Given: 0.705 mg Bi

Unknown: number of atoms Bi

$$0.705 \text{ mg Bi} \times \frac{1 \text{ g}}{1000 \text{ mg}} \times \frac{1 \text{ mol Bi}}{208.98 \text{ g Bi}} \times \frac{6.022 \times 10^{23} \text{ atoms}}{1 \text{ mol}}$$

$$= 2.03 \times 10^{18} \text{ atoms Bi}$$

f. Given: 37 µg U

Unknown: number of atoms U

$$37 \text{ µg U} \times \frac{1 \text{ g}}{10^{6} \text{ µg}} \times \frac{1 \text{ mol U}}{238.03 \text{ g U}} \times \frac{6.022 \times 10^{23} \text{ atoms}}{1 \text{ mol}} = 9.4 \times 10^{16} \text{ atoms U}$$

---

113. a. Given: 8.22×10^{23} atoms Rb

Unknown: mass Rb

$$8.22 \times 10^{23} \text{ atoms Rb} \times \frac{1 \text{ mol}}{6.022 \times 10^{23} \text{ atoms}} \times \frac{85.47 \text{ g Rb}}{1 \text{ mol Rb}} = 117 \text{ g Rb}$$

b. Given: 4.05 Avogadro's constants of Mn atoms

Unknown: mass Mn

$$4.05 \times 6.022 \times 10^{23} \text{ atoms Mn} \times \frac{1 \text{ mol}}{6.022 \times 10^{23} \text{ atoms}} \times \frac{54.94 \text{ g Mn}}{1 \text{ mol Mn}}$$

$$= 223 \text{ g Mn}$$

c. Given: 9.96×10^{26} atoms Te

Unknown: mass Te

$$9.96 \times 10^{26} \text{ atoms Te} \times \frac{1 \text{ mol}}{6.022 \times 10^{23} \text{ atoms}} \times \frac{127.60 \text{ g Te}}{1 \text{ mol Te}} = 2.11 \times 10^{5} \text{g Te}$$

d. Given: 0.000 025 Avogadro's constants of Rh atoms

Unknown: mass Rh

$$2.5 \times 10^{-5} \times 6.022 \times 10^{23} \text{ atoms Rh} \times \frac{1 \text{ mol}}{6.022 \times 10^{23} \text{ atoms}} \times \frac{102.91 \text{ g Rh}}{1 \text{ mol Rh}}$$

$$= 2.6 \times 10^{-3} \text{ g Rh}$$

e. Given: 88 300 000 000 000 atoms Ra

Unknown: mass Ra

$$8.83 \times 10^{13} \text{ atoms Ra} \times \frac{1 \text{ mol}}{6.022 \times 10^{23} \text{ atoms}} \times \frac{226.03 \text{ g Ra}}{1 \text{ mol Ra}}$$

$$= 3.31 \times 10^{-8} \text{ g Ra}$$

f. Given: 2.94×10^{17} atoms Hf

Unknown: mass Hf

$$2.94 \times 10^{17} \text{ atoms Hf} \times \frac{1 \text{ mol}}{6.022 \times 10^{23} \text{ atoms}} \times \frac{178.49 \text{ g Hf}}{1 \text{ mol Hf}} = 8.71 \times 10^{-5} \text{ g Hf}$$

---

114. a. Given: 45.0 g CH_3COOH

Unknown: moles CH_3COOH

formula mass $CH_3COOH = 2$ atoms $C \times \dfrac{12.01 \text{ amu}}{1 \text{ atom C}}$

$$+ 4 \text{ atoms H} \times \frac{1.01 \text{ amu}}{1 \text{ atom H}} + 2 \text{ atoms O} \times \frac{16.00 \text{ amu}}{1 \text{ atom O}} = 60.06 \text{ amu}$$

$$45.0 \text{ g } CH_3COOH \times \frac{1 \text{ mol } CH_3COOH}{60.06 \text{ g } CH_3COOH} = 0.749 \text{ mol } CH_3COOH$$

b. Given: 7.04 g $Pb(NO_3)_2$

Unknown: moles $Pb(NO_3)_2$

formula mass $Pb(NO_3)_2 = 1$ atom $Pb \times \dfrac{207.2 \text{ amu}}{1 \text{ atom Pb}} + 2$ atoms N

$$\times \frac{14.01 \text{ amu}}{1 \text{ atom N}} + 6 \text{ atoms O} \times \frac{16.00 \text{ amu}}{1 \text{ atom O}} = 331.22 \text{ amu}$$

$$7.04 \text{ g } Pb(NO_3)_2 \times \frac{1 \text{ mol } Pb(NO_3)_2}{331.22 \text{ g } Pb(NO_3)_2} = 0.0213 \text{ mol } Pb(NO_3)_2$$

c. Given: 5000 kg Fe_2O_3

Unknown: moles Fe_2O_3

formula mass $Fe_2O_3 = 2$ atoms $Fe \times \dfrac{55.85 \text{ amu}}{1 \text{ atom Fe}} + 3$ atoms $O \times \dfrac{16.00 \text{ amu}}{1 \text{ atom O}}$

$$= 159.70 \text{ amu}$$

$$5000 \text{ kg } Fe_2O_3 \times \frac{1000 \text{ g}}{1 \text{ kg}} \times \frac{1 \text{ mol } Fe_2O_3}{159.70 \text{ g } Fe_2O_3} = 3 \times 10^{4} \text{ mol } Fe_2O_3$$

d. Given: 12.0 mg
$C_2H_5NH_2$

Unknown: moles
$C_2H_5NH_2$

formula mass $C_2H_5NH_2$ = 2 atoms C $\times \dfrac{12.01 \text{ amu}}{1 \text{ atom C}}$ + 7 atoms H $\times \dfrac{1.01 \text{ amu}}{1 \text{ atom H}}$

+ 1 atom N $\times \dfrac{14.01 \text{ amu}}{1 \text{ atom N}}$ = 45.10 amu

12.0 mg $C_2H_5NH_2 \times \dfrac{1 \text{ g}}{1000 \text{ mg}} \times \dfrac{1 \text{ mol } C_2H_5NH_2}{45.10 \text{ g } C_2H_5NH_2}$

= 2.66×10^{-4} mol $C_2H_5NH_2$

e. Given: 0.003 22 g
$C_{17}H_{35}COOH$

Unknown: moles
$C_{17}H_{35}CO$
OH

formula mass $C_{17}H_{35}COOH$ = 18 atoms C $\times \dfrac{12.01 \text{ amu}}{1 \text{ atom C}}$

+ 36 atoms H $\times \dfrac{1.01 \text{ amu}}{1 \text{ atom H}}$ + 2 atoms O $\times \dfrac{16.00 \text{ amu}}{1 \text{ atom O}}$ = 284.54 amu

3.22×10^{-3} g $C_{17}H_{35}COOH \times \dfrac{1 \text{ mol } C_{17}H_{35}COOH}{284.54 \text{ g } C_{17}H_{35}COOH}$

= 1.13×10^{-5} mol $C_{17}H_{35}COOH$

f. Given: 50.0 kg
$(NH_4)_2SO_4$

Unknown: moles
$(NH_4)_2$
SO_4

formula mass $(NH_4)_2SO_4$ = 2 atoms N $\times \dfrac{14.01 \text{ amu}}{1 \text{ atom N}}$ + 8 atoms H

$\times \dfrac{1.01 \text{ amu}}{1 \text{ atom H}}$ + 1 atom S $\times \dfrac{32.07 \text{ amu}}{1 \text{ atom S}}$ + 4 atoms O $\times \dfrac{16.00 \text{ amu}}{1 \text{ atom O}}$

= 132.17 amu

50.0 kg $(NH_4)_2SO_4 \times \dfrac{1000 \text{ g}}{1 \text{ kg}} \times \dfrac{1 \text{ mol } (NH_4)_2SO_4}{132.17 \text{ g } (NH_4)_2SO_4}$

= 378 mol $(NH_4)_2SO_4$

---

115. a. Given: 3.00 mol
$SeOBr_2$

Unknown: mass
$SeOBr_2$

formula mass $SeOBr_2$ = 1 atom Se $\times \dfrac{78.96 \text{ amu}}{1 \text{ atom Se}}$

+ 1 atom O $\times \dfrac{16.00 \text{ amu}}{1 \text{ atom O}}$ + 2 atoms Br $\times \dfrac{79.90 \text{ amu}}{1 \text{ atom Br}}$

= 254.76 amu

3.00 mol $SeOBr_2 \times \dfrac{254.76 \text{ g } SeOBr_2}{1 \text{ mol } SeOBr_2}$ = 764 g $SeOBr_2$

b. Given: 488 mol
$CaCO_3$

Unknown: mass
$CaCO_3$

formula mass $CaCO_3$ = 1 atom Ca $\times \dfrac{40.08 \text{ amu}}{1 \text{ atom Ca}}$ + 1 atom C $\times \dfrac{12.01 \text{ amu}}{1 \text{ atom C}}$

+ 3 atoms O $\times \dfrac{16.00 \text{ amu}}{1 \text{ atom O}}$ = 100.09 amu

488 mol $CaCO_3 \times \dfrac{100.09 \text{ g } CaCO_3}{1 \text{ mol } CaCO_3}$ = 4.88×10^4 g $CaCO_3$

c. Given: 0.0091 mol $C_{20}H_{28}O_2$

Unknown: mass $C_{20}H_{28}O_2$

formula mass $C_{20}H_{28}O_2$ = 20 atoms C $\times \dfrac{12.01 \text{ amu}}{1 \text{ atom C}}$

+ 28 atoms H $\times \dfrac{1.01 \text{ amu}}{1 \text{ atom H}}$ + 2 atoms O $\times \dfrac{16.00 \text{ amu}}{1 \text{ atom O}}$ = 300.48 amu

0.0091 mol $C_{20}H_{28}O_2 \times \dfrac{300.48 \text{ g } C_{20}H_{28}O_2}{1 \text{ mol } C_{20}H_{28}O_2}$ = 2.7 g $C_{20}H_{28}O_2$

d. Given: 6.00×10^{-8} mol $C_{10}H_{14}N_2$

Unknown: mass $C_{10}H_{14}N_2$

formula mass $C_{10}H_{14}N_2$ = 10 atoms C $\times \dfrac{12.01 \text{ amu}}{1 \text{ atom C}}$ + 14 atoms H

$\times \dfrac{1.01 \text{ amu}}{1 \text{ atom H}}$ + 2 atoms N $\times \dfrac{14.01 \text{ amu}}{1 \text{ atom N}}$ = 162.26 amu

6.00×10^{-8} mol $C_{10}H_{14}N_2 \times \dfrac{162.26 \text{ g } C_{10}H_{14}N_2}{1 \text{ mol } C_{10}H_{14}N_2}$ = 9.74×10^{-6} g $C_{10}H_{14}N_2$

e. Given: 2.50 mol $Sr(NO_3)_2$

Unknown: mass $Sr(NO_3)_2$

formula mass $Sr(NO_3)_2$ = 1 atom Sr $\times \dfrac{87.62 \text{ amu}}{1 \text{ atom Sr}}$

+ 2 atoms N $\times \dfrac{14.01 \text{ amu}}{1 \text{ atom N}}$ + 6 atoms O $\times \dfrac{16.00 \text{ amu}}{1 \text{ atom O}}$

= 211.64 amu

2.50 mol $Sr(NO_3)_2 \times \dfrac{211.64 \text{ g } Sr(NO_3)_2}{1 \text{ mol } Sr(NO_3)_2}$ = 529 g $Sr(NO_3)_2$

f. Given: 3.50×10^{-6} mol UF_6

Unknown: mass UF_6

formula mass UF_6 = 1 atom U $\times \dfrac{238.03 \text{ amu}}{1 \text{ atom U}}$ + 6 atoms F $\times \dfrac{19.00 \text{ amu}}{1 \text{ atom F}}$

= 352.03 amu

3.50×10^{-6} mol $UF_6 \times \dfrac{352.03 \text{ g } UF_6}{1 \text{ mol } UF_6}$ = 1.23×10^{-3} g UF_6

---

116. a. Given: 4.72 mol WO_3

Unknown: number of formula units

4.27 mol $WO_3 \times \dfrac{6.022 \times 10^{23} \text{ formula units}}{1 \text{ mol}}$

= 2.57×10^{24} formula units WO_3

b. Given: 0.003 00 mol $Sr(NO_3)_2$

Unknown: number of formula units

3.00×10^{-3} mol $Sr(NO_3)_2 \times \dfrac{6.022 \times 10^{23} \text{ formula units}}{1 \text{ mol}}$

= 1.81×10^{21} formula units $Sr(NO_3)_2$

c. Given 72.5 mol $C_6H_5CH_3$

Unknown: number of molecules

72.5 mol $C_6H_5CH_3 \times \dfrac{6.022 \times 10^{23} \text{ molecules}}{1 \text{ mol}}$

= 4.37×10^{25} molecules $C_6H_5CH_3$

d. Given: 5.11×10^{-7} mol $C_{29}H_{50}O_2$

Unknown: number of molecules

$$5.11 \times 10^{-7} \text{ mol } C_{29}H_{50}O_2 \times \frac{6.022 \times 10^{23} \text{ molecules}}{1 \text{ mol}}$$

$$= 3.08 \times 10^{17} \text{ molecules } C_{29}H_{50}O_2$$

e. Given: 1500 mol N_2H_4

Unknown: number of molecules

$$1500 \text{ mol } N_2H_4 \times \frac{6.022 \times 10^{23} \text{ molecules}}{1 \text{ mol}} = 9.0 \times 10^{26} \text{ molecules } N_2H_4$$

f. Given: 0.989 mol $C_6H_5NO_2$

Unknown: number of molecules

$$0.989 \text{ mol } C_6H_5NO_2 \times \frac{6.022 \times 10^{23} \text{ molecules}}{1 \text{ mol}}$$

$$= 5.96 \times 10^{23} \text{ molecules } C_6H_5NO_2$$

---

117. a. Given: 285 g $FePO_4$

Unknown: number of formula units $FePO_4$

$$\text{formula mass } FePO_4 = 1 \text{ atom Fe} \times \frac{55.85 \text{ amu}}{1 \text{ atom Fe}} + 1 \text{ atom P} \times \frac{30.97 \text{ amu}}{1 \text{ atom P}}$$

$$+ 4 \text{ atoms O} \times \frac{16.00 \text{ amu}}{1 \text{ atom O}} = 150.82 \text{ amu}$$

$$285 \text{ g } FePO_4 \times \frac{1 \text{ mol } FePO_4}{150.82 \text{ g } FePO_4} \times \frac{6.022 \times 10^{23} \text{ formula units}}{1 \text{ mol}}$$

$$= 1.14 \times 10^{24} \text{ formula units } FePO_4$$

b. Given: 0.0084 g C_5H_5N

Unknown: number of molecules C_5H_5N

$$\text{formula mass } C_5H_5N = 5 \text{ atoms C} \times \frac{12.01 \text{ amu}}{1 \text{ atom C}} + 5 \text{ atoms H} \times \frac{1.01 \text{ amu}}{1 \text{ atom H}}$$

$$+ 1 \text{ atom N} \times \frac{14.01 \text{ amu}}{1 \text{ atom N}} = 79.11 \text{ amu}$$

$$0.0084 \text{ g } C_5H_5N \times \frac{1 \text{ mol } C_5H_5N}{79.11 \text{ g } C_5H_5N} \times \frac{6.022 \times 10^{23} \text{ molecules}}{1 \text{ mol}}$$

$$= 6.4 \times 10^{19} \text{ molecules } C_5H_5N$$

c. Given: 85 mg $(CH_3)_2CHCH_2OH$

Unknown: number of molecules $(CH_3)_2CHCH_2OH$

$$\text{formula mass } (CH_3)_2CHCH_2OH = 4 \text{ atoms C} \times \frac{12.01 \text{ amu}}{1 \text{ atom C}}$$

$$+ 10 \text{ atoms H} \times \frac{1.01 \text{ amu}}{1 \text{ atom H}} + 1 \text{ atom O} \times \frac{16.00 \text{ amu}}{1 \text{ atom O}} = 74.14 \text{ amu}$$

$$85 \text{ mg } (CH_3)_2CHCH_2OH \times \frac{1 \text{ g}}{1000 \text{ mg}} \times \frac{1 \text{ mol } (CH_3)_2CHCH_2OH}{74.14 \text{ g } (CH_3)_2CHCH_2OH}$$

$$\times \frac{6022 \times 10^{23} \text{ molecules}}{1 \text{ mol}} = 6.9 \times 10^{20} \text{ molecules } (CH_3)_2CHCH_2OH$$

d. Given: 4.6×10^{-4} g
$Hg(C_2H_3O_2)_2$

Unknown: number of formula units Hg $(C_2H_3O_2)_2$

formula mass $Hg(C_2H_3O_2)_2 = 1$ atom Hg $\times \dfrac{200.59 \text{ amu}}{1 \text{ atom Hg}} + 4$ atoms C

$\times \dfrac{12.01 \text{ amu}}{1 \text{ atom C}} + 6$ atoms H $\times \dfrac{1.01 \text{ amu}}{1 \text{ atom H}} + 4$ atoms O $\times \dfrac{16.00 \text{ amu}}{1 \text{ atom O}}$

$= 318.69$ amu

4.6×10^{-4} g $Hg(C_2H_3O_2)_2 \times \dfrac{1 \text{ mol } Hg(C_2H_3O_2)_2}{318.69 \text{ g } Hg(C_2H_3O_2)_2}$

$\times \dfrac{6.022 \times 10^{23} \text{ formula units}}{1 \text{ mol}} = 8.7 \times 10^{17}$ formula units $Hg(C_2H_3O_2)_2$

e. Given: 0.0067 g
Li_2CO_3

Unknown: number of formula units Li_2CO_3

formula mass $Li_2CO_3 = 2$ atoms Li $\times \dfrac{6.94 \text{ amu}}{1 \text{ atom Li}} + 1$ atom C $\times \dfrac{12.01 \text{ amu}}{1 \text{ atom C}}$

$+ 3$ atoms O $\times \dfrac{16.00 \text{ amu}}{1 \text{ atom O}} = 73.89$ amu

6.7×10^{-3} g $Li_2CO_3 \times \dfrac{1 \text{ mol } Li_2CO_3}{73.89 \text{ g } Li_2CO_3} \times \dfrac{6.022 \times 10^{23} \text{ formula units}}{1 \text{ mol}}$

$= 5.5 \times 10^{19}$ formula units Li_2CO_3

118. a. Given: 8.39×10^{23}
molecules F_2

Unknown: mass F_2

formula mass $F_2 = 2$ atoms F $\times \dfrac{19.00 \text{ amu}}{1 \text{ atom F}} = 38.00$ amu

8.39×10^{23} molecules $F_2 \times \dfrac{1 \text{ mol}}{6.022 \times 10^{23} \text{ molecules}} \times \dfrac{38.00 \text{ g } F_2}{1 \text{ mol } F_2} = 52.9$ g F_2

b. Given: 6.82×10^{24}
formula units
$BeSO_4$

Unknown: mass $BeSO_4$

formula mass $BeSO_4 = 1$ atom Be $\times \dfrac{9.01 \text{ amu}}{1 \text{ atom Be}} + 1$ atom S $\times \dfrac{32.07 \text{ amu}}{1 \text{ atom S}}$

$+ 4$ atoms O $\times \dfrac{16.00 \text{ amu}}{1 \text{ atom O}} = 105.08$ amu

6.82×10^{24} formula units $BeSO_4 \times \dfrac{1 \text{ mol}}{6.022 \times 10^{23} \text{ formula units}}$

$\times \dfrac{105.08 \text{ g } BeSO_4}{1 \text{ mol } BeSO_4} = 1190$ g $BeSO_4$

c. Given: 7.004×10^{26}
molecules of
$CHCl_3$

Unknown: mass $CHCl_3$

formula mass $CHCl_3 = 1$ atom C $\times \dfrac{12.01 \text{ amu}}{1 \text{ atom C}} + 1$ atom H $\times \dfrac{1.01 \text{ amu}}{1 \text{ atom H}}$

$+ 3$ atoms Cl $\times \dfrac{35.45 \text{ amu}}{1 \text{ atom Cl}} = 119.37$ amu

7.004×10^{26} molecules $CHCl_3 \times \dfrac{1 \text{ mol}}{6.022 \times 10^{23} \text{ molecules}}$

$\times \dfrac{119.37 \text{ g } CHCl_3}{1 \text{ mol } CHCl_3} = 1.388 \times 10^5$ g $CHCl_3$

d. Given: 31 billion formula units Cr$(CHO_2)_3$

Unknown: mass Cr$(CHO_2)_3$

formula mass Cr$(CHO_2)_3$ = 1 atom Cr $\times \dfrac{52.00 \text{ amu}}{1 \text{ atom Cr}}$

$+\ 3 \text{ atoms C} \times \dfrac{12.01 \text{ amu}}{1 \text{ atom C}} + 3 \text{ atoms H} \times \dfrac{1.01 \text{ amu}}{1 \text{ atom H}} + 6 \text{ atoms O} \times \dfrac{16.00 \text{ amu}}{1 \text{ atom O}}$

$=\ 187.06$ amu

$3.1 \times 10^{10} \text{ formula units Cr}(CHO_2)_3 \times \dfrac{1 \text{ mol}}{6.022 \times 10^{23} \text{ formula units}}$

$\times\ \dfrac{187.06 \text{ g Cr}(CHO_2)_3}{1 \text{ mol Cr}(CHO_2)_3} = 9.6 \times 10^{-12} \text{ g Cr}(CHO_2)_3$

e. Given: 6.3×10^{18} molecules HNO_3

Unknown: mass HNO_3

formula mass HNO = 1 atom H $\times \dfrac{1.01 \text{ amu}}{1 \text{ atom H}} + 1 \text{ atom N} \times \dfrac{14.01 \text{ amu}}{1 \text{ atom N}}$

$+\ 3 \text{ atoms O} \times \dfrac{16.00 \text{ amu}}{1 \text{ atom O}} = 63.02$ amu

$6.3 \times 10^{18} \text{ molecules HNO}_3 \times \dfrac{1 \text{ mol}}{6.022 \times 10^{23} \text{ molecules}} \times \dfrac{63.02 \text{ g HNO}_3}{1 \text{ mol HNO}_3}$

$=\ 6.6 \times 10^{-4} \text{ g HNO}_3$

f. Given: 8.37×10^{25} molecules $C_2Cl_2F_4$

Unknown: mass $C_2Cl_2F_4$

formula mass $C_2Cl_2F_4$ = 2 atoms C $\times \dfrac{12.01 \text{ amu}}{1 \text{ atom C}}$

$+\ 2 \text{ atoms Cl} \times \dfrac{35.45 \text{ amu}}{1 \text{ atom Cl}} + 4 \text{ atoms F} \times \dfrac{19.00 \text{ amu}}{1 \text{ atom F}} = 170.92$ amu

$8.37 \times 10^{25} \text{ molecules C}_2Cl_2F_4 \times \dfrac{1 \text{ mol}}{6.022 \times 10^{23} \text{ molecules}}$

$\times\ \dfrac{170.92 \text{ g C}_2Cl_2F_4}{1 \text{ mol C}_2Cl_2F_4} = 2.38 \times 10^4 \text{ g C}_2Cl_2F_4$

119. Given: 1 troy ounce = 31.1 g

Unknown: moles in a troy ounce of Au, Pt, Ag

$31.1 \text{ g Au} \times \dfrac{1 \text{ mol Au}}{196.97 \text{ g Au}} = 0.158 \text{ mol Au}$

$31.1 \text{ g Pt} \times \dfrac{1 \text{ mol Pt}}{195.08 \text{ g Pt}} = 0.159 \text{ mol Pt}$

$31.1 \text{ g Ag} \times \dfrac{1 \text{ mol Ag}}{107.87 \text{ g Ag}} = 0.288 \text{ mol Ag}$

120. Given: 22.0 g C_6H_5OH

Unknown: moles C_6H_5OH

formula mass C_6H_5OH = 6 atoms C $\times \dfrac{12.01 \text{ amu}}{1 \text{ atom C}}$

$+\ 6 \text{ atoms H} \times \dfrac{1.01 \text{ amu}}{1 \text{ atom H}} + 1 \text{ atom O} \times \dfrac{16.00 \text{ amu}}{1 \text{ atom O}} = 94.12$ amu

$22.0 \text{ g C}_6H_5OH \times \dfrac{1 \text{ mol C}_6H_5OH}{94.12 \text{ g C}_6H_5OH} = 0.234 \text{ mol C}_6H_5OH$

121. Given: 0.015 mol I_2

Unknown: mass I_2

$$\text{formula mass } I_2 = 2 \text{ atoms I} \times \frac{126.90 \text{ amu}}{1 \text{ atom I}} = 253.80 \text{ amu}$$

$$0.015 \text{ mol } I_2 \times \frac{253.80 \text{ g } I_2}{1 \text{ mol } I_2} = 3.8 \text{ g } I_2$$

---

122. Given: 1 carat = 200 mg

Unknown: number of C atoms in 1.00 carat

$$1 \text{ carat} \times \frac{200. \text{ mg}}{1 \text{ carat}} \times \frac{1 \text{ g}}{1000 \text{ mg}} \times \frac{1 \text{ mol C}}{12.01 \text{ g C}} \times \frac{6.022 \times 10^{23} \text{ atoms}}{1 \text{ mol}}$$

$$= 1.00 \times 10^{22} \text{ atoms C}$$

---

123. a. Given: 8.00 g $CaCl_2$; 1.000 kg water

Unknown: moles of $CaCl_2$ and water

$$\text{formula mass } CaCl_2 = 1 \text{ atom Ca} \times \frac{40.08 \text{ amu}}{1 \text{ atom Ca}}$$

$$+ 2 \text{ atoms Cl} \times \frac{35.45 \text{ amu}}{1 \text{ atom Cl}} = 110.98 \text{ amu}$$

$$8.00 \text{ g } CaCl_2 \times \frac{1 \text{ mol } CaCl_2}{110.98 \text{ g } CaCl_2} = 0.0721 \text{ mol } CaCl_2$$

$$\text{formula mass } H_2O = 2 \text{ atoms H} \times \frac{1.01 \text{ amu}}{1 \text{ atom H}} + 1 \text{ atom O} \times \frac{16.00 \text{ amu}}{1 \text{ atom O}}$$

$$= 18.02 \text{ amu}$$

$$1.000 \text{ kg } H_2O \times \frac{1000 \text{ g}}{1 \text{ kg}} \times \frac{1 \text{ mol } H_2O}{18.02 \text{ g } H_2O} = 55.49 \text{ mol } H_2O$$

b. Given: 0.0721 mol $CaCl_2$ from part **a**

Unknown: moles of Ca^{2+} and Cl^- ions

$$0.0721 \text{ mol } CaCl_2 \times \frac{1 \text{ mol } Ca^{2+}}{1 \text{ mol } CaCl_2} = 0.0721 \text{ mol } Ca^{2+}$$

$$0.0721 \text{ mol } CaCl_2 \times \frac{2 \text{ mol } Cl^-}{1 \text{ mol } CaCl_2} = 0.144 \text{ mol } Cl^-$$

---

124. a. Given: 453.6 g $C_{12}H_{22}O_{11}$

Unknown: moles $C_{12}H_{22}O_{11}$

$$\text{formula mass } C_{12}H_{22}O_{11} = 12 \text{ atoms O} \times \frac{12.01 \text{ amu}}{1 \text{ atom C}}$$

$$+ 22 \text{ atoms H} \times \frac{1.01 \text{ amu}}{1 \text{ atom H}} + 11 \text{ atoms O} \times \frac{16.00 \text{ amu}}{1 \text{ atom O}} = 342.34 \text{ amu}$$

$$453.6 \text{ g } C_{12}H_{22}O_{11} \times \frac{1 \text{ mol } C_{12}H_{22}O_{11}}{342.34 \text{ g } C_{12}H_{22}O_{11}} = 1.325 \text{ mol } C_{12}H_{22}O_{11}$$

b. Given: 453.6 g NaCl

Unknown: moles NaCl

$$\text{formula mass NaCl} = 1 \text{ atom Na} \times \frac{22.99 \text{ amu}}{1 \text{ atom Na}} + 1 \text{ atom Cl} \times \frac{35.45 \text{ amu}}{1 \text{ atom Cl}}$$

$$= 58.44 \text{ amu}$$

$$453.6 \text{ g NaCl} \times \frac{1 \text{ mol NaCl}}{58.44 \text{ g NaCl}} = 7.762 \text{ mol NaCl}$$

125. Given: 10.7 g NH_4Cl
Unknown: moles of ions

formula mass NH_4Cl = 1 atom N $\times \dfrac{14.01 \text{ amu}}{1 \text{ atom N}}$ + 4 atoms H $\times \dfrac{1.01 \text{ amu}}{1 \text{ atom H}}$

+ 1 atom Cl $\times \dfrac{35.45 \text{ amu}}{1 \text{ atom Cl}}$ = 53.50 amu

10.7 g $NH_4Cl \times \dfrac{1 \text{ mol } NH_4Cl}{53.50 \text{ g } NH_4Cl} \times \dfrac{2 \text{ mol ions}}{1 \text{ mol } NH_4Cl}$ = 0.400 mol ions

---

126. Given: 2.41×10^{24} atoms Cr; 1.51×10^{23} atoms Ni; 3.01×10^{23} atoms Cr
Unknown: total moles

2.41×10^{24} atoms + 0.15×10^{24} atoms + 0.301×10^{24} atoms

= 2.86×10^{24} atoms

2.86×10^{24} atoms $\times \dfrac{1 \text{ mol}}{6.022 \times 10^{23} \text{ atoms}}$ = 4.75 mol

---

127. a. Given: 250.0 mL H_2O; D_{H_2O} = 0.997 g/mL
Unknown: mass H_2O

250.0 mL $H_2O \times \dfrac{0.997 \text{ g } H_2O}{1 \text{ mL } H_2O}$ = 249 g H_2O

b. Given: 249 g H_2O (from part **a**)
Unknown: moles H_2O

formula mass H_2O = 2 atoms H $\times \dfrac{1.01 \text{ amu}}{1 \text{ atom H}}$ + 1 atom O $\times \dfrac{16.00 \text{ amu}}{1 \text{ atom O}}$

= 18.02 amu

249 g $H_2O \times \dfrac{1 \text{ mol } H_2O}{18.02 \text{ g } H_2O}$ = 13.8 mol H_2O

c. Given: D_{H_2O} = 0.997 g/mL; 2000 mol H_2O
Unknown: volume

2.000 mol $H_2O \times \dfrac{18.02 \text{ g } H_2O}{1 \text{ mol } H_2O} \times \dfrac{1 \text{ mL } H_2O}{0.997 \text{ g } H_2O}$ = 36.1 mL H_2O

d. Given: 2.000 mol H_2O
Unknown: mass

2.000 mol $H_2O \times \dfrac{18.02 \text{ g } H_2O}{1 \text{ mol } H_2O}$ = 36.04 g H_2O

---

129. Given: 6.35 g Cd
Unknown: mass of same number of Al atoms

6.35 g Cd $\times \dfrac{1 \text{ mol}}{112.41 \text{ g Cd}} \times \dfrac{26.98 \text{ g Al}}{1 \text{ mol}}$ = 1.52 g Al

---

130. Given: Oxygen in cylinder: initial = 1027.8 g; final = 1023.2 g
Unknown: moles of O_2 used

formula mass O_2 = 2 atoms O $\times \dfrac{16.00 \text{ amu}}{1 \text{ atom O}}$ = 32.00 amu

mass of O_2 used = 1027.8 g − 1023.2 g = 4.6 g

4.6 g $O_2 \times \dfrac{1 \text{ mol } O_2}{32.00 \text{ g } O_2}$ = 0.14 mol O_2

---

131. a. Given: 0.250 mol Ag_2S
Unknown: moles of Ag and S

0.250 mol $Ag_2S \times \dfrac{2 \text{ mol Ag}}{1 \text{ mol } Ag_2S}$ = 0.500 mol Ag

0.250 mol $Ag_2S \times \dfrac{1 \text{ mol S}}{1 \text{ mol } Ag_2S}$ = 0.250 mol S

b. Given: 38.8 g Ag_2S

Unknown: moles Ag_2S, Ag, and S

$$\text{formula mass } Ag_2S = 2 \text{ atoms Ag} \times \frac{107.87 \text{ Amu}}{1 \text{ atom Ag}} + 1 \text{ atom S} \times \frac{32.07 \text{ amu}}{1 \text{ atom S}}$$

$$= 247.81 \text{ amu}$$

$$38.8 \text{ g } Ag_2S \times \frac{1 \text{ mol } Ag_2S}{247.81 \text{ g } Ag_2S} = 0.157 \text{ mol } Ag_2S$$

$$0.157 \text{ mol } Ag_2S \times \frac{2 \text{ mol Ag}}{1 \text{ mol } Ag_2S} = 0.314 \text{ mol Ag}$$

$$0.157 \text{ mol } Ag_2S \times \frac{1 \text{ mol S}}{1 \text{ mol } Ag_2S} = 0.157 \text{ mol S}$$

c. Given: 0.314 mol Ag; 0.157 mol S

Unknown: masses of Ag and S

$$0.314 \text{ mol Ag} \times \frac{107.87 \text{ g Ag}}{1 \text{ mol Ag}} = 133.9 \text{ g Ag}$$

$$0.157 \text{ mol S} \times \frac{32.07 \text{ g S}}{1 \text{ mol S}} = 5.03 \text{ g S}$$

---

132. a. Given: $Na_2C_2O_4$

Unknown: percentage composition

$$\text{molar mass } Na_2C_2O_4 = 2 \text{ mol Na} \times \frac{22.99 \text{ g Na}}{1 \text{ mol Na}} + 2 \text{ mol C} \times \frac{12.01 \text{ g C}}{1 \text{ mol C}}$$

$$+ 4 \text{ mol O} \times \frac{16.00 \text{ g O}}{1 \text{ mol O}} = 134.00 \text{ g}$$

$$\frac{2 \times 22.99 \text{ g Na}}{134.00 \text{ g } Na_2C_2O_4} \times 100 = 34.31\% \text{ Na}$$

$$\frac{2 \times 12.01 \text{ g C}}{134.00 \text{ g } Na_2C_2O_4} \times 100 = 17.93\% \text{ C}$$

$$\frac{4 \times 16.00 \text{ g O}}{134.00 \text{ g } Na_2C_2O_4} \times 100 = 47.76\% \text{ O}$$

b. Given: C_2H_5OH

Unknown: percentage composition

$$\text{molar mass } C_2H_5OH = 2 \text{ mol C} \times \frac{12.01 \text{ g C}}{1 \text{ mol C}} + 6 \text{ mol H} \times \frac{1.01 \text{ g H}}{1 \text{ mol H}}$$

$$+ 1 \text{ mol O} \times \frac{16.00 \text{ g O}}{1 \text{ mol O}} = 46.08 \text{ g}$$

$$\frac{2 \times 12.01 \text{ g C}}{46.08 \text{ g } C_2H_5OH} \times 100 = 52.13\% \text{ C}$$

$$\frac{6 \times 1.01 \text{ g H}}{46.08 \text{ g } C_2H_5OH} \times 100 = 13.15\% \text{ H}$$

$$\frac{1 \times 16.00 \text{ g O}}{46.08 \text{ g } C_2H_5OH} \times 100 = 34.72\% \text{ O}$$

c. Given: Al_2O_3

Unknown: percentage composition

$$\text{molar mass } Al_2O_3 = 2 \text{ mol Al} \times \frac{26.98 \text{ g Al}}{1 \text{ mol Al}} + 3 \text{ mol O} \times \frac{16.00 \text{ g O}}{1 \text{ mol O}} = 101.96 \text{ g}$$

$$\frac{2 \times 26.98 \text{ Al}}{101.96 \text{ } Al_2O_3} \times 100 = 52.92\% \text{ Al}$$

$$\frac{3 \times 16.00 \text{ g O}}{101.96 \text{ g } Al_2O_3} \times 100 = 47.08\% \text{ O}$$

d. Given: K_2SO_4
Unknown: percentage composition

$$\text{molar mass } K_2SO_4 = 2 \text{ mol } K \times \frac{39.10 \text{ g } K}{1 \text{ mol } K} + 1 \text{ mol } S \times \frac{32.07 \text{ g } S}{1 \text{ mol } S}$$

$$+ 4 \text{ mol } O \times \frac{16.00 \text{ g } O}{1 \text{ mol } O} = 174.27 \text{ g}$$

$$\frac{2 \times 39.10 \text{ g } K}{174.27 \text{ g } K_2SO_4} \times 100 = 44.87\% \text{ K}$$

$$\frac{1 \times 32.07 \text{ g } S}{174.27 \text{ g } K_2SO_4} \times 100 = 18.40\% \text{ S}$$

$$\frac{4 \times 16.00 \text{ O}}{174.27 \text{ g } K_2SO_4} \times 100 = 36.72\% \text{ O}$$

---

133. Given: percentage composition
Unknown: identity of the compound

100.0 g compound contains 42.59 g Na, 12.02 g C, and 44.99 g O.

$$\frac{42.59 \text{ g Na}}{22.99 \text{ g/mol}} = 1.853 \text{ mol Na} \cong 2 \text{ mol Na}$$

$$\frac{12.02 \text{ g C}}{12.01 \text{ g/mol}} = 1.001 \text{ mol C} \cong 1 \text{ mol C}$$

$$\frac{44.99 \text{ g O}}{16.00 \text{ g/mol}} = 2.812 \text{ mol O} \cong 3 \text{ mol O}$$

Na_2CO_3, or sodium carbonate

---

134. a. Given: 50.0 g KBr
Unknown: mass Br

$$\text{molar mass } KBr = 1 \text{ mol } K \times \frac{39.10 \text{ g } K}{1 \text{ mol } K} + 1 \text{ mol } Br \times \frac{79.90 \text{ g } Br}{1 \text{ mol } Br} = 119.00 \text{ g}$$

$$50.0 \text{ g } KBr \times \frac{79.90 \text{ g } Br}{119.00 \text{ g } KBr} = 33.6 \text{ g } Br$$

b. Given: 1.00 kg $Na_2Cr_2O_7$
Unknown: mass Cr

$$\text{molar mass } Na_2Cr_2O_7 = 2 \text{ mol Na} \times \frac{22.99 \text{ g Na}}{1 \text{ mol Na}} + 2 \text{ mol Cr} \times \frac{52.00 \text{ g Cr}}{1 \text{ mol Cr}}$$

$$+ 7 \text{ mol O} \times \frac{16.00 \text{ g O}}{1 \text{ mol O}} = 261.98 \text{ g}$$

$$1.00 \text{ kg } Na_2Cr_2O_7 \times \frac{1000 \text{ g}}{1 \text{ kg}} \times \frac{2 \times 52.00 \text{ g Cr}}{261.98 \text{ g } Na_2Cr_2O_7} = 397 \text{ g Cr}$$

c. Given: 85.0 mg $C_6H_{14}N_2O_2$
Unknown: mass N

$$\text{molar mass } C_6H_{14}N_2O_2 = 6 \text{ mol C} \times \frac{12.01 \text{ g C}}{1 \text{ mol C}} + 14 \text{ mol H} \times \frac{1.01 \text{ g H}}{1 \text{ mol H}}$$

$$+ 2 \text{ mol N} \times \frac{14.01 \text{ g N}}{1 \text{ mol N}} + 2 \text{ mol O} \times \frac{16.00 \text{ g O}}{1 \text{ mol O}}$$

$$= 146.22 \text{ g}$$

$$0.085 \text{ g } C_6H_{14}N_2O_2 \times \frac{28.02 \text{ g N}}{146.22 \text{ g } C_6H_{14}N_2O_2} = 0.0163 \text{ g} = 16.3 \text{ mg N}$$

d. Given: 2.84 g $Co(C_2H_3O_2)_2$

Unknown: mass of Co

molar mass $Co(C_2H_3O_2)_2$ = $1 \text{ mol Co} \times \dfrac{58.93 \text{ g Co}}{1 \text{ mol Co}} + 4 \text{ mol C} \times \dfrac{12.01 \text{ g C}}{1 \text{ mol C}}$

$+ 6 \text{ mol H} \times \dfrac{1.01 \text{ g H}}{1 \text{ mol H}} + 4 \text{ mol O} \times \dfrac{16.00 \text{ g O}}{1 \text{ mol O}} = 177.03 \text{ g}$

$2.84 \text{ g Co}(C_2H_3O_2)_2 \times \dfrac{58.93 \text{ g Co}}{177.03 \text{ g Co}(C_2H_3O_2)_2} = 0.945 \text{ g Co}$

---

135. a. Given: $Na_2CO_3 \cdot 10H_2O$

Unknown: percentage of water

molar mass $Na_2CO_3 \cdot 10H_2O$ = $2 \text{ mol Na} \times \dfrac{22.99 \text{ g Na}}{1 \text{ mol Na}}$

$+ 1 \text{ mol C} \times \dfrac{12.01 \text{ g C}}{1 \text{ mol C}} + 13 \text{ mol O} \times \dfrac{16.00 \text{ g O}}{1 \text{ mol O}} + 20 \text{ mol H} \times \dfrac{1.01 \text{ g H}}{1 \text{ mol H}} = 286.19 \text{ g}$

molar mass H_2O = $2 \text{ mol H} \times \dfrac{1.01 \text{ g H}}{1 \text{ mol H}} + 1 \text{ mol O} \times \dfrac{16.00 \text{ g O}}{1 \text{ mol O}} = 18.02 \text{ g}$

$\dfrac{10(18.02) \text{ g } H_2O}{286.19 \text{ g } Na_2CO_3 \cdot 10 \, H_2O} \times 100 = 62.97\% \, H_2O$

b. Given: $NiI_2 \cdot 6H_2O$

Unknown: percentage of water

molar mass $NiI_2 \cdot 6H_2O$ = $1 \text{ mol Ni} \times \dfrac{58.69 \text{ g Ni}}{1 \text{ mol Ni}} + 2 \text{ mol I} \times \dfrac{126.90 \text{ g I}}{1 \text{ mol I}}$

$+ 12 \text{ mol H} \times \dfrac{1.01 \text{ g H}}{1 \text{ mol H}} + 6 \text{ mol O} \times \dfrac{16.00 \text{ g O}}{1 \text{ mol O}} = 420.61 \text{ g}$

$\dfrac{6(18.02) \text{ g } H_2O}{420.61 \text{ g } NiI_2 \cdot 6H_2O} \times 100 = 25.71\% \, H_2O$

c. Given: $(NH_4)_2 Fe(CN)_6 \cdot 3H_2O$

Unknown: percentage of water

molar mass $(NH_4)_2Fe(CN)_6 \cdot 3H_2O$ = $8 \text{ mol N} \times \dfrac{14.01 \text{ g N}}{1 \text{ mol N}}$

$+ 14 \text{ mol H} \times \dfrac{1.01 \text{ H}}{1 \text{ mol H}} + 1 \text{ mol Fe} \times \dfrac{55.85 \text{ g Fe}}{1 \text{ mol Fe}} + 6 \text{ mol C} \times \dfrac{12.01 \text{ g C}}{1 \text{ mol C}}$

$+ 3 \text{ mol O} \times \dfrac{16.00 \text{ g O}}{1 \text{ mol O}} = 302.13 \text{ g}$

$\dfrac{3(18.02) \text{ g } H_2O}{302.13 \text{ g } (NH_4)_2Fe(CN)_6 \cdot 3H_2O} \times 100 = 17.89\% \, H_2O$

d. Given: $AlBr_3 \cdot 6H_2O$
Unknown: percentage of water

$$\text{molar mass } AlBr_3 \cdot 6H_2O = 1 \text{ mol Al} \times \frac{26.98 \text{ g Al}}{1 \text{ mol Al}}$$

$$+ \; 3 \text{ mol Br} \times \frac{79.90 \text{ g Br}}{1 \text{ mol Br}} + 12 \text{ mol H} \times \frac{1.01 \text{ g H}}{1 \text{ mol H}}$$

$$+ \; 6 \text{ mol O} \times \frac{16.00 \text{ g O}}{1 \text{ mol O}} = 374.80 \text{ g}$$

$$\frac{6(18.02) \text{ g H}_2O}{374.80 \text{ g } AlBr_3 \cdot 6 H_2O} \times 100 = 28.85\% \text{ H}_2O$$

---

136. a. Given: nitric acid
Unknown: formula; percentage composition

formula is HNO_3

$$\text{molar mass } HNO_3 = 1 \text{ mol H} \times \frac{1.01 \text{ g H}}{1 \text{ mol H}} + 1 \text{ mol N} \times \frac{14.01 \text{ g N}}{1 \text{ mol N}}$$

$$+ \; 3 \text{ mol O} \times \frac{16.00 \text{ g O}}{1 \text{ mol O}} = 63.02 \text{ g}$$

$$\frac{1.01 \text{ g H}}{63.02 \text{ g } HNO_3} \times 100 = 1.60\% \text{ H}$$

$$\frac{14.01 \text{ g N}}{63.02 \text{ g } HNO_3} \times 100 = 22.23\% \text{ N}$$

$$\frac{3 \times 16.00 \text{ g O}}{63.02 \text{ g } HNO_3} \times 100 = 76.17\% \text{ O}$$

b. Given: ammonia
Unknown: formula; percentage composition

formula is NH_3

$$\text{molar mass } NH_3 = 1 \text{ mol N} \times \frac{14.01 \text{ g N}}{1 \text{ mol N}} + 3 \text{ mol H} \times \frac{1.01 \text{ g H}}{1 \text{ mol H}} = 17.04 \text{ g}$$

$$\frac{14.01 \text{ g N}}{17.04 \text{ g } NH_3} \times 100 = 82.22\% \text{ N}$$

$$\frac{3 \times 1.01 \text{ g H}}{17.04 \text{ g } NH_3} \times 100 = 17.78\% \text{ H}$$

c. Given: mercury (II) sulfate
Unknown: formula; percentage composition

formula is $HgSO_4$

$$\text{molar mass } HgSO_4 = 1 \text{ mol Hg} \times \frac{200.59 \text{ g Hg}}{1 \text{ mol Hg}} + 1 \text{ mol S} \times \frac{32.07 \text{ g S}}{1 \text{ mol S}}$$

$$+ \; 4 \text{ mol O} \times \frac{16.00 \text{ g O}}{1 \text{ mol O}} = 296.66 \text{ g}$$

$$\frac{200.59 \text{ g Hg}}{296.66 \text{ g } HgSO_4} \times 100 = 67.616\% \text{ Hg}$$

$$\frac{32.07 \text{ g S}}{296.66 \text{ g } HgSO_4} \times 100 = 10.81\% \text{ S}$$

$$\frac{4 \times 16.00 \text{ g O}}{296.66 \text{ g } HgSO_4} \times 100 = 21.57\% \text{ O}$$

d. Given: antimony (V) flouride

Unknown: formula; percentage composition

formula is SbF_5

$$\text{molar mass } SbF_5 = 1 \text{ mol Sb} \times \frac{121.76 \text{ g Sb}}{1 \text{ mol Sb}} + 5 \text{ mol F} \times \frac{19.00 \text{ g F}}{1 \text{ mol F}} = 216.76 \text{ g}$$

$$\frac{121.76 \text{ g Sb}}{216.76 \text{ g } SbF_5} \times 100 = 56.173\% \text{ Sb}$$

$$\frac{5 \times 19.00 \text{ g F}}{216.76 \text{ g } SbF_5} \times 100 = 43.83\% \text{ F}$$

---

137. a. Given: LiBr

Unknown: percentage composition

$$\text{molar mass } LiBr = 1 \text{ mol Li} \times \frac{6.94 \text{ g Li}}{1 \text{ mol Li}} + 1 \text{ mol Br} \times \frac{79.90 \text{ g Br}}{1 \text{ mol Br}} = 86.84 \text{ g}$$

$$\frac{6.94 \text{ g Li}}{86.84 \text{ g } LiBr} \times 100 = 7.99\% \text{ Li}$$

$$\frac{79.90 \text{ g Br}}{86.84 \text{ } LiBr} \times 100 = 92.01\% \text{ Br}$$

b. Given: $C_{14}H_{10}$

Unknown: percentage composition

$$\text{molar mass } C_{14}H_{10} = 14 \text{ mol C} \times \frac{12.01 \text{ g C}}{1 \text{ mol C}} + 10 \text{ mol H} \times \frac{1.01 \text{ g H}}{1 \text{ mol H}}$$

$$= 178.24 \text{ g}$$

$$\frac{14 \times 12.01 \text{ g C}}{178.24 \text{ g } C_{14}H_{10}} \times 100 = 94.33\% \text{ C}$$

$$\frac{10 \times 1.01 \text{ g H}}{178.24 \text{ g } C_{14}H_{10}} \times 100 = 5.67\% \text{ H}$$

c. Given: NH_4NO_3

Unknown: percentage composition

$$\text{molar mass } NH_4NO_3 = 2 \text{ mol N} \times \frac{14.01 \text{ g N}}{1 \text{ mol N}} + 4 \text{ mol H} \times \frac{1.01 \text{ g H}}{1 \text{ mol H}}$$

$$+ 3 \text{ mol O} \times \frac{16.00 \text{ g O}}{1 \text{ mol O}} = 80.06 \text{ g}$$

$$\frac{2 \times 14.01 \text{ g N}}{80.06 \text{ g } NH_4NO_3} \times 100 = 35.00\% \text{ N}$$

$$\frac{4 \times 1.01 \text{ g H}}{80.06 \text{ g } NH_4NO_3} \times 100 = 5.05\% \text{ H}$$

$$\frac{3 \times 16.00 \text{ g O}}{80.06 \text{ g } NH_4NO_3} \times 100 = 59.96\% \text{ O}$$

d. Given: HNO_2

Unknown: percentage composition

$$\text{molar mass } HNO_2 = 1 \text{ mol H} \times \frac{1.01 \text{ g H}}{1 \text{ mol H}} + 1 \text{ mol N} \times \frac{14.01 \text{ g N}}{1 \text{ mol N}}$$

$$+ 2 \text{ mol O} \times \frac{16.00 \text{ g O}}{1 \text{ mol O}} = 47.02 \text{ g}$$

$$\frac{1.01 \text{ g H}}{47.02 \text{ g } HNO_2} \times 100 = 2.15\% \text{ H}$$

$$\frac{14.01 \text{ g N}}{47.02 \text{ g } HNO_2} \times 100 = 29.80\% \text{ N}$$

$$\frac{2 \times 16.00 \text{ g O}}{47.02 \text{ g } HNO_2} \times 100 = 68.06\% \text{ O}$$

e. Given: Ag_2S

Unknown: percentage composition

molar mass $Ag_2S = 2 \text{ mol Ag} \times \dfrac{107.87 \text{ g Ag}}{1 \text{ mol Ag}} + 1 \text{ mol S} \times \dfrac{32.07 \text{ g S}}{1 \text{ mol S}} = 247.81 \text{ g}$

$\dfrac{2 \times 107.87 \text{ g Ag}}{247.81 \text{ g Ag}_2\text{S}} \times 100 = 87.059\% \text{ Ag}$

$\dfrac{32.07 \text{ g S}}{247.81 \text{ g Ag}_2\text{S}} \times 100 = 12.94\% \text{ S}$

f. Given: $Fe(SCN)_2$

Unknown: percentage composition

molar mass $Fe(SCN)_2 = 1 \text{ mol Fe} \times \dfrac{55.85 \text{ g Fe}}{1 \text{ mol Fe}} + 2 \text{ mol S} \times \dfrac{32.07 \text{ g S}}{1 \text{ mol S}}$

$+ 2 \text{ mol C} \times \dfrac{12.01 \text{ g C}}{1 \text{ mol C}} + 2 \text{ mol N} \times \dfrac{14.01 \text{ g N}}{1 \text{ mol N}} = 172.03 \text{ g}$

$\dfrac{55.85 \text{ g Fe}}{172.03 \text{ g Fe(SCN)}_2} \times 100 = 32.47\% \text{ Fe}$

$\dfrac{2 \times 32.00 \text{ g S}}{172.03 \text{ g Fe(SCN)}_2} \times 100 = 37.28\% \text{ S}$

$\dfrac{2 \times 12.01 \text{ g C}}{172.03 \text{ g Fe(SCN)}_2} \times 100 = 13.96\% \text{ C}$

$\dfrac{2 \times 14.01 \text{ g N}}{172.03 \text{ g Fe(SCN)}_2} \times 100 = 16.29\% \text{ N}$

g. Given: lithium acetate

Unknown: percentage composition

molar mass $LiC_2H_3O_2 = 1 \text{ mol Li} \times \dfrac{6.94 \text{ g Li}}{1 \text{ mol Li}} + 2 \text{ mol C} \times \dfrac{12.01 \text{ g C}}{1 \text{ mol C}}$

$+ 3 \text{ mol H} \times \dfrac{1.01 \text{ g H}}{1 \text{ mol H}} + 2 \text{ mol O} \times \dfrac{16.00 \text{ g O}}{1 \text{ mol O}} = 65.99 \text{ g}$

$\dfrac{6.94 \text{ g Li}}{65.99 \text{ g LiC}_2\text{H}_3\text{O}_2} \times 100 = 10.52\% \text{ Li}$

$\dfrac{2 \times 12.01 \text{ g C}}{65.99 \text{ g LiC}_2\text{H}_3\text{O}_2} \times 100 = 36.40\% \text{ C}$

$\dfrac{3 \times 1.01 \text{ g H}}{65.99 \text{ g LiC}_2\text{H}_3\text{O}_2} \times 100 = 4.59\% \text{ H}$

$\dfrac{2 \times 16.00 \text{ g O}}{65.99 \text{ g LiC}_2\text{H}_3\text{O}_2} \times 100 = 48.49\% \text{ O}$

h. Given: nickel (II) formate

Unknown: percentage composition

$$\text{molar mass Ni(CHO}_2)_2 = 1 \text{ mol Ni} \times \frac{58.69 \text{ g Ni}}{1 \text{ mol Ni}} + 2 \text{ mol C} \times \frac{12.01 \text{ g C}}{1 \text{ mol C}}$$

$$+ 2 \text{ mol H} \times \frac{1.01 \text{ g H}}{1 \text{ mol H}} + 4 \text{ mol O} \times \frac{16.00 \text{ g O}}{1 \text{ mol O}} = 148.73 \text{ g}$$

$$\frac{58.69 \text{ g Ni}}{148.73 \text{ g Ni(CHO}_2)_2} \times 100 = 39.46\% \text{ Ni}$$

$$\frac{2 \times 12.01 \text{ g C}}{148.73 \text{ g Ni(CHO}_2)_2} \times 100 = 16.15\% \text{ C}$$

$$\frac{2 \times 1.01 \text{ g H}}{148.73 \text{ Ni(CHO}_2)_2} \times 100 = 1.36\% \text{ H}$$

$$\frac{3 \times 16.00 \text{ g O}}{148.73 \text{ g Ni(CHO}_2)_2} \times 100 = 43.03\% \text{ O}$$

138. a. Given: NH_2CONH_2

Unknown: percentage of nitrogen

$$\text{molar mass NH}_2\text{CONH}_2 = 2 \text{ mol N} \times \frac{14.01 \text{ g N}}{1 \text{ mol N}} + 1 \text{ mol C} \times \frac{12.01 \text{ g C}}{1 \text{ mol C}}$$

$$+ 4 \text{ mol H} \times \frac{1.01 \text{ g H}}{1 \text{ mol H}} + 1 \text{ mol O} \times \frac{16.00 \text{ g O}}{1 \text{ mol O}} = 60.07 \text{ g}$$

$$\frac{2 \times 14.01 \text{ g N}}{60.07 \text{ g NH}_2\text{CONH}_2} \times 100 = 46.65\% \text{ N}$$

b. Given: SO_2Cl_2

Unknown: percentage of sulfur

$$\text{molar mass SO}_2\text{Cl}_2 = 1 \text{ mol S} \times \frac{32.07 \text{ g S}}{1 \text{ mol S}} + 2 \text{ mol O} \times \frac{16.00 \text{ g O}}{1 \text{ mol O}}$$

$$+ 2 \text{ mol Cl} \times \frac{35.45 \text{ g Cl}}{1 \text{ mol Cl}} = 134.97 \text{ g}$$

$$\frac{32.07 \text{ g S}}{134.97 \text{ g SO}_2\text{Cl}_2} \times 100 = 23.76\% \text{ S}$$

c. Given: Tl_2O_3

Unknown: percentage of thallium

$$\text{molar mass Tl}_2\text{O}_3 = 2 \text{ mol Tl} \times \frac{204.38 \text{ g Tl}}{1 \text{ mol Tl}} + 3 \text{ mol O} \times \frac{16.00 \text{ g O}}{1 \text{ mol O}} = 456.76 \text{ g}$$

$$\frac{2 \times 204.38 \text{ g Tl}}{456.76 \text{ g Tl}_2\text{O}_3} \times 100 = 89.491\% \text{ Tl}$$

d. Given: $KClO_3$

Unknown: percentage of oxygen

$$\text{molar mass KClO}_3 = 1 \text{ mol K} \times \frac{39.10 \text{ g K}}{1 \text{ mol K}} + 1 \text{ mol Cl} \times \frac{35.45 \text{ g Cl}}{1 \text{ mol Cl}}$$

$$+ 3 \text{ mol O} \times \frac{16.00 \text{ g O}}{1 \text{mol O}} = 122.55 \text{ g}$$

$$\frac{3 \times 16.00 \text{ g O}}{122.55 \text{ g KClO}_3} \times 100 = 39.17\% \text{ O}$$

e. Given: $CaBr_2$
Unknown: percentage of bromine

$$\text{molar mass } CaBr_2 = 1 \text{ mol Ca} \times \frac{40.08 \text{ g Ca}}{1 \text{ mol Ca}} + 2 \text{ mol Br} \times \frac{79.90 \text{ g Br}}{1 \text{ mol Br}} = 199.88 \text{ g}$$

$$\frac{2 \times 79.9 \text{ g Br}}{199.88 \text{ g } CaBr_2} \times 100 = 79.95\% \text{ Br}$$

f. Given: SnO_2
Unknown: percentage of tin

$$\text{molar mass } SnO_2 = 1 \text{ mol Sn} \times \frac{118.71 \text{ g Sn}}{1 \text{ mol Sn}} + 2 \text{ mol O} \times \frac{16.00 \text{ g O}}{1 \text{ mol O}}$$

$$= 150.71 \text{ g}$$

$$\frac{118.71 \text{ g Sn}}{150.71 \text{ g } SnO_2} \times 100 = 78.767\% \text{ Sn}$$

---

139. a. Given: 4.00 g MnO_2
Unknown: mass of oxygen

$$\text{molar mass } MnO_2 = 1 \text{ mol Mn} \times \frac{54.94 \text{ g Mn}}{1 \text{ mol Mn}} + 2 \text{ mol O} \times \frac{16.00 \text{ g O}}{1 \text{ mol O}} = 86.94 \text{ g}$$

$$\frac{4.00 \text{ g } MnO_2 \times 2 \times 16.00 \text{ g O}}{86.94 \text{ g } MnO_2} = 1.47 \text{ g O}$$

b. Given: 50.0 metric tons Al_2O_3
Unknown: mass of aluminum

$$\text{molar mass } Al_2O_3 = 2 \text{ mol Al} \times \frac{26.98 \text{ g Al}}{1 \text{ mol Al}} + 3 \text{ mol O} \times \frac{16.00 \text{ g O}}{1 \text{ mol O}} = 101.96 \text{ g}$$

$$50.0 \text{ metric tons } Al_2O_3 \times \frac{2 \times 26.98 \text{ g Al}}{101.96 \text{ g } Al_2O_3} = 26.5 \text{ metric tons Al}$$

c. Given: 325 g AgCN
Unknown: mass of silver

$$\text{molar mass AgCN} = 1 \text{ mol Ag} \times \frac{107.87 \text{ g Ag}}{1 \text{ mol Ag}} + 1 \text{ mol C} \times \frac{12.01 \text{ g}}{1 \text{mol C}}$$

$$+ 1 \text{ mol N} \times \frac{14.01 \text{ g N}}{1 \text{ mol N}} = 133.89 \text{ g}$$

$$325 \text{ g AgCN} \times \frac{107.87 \text{ g Ag}}{133.89 \text{ g AgCN}} = 262 \text{ g Ag}$$

d. Given: 0.780 g Au_2Se_3
Unknown: mass of gold

$$\text{molar mass } Au_2Se_3 = 2 \text{ mol Au} \times \frac{196.97 \text{ g Au}}{1 \text{ mol Au}} + 3 \text{ mol Se} \times \frac{78.96 \text{ g Se}}{1 \text{ mol Se}}$$

$$= 630.82 \text{ g}$$

$$0.780 \text{ g } Au_2Se_3 \times \frac{2 \times 196.97 \text{ g Au}}{630.82 \text{ g } Au_2Se_3} = 0.487 \text{ g Au}$$

e. Given: 683 g Na_2SeO_3
Unknown: mass of selenium

$$\text{molar mass } Na_2SeO_3 = 2 \text{ mol Na} \times \frac{22.99 \text{ g Na}}{1 \text{ mol Na}} + 1 \text{ mol Se} \times \frac{78.96 \text{ g Se}}{1 \text{ mol Se}}$$

$$+ 3 \text{ mol O} \times \frac{16.00 \text{ g O}}{1 \text{ mol O}} = 172.94 \text{ g}$$

$$683 \text{ g } Na_2SeO_3 \times \frac{78.96 \text{ g Se}}{172.94 \text{ g } Na_2SeO_3} = 312 \text{ g Se}$$

f. Given: 5.0×10^4 g $CHCl_2CH_2CH_3$

Unknown: mass of chlorine

molar mass $CHCl_2CH_2CH_3 = 3$ mol C $\times \dfrac{12.01\text{ g C}}{1\text{ mol C}} + 6$ mol H $\times \dfrac{1.01\text{ g H}}{1\text{ mol H}}$

$+ 2$ mol Cl $\times \dfrac{35.45\text{ g Cl}}{1\text{ mol Cl}} = 112.99$ g

5.0×10^4 g $CHCl_2CH_2CH_3 \times \dfrac{2 \times 35.45\text{ g Cl}}{112.99\text{ g }CHCl_2CH_2CH_3} = 3.1 \times 10^4$ g Cl

---

140. a. Given: $SrCl_2 \cdot 6H_2O$

Unknown: percentage of water

molar mass $SrCl_2 \cdot 6\,H_2O = 1$ mol Sr $\times \dfrac{87.62\text{ g Sr}}{1\text{ mol Sr}} + 2$ mol Cl $\times \dfrac{35.45\text{ g Cl}}{1\text{ mol Cl}}$

$+ 12$ mol H $\times \dfrac{1.01\text{ g H}}{1\text{ mol H}} + 6$ mol O $\times \dfrac{16.00\text{ g O}}{1\text{ mol O}} = 266.64$ g

$\dfrac{6(18.02)\text{ g }H_2O}{266.64\text{ g }SrCl_2 \cdot 6H_2O} \times 100 = 40.55\%\ H_2O$

b. Given: $ZnSO_4 \cdot 7H_2O$

Unknown: percentage of water

molar mass $ZnSO_4 \cdot 7H_2O = 1$ mol Zn $\times \dfrac{65.39\text{ g Zn}}{1\text{ mol Zn}} + 1$ mol S $\times \dfrac{32.07\text{ g S}}{1\text{ mol S}}$

$+ 11$ mol O $\times \dfrac{16.00\text{ g O}}{1\text{ mol O}} + 14$ mol H $\times \dfrac{1.01\text{ g H}}{1\text{ mol H}} = 287.60$ g

$\dfrac{7(18.02)\text{ g }H_2O}{287.60\text{ g }ZnSO_4 \cdot 7H_2O} \times 100 = 43.86\%\ H_2O$

c. Given: $CaFPO_3 \cdot 2H_2O$

Unknown: percentage of water

molar mass $CaFPO_3 \cdot 2H_2O = 1$ mol Ca $\times \dfrac{40.08\text{ g Ca}}{1\text{ mol Ca}}$

$+ 1$ mol F $\times \dfrac{19.00\text{ g F}}{1\text{ mol F}} + 1$ mol P $\times \dfrac{30.97\text{ g P}}{1\text{ mol P}} + 5$ mol O $\times \dfrac{16.00\text{ g O}}{1\text{ mol O}}$

$+ 4$ mol H $\times \dfrac{1.01\text{ g H}}{1\text{ mol H}} = 174.09$ g

$\dfrac{2(18.02)\text{ g }H_2O}{174.09\text{ g }CaFPO_3 \cdot 2H_2O} \times 100 = 20.70\%\ H_2O$

d. Given: $Be(NO_3)_2 \cdot 3H_2O$

Unknown: percentage of water

molar mass $Be(NO_3)_2 \cdot 3H_2O = 1$ mol Be $\times \dfrac{9.01\text{ g Be}}{1\text{ mol Be}}$

$+ 2$ mol N $\times \dfrac{14.01\text{ g N}}{1\text{ mol N}} \times 9$ mol O $\times \dfrac{16.00\text{ g O}}{1\text{ mol O}}$

$+ 6$ mol H $\times \dfrac{1.01\text{ g H}}{1\text{ mol H}} = 187.09$ g

$\dfrac{3(18.02)\text{ g }H_2O}{187.09\text{ g }Be(NO_3)_2 \cdot 3H_2O} \times 100 = 28.90\%\ H_2O$

141. **a.** Given: nickel (II) acetate tetrahydrate

Unknown: formula; percentage of nickel

formula is $Ni(C_2H_3O_2)_2 \cdot 4H_2O$

molar mass $Ni(C_2H_3O_2)_2 \cdot 4H_2O = 1 \text{ mol Ni} \times \dfrac{58.69 \text{ g Ni}}{1 \text{ mol Ni}}$

$+ \, 4 \text{ mol C} \times \dfrac{12.01 \text{ g C}}{1 \text{ mol C}} + 14 \text{ mol H} \times \dfrac{1.01 \text{ g H}}{1 \text{ mol H}} + 8 \text{ mol O} \times \dfrac{16.00 \text{ g O}}{1 \text{ mol O}}$

$= 248.87 \text{ g}$

$\dfrac{58.69 \text{ g Ni}}{248.87 \text{ g Ni}(C_2H_3O_2)_2 \cdot 4H_2O} \times 100 = 23.58\% \text{ Ni}$

b. Given: sodium chromate tetrahydrate

Unknown: formula; percentage of chromium

formula is $Na_2CrO_4 \cdot 4H_2O$

molar mass $Na_2CrO_4 \cdot 4H_2O = 2 \text{ mol Na} \times \dfrac{22.99 \text{ g Na}}{1 \text{ mol Na}}$

$+ \, 1 \text{ mol Cr} \times \dfrac{52.00 \text{ g Cr}}{1 \text{ mol Cr}} + 8 \text{ mol O} \times \dfrac{16.00 \text{ g O}}{1 \text{ mol O}} + 8 \text{ mol H} \times \dfrac{1.01 \text{ g H}}{1 \text{ mol H}}$

$= 234.06 \text{ g}$

$\dfrac{52.00 \text{ g Cr}}{234.06 \text{ g Na}_2CrO_4 \cdot 4H_2O} \times 100 = 22.22\% \text{ Cr}$

c. Given: cerium (IV) sulfate tetrahydrate

Unknown: percentage of cerium

formula is $Ce(SO_4)_2 \cdot 4H_2O$

molar mass $Ce(SO_4)_2 \cdot 4H_2O = 1 \text{ mol Ce} \times \dfrac{140.12 \text{ g Ce}}{1 \text{ mol Ce}}$

$+ \, 2 \text{ mol S} \times \dfrac{32.07 \text{ g S}}{1 \text{ mol S}} + 12 \text{ mol O} \times \dfrac{16.00 \text{ g O}}{1 \text{ mol O}} + 8 \text{ mol H} \times \dfrac{1.01 \text{ g H}}{1 \text{ mol H}}$

$= 404.34 \text{ g}$

$\dfrac{140.12 \text{ g Ce}}{404.34 \text{ g Ce}(SO_4)_2 \cdot 4H_2O} \times 100 = 34.65\% \text{ Ce}$

142. Given: 50.0 kg HgS

Unknown: mass of mercury

molar mass $HgS = 1 \text{ mol Hg} \times \dfrac{200.59 \text{ g Hg}}{1 \text{ mol Hg}} + 1 \text{ mol S} \times \dfrac{32.07 \text{ g S}}{1 \text{ mol S}} = 232.68 \text{ g}$

$50.0 \text{ kg HgS} \times \dfrac{200.59 \text{ g Hg}}{232.68 \text{ g HgS}} = 43.1 \text{ kg Hg}$

143. Given: 1.00×10^3 kg of each of $Ca_2(OH)_2CO_3$ and $CuFeS_2$

Unknown: mass of copper for each; which has more Cu

molar mass $Cu_2(OH)_2CO_3 = 2 \text{ mol Cu} \times \dfrac{63.55 \text{ g Cu}}{1 \text{ mol Cu}} + 5 \text{ mol O} \times \dfrac{16.00 \text{ g O}}{1 \text{ mol O}}$

$+ 2 \text{ mol H} \times \dfrac{1.01 \text{ g H}}{1 \text{ mol H}} + 1 \text{ mol C} \times \dfrac{12.01 \text{ g C}}{1 \text{mol C}} = 221.13 \text{ g}$

$1.00 \times 10^3 \text{ kg } Cu_2(OH)_2CO_3 \times \dfrac{2 \times 63.55 \text{ g Cu}}{221.13 \text{ g } Cu_2(OH)_2CO_3} = 575 \text{ kg Cu}$

molar mass $CuFeS_2 = 1 \text{ mol Cu} \times \dfrac{63.55 \text{ g Cu}}{1 \text{ mol Cu}} + 1 \text{ mol Fe} \times \dfrac{55.85 \text{ g Fe}}{1 \text{ mol F}}$

$+ 2 \text{ mol S} \times \dfrac{32.07 \text{ g S}}{1 \text{ mol S}} = 183.54 \text{ g}$

$1.00 \times 10^3 \text{ kg } CuFeS_2 \times \dfrac{63.55 \text{ g Cu}}{183.54 \text{ g } CuFeS_2} = 346 \text{ kg Cu}$

Malachite, $Cu_2(OH)_2CO_3$, has more copper.

144. a. Given: $VOSO_4 \cdot 2H_2O$

Unknown: percentage of vanadium

molar mass $VOSO_4 \cdot 2H_2O = 1 \text{ mol V} \times \dfrac{50.94 \text{ g V}}{1 \text{ mol V}} + 7 \text{ mol O} \times \dfrac{16.00 \text{ g O}}{1 \text{ mol O}}$

$+ 1 \text{ mol S} \times \dfrac{32.07 \text{ g S}}{1 \text{ mol S}} + 4 \text{ mol H} \times \dfrac{1.01 \text{ g H}}{1 \text{ mol H}} = 199.05 \text{ g}$

$\dfrac{50.94 \text{ g V}}{199.05 \text{ g } VOSO_4 \cdot 2 H_2O} \times 100 = 25.59\% \text{ V}$

b. Given: $K_2SnO_3 \cdot 3H_2O$

Unknown: percentage of tin

molar mass $K_2SnO_3 \cdot 3H_2O = 2 \text{ mol K} \times \dfrac{39.10 \text{ g K}}{1 \text{ mol K}}$

$+ 1 \text{ mol Sn} \times \dfrac{118.71 \text{ g Sn}}{1 \text{ mol Sn}} + 6 \text{ mol O} \times \dfrac{16.00 \text{ g O}}{1 \text{ mol O}} + 6 \text{ mol H} \times \dfrac{1.01 \text{ g H}}{1 \text{ mol H}} = 298.97$

$\dfrac{118.71 \text{ g Sn}}{298.97 \text{ g } K_2SnO_3 \cdot 3H_2O} \times 100 = 39.71\% \text{ Sn}$

c. Given: $CaClO_3 \cdot 2H_2O$

Unknown: percentage of chlorine

molar mass $CaClO_3 \cdot 2H_2O = 1 \text{ mol Ca} \times \dfrac{40.08 \text{ g Ca}}{1 \text{ mol Ca}}$

$+ 1 \text{ mol Cl} \times \dfrac{35.45 \text{ g Cl}}{1 \text{ mol Cl}} + 5 \text{ mol O} \times \dfrac{16.00 \text{ g O}}{1 \text{mol O}} + 4 \text{ mol H} \times \dfrac{1.01 \text{ g H}}{1 \text{ mol H}}$

$= 159.57 \text{ g}$

$\dfrac{35.45 \text{ g Cl}}{159.57 \text{ g } CaClO_3 \cdot 2H_2O} \times 100 = 22.22\% \text{ Cl}$

145. Given: 500.0 g CuSO$_4$ · 5H$_2$O

Unknown: mass of anhydrous CuSO$_4$

molar mass CuSO$_4$ = 1 mol Cu $\times \dfrac{63.55 \text{ g Cu}}{1 \text{ mol Cu}}$ + 1 mol S $\times \dfrac{32.07 \text{ g}}{1 \text{ mol S}}$

+ 4 mol O $\times \dfrac{16.00 \text{ g O}}{1 \text{ mol O}}$ = 159.62 g

molar mass CuSO$_4$ · 5H$_2$O = 159.62 g + 5 mol H$_2$O $\times \dfrac{18.02 \text{ g H}_2\text{O}}{1 \text{ mol H}_2\text{O}}$ = 249.72 g

500.0 g CuSO$_4$ · 5H$_2$O $\times \dfrac{159.62 \text{ g CuSO}_4}{249.72 \text{ g CuSO}_4 \cdot 5\text{H}_2\text{O}}$ = 319.6 g CuSO$_4$

---

146. Given: 1.00 g Ag

Unknown: mass of AgNO$_3$

molar mass AgNO$_3$ = 1 mol Ag $\times \dfrac{107.87 \text{ g Ag}}{1 \text{ mol Ag}}$ + 1 mol N $\times \dfrac{14.01 \text{ g N}}{1 \text{ mol N}}$

+ 3 mol O $\times \dfrac{16.00 \text{ g O}}{1 \text{ mol O}}$ = 169.88 g

1.00 g Ag $\times \dfrac{169.88 \text{ g AgNO}_3}{107.87 \text{ g Ag}}$ = 1.57 g AgNO$_3$

---

147. Given: 62.4 g Ag$_2$S

Unknown: mass of Ag and S

molar mass Ag$_2$S = 2 mol Ag $\times \dfrac{107.87 \text{ g Ag}}{1 \text{ mol Ag}}$ + 1 mol S $\times \dfrac{32.07 \text{ g S}}{1 \text{ mol S}}$ = 247.81 g

62.4 g Ag$_2$S $\times \dfrac{2(107.87) \text{ g Ag}}{247.81 \text{ g Ag}_2\text{S}}$ = 54.3 g Ag

62.4 g Ag$_2$S $\times \dfrac{32.07 \text{ g S}}{247.81 \text{ g Ag}_2\text{S}}$ = 8.08 g S

---

148. Given: MgSO$_4$ · 7H$_2$O; 11.8 g H$_2$O

Unknown: mass of MgSO$_4$ · 7H$_2$O

molar mass MgSO$_4$ · 7H$_2$O = 1 mol Mg $\times \dfrac{24.31 \text{ g Mg}}{1 \text{ mol Mg}}$

+ 1 mol S $\times \dfrac{32.07 \text{ g S}}{1 \text{ mol S}}$ + 11 mol O $\times \dfrac{16.00 \text{ g O}}{1 \text{ mol O}}$ + 14 mol H $\times \dfrac{1.01 \text{ g H}}{1 \text{ mol H}}$

= 246.52 g

11.8 g H$_2$O $\times \dfrac{246.52 \text{ g MgSO}_4 \cdot 7\text{H}_2\text{O}}{7(18.02) \text{ g H}_2\text{O}}$ = 23.1 g MgSO$_4$ · 7H$_2$O

---

149. Given: 1.00 kg H$_2$SO$_4$

Unknown: mass of sulfur

molar mass H$_2$SO$_4$ = 2 mol H $\times \dfrac{1.01 \text{ g H}}{1 \text{ mol H}}$ + 1 mol S $\times \dfrac{32.07 \text{ S}}{1 \text{ mol S}}$

+ 4 mol O $\times \dfrac{16.00 \text{ g O}}{1 \text{ mol O}}$ = 98.09 g

1.00 kg H$_2$SO$_4$ $\times \dfrac{32.07 \text{ g S}}{98.09 \text{ g H}_2\text{SO}_4} \times \dfrac{1000 \text{ g}}{1 \text{ kg}}$ = 3.27 $\times$ 10^2 g S

---

150. a. Given: 28.4% Cu; 71.6% Br

Unknown: empirical formula of compound

100.0 g of compound contains 28.4 g Cu and 71.6 g Br.

28.4 g Cu $\times \dfrac{1 \text{ mol Cu}}{63.55 \text{ g Cu}}$ = 0.447 mol Cu

71.6 g Br $\times \dfrac{1 \text{ mol Br}}{79.90 \text{ g Br}}$ = 0.896 mol Br

$\dfrac{0.447 \text{ mol Cu}}{0.447} : \dfrac{0.896 \text{ mol Br}}{0.447}$ = 1.00 mol Cu : 2.00 mol Br $\rightarrow$ CuBr$_2$

b. Given: 39.0% K;
12.0% C;
1.01% H;
47.9% O

Unknown: empirical formual of compound

100.0 g of compound contains 39.0 g K, 12.0 g C, 1.01 g H, and 47.9 g O.

$$39.0 \text{ g K} \times \frac{1 \text{ mol K}}{39.10 \text{ g K}} = 0.997 \text{ mol K}$$

$$12.0 \text{ g C} \times \frac{1 \text{ mol C}}{12.01 \text{ g C}} = 0.999 \text{ mol C}$$

$$1.01 \text{ g H} \times \frac{1 \text{ mol H}}{1.01 \text{ g H}} = 1.00 \text{ mol H}$$

$$47.9 \text{ g O} \times \frac{1 \text{ mol O}}{16.00 \text{ g O}} = 2.99 \text{ mol O}$$

$$\frac{0.997 \text{ mol k}}{0.997} : \frac{0.999 \text{ mol C}}{0.997} : \frac{1.00 \text{ mol H}}{0.997} : \frac{2.99 \text{ mol O}}{0.997} = 1.00 \text{ mol K} : 1.00 \text{ mol}$$

C : 1.00 mol H : 3.00 mol O $\rightarrow$ KHCO$_3$

c. Given: 77.3% Ag;
7.4% P;
15.3% O

Unknown: empirical formula of compound

100.0 g of compound contains 77.3 g Ag, 7.4 g P, and 15.3 g O.

$$77.3 \text{ g Ag} \times \frac{1 \text{ mol Ag}}{107.87 \text{ g Ag}} = 0.717 \text{ mol Ag}$$

$$7.4 \text{ g P} \times \frac{1 \text{ mol P}}{30.97 \text{ g P}} = 0.24 \text{ mol P}$$

$$15.3 \text{ g O} \times \frac{1 \text{ mol O}}{16.00 \text{ g O}} = 0.956 \text{ mol O}$$

$$\frac{0.717 \text{ mol Ag}}{0.24} : \frac{0.24 \text{ mol P}}{0.24} : \frac{0.956 \text{ mol O}}{0.24} = 3.0 \text{ mol Ag} : 1.0 \text{ mol P} :$$

4.0 mol O $\rightarrow$ Ag$_3$PO$_4$

d. Given: 0.57% H;
72.1% I;
27.3% O

Unknown: empirical formula of compound

100.0 g of compound contains 0.57 g H, 72.1 g I, and 27.3 g O

$$0.57 \text{ g H} \times \frac{1 \text{ mol H}}{1.01 \text{ g H}} = 0.56 \text{ mol H}$$

$$72.1 \text{ g I} \times \frac{1 \text{ mol I}}{126.90 \text{ g I}} = 0.57 \text{ mol I}$$

$$27.3 \text{ g O} \times \frac{1 \text{ mol O}}{16.00 \text{ g O}} = 1.7 \text{ mol O}$$

$$\frac{0.56 \text{ mol H}}{0.56} : \frac{0.57 \text{ mol I}}{0.56} : \frac{1.7 \text{ mol O}}{0.56} = 1.0 \text{ mol H} : 1.0 \text{ mol I} : 3.0 \text{ mol O}$$

$\rightarrow$ HIO$_3$

151. a. Given: 36.2% Al;
63.8% S

Unknown: empirical formula of compound

100.0 g of compound contains 36.2 g Al and 63.8 g S.

$$36.2 \text{ g Al} \times \frac{1 \text{ mol Al}}{26.98 \text{ g Al}} = 1.34 \text{ mol Al}$$

$$63.8 \text{ g S} \times \frac{1 \text{ mol S}}{32.07 \text{ g S}} = 1.99 \text{ mol S}$$

$$\frac{1.34 \text{ mol Al}}{1.34} : \frac{1.99 \text{ mol S}}{1.34} = 1.0 \text{ mol Al} : 1.5 \text{ mol S}$$

2(1.0 mol Al : 1.5 mol S) = 2.0 mol Al : 3.0 mol S $\rightarrow$ Al$_2$S$_3$

b. Given: 93.5% Nb; 6.50% O

Unknown: empirical formula of compound

100.0 g of compound contains 93.5 g Nb and 6.50 g O.

$$93.5 \text{ g Nb} \times \frac{1 \text{ mol Nb}}{92.91 \text{ g Nb}} = 1.01 \text{ mol Nb}$$

$$6.50 \text{ g O} \times \frac{1 \text{ mol O}}{16.00 \text{ g O}} = 0.406 \text{ mol O}$$

$$\frac{1.01 \text{ mol Nb}}{0.406} : \frac{0.406 \text{ mol O}}{0.406} = 2.49 \text{ mol Nb} : 1.00 \text{ mol O}$$

$$2(2.49 \text{ mol Nb} : 1.00 \text{ mol O}) = 4.98 \text{ mol Nb} : 2 \text{ mol O} \rightarrow Nb_5O_2$$

c. Given: 57.6% Sr; 13.8% P; 28.6% O

Unknown: empirical formula of compound

100.0 g of compound contains 57.6 g Sr, 13.8 g P, and 28.6 g O

$$57.6 \text{ g Sr} \times \frac{1 \text{ mol Sr}}{87.62 \text{ g Sr}} = 0.657 \text{ mol Sr}$$

$$13.8 \text{ g P} \times \frac{1 \text{ mol P}}{30.97 \text{ g P}} = 0.446 \text{ mol P}$$

$$28.6 \text{ g O} \times \frac{1 \text{ mol O}}{16.00 \text{ g O}} = 1.79 \text{ mol O}$$

$$\frac{0.657 \text{ mol Sr}}{0.446} : \frac{0.446 \text{ mol P}}{0.446} : \frac{1.79 \text{ mol O}}{0.446} = 1.47 \text{ mol Sr} : 1.00 \text{ mol P} : 4.01 \text{ mol O}$$

$$2(1.47 \text{ mol Sr} : 1.00 \text{ mol P} : 4.01 \text{ mol O}) = 2.94 \text{ mol Sr} : 2.00 \text{ mol P} :$$
$$8.02 \text{ mol O} \rightarrow Sr_3P_2O_8$$

d. Given: 28.5% Fe; 48.6% O; 22.9% S

Unknown: empirical formula of compound

100.0 g of compound contains 28.5 g Fe, 48.6 g O, and 22.9 g S

$$28.5 \text{ g Fe} \times \frac{1 \text{ mol Fe}}{55.85 \text{ g Fe}} = 0.510 \text{ mol Fe}$$

$$48.6 \text{ g O} \times \frac{1 \text{ mol O}}{16.00 \text{ g O}} = 3.04 \text{ mol O}$$

$$22.9 \text{ g S} \times \frac{1 \text{ mol S}}{32.07 \text{ g S}} = 0.714 \text{ mol S}$$

$$\frac{0.510 \text{ mol Fe}}{0.510} : \frac{3.04 \text{ mol O}}{0.510} : \frac{0.714 \text{ mol S}}{0.510} = 1.00 \text{ mol Fe} : 5.96 \text{ mol O} :$$

$$1.40 \text{ mol S}$$

$$2(1.00 \text{ mol Fe} : 5.96 \text{ mol O} : 1.40 \text{ mol S}) = 2.00 \text{ mol Fe} : 11.92 \text{ mol O} :$$
$$2.80 \text{ mol S} \rightarrow Fe_2S_3O_{12}$$

---

152. a. Given: empirical formula: CH_2; molar mass = 28 g/mol

Unknown: molecular formula

$$\text{molar mass } CH_2 = 1 \text{ mol C} \times \frac{12.01 \text{ g C}}{1 \text{ mol C}} + 2 \text{ mol H} \times \frac{1.01 \text{ g H}}{1 \text{ mol H}} = 14.03 \text{ g}$$

$$x = \frac{28 \text{ g}}{14.03 \text{ g}} = 2.0 \qquad C_xH_{2x} = C_2H_4$$

b. Given: empirical formula: B_2H_5; molar mass = 54 g/mol

Unknown: molecular formula

$$\text{molar mass } B_2H_5 = 2 \text{ mol B} \times \frac{10.81 \text{ g B}}{1 \text{ mol B}} + 5 \text{ mol H} \times \frac{1.01 \text{ g H}}{1 \text{ mol H}} = 26.67 \text{ g}$$

$$x = \frac{54 \text{ g}}{26.67 \text{ g}} = 2.0 \qquad B_{2x}H_{5x} = B_4H_{10}$$

c. Given: empirical formula: C_2HCl; molar mass = 179 g/mol

Unknown: molecular formula

$$\text{molar mass } C_2HCl = 2 \text{ mol C} \times \frac{12.01 \text{ g C}}{1 \text{ mol C}} + 1 \text{ mol H} \times \frac{1.01 \text{ g H}}{1 \text{ mol C}}$$

$$+ 1 \text{ mol Cl} \times \frac{35.45 \text{ g Cl}}{1 \text{ mol Cl}} = 60.48 \text{ g}$$

$$x = \frac{179 \text{ g}}{60.48 \text{ g}} = 2.96 \cong 3 \qquad C_{2x}H_xCl_x = C_6H_3Cl_3$$

d. Given: empirical formula: C_6H_8O; molar mass = 290 g/mol

Unknown: molecular formula

$$\text{molar mass } C_6H_8O = 6 \text{ mol C} \times \frac{12.01 \text{ g C}}{1 \text{ mol C}} + 8 \text{ mol H} \times \frac{1.01 \text{ g H}}{1 \text{ mol H}}$$

$$+ 1 \text{ mol O} \times \frac{16.00 \text{ g O}}{1 \text{ mol O}} = 96.14 \text{ g}$$

$$x = \frac{290 \text{ g}}{96.14 \text{ g}} = 3.0 \qquad C_{6x}H_{8x}O_x = C_{18}H_{24}O_3$$

e. Given: empirical formula: C_3H_2O; molar mass = 216 g/mol

Unknown: molecular formula

$$\text{molar mass } C_3H_2O = 3 \text{ mol C} \times \frac{12.01 \text{ g C}}{1 \text{ mol C}} + 2 \text{ mol H} \times \frac{1.01 \text{ g H}}{1 \text{ mol H}}$$

$$+ 1 \text{ mol O} \times \frac{16.00 \text{ g O}}{1 \text{ mol O}} = 54.05 \text{ g}$$

$$x = \frac{216 \text{ g}}{54.05} = 4.0 \qquad C_{3x}H_{2x}O_x = C_{12}H_8O_4$$

---

153. a. Given: 66.0% Ba; 34.0% Cl

Unknown: empircal formula of compound

100.0 g of compound contains 66.0 g Ba and 34.0 g Cl

$$66.0 \text{ g Ba} \times \frac{1 \text{ mol Ba}}{137.33 \text{ g Ba}} = 0.481 \text{ mol Ba}$$

$$34.0 \text{ g Cl} \times \frac{1 \text{ mol Cl}}{35.45 \text{ g Cl}} = 0.959 \text{ mol Cl}$$

$$\frac{0.481 \text{ mol Ba}}{0.481} : \frac{0.959 \text{ mol Cl}}{0.481} = 1.00 \text{ mol Ba} : 1.99 \text{ mol Cl} \rightarrow BaCl_2$$

b. Given: 80.38% Bi; 18.46% O; 1.16% H

Unknown: empirical formula of compound

100.00 g of compound contains 80.38 g Bi, 18.46 g O, and 1.16 g H

$$80.38 \text{ g Bi} \times \frac{1 \text{ mol Bi}}{28.98 \text{ g Bi}} = 0.3846 \text{ mol Bi}$$

$$18.46 \text{ g O} \times \frac{1 \text{ mol O}}{16.00 \text{ g O}} = 1.154 \text{ mol O}$$

$$1.16 \text{ g H} \times \frac{1 \text{ mol H}}{1.01 \text{ g H}} = 1.149 \text{ mol H}$$

$$\frac{0.3846 \text{ mol Bi}}{0.3846} : \frac{1.154 \text{ mol O}}{0.3846} : \frac{1.149 \text{ mol H}}{0.3846} = 1.000 \text{ mol Bi} : 3.001 \text{ mol O} :$$

$$2.964 \text{ mol H} \rightarrow BiO_3H_3$$

c. Given: 12.67% Al;
19.73% N;
67.60% O

Unknown: empirical
formula of
compound

100.00 g of compound contains 12.67 g Al, 19.73 g N, and 67.60 g O.

$$12.67 \text{ g Al} \times \frac{1 \text{ mol Al}}{26.98 \text{ g Al}} = 0.4696 \text{ mol Al}$$

$$19.73 \text{ g N} \times \frac{1 \text{ mol N}}{14.01 \text{ g N}} = 1.408 \text{ mol N}$$

$$67.60 \text{ g O} \times \frac{1 \text{ mol O}}{16.00 \text{ g O}} = 4.225 \text{ mol O}$$

$$\frac{0.4696 \text{ mol Al}}{0.4696} : \frac{1.408 \text{ mol N}}{0.4696} : \frac{4.225 \text{ mol O}}{0.4696} = 1.000 \text{ mol Al} : 2.998 \text{ mol N} :$$

$$8.997 \text{ mol O} \rightarrow AlN_3O_9$$

d. Given: 35.64% Zn;
26.18% C;
34.88% O;
3.30% H

Unknown: empirical
formula of
compound

100.00 g of compound contains 35.64 g Zn, 26.18 g C, 34.88 g O, and 3.30 g H.

$$35.64 \text{ g Zn} \times \frac{1 \text{ mol Zn}}{65.39 \text{ g Zn}} = 0.5450 \text{ mol Zn}$$

$$26.18 \text{ g C} \times \frac{1 \text{ mol C}}{12.01 \text{ g C}} = 2.180 \text{ mol C}$$

$$34.88 \text{ g O} \times \frac{1 \text{ mol O}}{16.00 \text{ g O}} = 2.180 \text{ mol O}$$

$$3.30 \text{ g H} \times \frac{1 \text{ mol H}}{1.01 \text{ g H}} = 3.267 \text{ mol H}$$

$$\frac{0.5450 \text{ mol Zn}}{0.5450} : \frac{2.180 \text{ mol C}}{0.5450} : \frac{2.180 \text{ mol O}}{0.5450} : \frac{3.267 \text{ mol H}}{0.5450} = 1.000 \text{ mol Zn} :$$

$$4.000 \text{ mol C} : 4.000 \text{ mol O} : 5.994 \text{ mol H} \rightarrow ZnC_4H_6O_4$$

e. Given: 2.8% H; 9.8%
N; 20.5% Ni;
44.5% O;
22.4% S

Unknown: empirical
formula of
compound

100.0 g of compound contains 2.8 g H, 9.8 g N, 20.5 g Ni, 44.5 g O, and 22.4 g S.

$$2.8 \text{ g H} \times \frac{1 \text{ mol H}}{1.01 \text{ g H}} = 2.8 \text{ mol H}$$

$$9.8 \text{ g N} \times \frac{1 \text{ mol N}}{14.01 \text{ g N}} = 0.70 \text{ mol N}$$

$$20.5 \text{ g Ni} \times \frac{1 \text{ mol Ni}}{58.69 \text{ g Ni}} = 0.35 \text{ mol Ni}$$

$$44.5 \text{ g O} \times \frac{1 \text{ mol O}}{16.00 \text{ g O}} = 2.8 \text{ mol O}$$

$$22.4 \text{ g S} \times \frac{1 \text{ mol S}}{32.07 \text{ g S}} = 0.70 \text{ mol S}$$

$$\frac{2.8 \text{ mol H}}{0.35} : \frac{0.70 \text{ mol N}}{0.35} : \frac{0.35 \text{ mol Ni}}{0.35} : \frac{2.8 \text{ mol O}}{0.35} : \frac{0.70 \text{ mol S}}{0.35} = 8.0 \text{ mol H} :$$

$$2.0 \text{ mol N} : 1.0 \text{ mol Ni} : 8.0 \text{ mol O} : 2.0 \text{ mol S} \rightarrow NiN_2S_2H_8O_8$$

f. Given: 8.09% C; 0.34% H; 10.78% O; 80.78% Br

Unknown: empirical formula of compound

100.00 g of compound contains 8.09 g C, 0.34 g H, 10.78 g O, and 80.78 g Br.

$$8.09 \text{ g C} \times \frac{1 \text{ mol C}}{12.01 \text{ g C}} = 0.674 \text{ mol C}$$

$$0.34 \text{ g H} \times \frac{1 \text{ mol H}}{1.01 \text{ g H}} = 0.34 \text{ mol H}$$

$$10.78 \text{ g O} \times \frac{1 \text{ mol O}}{16.00 \text{ g O}} = 0.674 \text{ mol O}$$

$$80.78 \text{ g Br} \times \frac{1 \text{ mol Br}}{79.90 \text{ g Br}} = 1.011 \text{ mol Br}$$

$$\frac{0.674 \text{ mol C}}{0.34} : \frac{0.34 \text{ mol H}}{0.34} : \frac{0.674 \text{ mol O}}{0.34} : \frac{1.011 \text{ mol Br}}{0.34} = 2.0 \text{ mol C} :$$

$$1.00 \text{ mol H} : 2.0 \text{ mol O} : 3.0 \text{ mol Br} \rightarrow C_2HBrO_2$$

---

154. a. Given: 0.537 g Cu; 0.321 g F

Unknown: empirical formula of compound

$$0.537 \text{ g Cu} \times \frac{1 \text{ mol Cu}}{63.55 \text{ g Cu}} = 0.00845 \text{ mol Cu}$$

$$0.321 \text{ g F} \times \frac{1 \text{ mol F}}{19.00 \text{ g F}} = 0.0169 \text{ mol F}$$

$$\frac{0.00845 \text{ mol Cu}}{0.00845} : \frac{0.0169 \text{ Mol F}}{0.00845} = 1.00 \text{ mol Cu} : 2.00 \text{ mol F} \rightarrow CuF_2$$

b. Given: 9.48 g Ba; 1.66 g C; 1.93 g N

Unknown: empirical formula of compound

$$9.48 \text{ g Ba} \times \frac{1 \text{ mol Ba}}{137.33 \text{ g Ba}} = 0.0690 \text{ mol Ba}$$

$$1.66 \text{ g C} \times \frac{1 \text{ mol C}}{12.01 \text{ g C}} = 0.138 \text{ mol C}$$

$$1.93 \text{ g N} \times \frac{1 \text{ mol N}}{14.01 \text{ g N}} = 0.138 \text{ mol N}$$

$$\frac{0.0690 \text{ mol Ba}}{0.0690} : \frac{0.138 \text{ mol C}}{0.0690} : \frac{0.138 \text{ mol N}}{0.0690} = 1.00 \text{ mol Ba} : 2.00 \text{ mol C} :$$

$$2.00 \text{ mol N} \rightarrow BaC_2N_2 = Ba(CN)_2$$

c. Given: 0.0091 g Mn; 0.0106 g O; 0.0053 g S

Unknown: empirical formula of compound

$$0.0091 \text{ g Mn} \times \frac{1 \text{ mol Mn}}{54.94 \text{ Mn}} = 1.7 \times 10^{-4} \text{ mol Mn}$$

$$0.0106 \text{ g O} \times \frac{1 \text{ mol O}}{16.00 \text{ g O}} = 6.63 \times 10^{-4} \text{ mol O}$$

$$0.0053 \text{ g S} \times \frac{1 \text{ mol S}}{32.07 \text{ g S}} = 1.7 \times 10^{-4} \text{ mol S}$$

$$\frac{1.7 \times 10^{-4} \text{ mol Mn}}{1.7 \times 10^{-4}} : \frac{6.63 \times 10^{-4} \text{ mol O}}{1.7 \times 10^{-4}} : \frac{1.7 \times 10^{-4} \text{ mol S}}{1.7 \times 10^{-4}}$$

$$= 1.0 \text{ mol Mn} : 3.9 \text{ mol O} : 1.0 \text{ mol S} \rightarrow MnO_4S = MnSO_4$$

155. a. Given: 0.0015 g Ni;
0.0067 g I

Unknown: empirical formula of compound

$$0.0015 \text{ g Ni} \times \frac{1 \text{ mol Ni}}{58.69 \text{ g Ni}} = 2.6 \times 10^{-5} \text{ mol Ni}$$

$$0.0067 \text{ g I} \times \frac{1 \text{ mol I}}{126.90 \text{ g I}} = 5.3 \times 10^{-5} \text{ mol I}$$

$$\frac{2.6 \times 10^{-5} \text{ mol Ni}}{2.6 \times 10^{-5}} : \frac{5.3 \times 10^{-5} \text{ mol I}}{2.6 \times 10^{-5}} = 1.0 \text{ mol Ni} : 2.0 \text{ mol I} \rightarrow NiI_2$$

b. Given: 0.144 g Mn;
0.074 g N;
0.252 g O

Unknown: empirical formula of compound

$$0.144 \text{ g Mn} \times \frac{1 \text{ mol Mn}}{54.94 \text{ g Mn}} = 2.62 \times 10^{-3} \text{ mol Mn}$$

$$0.074 \text{ g N} \times \frac{1 \text{ mol N}}{14.01 \text{ g N}} = 5.3 \times 10^{-3} \text{ mol N}$$

$$0.252 \text{ g O} \times \frac{1 \text{ mol O}}{16.00 \text{ g O}} = 1.58 \times 10^{-2} \text{ mol O}$$

$$\frac{2.62 \times 10^{-3} \text{ mol Mn}}{2.62 \times 10^{-3}} : \frac{5.3 \times 10^{-3} \text{ mol N}}{2.62 \times 10^{-3}} : \frac{1.58 \times 10^{-2} \text{ mol O}}{2.62 \times 10^{-3}} =$$

$$1.00 \text{ mol Mn} : 2.0 \text{ mol N} : 6.0 \text{ mol O} \rightarrow MnN_2O_6 = Mn(NO_3)_2$$

c. Given: 0.691 g Mg;
1.824 g S;
1.365 g O

Unknown: empirical formula of compound

$$0.691 \text{ g Mg} \times \frac{1 \text{ mol Mg}}{24.31 \text{ g Mg}} = 0.0284 \text{ mol Mg}$$

$$1.824 \text{ g S} \times \frac{1 \text{ mol S}}{32.07 \text{ g S}} = 0.05688 \text{ mol S}$$

$$1.365 \text{ g O} \times \frac{1 \text{ mol O}}{16.00 \text{ g O}} = 0.08531 \text{ mol O}$$

$$\frac{0.0284 \text{ mol Mg}}{0.0284} : \frac{0.05688 \text{ mol S}}{0.0284} : \frac{0.08531 \text{ mol O}}{0.0284} = 1.00 \text{ mol Mg} :$$

$$2.00 \text{ mol S} : 3.00 \text{ mol O} \rightarrow MgS_2O_3$$

d. Given: 14.77 g K;
9.06 g O;
2.42 g Sn

Unknown: empirical formula of compound

$$14.77 \text{ g K} \times \frac{1 \text{ mol K}}{39.10 \text{ g K}} = 0.3777 \text{ mol K}$$

$$9.06 \text{ g O} \times \frac{1 \text{ mol O}}{16.00 \text{ g O}} = 0.566 \text{ mol O}$$

$$22.42 \text{ g Sn} \times \frac{1 \text{ mol Sn}}{118.71 \text{ g Sn}} = 0.1889 \text{ mol Sn}$$

$$\frac{0.3777 \text{ mol K}}{0.3777} : \frac{0.566 \text{ mol O}}{0.3777} : \frac{0.1889 \text{ mol Sn}}{0.3777} = 1.000 \text{ mol K} : 1.50 \text{ mol O} :$$

$$0.5001 \text{ mol Sn}$$

$$2(1.0 \text{ mol K} : 1.5 \text{ mol O} : 0.5 \text{ mol Sn}) = 2 \text{ mol K} : 3 \text{ mol O} : 1 \text{ mol Sn}$$
$$\rightarrow K_2O_3Sn = K_2SnO_3$$

156. a. Given: 60.9% As; 39.1% S

Unknown: empirical formula of compound

100.0 g of compound contains 60.9 g As and 39.1 g S.

$$60.9 \text{ g As} \times \frac{1 \text{ mol As}}{74.92 \text{ g As}} = 0.813 \text{ mol As}$$

$$39.1 \text{ g S} \times \frac{1 \text{ mol S}}{32.07 \text{ g S}} = 1.22 \text{ mol S}$$

$$\frac{0.813 \text{ mol As}}{0.813} : \frac{1.22 \text{ mol S}}{0.813} = 1.00 \text{ mol As: } 1.50 \text{ mol S}$$

$$2(1.00 \text{ mol As : } 1.50 \text{ mol S}) = 2 \text{ mol As : } 3 \text{ mol S} \rightarrow As_2S_3$$

b. Given: 76.89% Re; 23.12% O

Unknown: empirical formula of compound

100.00 g of compound contains 76.89 g Re and 23.12 g O.

$$76.89 \text{ g Re} \times \frac{1 \text{ mol Re}}{186.21 \text{ g Re}} = 0.4129 \text{ mol Re}$$

$$23.12 \text{ g O} \times \frac{1 \text{ mol O}}{16.00 \text{ g O}} = 1.445 \text{ mol O}$$

$$\frac{0.4129 \text{ mol Re}}{0.4129} : \frac{1.445 \text{ mol O}}{0.4129} = 1.000 \text{ mol Re : } 3.500 \text{ mol O}$$

$$2(1.0 \text{ mol Re : } 3.5 \text{ mol O}) = 2 \text{ mol Re : } 7 \text{ mol O} \rightarrow Re_2O_7$$

c. Given: 5.04% H; 35.00% N; 59.96% O

Unknown: empirical formula of compound

100.00 g of compound contains 5.04 g H, 35.00 g N, and 59.96 g O

$$5.04 \text{ g H} \times \frac{1 \text{ mol H}}{1.01 \text{ g H}} = 4.99 \text{ mol H}$$

$$35.00 \text{ g N} \times 1 \frac{\text{mol N}}{14.01 \text{ g N}} = 2.498 \text{ mol N}$$

$$59.96 \text{ g O} = \frac{1 \text{ mol O}}{16.00 \text{ g O}} = 3.748 \text{ mol O}$$

$$\frac{4.99 \text{ mol H}}{2.498} : \frac{2.498 \text{ mol N}}{2.498} : \frac{3.748 \text{ mol O}}{2.498} = 2.00 \text{ mol H : } 1.000 \text{ mol N : }$$

1.500 mol O

$$2(2.0 \text{ mol H : } 1.0 \text{ mol N : } 1.5 \text{ mol O}) = 4 \text{ mol H : } 2 \text{ mol N : } 3 \text{ mol O}$$
$$\rightarrow H_4N_2O_3 = NH_4NO_3$$

d. Given: 24.3% Fe; 33.9% Cr; 41.8% O

Unknown: empirical formula of compound

100.0 g of compound contains 24.3 g Fe, 33.9 g Cr and 41.8 g O

$$24.3 \text{ g Fe} \times \frac{1 \text{ mol Fe}}{55.85 \text{ g Fe}} = 0.435 \text{ mol Fe}$$

$$33.9 \text{ g Cr} \times \frac{1 \text{ mol Cr}}{52.00 \text{ g Cr}} = 0.652 \text{ mol Cr}$$

$$41.8 \text{ g O} \times \frac{1 \text{ mol O}}{16.00 \text{ g O}} = 2.61 \text{ mol O}$$

$$\frac{0.435 \text{ mol Fe}}{0.435} : \frac{0.652 \text{ mol Cr}}{0.435} : \frac{2.61 \text{ mol O}}{0.435} = 1.00 \text{ mol Fe : } 1.50 \text{ mol Cr : }$$

6.00 mol O

$$2(1.0 \text{ mol Fe : } 1.5 \text{ mol Cr : } 6.0 \text{ mol O}) = 2 \text{ mol Fe : } 3 \text{ mol Cr : } 12 \text{ mol O}$$
$$\rightarrow Fe_2Cr_3O_{12} = Fe_2(CrO_4)_3$$

e. Given: 54.03% C;
37.81% N;
8.16% H

Unknown: empirical formula of compound

100.00 g of compound contains 54.03 g C, 37.81 g N, and 8.16 g H.

$$54.03 \text{ g C} \times \frac{1 \text{ mol C}}{12.01 \text{ g C}} = 4.499 \text{ mol C}$$

$$37.81 \text{ g N} \times \frac{1 \text{ mol N}}{14.01 \text{ g N}} = 2.699 \text{ mol N}$$

$$8.16 \text{ g H} \times \frac{1 \text{ mol H}}{1.01 \text{ g H}} = 8.08 \text{ mol H}$$

$$\frac{4.499 \text{ mol C}}{2.699} : \frac{2.699 \text{ mol N}}{2.699} : \frac{8.08 \text{ mol H}}{2.699} = 1.67 \text{ mol C} : 1.00 \text{ mol N} :$$

$$2.99 \text{ mol H}$$

$$3(1.67 \text{ mol C} : 1.00 \text{ mol N} : 2.99 \text{ mol H}) = 5 \text{ mol C} : 3 \text{ mol N} : 9 \text{ mol H}$$
$$\rightarrow C_5N_3H_9 = C_5H_9N_3$$

f. Given: 55.81% C;
3.90% H;
29.43% F;
10.85% N

Unknown: empirical formula of compound

100.00 g of compound contains 55.81 g C, 3.90 g H, 29.43 g F, and 10.85 g N.

$$55.81 \text{ g C} \times \frac{1 \text{ mol C}}{12.01 \text{ g C}} = 4.647 \text{ mol C}$$

$$3.90 \text{ g H} \times \frac{1 \text{ mol H}}{1.01 \text{ g H}} = 3.86 \text{ mol H}$$

$$29.43 \text{ g F} \times \frac{1 \text{ mol F}}{19.00 \text{ g F}} = 1.549 \text{ mol F}$$

$$10.85 \text{ g N} \times \frac{1 \text{ mol N}}{14.01 \text{ g N}} = 0.7744 \text{ mol N}$$

$$\frac{4.647 \text{ mol C}}{0.7744} : \frac{3.86 \text{ mol H}}{0.7744} : \frac{1.549 \text{ mol F}}{0.7744} : \frac{0.7744 \text{ mol N}}{0.7744} = 6.000 \text{ mol C} :$$

$$4.98 \text{ mol H} ; 2.000 \text{ mol F} : 1.000 \text{ mol N} \rightarrow C_6H_5F_2N = C_6H_3F_2NH_2$$

157. a. Given: empirical formula: C_2H_4S; molar mass = 179

Unknown: molecular formula of compound

$$\text{molar mass } C_2H_4S = 2 \text{ mol C} \times \frac{12.01 \text{ g C}}{1 \text{ mol C}} + 4 \text{ mol H} \times \frac{1.01 \text{ g H}}{1 \text{ mol H}}$$

$$+ 1 \text{ mol S} \times \frac{32.07 \text{ g S}}{1 \text{ mol S}} = 60.13 \text{ g}$$

$$x = \frac{179 \text{ g}}{60.13 \text{ g}} = 2.98 \cong 3; \; C_{2x}H_{4x}S_x = C_6H_{12}S_3$$

b. Given: empirical formula: C_2H_4O; molar mass = 176

Unknown: molecular formula of compound

$$\text{molar mass } C_2H_4O = 2 \text{ mol C} \times \frac{12.01 \text{ g C}}{1 \text{ mol C}} + 4 \text{ mol H} \times \frac{1.01 \text{ g H}}{1 \text{ mol H}}$$

$$+ 1 \text{ mol O} \times \frac{16.00 \text{ g O}}{1 \text{ mol O}} = 44.06 \text{ g}$$

$$x = \frac{176 \text{ g}}{44.06 \text{ g}} = 3.99 \cong 4; \; C_{2x}H_{4x}O_x = C_8H_{16}O_4$$

c. Given: empirical formula: $C_2H_3O_2$; molar mass = 119

Unknown: molecular formula of compound

$$\text{molar mass } C_2H_3O_2 = 2 \text{ mol C} \times \frac{12.01 \text{ g C}}{1 \text{ mol C}} + 3 \text{ mol H} \times \frac{1.01 \text{ g H}}{1 \text{ mol H}}$$

$$+ 2 \text{ mol O} \times \frac{16.00 \text{ g O}}{1 \text{ mol O}} = 59.058$$

$$x = \frac{119 \text{ g}}{59.05 \text{ g}} = 2.02 \cong 2; \; C_{2x}H_{3x}O_{2x} = C_4H_6O_4$$

d. Given: empirical formula: C_2H_2O; molar mass = 254

Unknown: molecular formula of compound

$$\text{molar mass } C_2H_2O = 2 \text{ mol } C \times \frac{12.01 \text{ g C}}{1 \text{ mol C}} + 2 \text{ mol H} \times \frac{1.01 \text{ g H}}{1 \text{ mol H}}$$

$$+ 1 \text{ mol O} \times \frac{16.00 \text{ g O}}{1 \text{ mol O}} = 42.04 \text{ g}$$

$$x = \frac{254 \text{ g}}{42.04 \text{ g}} = 6.04 \cong 6; \ C_{2x}H_{2x}O_x = C_{12}H_{12}O_6$$

---

158. a. Given: percent composition; molar mass = 116.07

Unknown: molecular formula of compound

100.00 g of compound contains 41.39 g C, 3.47 g H, and 55.14 g O.

$$41.39 \text{ g C} \times \frac{1 \text{ mol C}}{12.01 \text{ g C}} = 3.446 \text{ mol C}$$

$$3.47 \text{ g H} \times \frac{1 \text{ mol H}}{1.01 \text{ g H}} = 3.44 \text{ mol H}$$

$$55.14 \text{ g O} \times \frac{1 \text{ mol O}}{16.00 \text{ g O}} = 3.446 \text{ mol O}$$

$$\frac{3.446 \text{ mol C}}{3.44} : \frac{3.44 \text{ mol H}}{3.44} : \frac{3.446 \text{ mol O}}{3.44} = 1.00 \text{ mol C} : 1.00 \text{ mol H}: 1.00 \text{ mol}$$

empirical formula = CHO

$$\text{molar mass CHO} = 1 \text{ mol C} \times \frac{12.01 \text{ g C}}{1 \text{ mol C}} + 1 \text{ mol H} \times \frac{1.01 \text{ g H}}{1 \text{ mol H}}$$

$$+ 1 \text{ mol O} \times \frac{16.00 \text{ g O}}{1 \text{ mol O}} = 29.02 \text{ g}$$

$$x = \frac{116.07 \text{ g}}{29.02 \text{ g}} = 4.000; \ C_xH_xO_x = C_4H_4O_4$$

b. Given: percent composition; molar mass = 88

Unknown: molecular formula of compound

100.00 g of compound contains 54.53 g C, 9.15 g H, and 36.32 g O.

$$54.53 \text{ g C} \times \frac{1 \text{ mol C}}{12.01 \text{ g C}} = 4.540 \text{ mol C}$$

$$9.15 \text{ g H} \times \frac{1 \text{ mol H}}{1.01 \text{ g H}} = 9.06 \text{ mol H}$$

$$36.32 \text{ g O} \times \frac{1 \text{ mol O}}{16.00 \text{ g O}} = 2.270 \text{ mol O}$$

$$\frac{4.540 \text{ mol C}}{2.270} : \frac{2.06 \text{ mol H}}{2.270} : \frac{2.270 \text{ mol O}}{2.270} = 2.000 \text{ mol C}: 3.99 \text{ mol H} :$$

$$1.000 \text{ mol O}$$

empirical formula = C_2H_4O

$$\text{molar mass } C_2H_4O = 2 \text{ mol C} \times \frac{12.01 \text{ g C}}{1 \text{ mol C}} + 4 \text{ mol H} \times \frac{1.01 \text{ g H}}{1 \text{ mol H}}$$

$$+ 1 \text{ mol O} \times \frac{16.00 \text{ g O}}{1 \text{ mol O}} = 44.06 \text{ g}$$

$$x = \frac{88 \text{ g}}{44.06 \text{ g}} = 2.0; \ C_{2x}H_{4x}O_x = C_4H_8O_2$$

c. Given: percent composition; molar mass = 168.19

Unknown: molecular formula of compound

100.00 g of compound contains 64.27 g C; 7.19 g H, and 28.54 g O.

$$64.27 \text{ g C} \times \frac{1 \text{ mol C}}{12.01 \text{ g C}} = 5.351 \text{ mol C}$$

$$7.19 \text{ g H} \times \frac{1 \text{ mol H}}{1.01 \text{ g H}} = 7.12 \text{ mol H}$$

$$28.54 \text{ g O} \times \frac{1 \text{ mol O}}{16.00 \text{ g O}} = 1.784 \text{ mol O}$$

$$\frac{5.351 \text{ mol C}}{1.784} : \frac{7.12 \text{ mol H}}{1.784} : \frac{1.784 \text{ mol O}}{1.784} = 2.999 \text{ mol C} : 3.99 \text{ mol H} :$$

1.000 mol O

empirical formula = C_3H_4O

$$\text{molar mass } C_3H_4O = 3 \text{ mol C} \times \frac{12.01 \text{ g C}}{1 \text{ mol C}} + 4 \text{ mol H} \times \frac{1.01 \text{ g H}}{1 \text{ mol H}}$$

$$+ 1 \text{ mol O} \times \frac{16.00 \text{ g O}}{1 \text{ mol O}} = 56.07 \text{ g}$$

$$x = \frac{168.19 \text{ g}}{56.07 \text{ g}} = 3.000; \ C_{3x}H_{4x}O_x = C_9H_{12}O_3$$

---

159. Given: 0.141 g K; 0.115 g S; 0.144 g O

Unknown: empirical formula of compound

$$0.141 \text{ g K} \times \frac{1 \text{ mol K}}{39.10 \text{ g K}} = 3.61 \times 10^{-3} \text{ mol K}$$

$$0.115 \text{ g S} \times \frac{1 \text{ mol S}}{32.07 \text{ g S}} = 3.59 \times 10^{-3} \text{ mol S}$$

$$0.144 \text{ g O} \times \frac{1 \text{ mol O}}{16.00 \text{ g O}} = 9.00 \times 10^{-3} \text{ mol O}$$

$$\frac{3.61 \times 10^{-3} \text{ mol K}}{3.59 \times 10^{-3}} : \frac{3.59 \times 10^{-3} \text{ mol S}}{3.59 \times 10^{-3}} : \frac{9.00 \times 10^{-3} \text{ mol O}}{3.59 \times 10^{-3}}$$

= 1.01 mol K : 1.00 mol S : 2.51 mol O

2(1.01 mol K : 1.00 mol S : 2.51 mol O) = 2 mol K : 2 mol S : 5 mol O
→ $K_2S_2O_5$

---

160. a. Given: 9.65 g Pb; 0.99 g O

Unknown: empirical formula of compound

$$9.65 \text{ g Pb} \times \frac{1 \text{ mol Pb}}{207.2 \text{ g Pb}} = 0.0466 \text{ mol Pb}$$

$$0.99 \text{ g O} \times \frac{1 \text{ mol O}}{16.00 \text{ g O}} = 0.062 \text{ mol O}$$

$$\frac{0.466 \text{ mol Pb}}{0.0466} : \frac{0.062 \text{ mol O}}{0.0466} = 1.0 \text{ mol Pb} : 1.3 \text{ mol O}$$

3 (1.0 mol Pb : 1.3 mol 0) = 3 mol Pb : 4 mol O → Pb_3O_4

161. Given: 0.70 g Cr; 0.65 g S; 1.30 g O; molar mass = 392.2

Unknown: molecular formula of compound

$$0.70 \text{ g Cr} \times \frac{1 \text{ mol Cr}}{52.00 \text{ g Cr}} = 0.013 \text{ mol Cr}$$

$$0.65 \text{ g S} \times \frac{1 \text{ mol S}}{32.07 \text{ g S}} = 0.0203 \text{ mol S}$$

$$1.30 \text{ g O} \times \frac{1 \text{ mol O}}{16.00 \text{ g O}} = 0.812 \text{ mol O}$$

$$\frac{0.0135 \text{ mol Cr}}{0.0135} : \frac{0.0203 \text{ mol S}}{0.0135} : \frac{0.0812 \text{ mol O}}{0.0135} = 1.0 \text{ mol Cr} : 1.5 \text{ mol S} :$$

6.0 mol O

$$2(1.0 \text{ mol Cr} : 1.5 \text{ mol S} : 6.0 \text{ mol O}) = 2 \text{ mol Cr} : 3 \text{ mol S} : 12 \text{ mol O}$$
$$\rightarrow Cr_2S_3O_{12} = Cr_2(SO_4)_3$$

---

162. Given: 60.68% C; 3.40% H; 35.92% O

Unknown: empirical formula of compound

100.00 compound contain 60.68 g C, 3.40 g H, and 35.92 g O

$$60.68 \text{ g C} \times \frac{1 \text{ mol C}}{12.01 \text{ g C}} = 5.052 \text{ mol C}$$

$$3.40 \text{ g H} \times \frac{1 \text{ mol H}}{1.01 \text{ g H}} = 3.37 \text{ mol H}$$

$$35.92 \text{ g O} \times \frac{1 \text{ mol O}}{16.00 \text{ g O}} = 2.245 \text{ mol O}$$

$$\frac{5.052 \text{ mol C}}{2.245} : \frac{3.37 \text{ mol H}}{2.245} : \frac{2.245 \text{ mol O}}{2.245} = 2.25 \text{ mol C} : 1.50 \text{ mol H} : 1.00 \text{ mol O}$$

$$4(2.25 \text{ mol C} : 1.50 \text{ mol H} : 1.00 \text{ mol O}) = 9 \text{ mol C} : 6 \text{ mol H} : 4 \text{ mol O}$$
$$\rightarrow C_9H_6O_4$$

---

163. Given: 208 mg C; 31 mg H; 146 mg N; molar mass = 111

Unknown: molecular formula of compound

$$208 \text{ mg C} \times \frac{1 \text{ mol C}}{12.01 \text{ g C}} \times \frac{1 \text{ g}}{1000 \text{ mg}} = 0.0173 \text{ mol C}$$

$$31 \text{ mg H} \times \frac{1 \text{ mol H}}{1.01 \text{ g H}} \times \frac{1 \text{ g}}{1000 \text{ mg}} = 0.031 \text{ mol H}$$

$$146 \text{ mg N} \times \frac{1 \text{ mol N}}{14.01 \text{ g N}} \times \frac{1 \text{ g}}{1000 \text{ mg}} = 0.0104 \text{ mol N}$$

$$\frac{0.0173 \text{ mol C}}{0.0104} : \frac{0.031 \text{ mol H}}{0.0104} : \frac{0.0104 \text{ mol N}}{0.0104} = 1.66 \text{ mol C} : 3.00 \text{ mol H} :$$

1.00 mol N

$$3(1.66 \text{ mol C} : 3.00 \text{ mol H} : 1.00 \text{ mol N}) = 5 \text{ mol C} : 9 \text{ mol H} : 3 \text{ mol N}$$

empirical formula = $C_5H_9N_3$

$$\text{molar mass } C_5H_9N_3 = 5 \text{ mol C} \times \frac{12.01 \text{ g C}}{1 \text{ mol C}} + 9 \text{ mol H} \times \frac{1.01 \text{ g H}}{1 \text{ mol H}}$$

$$+ 3 \text{ mol N} \times \frac{14.01 \text{ g N}}{1 \text{ mol N}} = 111.17 \text{ g}$$

$$\frac{111 \text{ g}}{111.17 \text{ g}} = 0.998 \cong 1$$

molecular formula = $C_5H_9N_3$

165. Given: balanced equation; 4.0 mol H_2

Unknown: moles Na

$$4.0 \text{ mol } H_2 \times \frac{2 \text{ mol Na}}{1 \text{ mol } H_2} = 8.0 \text{ mol Na}$$

166. Given: balanced equation; 0.046 mol LiBr

Unknown: moles LiCl

$$0.046 \text{ mol LiBr} \times \frac{2 \text{ mol LiCl}}{2 \text{ mol LiBr}} = 0.046 \text{ mol LiCl}$$

167. a. Given: balanced equation; 18 mol Al

Unknown: moles H_2SO_4

$$18 \text{ mol Al} \times \frac{3 \text{ mol } H_2SO_4}{2 \text{ mol Al}} = 27 \text{ mol } H_2SO_4$$

b. Given: balanced equation; 18 mol Al

Unknown: moles of each product

$$18 \text{ mol Al} \times \frac{1 \text{ mol } Al_2(SO_4)_3}{2 \text{ mol Al}} = 9 \text{ mol } Al_2(SO_4)_3$$

$$18 \text{ mol Al} \times \frac{3 \text{ mol } H_2}{2 \text{ mol Al}} = 27 \text{ mol } H_2$$

168. a. Given: balanced equation; 3.85 mol C_3H_8

Unknown: moles of CO_2 and H_2O

$$3.85 \text{ mol } C_3H_8 \times \frac{3 \text{ mol } CO_2}{1 \text{ mol } C_3H_8} = 11.6 \text{ mol } CO_2$$

$$3.85 \text{ mol } C_3H_8 \times \frac{4 \text{ mol } H_2O}{1 \text{ mol } C_3H_8} = 15.4 \text{ mol } H_2O$$

b. Given: balanced equation; 0.647 mol O_2

Unknown: moles of CO_2, H_2O, and C_3H_8

$$0.647 \text{ mol } O_2 \times \frac{3 \text{ mol } CO_2}{5 \text{ mol } O_2} = 0.388 \text{ mol } CO_2$$

$$0.647 \text{ mol } O_2 \times \frac{4 \text{ mol } H_2O}{5 \text{ mol } O_2} = 0.518 \text{ mol } H_2O$$

$$0.647 \text{ mol } O_2 \times \frac{1 \text{ mol } C_3H_8}{5 \text{ mol } O_2} = 0.129 \text{ mol } C_3H_8$$

169. a. Given: balanced equation; 3.25 mol P_4O_{10}

Unknown: mass of P

$$3.25 \text{ mol } P_4O_{10} \times \frac{4 \text{ mol P}}{1 \text{ mol } P_4O_{10}} \times \frac{30.97 \text{ g P}}{1 \text{ mol P}} = 403 \text{ g P}$$

b. Given: balanced equation; 0.489 mol P

Unknown: mass of O_2 and P_4O_{10}

$$0.489 \text{ mol P} \times \frac{5 \text{ mol } O_2}{4 \text{ mol P}} \times \frac{32.00 \text{ g } O_2}{1 \text{ mol } O_2} = 19.6 \text{ g } O_2$$

$$0.489 \text{ mol P} \times \frac{1 \text{ mol } P_4O_{10}}{4 \text{ mol P}} \times \frac{283.88 \text{ g } P_4O_{10}}{1 \text{ mol } P_4O_{10}} = 34.7 \text{ g } P_4O_{10}$$

170. a. Given: balanced equation; 1.840 mol H_2O_2

Unknown: mass of O_2

$$1.840 \text{ mol } H_2O_2 \times \frac{1 \text{ mol } O_2}{2 \text{ mol } H_2O_2} \times \frac{32.00 \text{ g } O_2}{1 \text{ mol } O_2} = 29.44 \text{ g } O_2$$

b. Given: balanced equation; 5.0 mol O_2

Unknown: mass of water

$$5.0 \text{ mol } O_2 \times \frac{2 \text{ mol } H_2O}{1 \text{ mol } O_2} \times \frac{18.02 \text{ g } H_2O}{1 \text{ mol } H_2O} = 180 \text{ g } H_2O$$

171. a. Given: balanced equation; 100.0 g $NaNO_3$

Unknown: moles of Na_2CO_3

$$100.0 \text{ g } NaNO_3 \times \frac{1 \text{ mol } NaNO_3}{85.01 \text{ g } NaNO_3} \times \frac{1 \text{ mol } Na_2CO_3}{2 \text{ mol } NaNO_3} = 0.5882 \text{ mol } Na_2CO_3$$

b. Given: balanced equation; 7.50 g Na_2CO_3

Unknown: moles of CO_2

$$7.50 \text{ g } Na_2CO_3 \times \frac{1 \text{ mol } Na_2CO_3}{105.99 \text{ g } Na_2CO_3} \times \frac{1 \text{ mol } CO_2}{1 \text{ mol } Na_2CO_3} = 0.0708 \text{ mol } CO_2$$

172. a. Given: balanced equation; 625 g Fe_3O_4

Unknown: moles of H_2

$$625 \text{ g } Fe_3O_4 \times \frac{1 \text{ mol } Fe_3O_4}{231.55 \text{ g } Fe_3O_4} \times \frac{4 \text{ mol } H_2}{1 \text{ mol } Fe_3O_4} = 10.8 \text{ mol } H_2$$

b. Given: balanced equation; 27 g H_2

Unknown: moles of Fe

$$27 \text{ g } H_2 \times \frac{1 \text{ mol } H_2}{2.02 \text{ g } H_2} \times \frac{3 \text{ mol Fe}}{4 \text{ mol } H_2} = 10. \text{ mol Fe}$$

173. a. Given: balanced equation; 22.5 g $AgNO_3$

Unknown: mass of AgBr

$$22.5 \text{ g } AgNO_3 \times \frac{1 \text{ mol } AgNO_3}{169.88 \text{ g } AgNO_3} \times \frac{2 \text{ mol AgBr}}{2 \text{ mol } AgNO_3} \times \frac{187.77 \text{ g AgBr}}{1 \text{ mol AgBr}}$$
$$= 24.9 \text{ g AgBr}$$

174. a. Given: balanced equation; 90. g CaC_2

Unknown: mass C_2H_2

$$90. \text{ g } CaC_2 \times \frac{1 \text{ mol } CaC_2}{64.10 \text{ g } CaC_2} \times \frac{1 \text{ mol } C_2H_2}{1 \text{ mol } CaC_2} \times \frac{26.04 \text{ g } C_2H_2}{1 \text{ mol } C_2H_2} = 37 \text{ g } C_2H_2$$

175. a. Given: balanced equation; 25.0 g Cl_2

Unknown: mass MnO_2

$$25.0 \text{ g } Cl_2 \times \frac{1 \text{ mol } Cl_2}{70.90 \text{ g } Cl_2} \times \frac{1 \text{ mol } MnO_2}{1 \text{ mol } Cl_2} \times \frac{86.94 \text{ g } MnO_2}{1 \text{ mol } MnO_2} = 30.7 \text{ g } MnO_2$$

b. Given: balanced equation; 0.091 g Cl_2

Unknown: mass $MnCl_2$

$$0.091 \text{ g } Cl_2 \times \frac{1 \text{ mol } Cl_2}{70.90 \text{ g } Cl_2} \times \frac{1 \text{ mol } MnCl_2}{1 \text{ mol } Cl_2} \times \frac{125.84 \text{ g } MnCl_2}{1 \text{ mol } MnCl_2} = 0.16 \text{ g } MnCl_2$$

176. Given: balanced equation; 30.0 mol NH_3

Unknown: moles $(NH_4)_2SO_4$

$$30.0 \text{ mol } NH_3 \times \frac{1 \text{ mol } (NH_4)_2SO_4}{2 \text{ mol } NH_3} = 15.0 \text{ mol } (NH_4)_2SO_4$$

177. a. Given: balanced equation; 150 g Fe_2O_3

Unknown: mass Al

$$150 \text{ g } Fe_2O_3 \times \frac{1 \text{ mol } Fe_2O_3}{159.70 \text{ g } Fe_2O_3} \times \frac{2 \text{ mol } Al}{1 \text{ mol } Fe_2O_3} \times \frac{26.98 \text{ g } Al}{1 \text{ mol } Al} = 51 \text{ g } Al$$

b. Given: balanced equation; 0.905 mol Al_2O_3

Unknown: mass Fe

$$0.905 \text{ mol } Al_2O_3 \times \frac{2 \text{ mol } Fe}{1 \text{ mol } Al_2O_3} \times \frac{55.85 \text{ g } Fe}{1 \text{ mol } Fe} = 101 \text{ g } Fe$$

c. Given: balanced equation; 99.0 g Al

Unknown: moles Fe_2O_3

$$99.0 \text{ g } Al \times \frac{1 \text{ mol } Al}{26.98 \text{ g } Al} \times \frac{1 \text{ mol } Fe_2O_3}{2 \text{ mol } Al} = 1.83 \text{ mol } Fe_2O_3$$

178. Given: 1.40 g N_2; balanced equation

Unknown: mass H_2

$$1.40 \text{ g } N_2 \times \frac{1 \text{ mol } N_2}{28.02 \text{ g } N_2} \times \frac{3 \text{ mol } H_2}{1 \text{ mol } N_2} \times \frac{2.02 \text{ g } H_2}{1 \text{ mol } H_2} = 0.303 \text{ g } H_2$$

179. Given: 1.27 g KOH

Unknown: mass of H_2SO_4

$$2KOH + H_2SO_4 \rightarrow K_2SO_4 + 2H_2O$$

$$1.27 \text{ g } KOH \times \frac{1 \text{ mol } KOH}{56.11 \text{ g } KOH} \times \frac{1 \text{ mol } H_2SO_4}{2 \text{ mol } KOH} \times \frac{98.09 \text{ g } H_2SO_4}{1 \text{ mol } H_2SO_4}$$

$$= 1.11 \text{ g } H_2SO_4$$

180. a. Given: reactants and products

Unknown: balanced equation

$$H_3PO_4 + 2NH_3 \rightarrow (NH_4)_2HPO_4$$

b. Given: 10.00 g NH_3

Unknown: moles $(NH_4)_2HPO_4$

$$10.00 \text{ g } NH_3 \times \frac{1 \text{ mol } NH_3}{17.04 \text{ g } NH_3} \times \frac{1 \text{ mol } (NH_4)_2HPO_4}{2 \text{ mol } NH_3} = 0.293 \text{ mol } (NH_4)_2HPO_4$$

c. Given: 2800 kg H_3PO_4

Unknown: mass NH_3

$$2800 \text{ kg } H_3PO_4 \times \frac{1 \text{ mol } H_3PO_4}{98.00 \text{ g } H_3PO_4} \times \frac{2 \text{ mol } NH_3}{1 \text{ mol } H_3PO_4} \times \frac{17.04 \text{ g } NH_3}{1 \text{ mol } NH_3}$$

$$= 970 \text{ kg } NH_3$$

181. a. Given: balanced equation; 30.0 mol $Zn_3(C_6H_5O_7)_2$

Unknown: moles $ZnCO_3$ and $C_6H_8O_7$

$$30.0 \text{ mol } Zn_3(C_6H_5O_7)_2 \times \frac{3 \text{ mol } ZnCO_3}{1 \text{ mol } Zn_3(C_6H_5O_7)_2} = 90.0 \text{ mol } ZnCO_3$$

$$30.0 \text{ mol } Zn_3(C_6H_5O_7)_2 \times \frac{2 \text{ mol } C_6H_8O_7}{1 \text{ mol } Zn_3(C_6H_5O_7)_2} = 60.0 \text{ mol } C_6H_8O_7$$

b. Given: balanced equation; 500. mol $C_6H_8O_7$

Unknown: mass in kg of H_2O and CO_2

$$500. \text{ mol } C_6H_8O_7 \times \frac{3 \text{ mol } H_2O}{2 \text{ mol } C_6H_8O_7} \times \frac{18.02 \text{ g } H_2O}{1 \text{ mol } H_2O} \times \frac{1 \text{ kg}}{1000 \text{ g}} = 13.5 \text{ kg } H_2O$$

$$500. \text{ mol } C_6H_8O_7 \times \frac{3 \text{ mol } CO_2}{2 \text{ mol } C_6H_8O_7} \times \frac{44.01 \text{ g } CO_2}{1 \text{ mol } CO_2} \times \frac{1 \text{ kg}}{1000 \text{ g}} = 33.0 \text{ kg } CO_2$$

182. a. Given: balanced equation; 52.5 g C_3H_7COOH

Unknown: mass $C_3H_7COOCH_3$

$$52.5 \text{ g } C_3H_7COOH \times \frac{1 \text{ mol } C_3H_7COOH}{88.12 \text{ g } C_3H_7COOH} \times \frac{1 \text{ mol } C_3H_7COOCH_3}{1 \text{ mol } C_3H_7COOH}$$

$$\times \frac{102.15 \text{ g } C_3H_7COOCH_3}{1 \text{ mol } C_3H_7COOCH_3} = 60.9 \text{ g } C_3H_7COOCH_3$$

b. Given: balanced equation; 5800. g CH_3OH

Unknown: mass H_2O

$$5800. \text{ g } CH_3OH \times \frac{1 \text{ mol } CH_3OH}{32.05 \text{ g } CH_3OH} \times \frac{1 \text{ mol } H_2O}{1 \text{ mol } CH_3OH} \times \frac{18.02 \text{ g } H_2O}{1 \text{ mol } H_2O} = 3261 \text{ g } H_2O$$

183. a. Given: balanced equation; 36.0 g NH_4NO_3

Unknown: moles N_2

$$36.0 \text{ g } NH_4NO_3 \times \frac{1 \text{ mol } NH_4NO_3}{80.06 \text{ g } NH_4NO_3} \times \frac{2 \text{ mol } N_2}{2 \text{ mol } NH_4NO_3} = 0.450 \text{ mol } N_2$$

b. Given: balanced equation; 7.35 mol H_2O

Unknown: mass NH_4NO_3

$$7.35 \text{ mol } H_2O \times \frac{2 \text{ mol } NH_4NO_3}{4 \text{ mol } H_2O} \times \frac{80.06 \text{ g } NH_4NO_3}{1 \text{ mol } NH_4NO_3} = 294 \text{ g } NH_4NO_3$$

184. Given: 1.23 mg $Pb(NO_3)_2$

Unknown: mass KNO_3

$$Pb(NO_3)_2 + 2KI \rightarrow PbI_2 + 2KNO_3$$

$$1.23 \text{ mg } Pb(NO_3)_2 \times \frac{1 \text{ mol } Pb(NO_3)_2}{331.22 \text{ g } Pb(NO_3)_2} \times \frac{2 \text{ mol } KNO_3}{1 \text{ mol } Pb(NO_3)_2}$$

$$\times \frac{101.11 \text{ g } KNO_3}{1 \text{ mol } KNO_3} = 0.751 \text{ mg } KNO_3$$

185. Given: balanced equation; 0.34 kg Pb

Unknown: moles $PbSO_4$

$$0.34 \text{ kg Pb} \times \frac{1000 \text{ g}}{1 \text{ kg}} \times \frac{1 \text{ mol Pb}}{207.2 \text{ g Pb}} \times \frac{2 \text{ mol } PbSO_4}{1 \text{ mol Pb}} = 3.3 \text{ mol } PbSO_4$$

186. Given: 20.0 mol CO_2
Unknown: mass H_2O

$CO_2 + 2LiOH \rightarrow H_2O + Li_2CO_3$

$20.0 \text{ mol } CO_2 \times \dfrac{1 \text{ mol } H_2O}{1 \text{ mol } CO_2} \times \dfrac{18.02 \text{ g } H_2O}{1 \text{ mol } H_2O} = 360. \text{ g } H_2O$

---

187. a. Given: balanced equation; 1.00×10^2 g P_4O_{10}
Unknown: mass H_2O

$1.00 \times 10^2 \text{ g } P_4O_{10} \times \dfrac{1 \text{ mol } P_4O_{10}}{283.88 \text{ g } P_4O_{10}} \times \dfrac{6 \text{ mol } H_2O}{1 \text{ mol } P_4O_{10}} \times \dfrac{18.02 \text{ g } H_2O}{1 \text{ mol } H_2O}$

$= 38.1 \text{ g } H_2O$

b. Given: balanced equation; 0.614 mol H_2O
Unknown: mass H_3PO_4

$0.614 \text{ mol } H_2O \times \dfrac{4 \text{ mol } H_3PO_4}{6 \text{ mol } H_2O} \times \dfrac{98.00 \text{ g } H_3PO_4}{1 \text{ mol } H_3PO_4} = 40.1 \text{ g } H_3PO_4$

c. Given: mass of H_2O
Unknown: moles H_2O

$(63.70 \text{ g} - 56.64 \text{ g}) \, H_2O \times \dfrac{1 \text{ mol } H_2O}{18.02 \text{ g } H_2O} = 0.392 \text{ mol } H_2O$

---

188. Given: 95.0 g H_2O
Unknown: mass C_2H_5OH

$C_2H_5OH + 3O_2 \rightarrow 2CO_2 + 3H_2O$

$95.0 \text{ g } H_2O \times \dfrac{1 \text{ mol } H_2O}{18.02 \text{ g } H_2O} \times \dfrac{1 \text{ mol } C_2H_5OH}{3 \text{ mol } H_2O} \times \dfrac{46.08 \text{ g } C_2H_5OH}{1 \text{ mol } C_2H_5OH}$

$= 81.0 \text{ g } C_2H_5OH$

---

189. Given: balanced equation; 50.0 g SO_2
Unknown: mass H_2SO_4 and O_2

$50.0 \text{ g } SO_2 \times \dfrac{1 \text{ mol } SO_2}{64.07 \text{ g } SO_2} \times \dfrac{2 \text{ mol } H_2SO_4}{2 \text{ mol } SO_2} \times \dfrac{98.09 \text{ g } H_2SO_4}{1 \text{ mol } H_2SO_4} = 76.5 \text{ g } H_2SO_4$

$50.0 \text{ g } SO_2 \times \dfrac{1 \text{ mol } SO_2}{64.07 \text{ g } SO_2} \times \dfrac{1 \text{ mol } O_2}{2 \text{ mol } SO_2} \times \dfrac{32.00 \text{ g } O_2}{1 \text{ mol } O_2} = 12.5 \text{ g } O_2$

---

190. Given: 5.00 g $NaHCO_3$
Unknown: mass CO_2

$2NaHCO_3 \rightarrow Na_2CO_3 + H_2O + CO_2$

$5.00 \text{ g } NaHCO_3 \times \dfrac{1 \text{ mol } NaHCO_3}{84.01 \text{ g } NaHCO_3} \times \dfrac{1 \text{ mol } CO_2}{2 \text{ mol } NaHCO_3} \times \dfrac{44.01 \text{ g } CO_2}{1 \text{ mol } CO_2}$

$= 1.31 \text{ g } CO_2$

---

191. c. Given: 20 000 mol N_2H_4
Unknown: mol N_2

$20\,000 \text{ mol } N_2H_4 \times \dfrac{3 \text{ mol } N_2}{2 \text{ mol } N_2H_4} = 30\,000 \text{ mol } N_2$

d. Given: 450. kg N_2O_4
Unknown: mass H_2O

$450. \text{ kg } N_2O_4 \times \dfrac{1000 \text{ g}}{1 \text{ kg}} \times \dfrac{1 \text{ mol } N_2O_4}{92.02 \text{ g } N_2O_4} \times \dfrac{4 \text{ mol } H_2O}{1 \text{ mol } N_2O_4} \times \dfrac{18.02 \text{ g } H_2O}{1 \text{ mol } H_2O}$

$= 3.52 \times 10^5 \text{ g } H_2O$

192. Given: 517.84 g HgO
Unknown: mol O_2

$$2HgO \rightarrow 2Hg + O_2$$

$$517.84 \text{ g HgO} \times \frac{1 \text{ mol HgO}}{216.59 \text{ g HgO}} \times \frac{1 \text{ mol } O_2}{2 \text{ mol HgO}} = 1.1954 \text{ mol } O_2$$

193. Given: 58.0 g Cl_2
Unknown: mass Fe

$$2Fe + 3Cl_2 \rightarrow 2FeCl_3$$

$$58.0 \text{ g Cl}_2 \times \frac{1 \text{ mol Cl}_2}{70.90 \text{ g Cl}_2} \times \frac{2 \text{ mol Fe}}{3 \text{ mol Cl}_2} \times \frac{55.85 \text{ g Fe}}{1 \text{ mol Fe}} = 30.5 \text{ g Fe}$$

194. Given: balanced equation; 5.00 mg Na_2S

Unknown: mass CdS in mg

$$5.00 \text{ mg Na}_2S \times \frac{1 \text{ mol Na}_2S}{78.05 \text{ g Na}_2 S} \times \frac{1 \text{ mol CdS}}{1 \text{ mol Na}_2S} \times \frac{144.48 \text{ g CdS}}{1 \text{ mol CdS}} = 9.26 \text{ mg CdS}$$

195. a. Given: balanced equation; 4.44 mol $KMnO_4$

Unknown: mol CO_2

$$4.44 \text{ mol KMnO}_4 \times \frac{5 \text{ mol CO}_2}{14 \text{ mol KMnO}_4} = 1.59 \text{ mol CO}_2$$

b. Given: 5.21 g H_2O
Unknown: mol $C_3H_5(OH)_3$

$$5.21 \text{ g H}_2O \times \frac{1 \text{ mol H}_2O}{18.02 \text{ g H}_2O} \times \frac{4 \text{ mol C}_3H_5(OH)_3}{16 \text{ mol H}_2O} = 0.0723 \text{ mol C}_3H_5(OH)_3$$

c. Given: 3.39 mol K_2CO_3

Unknown: mass Mn_2O_3 in grams

$$3.39 \text{ mol K}_2CO_3 \times \frac{7 \text{ mol Mn}_2O_3}{7 \text{ mol K}_2CO_3} \times \frac{157.88 \text{ g Mn}_2O_3}{1 \text{ mol Mn}_2O_3} = 535 \text{ g Mn}_2O_3$$

d. Given: 50.0 g $KMnO_4$
Unknown: mass $C_3H_5(OH)_3$ and CO_2 in grams

$$50.0 \text{ g KMnO}_4 \times \frac{1 \text{ mol KMnO}_4}{158.04 \text{ g KMnO}_4} \times \frac{4 \text{ mol C}_3H_5(OH)_3}{14 \text{ mol KMnO}_4}$$

$$\times \frac{92.11 \text{ g C}_3H_5(OH)_3}{1 \text{ mol C}_3H_5(OH)_3} = 8.33 \text{ g C}_3H_5(OH)_3$$

$$50.0 \text{ g KMnO}_4 \times \frac{1 \text{ mol KMnO}_4}{158.04 \text{ g KMnO}_4} \times \frac{5 \text{ mol CO}_2}{14 \text{ mol KMnO}_4} \times \frac{44.01 \text{ g CO}_2}{1 \text{ mol CO}_2}$$

$$= 4.97 \text{ g CO}_2$$

196. a. Given: balanced equation; 5.00×10^3 kg $CaCl_2$

Unknown: mass HCl

$$5.00 \times 10^3 \text{ kg CaCl}_2 \times \frac{1 \text{ mol CaCl}_2}{110.98 \text{ g CaCl}_2} \times \frac{2 \text{ mol HCl}}{1 \text{ mol CaCl}_2} \times \frac{36.46 \text{ g HCl}}{1 \text{ mol HCl}}$$

$$= 3.29 \times 10^3 \text{ kg HCl}$$

b. Given: balanced equation; 750 g $CaCO_3$

Unknown: mass CO_2

$$750 \text{ g } CaCO_3 \times \frac{1 \text{ mol } CaCO_3}{100.09 \text{ g } CaCO_3} \times \frac{1 \text{ mol } CO_2}{1 \text{ mol } CaCO_3} \times \frac{44.01 \text{ g } CO_2}{1 \text{ mol } CO_2} = 330 \text{ g } CO_2$$

---

197. a. Given: balanced equation; 1.50×10^5 g Al

Unknown: mass NH_4ClO_4

$$1.50 \times 10^5 \text{ g Al} \times \frac{1 \text{ mol Al}}{26.98 \text{ g Al}} \times \frac{3 \text{ mol } NH_4ClO_4}{3 \text{ mol Al}} \times \frac{117.50 \text{ g } NH_4ClO_4}{1 \text{ mol } NH_4ClO_4}$$

$$= 6.53 \times 10^5 \text{ g } NH_4ClO_4$$

b. Given: balanced equation; 620 kg NH_4ClO_4

Unknown: mass NO

$$620 \text{ kg } NH_4ClO_4 \times \frac{1 \text{ mol } NH_4ClO_4}{117.50 \text{ g } NH_4ClO_4} \times \frac{3 \text{ mol NO}}{3 \text{ mol } NH_4ClO_4} \times \frac{30.01 \text{ g NO}}{1 \text{ mol NO}}$$

$$= 160 \text{ kg NO}$$

---

198. a. Given: balanced equation; 2.50×10^5 kg H_2SO_4

Unknown: moles H_3PO_4

$$2.50 \times 10^5 \text{ kg } H_2SO_4 \times \frac{1000 \text{ g}}{1 \text{ kg}} \times \frac{1 \text{ mol } H_2SO_4}{98.09 \text{ g } H_2SO_4} \times \frac{2 \text{ mol } H_3PO_4}{3 \text{ mol } H_2SO_4}$$

$$= 1.70 \times 10^6 \text{ mol } H_3PO_4$$

b. Given: balanced equation; 400. kg $Ca_3(PO_4)_2$

Unknown: mass $CaSO_4 \cdot 2H_2O$

$$400 \text{ kg } Ca(PO_4)_2 \times \frac{1 \text{ mol } Ca_3(PO_4)_2}{310.18 \text{ g } Ca_3(PO_4)_2} \times \frac{3 \text{ mol } CaSO_4 \cdot 2H_2O}{1 \text{ mol } Ca_3(PO_4)_2}$$

$$\times \frac{172.19 \text{ g } CaSO_4 \cdot 2H_2O}{1 \text{ mol } CaSO_4 \cdot 2H_2O} = 666 \text{ kg } CaSO_4 \cdot 2H_2O$$

c. Given: balanced equation; 68 metric tons rock; 78.8% $Ca_3(PO_4)_2$

Unknown: mass H_3PO_4 in metric tons

$$68 \text{ metric tons rock} \times \frac{0.788 \text{ g } Ca_3(PO_4)_2}{1 \text{ g rock}} \times \frac{1 \text{ mol } Ca_3(PO_4)_2}{310.18 \text{ g } Ca_3(PO_4)_2}$$

$$\times \frac{2 \text{ mol } H_3PO_4}{1 \text{ mol } Ca_3(PO_4)_2} \times \frac{98.00 \text{ g } H_3PO_4}{1 \text{ mol } H_3PO_4} = 34 \text{ metric tons } H_3PO_4$$

---

199. Given: balanced equation; mass Fe = 3.19% × 1650 kg

Unknown: mass of steel scrap after 1 yr

$$0.0319 \times 1650 \text{ kg Fe} = 52.6 \text{ kg Fe}$$

$$52.6 \text{ kg Fe} \times \frac{\text{mol Fe}}{55.85 \text{ g Fe}} \times \frac{2 \text{ mol } Fe_2O_3}{4 \text{ mol Fe}} \times \frac{159.70 \text{ g } Fe_2O_3}{1 \text{ mol } Fe_2O_3} = 75.2 \text{ kg } Fe_2O_3$$

$$1650 \text{ kg} - 52.6 \text{ kg} + 75.2 \text{ kg} = 1670 \text{ kg}$$

---

200. Given: balanced equation; 0.048 mol Al; 0.030 mol O_2

$$0.048 \text{ mol Al} \times \frac{3 \text{ mol } O_2}{4 \text{ mol Al}} = 0.036 \text{ mol } O_2$$

0.036 mol O_2 needed; 0.030 mol O_2 available

limiting reactant: O_2

201. Given: balanced equation; 862 g $ZrSiO_4$; 950. g Cl_2

$$862 \text{ g } ZrSiO_4 \times \frac{1 \text{ mol } ZrSiO_4}{183.31 \text{ g } ZrSiO_4} \times \frac{2 \text{ mol } Cl_2}{1 \text{ mol } ZrSiO_4} \times \frac{70.90 \text{ g } Cl_2}{1 \text{ mol } Cl_2} = 667 \text{ g } Cl_2$$

Unknown: limiting reactant; mass $ZrCl_4$

667 g Cl_2 needed; 950. g Cl_2 available; limiting reactant is $ZrSiO_4$

$$862 \text{ g } ZrSiO_4 \times \frac{1 \text{ mol } ZrSiO_4}{183.31 \text{ g } ZrSiO_4} \times \frac{1 \text{ mol } ZrCl_4}{1 \text{ mol } ZrSiO_4} \times \frac{233.02 \text{ g } ZrCl_4}{1 \text{ mol } ZrCl_4}$$

$$= 1.10 \times 10^3 \text{ g } ZrCl_4$$

202. Given: 1.72 mol ZnS; 3.04 mol O_2

$$2ZnS + 3O_2 \rightarrow 2ZnO + 2SO_2$$

Unknown: balanced equation; limiting reactant

$$1.72 \text{ mol ZnS} \times \frac{3 \text{ mol } O_2}{2 \text{ mol ZnS}} = 2.58 \text{ mol } O_2$$

2.58 mol O_2 needed; 3.04 mol O_2 available; limiting reactant is ZnS.

203. a. Given: balanced equation; 0.32 mol Al; 0.26 mol O_2

$$0.32 \text{ mol Al} \times \frac{3 \text{ mol } O_2}{4 \text{ mol Al}} = 0.24 \text{ mol } O_2$$

0.24 mol O_2 needed; 0.26 mol O_2 available; limiting reactant is Al

Unknown: limiting reactant

b. Given: balanced equation; 6.38×10^{-3} mol O_2; 9.15×10^{-3} mol Al

$$6.38 \times 10^{-3} \text{ mol } O_2 \times \frac{4 \text{ mol Al}}{3 \text{ mol } O_2} = 8.51 \times 10^{-3} \text{ mol Al}$$

8.51×10^{-3} mol Al needed; 9.15×10^{-3} mol Al available; limiting reactant: O_2

Unknown: moles Al_2O_3

$$6.38 \times 10^{-3} \text{ mol } O_2 \times \frac{2 \text{ mol } Al_2O_3}{3 \text{ mol } O_2} = 4.25 \times 10^{-3} \text{ mol } Al_2O_3$$

c. Given: balanced equation; 3.17 g Al; 2.55 g O_2

$$3.17 \text{ g Al} \times \frac{1 \text{ mol Al}}{26.98 \text{ g Al}} \times \frac{3 \text{ mol } O_2}{4 \text{ mol Al}} \times \frac{32.00 \text{ g } O_2}{1 \text{ mol } O_2} = 2.82 \text{ g } O_2$$

2.82 g O_2 needed; 2.55 O_2 available; limiting reactant: O_2

Unknown: limiting reactant

204. a. Given: balanced equation; 100. g CuS; 56 g O_2

$$100. \text{ g CuS} \times \frac{1 \text{ mol CuS}}{95.62 \text{ g CuS}} \times \frac{3 \text{ mol } O_2}{2 \text{ mol CuS}} \times \frac{32.00 \text{ g } O_2}{1 \text{ mol } O_2} = 50.2 \text{ g } O_2$$

50.2 g O_2 needed; 56 g O_2 available; limiting reactant: CuS

Unknown: limiting reactant

b. Given: balanced equation; 18.7 g CuS; 12.0 g O_2

$$18.7 \text{ g CuS} \times \frac{1 \text{ mol CuS}}{95.62 \text{ g CuS}} \times \frac{3 \text{ mol } O_2}{2 \text{ mol CuS}} \times \frac{32.00 \text{ g } O_2}{1 \text{ mol } O_2} = 9.39 \text{ g } O_2$$

9.39 g O_2 needed; 12.0 g O_2 available; limiting reactant: CuS

Unknown: mass CuO

$$18.7 \text{ g CuS} \times \frac{1 \text{ mol CuS}}{95.62 \text{ CuS}} \times \frac{2 \text{ mol CuO}}{2 \text{ mol CuS}} \times \frac{79.55 \text{ g CuO}}{1 \text{ mol CuO}} = 15.6 \text{ g CuO}$$

205. Given: balanced equation; 0.092 mol Fe; 0.158 mol $CuSO_4$

Unknown: limiting reactant; moles Cu

$$0.092 \text{ mol Fe} \times \frac{3 \text{ mol } CuSO_4}{2 \text{ mol Fe}} = 0.14 \text{ mol } CuSO_4$$

0.14 mol $CuSo_4$ needed; 0.158 mol $CuSO_4$ available; limiting reactant: Fe

$$0.092 \text{ mol Fe} \times \frac{3 \text{ mol Cu}}{2 \text{ mol Fe}} = 0.14 \text{ mol Cu}$$

206. Given: balanced equation; 55 g $BaCO_3$; 26 g HNO_3

Unknown: mass Ba $(NO_3)_2$

$$55 \text{ g } BaCO_3 \times \frac{1 \text{ mol } BaCO_3}{197.34 \text{ g } BaCO_3} \times \frac{2 \text{ mol } HNO_3}{1 \text{ mol } BaCO_3} \times \frac{63.02 \text{ g } HNO_3}{1 \text{ mol } HNO_3}$$

$$= 35 \text{ g } HNO_3$$

35 g HNO_3 needed; 26 HNO_3 available; limiting reactant: HNO_3

$$26 \text{ g } HNO_3 \times \frac{1 \text{ mol } HNO_3}{63.02 \text{ g } HNO_3} \times \frac{1 \text{ mol } Ba(NO_3)_2}{2 \text{ mol } HNO_3} \times \frac{261.35 \text{ g } Ba(NO_3)_2}{1 \text{ mol } Ba(NO_3)_2}$$

$$= 54 \text{ g } Ba(NO_3)_2$$

207. a. Given: balanced equation; 560 g MgI_2; 360 g Br_2

Unknown: excess reactant; remaining mass

$$560 \text{ g } MgI_2 \times \frac{1 \text{ mol } MgI_2}{278.11 \text{ g } MgI_2} \times \frac{1 \text{ mol } Br_2}{1 \text{ mol } MgI_2} \times \frac{159.80 \text{ g } Br_2}{1 \text{ mol } Br_2} = 322 \text{ g } Br_2$$

Br_2 is in excess; 360 g Br_2 – 322 g Br_2 = 38 g Br_2 excess

b. Given: balanced equation; 560 g MgI_2

Unknown: mass I_2

$$560 \text{ g } MgI_2 \times \frac{1 \text{ mol } MgI_2}{278.11 \text{ g } MgI_2} \times \frac{1 \text{ mol } I_2}{1 \text{ mol } MgI_2} \times \frac{253.80 \text{ g } I_2}{1 \text{ mol } I_2} = 510 \text{ g } I_2$$

208. a. Given: balanced equation; 22.9 g Ni; 112 g $AgNO_3$

Unknown: excess reactant

$$22.9 \text{ g Ni} \times \frac{1 \text{ mol Ni}}{58.69 \text{ g Ni}} \times \frac{2 \text{ mol } AgNO_3}{1 \text{ mol Ni}} \times \frac{169.88 \text{ g } AgNO_3}{1 \text{ mol } AgNO_3} = 133 \text{ g } AgNO_3$$

Ni is in excess

b. Given: balanced equation; 112 g $AgNO_3$

Unknown: mass $Ni(NO_3)_2$

$$112 \text{ g } AgNO_3 \times \frac{1 \text{ mol } AgNO_3}{169.88 \text{ g } AgNO_3} \times \frac{1 \text{ mol } Ni(NO_3)_2}{2 \text{ mol } AgNO_3} \times \frac{182.71 \text{ g } Ni(NO_3)_2}{1 \text{ mol } Ni(NO_3)_2}$$

$$= 60.2 \text{ g } Ni(NO_3)_2$$

209. Given: 1.60 mol CS_2; 5.60 mol O_2

Unknown: balanced equation; moles of excess, reactant

$$CS_2(g) + 3O_2(g) \rightarrow 2SO_2(g) + CO_2(g)$$

$$1.60 \text{ mol } CS_2 \times \frac{3 \text{ mol } O_2}{1 \text{ mol } CS_2} = 4.80 \text{ mol } O_2$$

5.60 mol O_2 – 4.80 mol O_2 = 0.80 mol O_2 excess

210. a. Given: balanced equation; 0.91 g $HgCl_2$

Unknown: mass $Hg(NH_2)Cl$

$$0.91 \text{ g } HgCl_2 \times \frac{1 \text{ mol } HgCl_2}{271.49 \text{ g } HgCl_2} \times \frac{1 \text{ mol } Hg(NH_2)Cl}{1 \text{ mol } HgCl_2}$$

$$\times \frac{252.07 \text{ g } Hg(NH_2)Cl}{1 \text{ mol } Hg(NH_2)Cl} = 0.84 \text{ g } Hg(NH_2)Cl$$

b. Given: balanced equation; 0.91 g $HgCl_2$; 0.15 g NH_3

$$0.91 \text{ g } HgCl_2 \times \frac{1 \text{ mol } HgCl_2}{271.49 \text{ g } HgCl_2} \times \frac{2 \text{ mol } NH_3}{1 \text{ mol } HgCl_2} \times \frac{17.04 \text{ g } NH_3}{1 \text{ mol } NH_3} = 0.11 \text{ g } NH_3$$

0.11 g NH_3 needed; 0.15 g NH_3 available; limiting reactant: $HgCl_2$

Unknown: mass $Hg(NH_2)Cl$

$$0.91 \text{ g } HgCl_2 \times \frac{1 \text{ mol } HgCl_2}{271.49 \text{ g } HgCl_2} \times \frac{1 \text{ mol } Hg(NH_2)Cl}{1 \text{ mol } HgCl_2}$$

$$\times \frac{252.07 \text{ g } Hg(NH_2)Cl}{1 \text{ mol } Hg(NH_2)Cl} = 0.84 \text{ g } Hg(NH_2)Cl$$

211. b. Given: balanced equation from **a**; 0.57 mol Al; 0.37 mol NaOH; excess water

$$0.57 \text{ mol Al} \times \frac{2 \text{ mol NaOH}}{2 \text{ mol Al}} = 0.57 \text{ mol NaOH}$$

0.57 mol NaOH needed; 0.37 mol NaOH available; limiting reactant: NaOH

Unknown: moles H_2

$$0.37 \text{ mol NaOH} \times \frac{3 \text{ mol } H_2}{2 \text{ mol NaOH}} = 0.56 \text{ mol } H_2$$

212. a. Given: balanced equation; 0.0845 mol NO_2

$$0.0845 \text{ mol } NO_2 \times \frac{4 \text{ mol } HNO_3}{2 \text{ mol } NO_2} = 0.169 \text{ mol } HNO_3$$

Unknown: moles of HNO_3 and Cu

$$0.0845 \text{ mol } NO_2 \times \frac{1 \text{ mol Cu}}{2 \text{ mol } NO_2} = 0.0422 \text{ mol Cu}$$

b. Given: balanced equation; 5.94 g Cu; 23.23 g HNO_3

$$5.94 \text{ g Cu} \times \frac{1 \text{ mol Cu}}{63.55 \text{ g Cu}} \times \frac{4 \text{ mol } HNO_3}{1 \text{ mol Cu}} \times \frac{63.02 \text{ g } HNO_3}{1 \text{ mol } HNO_3} = 23.6 \text{ g } HNO_3$$

23.6 g HNO_3 needed; 23.23 g HNO_3 available: Cu is in excess.

Unknown: excess reactant

213. a. Given: balanced equation; 2.90 mol NH_3; 3.75 mol O_2

$$2.90 \text{ mol } NH_3 \times \frac{5 \text{ mol } O_2}{4 \text{ mol } NH_3} = 3.62 \text{ mol } O_2; \ NH_3 \text{ is limiting.}$$

Unknown: moles of NO and H_2O

$$2.90 \text{ mol } NH_3 \times \frac{4 \text{ mol NO}}{4 \text{ mol } NH_3} = 2.90 \text{ mol NO}$$

$$2.90 \text{ mol } NH_3 \times \frac{6 \text{ mol } H_2O}{4 \text{ mol } NH_3} = 4.35 \text{ mol } H_2O$$

b. Given: balanced equation; 4.20×10^4 g NH_3; 1.31×10^5 g O_2

Unknown: limiting reactant

$$4.20 \times 10^4 \text{ g } NH_3 \times \frac{1 \text{ mol } NH_3}{17.04 \text{ g } NH_3} \times \frac{5 \text{ mol } O_2}{4 \text{ mol } NH_3} \times \frac{32.00 \text{ g } O_2}{1 \text{ mol } O_2}$$

$$= 9.86 \times 10^4 \text{ g } O_2$$

9.86×10^4 g O_2 needed; 1.31×10^5 g O_2 available; limiting reactant: NH_3

c. Given: balanced equation; 869 kg NH_3; 2480 kg O_2

Unknown: mass NO

$$869 \text{ kg } NH_3 \times \frac{1 \text{ mol } NH_3}{17.04 \text{ g } NH_3} \times \frac{5 \text{ mol } O_2}{4 \text{ mol } NH_3} \times \frac{32.00 \text{ g } O_2}{1 \text{ mol } O_2} = 2040 \text{ kg } O_2$$

2040 kg O_2 needed; 2480 kg O_2 available; limiting reactant: NH_3

$$869 \text{ kg } NH_3 \times \frac{1 \text{ mol } NH_3}{17.04 \text{ g } NH_3} \times \frac{4 \text{ mol } NO}{4 \text{ mol } NH_3} \times \frac{30.01 \text{ g } NO}{1 \text{ mol } NO}$$

$$= 1.53 \times 10^3 \text{ kg } NO$$

214. Given: balanced equation; 620 g C_2H_5OH; 1020 g CuO

Unknown: mass CH_3CHO; mass excess reactant left

$$620 \text{ g } C_2H_5OH \times \frac{1 \text{ mol } C_2H_5OH}{46.08 \text{ g } C_2H_5OH} \times \frac{1 \text{ mol } CuO}{1 \text{ mol } C_2H_5OH} \times \frac{79.55 \text{ g } CuO}{1 \text{ mol } CuO}$$

$$= 1070 \text{ g } CuO$$

1070 g CuO needed; 1020 g CuO available; limiting reactant: CuO

$$1020 \text{ g } CuO \times \frac{1 \text{ mol } CuO}{79.55 \text{ g } CuO} \times \frac{1 \text{ mol } CH_3CHO}{1 \text{ mol } CuO} \times \frac{44.06 \text{ g } CH_3CHO}{1 \text{ mol } CH_3CHO}$$

$$= 565 \text{ g } CH_3CHO$$

$$1020 \text{ g } CuO \times \frac{1 \text{ mol } CuO}{79.55 \text{ g } CuO} \times \frac{1 \text{ mol } C_2H_5OH}{1 \text{ mol } CuO} \times \frac{46.08 \text{ g } C_2H_5OH}{1 \text{ mol } C_2H_5OH}$$

$$= 591 \text{ g } C_2H_5OH$$

$620 \text{ g } C_2H_5OH - 591 \text{ g } C_2H_5OH = 29 \text{ g } C_2H_5OH$ excess

215. Given: balanced equation; 250 g SO_2; 650 g Br_2; excess H_2O

Unknown: mass HBr

$$250 \text{ g } SO_2 \times \frac{1 \text{ mol } SO_2}{64.07 \text{ g } SO_2} \times \frac{1 \text{ mol } Br_2}{1 \text{ mol } SO_2} \times \frac{159.80 \text{ g } Br_2}{1 \text{ mol } Br_2} = 624 \text{ g } Br_2$$

624 g Br_2 needed; 650 Br_2 available; limiting reactant: SO_2

$$250 \text{ g } SO_2 \times \frac{1 \text{ mol } SO_2}{64.07 \text{ g } SO_2} \times \frac{2 \text{ mol } HBr}{1 \text{ mol } SO_2} \times \frac{80.91 \text{ g } HBr}{1 \text{ mol } HBr} = 630 \text{ g } HBr$$

216. Given: balanced equation; 25.0 g Na_2SO_3; 22.0 g HCl

Unknown: mass SO_2

$$25.0 \text{ g } Na_2SO_3 \times \frac{1 \text{ mol } Na_2SO_3}{126.05 \text{ g } Na_2SO_3} \times \frac{2 \text{ mol } HCl}{1 \text{ mol } Na_2SO_3} \times \frac{36.46 \text{ g } HCl}{1 \text{ mol } HCl} = 14.5 \text{ g HCl}$$

14.5 g HCl needed; 22.0 g HCl available; limiting reactant: Na_2SO_3

$$25.0 \text{ g } Na_2SO_3 \times \frac{1 \text{ mol } Na_2SO_3}{126.05 \text{ g } Na_2SO_3} \times \frac{1 \text{ mol } SO_2}{1 \text{ mol } Na_2SO_3} \times \frac{64.07 \text{ g } SO_2}{1 \text{ mol } SO_2}$$

$$= 12.7 \text{ g } SO_2$$

217. a. Given: balanced equation; 27.5 g TbF_3; 6.96 g Ca

Unknown: mass Tb

$$27.5 \text{ g TbF}_3 \times \frac{1 \text{ mol TbF}_3}{215.93 \text{ g TbF}_3} \times \frac{3 \text{ mol Ca}}{2 \text{ mol TbF}_3} \times \frac{40.08 \text{ g Ca}}{1 \text{ mol Ca}} = 7.66 \text{ g Ca}$$

7.66 g Ca needed; 6.96 g Ca available; limiting reactant: Ca

$$6.96 \text{ g Ca} \times \frac{1 \text{ mol Ca}}{40.08 \text{ g Ca}} \times \frac{2 \text{ mol Tb}}{3 \text{ mol Ca}} \times \frac{158.93 \text{ g Tb}}{1 \text{ mol Tb}} = 18.4 \text{ g Tb}$$

b. Given: balanced equation; 6.96 g Ca; 27.5 g TbF_3; Ca is limiting

Unknown: mass TbF_3 remaining

$$6.96 \text{ g Ca} \times \frac{1 \text{ mol Ca}}{40.08 \text{ g Ca}} \times \frac{2 \text{ mol TbF}_3}{3 \text{ mol Ca}} \times \frac{215.93 \text{ g TbF}_3}{1 \text{ mol TbF}_3} = 25.0 \text{ g TbF}_3$$

$$27.5 \text{ g TbF}_3 - 25.0 \text{ g TbF}_3 = 2.5 \text{ g TbF}_3 \text{ remaining}$$

218. a. Given: theoretical yield = 50.0 g; actual yield = 41.9 g

Unknown: percent yield

$$\frac{41.9 \text{ g}}{50.0 \text{ g}} \times 100 = 83.8\% \text{ yield}$$

b. Given: theoretical yield = 290 kg; actual yield = 270 kg

Unknown: percent yield

$$\frac{270 \text{ kg}}{290 \text{ kg}} \times 100 = 93\% \text{ yield}$$

c. Given: theoretical yield = 6.05×10^4 kg; actual yield = 4.18×10^4 kg

Unknown: percent yield

$$\frac{4.18 \times 10^4 \text{ kg}}{6.05 \times 10^4 \text{ kg}} \times 100 = 69.1\% \text{ yield}$$

d. Given: theoretical yield = 0.00192 g; actual yield = 0.00089 g

Unknown: percent yield

$$\frac{0.00089 \text{ g}}{0.00192 \text{ g}} \times 100 = 46\% \text{ yield}$$

219. a. Given: balanced equation; 8.87 g As_2O_3; actual yield As = 5.33 g

Unknown: percent yield

$$\text{theoretical yield} = 8.87 \text{ g As}_2\text{O}_3 \times \frac{1 \text{ mol As}_2\text{O}_3}{197.84 \text{ g As}_2\text{O}_3} \times \frac{4 \text{ mol As}}{2 \text{ mol As}_2\text{O}_3}$$

$$\times \frac{74.92 \text{ g As}}{1 \text{ mol As}} = 6.72 \text{ g As}$$

$$\frac{5.33 \text{ g As}}{6.72 \text{ g As}} \times 100 = 79.3\% \text{ yield}$$

b. Given: balanced equation; 67 g C, actual yield As = 425 g

Unknown: percent yield

$$\text{theoretical yield} = 67 \text{ g C} \times \frac{1 \text{ mol C}}{12.01 \text{ g C}} \times \frac{4 \text{ mol As}}{3 \text{ mol C}} \times \frac{74.92 \text{ g As}}{1 \text{ mol As}} = 560 \text{ g As}$$

$$\frac{425 \text{ g As}}{560 \text{ g As}} \times 100 = 76\% \text{ yield}$$

220. a. Given: theoretical
yield = 68.3 g;
actual yield
= 43.9 g

Unknown: percent
yield

$\dfrac{43.9 \text{ g}}{68.3 \text{ g}} \times 100 = 64.3\%$ yield

b. Given: theoretical
yield =
0.0722 mol;
actual yield =
0.0419 mol

Unknown: percent
yield

$\dfrac{0.0419 \text{ mol}}{0.0722 \text{ mol}} \times 100 = 58.0\%$ yield

c. Given: 4.29 mol
C_2H_5OH;
actual yield
$CH_3COOC_2H_5$
= 2.98 mol;
balanced
equation

Unknown: percent
yield

theoretical yield $CH_3COOC_2H_5 =$

$4.29 \text{ mol } C_2H_5OH \times \dfrac{1 \text{ mol } CH_3COOC_2H_5}{1 \text{ mol } C_2H_5OH} = 4.29 \text{ mol } CH_3COOC_2H_5$

$\dfrac{2.98 \text{ mol } CH_3COOC_2H_5}{4.29 \text{ mol } CH_3COOC_2H_5} \times 100 = 69.5\%$ yield

d. Given: balanced
equation; 0.58
mol C_2H_5OH;
0.82 mol
CH_3COOH;
actual yield
$CH_3COOC_2H_5$
= 0.46 mol

Unknown: percent
yield

$0.58 \text{ mol } C_2H_5OH \times \dfrac{1 \text{ mol } CH_3COOH}{1 \text{ mol } C_2H_5OH} = 0.58 \text{ mol } CH_3COOH$

C_2H_5OH is limiting.

$0.58 \text{ mol } C_2H_5OH \times \dfrac{1 \text{ mol } CH_3COOC_2H_5}{1 \text{ mol } C_2H_5OH} = 0.58 \text{ mol } CH_3COOC_2H_5$

$\dfrac{0.46 \text{ mol}}{0.58 \text{ mol}} \times 100 = 79\%$ yield

---

221. a. Given: balanced
equation;
0.0251 mol A;
actual yield C
= 0.0349 mol

Unknown: percent
yield

theoretical yield $C = 0.0251 \text{ mol A} \times \dfrac{4 \text{ mol C}}{2 \text{ mol A}} = 0.0502 \text{ mol C}$

$\dfrac{0.0349 \text{ mol}}{0.0502 \text{ mol}} \times 100 = 69.5\%$ yield

b. Given: balanced
equation;
1.19 mol A;
actual yield
D = 1.41 mol

Unknown: percent
yield

theoretical yield $D = 1.19 \text{ mol A} \times \dfrac{3 \text{ mol D}}{2 \text{ mol A}} = 1.785 \text{ mol D}$

$\dfrac{1.41 \text{ mol}}{1.785 \text{ mol}} \times 100 = 79.0\%$ yield

c. Given: balanced
equation;
189 mol B;
actual yield
D = 39 mol

Unknown: percent
yield

theoretical yield $D = 189 \text{ mol B} \times \dfrac{3 \text{ mol D}}{7 \text{ mol B}} = 81.0 \text{ mol D}$

$\dfrac{39 \text{ mol}}{81.0 \text{ mol}} \times 100 = 48\%$ yield

d. Given: balanced equation; 3500 mol B; actual yield C = 1700 mol

Unknown: percent yield

theoretical yield C $= 3500 \text{ mol B} \times \dfrac{4 \text{ mol C}}{7 \text{ mol B}} = 2.0 \times 10^3 \text{ mol C}$

$\dfrac{1.7 \times 10^3 \text{ mol}}{2.0 \times 10^3 \text{ mol}} \times 100 = 85\% \text{ C}$

---

222. a. Given: balanced equation; 57 mol $Ca_3(PO_4)_2$; actual yield $CaSiO_3$ = 101 mol

Unknown: percent yield

theoretical yield $CaSiO_3 = 57 \text{ mol } Ca_3(PO_4)_2 \times \dfrac{3 \text{ mol } CaSiO_3}{1 \text{ mol } Ca_3(PO_4)_2}$

$= 170 \text{ mol } CaSiO_3$

$\dfrac{101 \text{ mol}}{170 \text{ mol}} \times 100 = 59\% \text{ yield}$

b. Given: balanced equation; 1280 mol C; actual yield $CaSiO_3$ = 622 mol

Unknown: percent yield

theoretical yield $CaSiO_3 = 1280 \text{ mol C} \times \dfrac{3 \text{ mol } CaSiO_3}{5 \text{ mol C}} = 768 \text{ mol } CaSiO_3$

$\dfrac{622 \text{ mol}}{768 \text{ mol}} \times 100 = 81.0\% \text{ yield}$

c. Given: balanced equation; 81.5% yield; 1.4×10^5 mol $Ca_3(PO_4)_2$

Unknown: actual mol P

$1.4 \times 10^5 \text{ mol } Ca_3(PO_4)_2 \times \dfrac{2 \text{ mol P}}{1 \text{ mol } Ca_3(PO_4)_2} \times 0.815 = 2.3 \times 10^5 \text{ mol}$

---

223. a. Given: balanced equation; 56.9 g WO_3; actual yield W = 41.4 g

Unknown: percent yield

$56.9 \text{ g } WO_3 \times \dfrac{1 \text{ mol } WO_3}{231.84 \text{ g } WO_3} \times \dfrac{1 \text{ mol W}}{1 \text{ mol } WO_3} \times \dfrac{183.84 \text{ g W}}{1 \text{ mol W}} = 45.1 \text{ g W}$

$\dfrac{41.4 \text{ g}}{45.1 \text{ g}} \times 100 = 91.8\% \text{ yield}$

b. Given: balanced equation; 3.72 g WO_3; 92.0% yield

Unknown: moles W

$3.72 \text{ g } WO_3 \times \dfrac{1 \text{ mol } WO_3}{231.84 \text{ g } WO_3} \times \dfrac{1 \text{ mol W}}{1 \text{ mol } WO_3} \times \dfrac{92.0\%}{100\%} = 0.0148 \text{ mol W}$

c. Given: balanced equation; actual yield W = 11.4 g; 89.4% yield

Unknown: mass WO_3

$\dfrac{11.4 \text{ g W}}{x} = \dfrac{89.4 \text{ g}}{100.0 \text{ g}}; x = 12.8 \text{ g W}$

$12.8 \text{ g W} \times \dfrac{1 \text{ mol W}}{183.84 \text{ g W}} \times \dfrac{1 \text{ mol } WO_3}{1 \text{ mol W}} \times \dfrac{231.84 \text{ g } WO_3}{1 \text{ mol } WO_3} = 16.1 \text{ g } WO_3$

224. a. Given: balanced equation; 410. kg CS_2; actual yield CCl_4 = 719 kg

Unknown: percent yield

theoretical yield = 410. kg $CS_2 \times \dfrac{1 \text{ mol } CS_2}{76.15 \text{ g } CS_2} \times \dfrac{1 \text{ mol } CCl_4}{1 \text{ mol } CS_2}$

$\times \dfrac{153.81 \text{ g } CCl_4}{1 \text{ mol } CCl_4}$ = 828 kg CCl_4

$\dfrac{719 \text{ kg}}{828 \text{ kg}} \times 100$ = 86.8% yield

b. Given: balanced equation; 67.5 g Cl_2; actual yield S_2Cl_2 = 39.5 g

Unknown: percent yield

theoretical yield = 67.5 g $Cl_2 \times \dfrac{1 \text{ mol } Cl_2}{70.90 \text{ g } Cl_2} \times \dfrac{1 \text{ mol } S_2Cl_2}{3 \text{ mol } Cl_2}$

$\times \dfrac{135.04 \text{ g } S_2Cl_2}{1 \text{ mol } S_2Cl_2}$ = 42.8 g S_2Cl_2

$\dfrac{39.5 \text{ g}}{42.8 \text{ g}} \times 100$ = 92.2% yield

c. Given: balanced equation; 83.3% yield; actual yield CCl_4 = 5.00×10^4 kg

Unknown: kg CS_2 and S_2Cl_2

5.00×10^4 kg $CCl_4 \times \dfrac{100\%}{83.3\%} \times \dfrac{1 \text{ mol } CCl_4}{153.81 \text{ g } CCl_4} \times \dfrac{1 \text{ mol } CS_2}{1 \text{ mol } CCl_4} \times \dfrac{76.15 \text{ g } CS_2}{1 \text{ mol } CS_2} =$

2.97×10^4 kg CS_2

5.00×10^4 kg $CCl_4 \times \dfrac{83.3\%}{100\%} \times \dfrac{1 \text{ mol } CCl_4}{153.81 \text{ g } CCl_4} \times \dfrac{1 \text{ mol } S_2Cl_2}{1 \text{ mol } CCl_4}$

$\times \dfrac{135.04 \text{ g } S_2Cl_2}{1 \text{ mol } S_2Cl_2}$ = 3.66×10^4 kg S_2Cl_2

225. a. Given: balanced equation; 0.38 g NO_2; actual yield N_2O_5 = 0.36 g

Unknown: percent yield

0.38 g $NO_2 \times \dfrac{1 \text{ mol } NO_2}{46.01 \text{ g } NO_2} \times \dfrac{1 \text{ mol } N_2O_5}{2 \text{ mol } NO_2} \times \dfrac{108.02 \text{ g } N_2O_5}{1 \text{ mol } N_2O_5}$ = 0.45 g N_2O_5

$\dfrac{0.36 \text{ g}}{0.45 \text{ g}} \times 100$ = 80.% g yield

b. Given: balanced equation; 6.0 mol NO_2; 61.1% yield

Unknown: mass N_2O_5

6.0 mol $NO_2 \times \dfrac{1 \text{ mol } N_2O_5}{2 \text{ mol } NO_2} \times \dfrac{108.02 \text{ g } N_2O_5}{1 \text{ mol } N_2O_5}$ = 320 g N_2O_5

320 g $N_2O_5 \times \dfrac{61.1\%}{100\%}$ = 2.0×10^2 g N_2O_5

226. Given: balanced equation; 30.0 g NaCl; 0.250 mol H_2SO_4; actual yield HCl = 14.6 g

Unknown: percent yield

30.0 g NaCl $\times \dfrac{1 \text{ mol NaCl}}{58.44 \text{ g NaCl}} \times \dfrac{1 \text{ mol } H_2SO_4}{2 \text{ mol NaCl}}$ = 0.257 mol H_2SO_4

0.250 mol H_2SO_4 available, 0.257 mol H_2SO_4 needed; H_2SO_4 is limiting.

0.250 mol $H_2SO_4 \times \dfrac{2 \text{ mol HCl}}{1 \text{ mol } H_2SO_4} \times \dfrac{36.46 \text{ g HCl}}{1 \text{ mol HCl}}$ = 18.2 g HCl

$\dfrac{14.6 \text{ g}}{18.2 \text{ g}} \times 100$ = 80.2% yield

MODERN CHEMISTRY APPENDIX D SOLUTIONS MANUAL

227. a. Given: balanced equation; 410 g Au; actual yield $NaAu(CN)_2$ = 540 g

Unknown: percent yield

$$\text{theoretical yield} = 410 \text{ g Au} \times \frac{1 \text{ mol Au}}{196.97 \text{ g Au}} \times \frac{4 \text{ mol NaAu(CN)}_2}{4 \text{ mol Au}}$$

$$\times \frac{272.00 \text{ g NaAu(CN)}_2}{1 \text{ mol NaAu(CN)}_2} = 570 \text{ g NaAu(CN)}_2$$

$$\frac{540 \text{ g}}{570 \text{ g}} \times 100 = 95\% \text{ yield}$$

b. Given: balanced equation; 79.6% yield; 1.00 kg $NaAu(CN)_2$

Unknown: mass Au

$$1.00 \text{ kg NaAu(CN)}_2 \times \frac{100\%}{79.6\%} \times \frac{1 \text{ mol NaAu(CN)}_2}{272.00 \text{ g NaAu(CN)}_2}$$

$$\times \frac{4 \text{ mol Au}}{4 \text{ mol NaAu(CN)}_2} \times \frac{196.97 \text{ g Au}}{1 \text{ mol Au}} = 0.910 \text{ kg Au} = 9.10 \times 10^2 \text{ g Au}$$

c. Given: 0.910 kg Au; ore is 0.001% Au

Unknown: mass of ore

$$\frac{x}{0.910 \text{ kg Au}} = \frac{100\%}{0.001\%}; x = 9 \times 10^4 \text{ kg ore}$$

228. a. Given: balanced equation; 2.00 g CO; actual yield I_2 = 3.17 g

Unknown: percent yield

$$\text{theoretical yield} = 2.00 \text{ g CO} \times \frac{1 \text{ mol CO}}{28.01 \text{ g CO}} \times \frac{1 \text{ mol I}_2}{5 \text{ mol CO}} \times \frac{253.80 \text{ g I}_2}{1 \text{ mol I}_2}$$

$$= 3.63 \text{ g I}_2$$

$$\frac{3.17 \text{ g}}{3.63 \text{ g}} \times 100 = 87.3\% \text{ yield}$$

b. Given: 87.6% yield; 2.00 g CO

Unknown: mass of unreacted CO

$$100.0\% - 87.6\% = 12.4\% \text{ unreacted}$$

$$0.124 \times 2.00 \text{ g CO} = 0.248 \text{ g CO}$$

229. a. Given: balanced equation; 1.2 kg Cl_2; actual yield NaClO = 0.90 kg

Unknown: percent yield

$$\text{theoretical yield} = 1.2 \text{ kg Cl}_2 \times \frac{1 \text{ mol Cl}_2}{70.90 \text{ g Cl}_2} \times \frac{1 \text{ mol NaClO}}{1 \text{ mol Cl}_2}$$

$$\times \frac{74.44 \text{ g NaClO}}{1 \text{ mol NaClO}} = 1.3 \text{ kg NaClO}$$

$$\frac{0.90 \text{ kg}}{1.3 \text{ kg}} \times 100 = 69\%$$

b. Given: balanced equation; 91.8% yield; 25 metric tons actual yield NaClO

Unknown: metric tons Cl_2

$$25 \text{ metric tons NaClO} \times \frac{100\%}{91.8\%} \times \frac{1 \text{ mol NaClO}}{65.46 \text{ g NaClO}} \times \frac{1 \text{ mol Cl}_2}{1 \text{ mol NaClO}}$$

$$\times \frac{70.90 \text{ g Cl}_2}{1 \text{ mol Cl}_2} = 29 \text{ metric tons Cl}_2$$

c. Given: balanced equation; 81.8% yield; 1 mol Cl_2

Unknown: mass NaCl

$$1.00 \text{ mol } Cl_2 \times \frac{1 \text{ mol NaCl}}{1 \text{ mol } Cl_2} \times \frac{58.44 \text{ g NaCl}}{1 \text{ mol NaCl}} \times \frac{81.8\%}{100\%} = 47.8 \text{ g NaCl}$$

d. Given: balanced equation; 79.5% yield; actual rate NaClO 370 kg/h

Unknown: rate NaOH in kg/h

$$\frac{370 \text{ kg NaClO}}{1 \text{ h}} \times \frac{100\%}{79.5\%} \times \frac{1 \text{ mol NaClO}}{65.46 \text{ g NaClO}} \times \frac{2 \text{ mol NaOH}}{1 \text{ mol NaClO}}$$

$$\times \frac{40.00 \text{ g NaOH}}{1 \text{ mol NaOH}} = 568 \text{ kg NaOH/h}$$

---

230. b. Given: theoretical yield = 2.04 g; actual yield = 1.79 g

Unknown: percent yield

$$\frac{1.79 \text{ g}}{2.04 \text{ g}} \times 100 = 87.7\% \text{ yield}$$

d. Given: balanced equation from **c**; 0.097 mol Mg; 0.027 mol Mg_3N_2

Unknown: percent yield

$$\text{theoretical yield} = 0.097 \text{ mol Mg} \times \frac{1 \text{ mol } Mg_3N_2}{3 \text{ mol Mg}} = 0.032 \text{ mol } Mg_3N_2$$

$$\frac{0.027 \text{ mol}}{0.032 \text{ mol}} \times 100 = 84\% \text{ yield}$$

---

231. a. Given: balanced equation; 0.89 g C_3H_7OH; actual yield C_2H_5COOH = 0.88 g

Unknown: percent yield

$$\text{theoretical yield} = 0.89 \text{ g } C_3H_7OH \times \frac{1 \text{ mol } C_3H_7OH}{60.11 \text{ g } C_3H_7OH}$$

$$\times \frac{3 \text{ mol } C_2H_5COOH}{3 \text{ mol } C_3H_7OH} \times \frac{74.09 \text{ g } C_2H_5COOH}{1 \text{ mol } C_2H_5COOH} = 1.1 \text{ g } C_2H_5COOH$$

$$\frac{0.88 \text{ g}}{1.1 \text{ g}} \times 100 = 80.\% \text{ yield}$$

b. Given: balanced equation; actual yield C_2H_5COOH = 1.50 mol; 136 g C_3H_7OH

Unknown: percent yield

$$\text{theoretical yield} = 136 \text{ g } C_3H_7OH \times \frac{1 \text{ mol } C_3H_7OH}{60.11 \text{ g } C_3H_7OH}$$

$$\times \frac{3 \text{ mol } C_2H_5COOH}{3 \text{ mol } C_3H_7OH} = 2.26 \text{ mol } C_2H_5COOH$$

$$\frac{1.50 \text{ mol}}{2.26 \text{ mol}} \times 100 = 66.4\% \text{ yield}$$

c. Given: balanced equation; 116 g $Na_2Cr_2O_7$; actual yield C_2H_5COOH = 28.1 g

Unknown: percent yield

$$\text{theoretical yield} = 116 \text{ g } Na_2Cr_2O_7 \times \frac{1 \text{ mol } Na_2Cr_2O_7}{261.98 \text{ g } Na_2Cr_2O_7}$$

$$\times \frac{3 \text{ mol } C_2H_5COOH}{2 \text{ mol } Na_2Cr_2O_7} \times \frac{74.09 \text{ g } C_2H_5COOH}{1 \text{ mol } C_2H_5COOH} = 49.2 \text{ g } C_2H_5COOH$$

$$\frac{28.1 \text{ g}}{49.2 \text{ g}} \times 100 = 57.1\% \text{ yield}$$

232. Given: unbalanced equation; 850. g C_3H_6; 300. g NH_3; excess O_2; actual yield C_3H_3N = 850. g

Unknown: balanced equation; limiting reactant; percent yield

$$2C_3H_6(g) + 2NH_3(g) + 3O_2(g) \rightarrow 2C_3H_3N(g) + 6H_2O(g)$$

$$850.\ g\ C_3H_6 \times \frac{1\ mol\ C_3H_6}{42.09\ g\ C_3H_6} \times \frac{2\ mol\ NH_3}{2\ mol\ C_3H_6} \times \frac{17.04\ g\ NH_3}{1\ mol\ NH_3} = 344\ g\ NH_3$$

300 g NH_3 available, 344 g NH_3 needed; NH_3 is limiting.

$$300.\ g\ NH_3 \times \frac{1\ mol\ NH_3}{17.04\ g\ NH_3} \times \frac{2\ mol\ C_3H_3N}{2\ mol\ NH_3} \times \frac{53.07\ g\ C_3H_3N}{1\ mol\ C_3H_3N}$$

$$= 934\ g\ C_3H_3N$$

$$\frac{850.\ g}{934\ g} \times 100 = 91.0\%\ yield$$

233. a. Given: 430 kg H_2; reactants and product

Unknown: balanced equation; mass CH_3OH

$$CO + 2H_2 \rightarrow CH_3OH$$

$$430.\ kg\ H_2 \times \frac{1\ mol\ H_2}{2.02\ g\ H_2} \times \frac{1\ mol\ CH_3OH}{2\ mol\ H_2} \times \frac{32.05\ g\ CH_3OH}{1\ mol\ CH_3OH}$$

$$= 3.41 \times 10^3\ kg\ CH_3OH$$

b. Given: balanced equation and theoretical yield from **a**; actual yield CH_3OH = 3.12×10^3 kg

Unknown: percent yield

$$\frac{3.12 \times 10^3\ kg}{3.41 \times 10^3\ kg} \times 100 = 91.5\%\ yield$$

234. Given: balanced equation; 750. g $C_6H_{10}O_4$; actual yield $C_6H_{16}N_2$ = 578 g

Unknown: percent yield

$$750.\ g\ C_6H_{10}O_4 \times \frac{1\ mol\ C_6H_{10}O_4}{146.16\ g\ C_6H_{10}O_4} \times \frac{1\ mol\ C_6H_{16}N_2}{1\ mol\ C_6H_{10}O_4}$$

$$\times \frac{116.24\ g\ C_6H_{16}N_2}{1\ mol\ C_6H_{16}N_2} = 596\ g\ C_6H_{16}N_2$$

$$\frac{578\ g}{596\ g} \times 100 = 97.0\%\ yield$$

235. Given: unbalanced equation; 1.37×10^4 g CO_2; 63.4% yield

Unknown: balanced equation; mass O_2

$$6CO_2 + 6H_2O \rightarrow C_6H_{12}O_6 + 6O_2$$

$$1.37 \times 10^4\ g\ CO_2 \times \frac{1\ mol\ CO_2}{44.01\ g\ CO_2} \times \frac{6\ mol\ O_2}{6\ mol\ CO_2} \times \frac{32.00\ g\ O_2}{1\ mol\ O_2}$$

$$= 9.96 \times 10^3\ g\ O_2$$

$$9.96 \times 10^3\ g\ O_2 \times \frac{63.4\%}{100\%} = 6.32 \times 10^3\ g\ O_2$$

236. Given: balanced equation; 2.67×10^2 mol $Ca(OH)_2$; 54.3% yield

Unknown: mass CaO in kg

$$2.67 \times 10^2\ mol\ Ca(OH)_2 \times \frac{100\%}{54.3\%} \times \frac{1\ mol\ CaO}{1\ mol\ Ca(OH)_2} \times \frac{56.08\ g\ CaO}{1\ mol\ CaO}$$

$$\times \frac{1\ kg}{1000\ g} = 27.6\ kg$$

237. a. Given: $P_1 = 3.0$ atm;
$V_1 = 25$ mL;
$P_2 = 6.0$ atom

Unknown: V_2

$$V_2 = \frac{P_1 V_1}{P_2} = 3.0 \text{ atm} \times \frac{25 \text{ mL}}{6.0 \text{ atm}} = 13 \text{ mL}$$

b. Given: $P_1 = 99.97$
kPa; $V_1 =$
550. mL; V_2
$= 275$ mL

Unknown: P_2

$$P_2 = \frac{P_1 V_1}{V_2} = \frac{99.97 \text{ kPa} \times 550. \text{ mL}}{275 \text{ mL}} = 200. \text{ kPa}$$

c. Given: $P_1 = 0.89$
atm; $P_2 =$
3.56 atm;
$V_2 = 20.0$ L

Unknown: V_1

$$V_1 = \frac{P_2 V_2}{P_1} = \frac{3.56 \text{ atm} \times 20.0 \text{ L}}{0.89 \text{ atm}} = 80. \text{ L}$$

d. Given: $V_1 = 800.$ mL;
$P_2 = 500.$ kPa;
$V_2 = 160.$ mL

Unknown: P_1

$$P_1 = \frac{P_2 V_2}{V_1} = \frac{500. \text{ kPa} \times 160. \text{ mL}}{800. \text{ mL}} = 100. \text{ kPa}$$

e. Given: $P_1 =$
0.040 atm;
$P_2 = 250$ atm;
$V_2 = 1.0 \times$
10^{-2} L

Unknown: V_1

$$V_1 = \frac{P_2 V_2}{P_1} = \frac{250 \text{ atm} \times 1.0 \times 10^{-2} \text{ L}}{0.040 \text{ atm}} = 63 \text{ L}$$

---

238. Given: $P_1 = 1.8$ atm;
$V_1 = 2.8$ L; P_2
$= 1.2$ atm

Unknown: V_2

$$V_2 = \frac{P_1 V_1}{P_2} = \frac{1.8 \text{ atm} \times 2.8 \text{ L}}{1.2 \text{ atm}} = 4.2 \text{ L}$$

---

239. Given: $P_1 = 99.3$ kPa;
$V_1 = 48.0$ L;
$V_2 = 16.0$ L

Unknown: P_2

$$P_2 = \frac{P_1 V_1}{V_2} = \frac{99.3 \text{ kPa} \times 48.0 \text{ L}}{16.0 \text{ L}} = 298 \text{ kPa}$$

---

240. Given: $P_1 = 0.989$ atm;
$V_1 = 59.0$ mL;
$P_2 = 0.967$ atm

Unknown: V_2

$$V_2 = \frac{P_1 V_1}{P_2} = \frac{0.989 \text{ atm} \times 59.0 \text{ mL}}{0.967 \text{ atm}} = 60.3 \text{ mL}$$

---

241. Given: $P_1 = 6.5$ atm;
$V_1 = 2.2$ L;
$P_2 = 1.15$ atm

Unknown: V_2

$$V_2 = \frac{P_1 V_1}{P_2} = \frac{6.5 \text{ atm} \times 2.2 \text{ L}}{1.15 \text{ atm}} = 12 \text{ L}$$

242. a. Given: $V_1 = 40.0$ mL;

$T_1 = 280.$ K;

$T_2 = 350.$ K;

Unknown: V_2

$$V_2 = \frac{V_1 T_2}{T_1} = \frac{40.0 \text{ mL} \times 350 \text{ K}}{280. \text{ K}} = 50.0 \text{ mL}$$

b. Given: $V_1 = 0.606$ L;

$T_1 = 300.$ K;

$V_2 = 0.404$ L

Unknown: T_2

$$T_2 = \frac{V_2 T_1}{V_1} = \frac{0.404 \text{ L} \times 300. \text{ K}}{0.606 \text{ L}} = 200. \text{ K}$$

c. Given: $T_1 = 292$ K;

$V_2 = 250.$ mL;

$T_2 = 365$ K

Unknown: V_1

$$V_1 = \frac{V_2 T_1}{T_2} = \frac{250. \text{ mL} \times 292 \text{ K}}{365 \text{ K}} = 200. \text{ mL}$$

d. Given: $V_1 = 100.$ mL;

$V_2 = 125$ mL;

$T_2 = 305$ K

Unknown: T_1

$$T_1 = \frac{T_2 V_1}{V_2} = \frac{305 \text{ K} \times 100. \text{ mL}}{125 \text{ mL}} = 244 \text{ K}$$

e. Given: $V_1 = 0.0024$ L;

$T_1 = 22°C$;

$T_2 = -14°C$;

$K = 273 + °C$

Unknown: V_2

$$V_2 = \frac{V_1 T_2}{T_1} = \frac{0.0024 \text{ L} \times (273 - 14) \text{ K}}{(273 + 22) \text{ K}} = \frac{0.0024 \text{ L} \times 259 \text{ K}}{259 \text{ K}} = 0.0021 \text{ L}$$

243. Given: $V_1 = 2.75$ L; $T_1 = 18°C$; $T_2 = 45°C$;

$K = 273 + °C$

Unknown: V_2

$$V_2 = \frac{V_1 T_2}{T_1} = \frac{2.75 \text{ L} \times (273 + 45) \text{ K}}{(273 + 18) \text{ K}} = \frac{2.75 \text{ L} \times 318 \text{ K}}{291 \text{ K}} = 3.01 \text{ L}$$

244. Given: $V_1 = 0.43$ mL;

$T_1 = 24°C$; $V_2 = 0.57$ mL; $K = 273 + °C$

Unknown: T_2

$$T_2 = \frac{T_1 V_2}{V_1} = \frac{(273 + 24) \text{ K} \times 0.57 \text{ mL}}{0.43 \text{ mL}} = 394 \text{ K}$$

$$394 \text{ K} - 273 = 121°C$$

245. a. Given: $P_1 = 1.50$ atm;

$T_1 = 273$ K;

$T_2 = 410$ K

Unknown: P_2

$$P_2 = \frac{P_1 T_2}{T_1} = \frac{1.50 \text{ atm} \times 410 \text{ K}}{273 \text{ K}} = 2.25 \text{ atm}$$

b. Given: $P_1 = 0.208$ atm;

$T_1 = 300.$ K;

$P_2 = 0.156$ atm

Unknown: T_2

$$T_2 = \frac{T_1 P_2}{P_1} = \frac{300. \text{ K} \times 0.156 \text{ atm}}{0.208 \text{ atm}} = 225 \text{ K}$$

c. Given: $T_1 = 52°C$;
  $P_2 = 99.7$ kPa;
  $T_2 = 77°C$;
  $K = 273 + °C$

  Unknown: P_1

$$P_1 = \frac{P_2 T_1}{T_2} = \frac{99.7 \text{ kPa} \times (52 + 273) \text{ K}}{(77 + 273) \text{ K}} = \frac{99.7 \text{ kPa} \times 325 \text{ K}}{350. \text{ K}} = 92.6 \text{ kPa}$$

d. Given: $P_1 = 5.20$ atm;
  $P_2 = 4.16$ atm;
  $T_2 = -13°C$;
  $K = 273 + °C$

  Unknown: T_1

$$T_1 = \frac{P_1 T_2}{P_1} = \frac{5.20 \text{ atm} \times (273 - 13) \text{ K}}{4.16 \text{ atm}} = \frac{5.20 \text{ atm} \times 260. \text{ K}}{4.16 \text{ atm}} = 325 \text{ K}$$

$325 \text{ K} - 273 = 52°C$

e. Given: $P_1 = 8.33 \times 10^{-4}$ atm;
  $T_1 = -84°C$;
  $P_2 = 3.92 \times 10^{-3}$ atm;
  $K = 273 + °C$

  Unknown: T_2

$$T_2 = \frac{T_1 P_2}{P_1} = \frac{(273 - 84) \text{ K} \times 3.92 \times 10^{-3} \text{ atm}}{8.33 \times 10^{-4} \text{ atm}} = \frac{189 \text{ K} \times 3.92 \times 10^{-3}}{8.33 \times 10^{-4}}$$

$= 889 \text{ K}$

$889 \text{ K} - 273 = 616°C$

---

246. Given: $P_1 = 4.882$ atm;
  $P_2 = 4.690$ atm;
  $T_2 = 8°C$;
  $K = 273 + °C$

  Unknown: T_1

$$T_1 = \frac{P_1 T_2}{P_2} = \frac{4.882 \text{ atm} \times (273 + 8) \text{ K}}{4.690 \text{ atm}} = \frac{4.882 \text{ atm} \times 281 \text{ K}}{4.690 \text{ atm}} = 293 \text{ K}$$

$293 \text{ K} - 273 = 20.°C$

---

247. Given: $P_1 = 107$ kPa;
  $T_1 = 22°C$;
  $T_2 = 45°C$;
  $K = 273 + °C$

  Unknown: P_2

$$P_2 = \frac{P_1 T_2}{T_1} = \frac{107 \text{ kPa} \times (273 + 45) \text{ K}}{(273 + 22) \text{ K}} = \frac{107 \text{ kPa} \times 318 \text{ K}}{295 \text{ K}} = 115 \text{ kPa}$$

---

248. a. Given: $P_1 = 99.3$ kPa;
  $V_1 = 225$ mL;
  $T_1 = 15°C$;
  $P_2 = 102.8$ kPa;
  $T_2 = 24°C$

  Unknown: V_2

$$V_2 = \frac{P_1 V_1 T_2}{T_1 P_2} = \frac{99.3 \text{ kPa} \times 225 \text{ mL} \times (273 + 24) \text{ K}}{(273 + 15) \text{ K} \times 102.8 \text{ kPa}} = 224 \text{ mL}$$

b. Given: $P_1 = 0.959$ atm;
  $V_1 = 3.50$ L;
  $T_1 = 45°C$;
  $V_2 = 3.70$ L;
  $T_2 = 37°C$

  Unknown: P_2

$$P_2 = \frac{P_1 V_1 T_2}{T_1 V_2} = \frac{0.959 \text{ atm} \times 3.50 \text{ L} \times (273 + 37) \text{ K}}{(273 + 45) \text{ K} \times 3.70 \text{ L}} = 0.884 \text{ atm}$$

c. Given: $P_1 = 0.0036$ atm;
  $V_1 = 62$ mL;
  $T_1 = 373$ K;
  $P_2 = 0.0029$ atm;
  $V_2 = 64$ mL

  Unknown: T_2

$$T_2 = \frac{T_1 P_2 V_2}{P_1 V_1} = \frac{373 \text{ K} \times 0.0029 \text{ atm} \times 64 \text{ mL}}{0.0036 \text{ atm} \times 62 \text{ mL}} = 310 \text{ K}$$

d. Given: $P_1 = 100.$ kPa;
$V_1 = 43.2$ mL;
$T_1 = 19°C$;
$P_2 = 101.3$
kPa; $T_2 = 0°C$

Unknown: V_2

$$V_2 = \frac{P_1V_1T_2}{T_1P_2} = \frac{100.\text{ kPa} \times 43.2\text{ mL} \times (273 + 0)\text{ K}}{(273 + 19)\text{ K} \times 101.3\text{ kPa}} = 39.9\text{ mL}$$

249. Given: $V_1 = 450.$ mL;
$P_1 = 100.$ kPa;
$T_1 = 17°C$;
$T_2 = 0°C$;
$P_2 = 101.3$ kPa

Unknown: V_2

$$V_2 = \frac{P_1V_1T_2}{T_1P_2} = \frac{100.\text{ kPa} \times 450.\text{ mL} \times (273 + 0)\text{ K}}{(273 + 17)\text{ K} \times 101.3\text{ kPa}} = 418\text{ mL}$$

250. Given: $T = 27°C$; H_2S
gas: $P_T = 207.33$
kPa; $V = 15$ mL

Unknown: P_{H_2O}; P_{H_2S}

Per Table A-8: $P_{H_2O} = 3.57$ kPa

$P_{H_2S} = P_T - P_{H_2O} = 207.33\text{ kPa} - 3.57\text{ kPa} = 203.76\text{ kPa}$

251. Given: $T = 10°C$;
$P_T = 105.5$ kPa;
$V = 1.93$ L;

$$\frac{P_1V_1}{T_1} = \frac{P_2V_2}{T_2}$$

Unknown: V_{H_2} at STP

Per Table A-8: $P_{H_2O} = 1.23$ kPa

$P_{H_2} = P_T - P_{H_2O} = 105.5\text{ kPa} - 1.23\text{ kPa} = 104.3\text{ kPa}$

$$V_2 = \frac{P_1V_1T_2}{T_1P_2} = \frac{104.3\text{ kPa} \times 1.93\text{ L} \times (273 + 0)\text{ K}}{(273 + 10)\text{ K} \times 101.3\text{ kPa}} = 1.92\text{ L}$$

252. Given: $V_1 = 338$ mL
CH_4 at $T_1 =$
$19°C$, $P_1 =$
0.9566 atm;
$T_2 = 26°C$,
$P_2 = 0.989$

Unknown: V_2 of CH_4

$P_{1(H_2O)} = 2.19$ kPa; $P_{2(H_2O)} = 3.36$ kPa

$$P_{1(CH_4)} = 0.9566\text{ atm} - \left(2.19\text{ kPa} \times \frac{1\text{ atm}}{101.3\text{ kPa}}\right) = 0.935\text{ atm}$$

$$P_{2(CH_4)} = 0.989\text{ atm} - \left(3.36\text{ kPa} \times \frac{1\text{ atm}}{101.3\text{ kPa}}\right) = 0.956\text{ atm}$$

$$V_2 = \frac{P_1V_1T_2}{T_1P_2} = \frac{0.935\text{ atm} \times 338\text{ mL} \times (273 + 26)\text{ K}}{(273 + 19)\text{ K} \times 0.956\text{ atm}} = 339\text{ mL}$$

$V_2 > V_1$; Student 2 collected more.

253. T is constant; $P_1V_1 = P_2V_2$

a. Given: $P_1 = 127.3$ kPa;
$V_1 = 796$ cm^3;
$V_2 = 965$ cm^3

Unknown: P_2

$$P_2 = \frac{P_1V_1}{V_2} = \frac{127.3\text{ kPa} \times 796\text{ cm}^3}{965\text{ cm}^3} = 105\text{ kPa}$$

b. Given: $P_1 = 7.1 \times 10^2$ atm; $\quad V_1 = \dfrac{P_2 V_2}{P_1} = \dfrac{9.6 \times 10^{-1} \text{ atm} \times 3.7 \times 10^3 \text{ mL}}{7.1 \times 10^2 \text{ atm}} = 5.0$ mL

$P_2 = 9.6 \times 10^{-1}$ atm;

$V_2 = 3.7 \times 10^3$ mL

Unknown: V_1

c. Given: $V_1 = 1.77$ L; $\quad P_1 = \dfrac{P_2 V_2}{V_1} = \dfrac{30.79 \text{ kPa} \times 2.44 \text{ L}}{1.77 \text{ L}} = 42.4$ kPa

$P_2 = 30.79$ kPa;

$V_2 = 2.44$ L

Unknown: P_1

d. Given: $P_1 = 114$ kPa; $\quad V_2 = \dfrac{P_1 V_1}{P_2} = \dfrac{114 \text{ kPa} \times 2.93 \text{ dm}^3}{4.93 \times 10^4 \text{ kPa}} = 6.78 \times 10^{-3} \text{ dm}^3$

$V_1 = 2.93$ dm^3;

$P_2 = 4.93 \times 10^4$ kPa

Unknown: V_2

e. Given: $P_1 = 1.00$ atm; $\quad P_2 = \dfrac{P_1 V_1}{V_2} = \dfrac{1.00 \text{ atm} \times 120. \text{ mL}}{97.0 \text{ mL}} = 1.24$ atm

$V_1 = 120.$ mL;

$V_2 = 97.0$ mL

Unknown: P_2

f. Given: $P_1 = 0.77$ atm; $\quad V_2 = \dfrac{P_1 V_1}{P_2} = \dfrac{0.77 \text{ atm} \times 3.6 \text{ m}^3}{1.90 \text{ atm}} = 1.5 \text{ m}^3$

$V_2 = 3.6$ m^3;

$P_2 = 1.90$ atm

Unknown: V_2

---

254. Given: $V_1 = 0.722$ m^3; $\quad V_2 = \dfrac{P_1 V_1}{P_2} = \dfrac{10.6 \text{ atm} \times 0.722 \text{ m}^3}{0.96 \text{ atm}} = 8.0 \text{ m}^3$

$P_1 = 10.6$ atm;

$P_2 = 0.96$ atm;

$P_1 V_1 = P_2 V_2$

Unknown: V_2

---

255. Given: $V_1 = 7.50 \times 10^3$ L; $V_2 = 195$ L; $\quad P_1 = \dfrac{P_2 V_2}{V_1} = \dfrac{0.993 \text{ atm} \times 195 \text{ L}}{7.50 \times 10^3 \text{ L}} = 0.0258$ atm

$P_2 = 0.993$ atm;

$P_1 V_1 = P_2 V_2$

Unknown: P_1

---

256. Given: $V_1 = 5.70 \times 10^{-1}$ dm^3; $\quad V_2 = \dfrac{P_1 V_1}{P_2} = \dfrac{1.05 \text{ atm} \times 5.70 \times 10^{-1} \text{ dm}^3}{7.47 \text{ atm}} = 8.01 \times 10^{-2} \text{ dm}^3$

$P_1 = 1.05$ atm;

$P_2 = 7.47$ atm;

$P_1 V_1 = P_2 V_2$

Unknown: V_2

257. P is constant; $\dfrac{V_1}{T_1} = \dfrac{V_2}{T_2}$;

$\text{K} = 273 + {}^\circ\text{C}$

a. Given: $V_1 = 26.5$ mL; $\quad T_1 = \dfrac{T_2 V_1}{V_2} = \dfrac{290.\ \text{K} \times 26.5\ \text{mL}}{32.9\ \text{mL}} = 234$ K

$\qquad V_2 = 32.9$ mL;

$\qquad T_2 = 290.$ K

Unknown: T_1

b. Given: $T_1 = 100{}^\circ\text{C}$; $\quad V_1 = \dfrac{T_1 V_2}{T_2} = \dfrac{(273 + 100)\ \text{K} \times 0.83\ \text{dm}^3}{(273 + 29)\ \text{K}} = 1.0\ \text{dm}^3$

$\qquad V_2 = 0.83\ \text{dm}^3$;

$\qquad T_2 = 29{}^\circ\text{C}$

Unknown: V_1

c. Given: $V_1 = 7.44 \times$ $\quad T_2 = \dfrac{T_1 V_2}{V_1} = \dfrac{(870.\ + 273)\ \text{K} \times 2.59 \times 10^2\ \text{mm}^3}{7.44 \times 10^4\ \text{mm}^3} = 3.98$ K

$\qquad 10^4\ \text{mm}^3$;

$\qquad T_1 = 870{}^\circ\text{C}$;

$\qquad V_2 = 2.59 \times$ $\qquad 3.98\ \text{K} - 273.15 = -269.17{}^\circ\text{C}$

$\qquad 10^2\ \text{mm}^3$

Unknown: T_2 in ${}^\circ\text{C}$

d. Given: $V_1 = 5.63 \times$ $\quad V_2 = \dfrac{V_1 T_2}{T_1} = \dfrac{5.63 \times 10^{-2}\ \text{L} \times 190.\ \text{K}}{132\ \text{K}} = 8.10 \times 10^{-2}$ L

$\qquad 10^{-2}$ L;

$\qquad T_1 = 132$ K;

$\qquad T_2 = 190.$ K

Unknown: V_2

e. Given: $T_1 = 243$ K; $\quad V_1 = \dfrac{V_2 T_1}{T_2} = \dfrac{819\ \text{cm}^3 \times 243\ \text{K}}{409\ \text{K}} = 487\ \text{cm}^3$

$\qquad V_2 = 819\ \text{cm}^3$;

$\qquad T_2 = 409$ K

Unknown: V_1

f. Given: $V_1 = 679\ \text{m}^3$; $\quad V_2 = \dfrac{V_1 T_2}{T_1} = \dfrac{679\ \text{m}^3 \times (273 - 246)\ \text{K}}{(273 - 3)\ \text{K}} = 67.9\ \text{m}^3$

$\qquad T_1 = -3{}^\circ\text{C}$;

$\qquad T_2 = -246{}^\circ\text{C}$

Unknown: V_2

258. Given: $V_1 = 1.15\ \text{cm}^3$; $\quad V_2 = \dfrac{V_1 T_2}{T_1} = \dfrac{1.15\ \text{cm}^3 \times (273 + 99)\ \text{K}}{(273 + 22)\ \text{K}} = 1.45\ \text{cm}^3$

$\qquad T_1 = 22{}^\circ\text{C}$;

$\qquad T_2 = 99{}^\circ\text{C}$;

$\qquad \dfrac{V_1}{T_1} = \dfrac{V_2}{T_2}$;

$\qquad \text{K} = 273 + {}^\circ\text{C}$

Unknown: V_2

259. Given: $V_1 = 6.75\ \text{dm}^3$; $\quad T_2 = \dfrac{V_2 T_1}{V_1} = \dfrac{5.03\ \text{dm}^3 \times (273 + 40.)\ \text{K}}{6.75\ \text{dm}^3} = 233$ K

$\qquad T_1 = 40.{}^\circ\text{C}$;

$\qquad V_2 = 5.03\ \text{dm}^3$;

$\qquad \dfrac{V_1}{T_1} = \dfrac{V_2}{T_2}$; $\qquad 233\ \text{K} - 273 = -40.{}^\circ\text{C}$

$\qquad \text{K} = 273 + {}^\circ\text{C}$

Unknown: T_2

260. V is constant;

$\dfrac{P_1}{T_1} = \dfrac{P_2}{T_2};$

$K = 273 + °C$

$T_1 = \dfrac{T_2 P_1}{P_2} = \dfrac{(273 + 192)\,K \times 0.777\,atm}{5.6\,atm} = 64.5\,K$

$64.5\,K - 273 = -208°C$

a. Given: $P_1 = 0.777$ atm;

$P_2 = 5.6$ atm;

$T_2 = 192°C$

Unknown: T_1 in °C

b. Given: $P_1 = 152$ kPa;

$T_1 = 302$ K;

$T_2 = 11$ K

Unknown: P_2

$P_2 = \dfrac{P_1 T_2}{T_1} = \dfrac{152\,kPa \times 11\,K}{302\,K} = 5.5\,kPa$

c. Given: $T_1 = -76°C$;

$P_2 = 3.97$ atm;

$T_2 = 27°C$

Unknown: P_1

$P_1 = \dfrac{P_2 T_1}{T_2} = \dfrac{3.97\,atm \times (273 - 76)\,K}{(273 + 27)\,K} = 2.61\,atm$

d. Given: $P_1 = 395$ atm;

$T_1 = 46°C$;

$P_2 = 706$ atm

Unknown: T_2 in °C

$T_2 = \dfrac{T_1 P_2}{P_1} = \dfrac{(273 + 46)\,K \times 706\,atm}{395\,atm} = 570.\,K$

$570.\,K - 273 = 297°C$

e. Given: $T_1 = -37°C$;

$P_2 = 350.$ atm;

$T_2 = 2050°C$

Unknown: P_1

$P_1 = \dfrac{P_2 T_1}{T_2} = \dfrac{350.\,atm \times (273 - 37)\,K}{(273 + 2050)\,K} = 35.6\,atm$

f. Given: $P_1 = 0.39$ atm;

$T_1 = 263$ K;

$P_2 = 0.058$ atm

Unknown: T_2

$T_2 = \dfrac{T_1 P_2}{P_1} = \dfrac{263\,K \times 0.058\,atm}{0.39\,atm} = 39\,K$

---

261. Given: $T_1 = 22°C$;

$P_1 = 0.982$ atm;

$T_2 = -3°C$;

$\dfrac{P_1}{T_1} = \dfrac{P_2}{T_2};$

$K = 273 + °C$

Unknown: P_2

$P_2 = \dfrac{T_2 P_1}{T_1} = \dfrac{(273 - 3)\,K \times 0.982\,atm}{(273 + 22)\,K} = 0.899\,atm$

---

262. Given: $P_1 = 2.50$ atm;

$T_1 = 33°C$;

$T_2 = 0°C$;

$\dfrac{P_1}{T_1} = \dfrac{P_2}{T_2};$

$K = 273 + °C$

Unknown: P_2

$P_2 = \dfrac{P_1 T_2}{T_1} = \dfrac{2.50\,atm \times (273 + 0)\,K}{(273 + 33)\,K} = 2.23\,atm$

---

263. Given: $P_1 = 127.5$ kPa;

$T_1 = 290.$ K;

$P_2 = 3.51$ kPa;

$\dfrac{P_1}{T_1} = \dfrac{P_2}{T_2};$

Unknown: T_2

$T_2 = \dfrac{T_1 P_2}{P_1} = \dfrac{290.\,K \times 3.51\,kPa}{127.5\,kPa} = 7.98\,K$

264. $\dfrac{V_1P_1}{T_1} = \dfrac{V_2P_2}{T_2};$

$K = 273 + °C$

$V_2 = \dfrac{V_1P_1T_2}{T_1P_2} = \dfrac{1.65 \text{ L} \times 1.03 \text{ atm} \times (273 + 46) \text{ K}}{(273 + 19) \text{ K} \times 0.920 \text{ atm}} = 2.02 \text{ L}$

a. Given: $P_1 = 1.03 \text{ atm};$
$V_1 = 1.65 \text{ L};$
$T_1 = 19°C;$
$P_2 = 0.920 \text{ atm};$
$T_2 = 46°C$

Unknown: V_2

b. Given: $P_1 = 107.0 \text{ kPa};$
$V_1 = 3.79 \text{ dm}^3;$
$T_1 = 73°C;$
$V_2 = 7.58 \text{ dm}^3;$
$T_2 = 217°C$

Unknown: P_2

$P_2 = \dfrac{V_1P_1T_2}{T_1V_2} = \dfrac{3.79 \text{ dm}^3 \times 107.0 \text{ kPa} \times (273 + 217) \text{ K}}{(273 + 73) \text{ K} \times 7.58 \text{ dm}^3} = 75.8 \text{ kPa}$

c. Given: $P_1 = 0.029 \text{ atm};$
$V_1 = 249 \text{ mL};$
$P_2 = 0.098 \text{ atm};$
$V_2 = 197 \text{ mL};$
$T_2 = 293 \text{ K}$

Unknown: T_1

$T_1 = \dfrac{V_1P_1T_2}{V_2P_2} = \dfrac{249 \text{ mL} \times 0.029 \text{ atm} \times 293 \text{ K}}{197 \text{ mL} \times 0.098 \text{ atm}} = 110 \text{ K}$

d. Given: $P_1 = 113 \text{ kPa};$
$T_1 = 12°C;$
$P_2 = 149 \text{ kPa};$
$V_2 = 3.18 \times 10^3 \text{ mm}^3;$
$T_2 = -18°C$

Unknown: V_1

$V_1 = \dfrac{V_2P_2T_1}{T_2P_1} = \dfrac{3.18 \times 10^3 \text{ mm}^3 \times 149 \text{ kPa} \times (273 + 12) \text{ K}}{(273 - 18) \text{ K} \times 113 \text{ kPa}}$

$= 4.69 \times 10^3 \text{ mm}^3$

e. Given: $P_1 = 1.15 \text{ atm};$
$V_1 = 0.93 \text{ m}^3;$
$T_1 = -22°C;$
$P_2 = 1.01 \text{ atm};$
$V_2 = 0.85 \text{ m}^3$

Unknown: T_2

$T_2 = \dfrac{V_2P_2T_1}{V_1P_1} = \dfrac{0.85 \text{ m}^3 \times 1.01 \text{ atm} \times (273 - 22) \text{ K}}{0.93 \text{ m}^3 \times 1.15 \text{ atm}} = 210 \text{ K}$

$201 \text{ K} - 273 = -72°C$

f. Given: $V_1 = 156 \text{ cm}^3;$
$T_1 = 195 \text{ K};$
$P_2 = 2.25 \text{ atm};$
$V_2 = 468 \text{ cm}^3;$
$T_2 = 585 \text{ K}$

Unknown: P_1

$P_1 = \dfrac{V_2P_2T_1}{T_2V_1} = \dfrac{468 \text{ cm}^3 \times 2.25 \text{ atm} \times 195 \text{ K}}{585 \text{ K} \times 156 \text{ cm}^3} = 2.25 \text{ atm}$

265. Given: $\dfrac{P_1V_1}{T_1} = \dfrac{P_2V_2}{T_2};$

$K = 273 + °C;$
$V_1 = 392 \text{ cm}^3;$
$P_1 = 0.987 \text{ atm};$
$T_1 = 21°C;$
$T_2 = 13°C;$
$P_2 = 0.992 \text{ atm}$

Unknown: V_2

$V_2 = \dfrac{V_1P_1T_2}{T_1P_2} = \dfrac{392 \text{ cm}^3 \times 0.987 \text{ atm} \times (273 + 13) \text{ K}}{(273 + 21) \text{ K} \times 0.992 \text{ atm}} = 379 \text{ cm}^3$

266. Given: $P_T = 0.989$ atm;
$\quad\quad\quad\quad$ $T = 17°C$

$\quad\quad$ Unknown: P_{H_2}

from Table A-8: $P_{H_2O} = 1.94 \text{ kPa} \times \dfrac{1 \text{ atm}}{101.3 \text{ kPa}} = 0.0192$ atm

$P_{H_2} = P_T - P_{H_2O} = 0.989 \text{ atm} - 0.0192 \text{ atm} = 0.970 \text{ atm or } 98.3 \text{ kPa}$

---

267. Given: $P_1 = 1.77$ atm;
$\quad\quad\quad\quad$ $V_1 = 1.00$ L;
$\quad\quad\quad\quad$ $V_2 = 1.50$ L;
$\quad\quad\quad\quad$ $P_2 = 0.487$ atm;
$\quad\quad\quad\quad$ $P_1V_1 = P_2V_2$

$\quad\quad$ Unknown: equalized
$\quad\quad\quad\quad\quad$ P in V_T

$V_T = V_1 + V_2 = 1.00 \text{ L} + 1.50 \text{ L} = 2.50$ L

$\dfrac{P_1V_1}{V_T} = \dfrac{1.77 \text{ atm} \times 1.00 \text{ L}}{2.50 \text{ L}} = 0.708$ atm

$\dfrac{P_2V_2}{V_T} = \dfrac{0.487 \text{ atm} \times 1.50 \text{ L}}{2.50 \text{ L}} = 0.292$ atm

$P_T = 0.708 \text{ atm} + 0.292 \text{ atm} = 1.00$ atm

---

268. Given: $T_1 = 10.°C$;
$\quad\quad\quad\quad$ $P_T = 1.02$ atm;
$\quad\quad\quad\quad$ $V_1 = 293$ mL;
$\quad\quad\quad\quad$ $\dfrac{P_1V_1}{T_1} = \dfrac{P_2V_2}{T_2}$;
$\quad\quad\quad\quad$ $P_2 = 1.00$ atm;
$\quad\quad\quad\quad$ $T_2 = 0°C$;
$\quad\quad\quad\quad$ $K = 273$

$\quad\quad$ Unknown: V_{O_2} at STP
$\quad\quad\quad\quad\quad$ (V_2)

From Table A-8: $P_{H_2O} = 1.23 \text{ kPa} \times \dfrac{1 \text{ atm}}{101.3 \text{ kPa}} = 0.0121$ atm

$P_{O_2} = P_T - P_{H_2O} = 1.02 \text{ atm} - 0.0121 \text{ atm} = 1.01 \text{ atm} = P_1$

$V_2 = \dfrac{P_1V_1T_2}{T_1P_2} = \dfrac{1.01 \text{ atm} \times 293 \text{ mL} \times (273 + 0) \text{ K}}{(273 + 10) \text{ K} \times 1.00 \text{ atm}} = 285$ mL

---

269. Given: $P_1 = 101.3$ kPa;
$\quad\quad\quad\quad$ $T_1 = 20°C$;
$\quad\quad\quad\quad$ $V_1 = 325 \text{ cm}^3$;
$\quad\quad\quad\quad$ $P_2 = 76.24$ kPa;
$\quad\quad\quad\quad$ $T_2 = 10°C$;
$\quad\quad\quad\quad$ gases are air
$\quad\quad\quad\quad$ over water;
$\quad\quad\quad\quad$ $K = 273 + °C$;
$\quad\quad\quad\quad$ $P_T = P_{air} + P_{H_2O}$;
$\quad\quad\quad\quad$ $P_{H_2O(20°C)} = 2.34$
$\quad\quad\quad\quad$ kPa; $P_{H_2O(10°C)} = $
$\quad\quad\quad\quad$ 1.23 kPa

$\quad\quad$ Unknown: V_2; V of
$\quad\quad\quad\quad\quad$ water lost

$P_{A_1} = P_1 - P_{H_2O(20°C)} = 101.3 \text{ kPa} - 2.34 \text{ kPa} = 99.0$ kPa

In sealed bottle on mountain: $P_{A_2} = P_{A_1} + P_{H_2O(10°C)}$

$= 99.0 \text{ kPa} + 1.23 \text{ kPa} = 100.2$ kPa

$V_2 = \dfrac{P_{A_2}V_1T_2}{T_1P_2} = \dfrac{100.2 \text{ kPa} \times 325 \text{ cm}^3 \times (273 + 10) \text{ K}}{(273 + 20) \text{ K} \times 76.24 \text{ kPa}} = 413 \text{ cm}^3$

$V_{H_2O} = 413 \text{ cm}^3 - 325 \text{ cm}^3 = 88 \text{ cm}^3 \text{ H}_2O$

---

270. Given: 1°C change in
$\quad\quad\quad\quad$ T produces a
$\quad\quad\quad\quad$ change of
$\quad\quad\quad\quad$ 0.20 cm^3 in V;
$\quad\quad\quad\quad$ $\dfrac{V_1}{T_1} = \dfrac{V_2}{T_2}$;
$\quad\quad\quad\quad$ $K = 273 + °C$

$\quad\quad$ Unknown: V at 20.°C

$\dfrac{V}{(273 + 20) \text{ K}} = \dfrac{V + 0.20 \text{ cm}^3}{(273 + 21) \text{ K}}$

$294 \, V = 293 \, V + 293 \times 0.20 \text{ cm}^3$

$V = 59 \text{ cm}^3$

---

271. Given: $V_1 = 62.25$ mL;
$\quad\quad\quad\quad$ $T = 22°C$;
$\quad\quad\quad\quad$ $P_T = 97.7$ kPa;
$\quad\quad\quad\quad$ $V_2 = 50.00$ mL;
$\quad\quad\quad\quad$ $P_{H_2O} = 2.64$ kPa

$\quad\quad$ Unknown: P_2

$P_{N_2} = P_T - P_{H_2O} = 97.7 \text{ kPa} - 2.64 \text{ kPa} = 95.1$ kPa

$P_2 = \dfrac{P_{N_2}V_1}{V_2} = \dfrac{95.1 \text{ kPa} \times 62.25 \text{ mL}}{50.00 \text{ mL}} = 118$ kPa

272. Given: $V_1 = 844$ mL;
$T_1 = 0.00°C$;
$P_1 = 1.000$ atm;
$P_T = 1.017$ atm;
$P_{H_2O} = 3.17$ kPa;
$T_2 = 25°C$;
$P_T = 1.017$ atm;
$$\frac{P_1V_1}{T_1} = \frac{P_2V_2}{T_2};$$
$K = 273 + °C$

Unknown: V_2; V_T at 25°C and 1.017 atm

$$P_2 = P_{NF_3} = P_T - P_{H_2O} = 1.017 \text{ atm} - 3.17 \text{ kPa} \left(\frac{1 \text{ atm}}{101.3 \text{ kPa}}\right) = 0.9857 \text{ atm}$$

$$V_2 = \frac{P_1V_1T_2}{T_1P_2} = \frac{1.000 \text{ atm} \times 844 \text{ mL} \times (273 + 25) \text{ K}}{(273 + 0) \text{ K} \times 0.9857 \text{ atm}} = 935 \text{ mL}$$

---

273. Given: $V_1 = 2.94$ kL;
$P_1 = 1.06$ atm;
$T_1 = 32°C$;
$P_2 = 0.092$ atm;
$T_2 = -35°C$;
$$\frac{P_1V_1}{T_1} = \frac{P_2V_2}{T_2};$$
$K = 273 + °C$

Unknown: V_2

$$V_2 = \frac{P_1V_1T_2}{T_1P_2} = \frac{1.06 \text{ atm} \times 2.94 \text{ kL} \times (273 - 35) \text{ K}}{(273 + 32) \text{ K} \times 0.092 \text{ atm}} = 26.4 \text{ kL}$$

---

274. Given: $P_1 = 2.96$ atm;
$T_1 = 17°C$;
$T_2 = 95°C$;
$$\frac{P_1}{T_1} = \frac{P_2}{T_2};$$
$K = 273 + °C$

Unknown: P_2

$$P_2 = \frac{P_1T_2}{T_1} = \frac{2.96 \text{ atm} \times (273 + 95) \text{ K}}{(273 + 17) \text{ K}} = 3.76 \text{ atm}$$

---

275. Given: $T_1 = 39°C$;
$V_2 = 108$ mL;
$T_2 = 21°C$;
$$\frac{V_1}{T_1} = \frac{V_2}{T_2};$$
$K = 273 + °C$

Unknown: V_1

$$V_1 = \frac{V_2T_1}{T_2} = \frac{108 \text{ mL} \times (273 + 39) \text{ K}}{(273 + 21) \text{ K}} = 115 \text{ mL}$$

---

276. Given: $V_1 = 624$ L;
$P_1 = 1.40$ atm;
$V_2 = 80.0$ L;
$P_1V_1 = P_2V_2$

Unknown: P_2

$$P_2 = \frac{P_1V_1}{V_2} = \frac{1.40 \text{ atm} \times 624 \text{ L}}{80.0 \text{ L}} = 10.9 \text{ atm}$$

---

277. a. Given: $P = 1.09$ atm;
$n = 0.0881$ mol;
$T = 302$ K
Unknown: V in L

$$V = \frac{nRT}{P} = \frac{0.0881 \text{ mol} \cdot 0.0821 \frac{\text{L} \cdot \text{atm}}{\text{mol} \cdot \text{K}} \times 302 \text{ K}}{1.09 \text{ atm}} = 2.00 \text{ L}$$

b. Given: $P = 94.9$ kPa;
$V = 0.0350$ L;
$T = 55°C$
Unknown: n

$$n = \frac{PV}{RT} = \frac{94.9 \text{ kPa} \times 0.0350 \text{ L}}{8.314 \frac{\text{L} \cdot \text{kPa}}{\text{mol} \cdot \text{K}} \times (273 + 55) \text{ K}} = 1.22 \times 10^{-3} \text{ mol}$$

c. Given: $V = 15.7$ L;
$n = 0.815$ mol;
$T = -20.°C$

Unknown: P in kPa

$$P = \frac{nRT}{V} = \frac{0.815 \text{ mol} \times 8.314 \frac{\text{L} \cdot \text{kPa}}{\text{mol} \cdot \text{K}} \times (273 - 20) \text{ K}}{15.7 \text{ L}} = 109 \text{ kPa}$$

d. Given: $P = 0.500$ atm;
$V = 629$ mL;
$n = 0.0337$ mol

Unknown: T in K

$$T = \frac{PV}{nR} = \frac{0.500 \text{ atm} \times 629 \text{ mL} \times 1 \text{ L}}{0.0337 \text{ mol} \times 0.0821 \frac{\text{L} \cdot \text{atm}}{\text{mol} \cdot \text{K}} \times 1000 \text{ mL}} = 114 \text{ K}$$

e. Given: $P = 0.950$ atm;
$n = 0.0818$ mol;
$T = 19°C$

Unknown: V in L

$$V = \frac{nRT}{P} = \frac{0.0818 \text{ mol} \times 0.0821 \frac{\text{L} \cdot \text{atm}}{\text{mol} \cdot \text{K}} \times (273 + 19) \text{ K}}{0.950 \text{ atm}} = 2.06 \text{ L}$$

f. Given: $P = 107$ kPa;
$V = 39.0$ mL;
$T = 27°C$

Unknown: n

$$n = \frac{PV}{RT} = \frac{107 \text{ kPa} \times 39.0 \text{ mL} \times 1 \text{ L}}{8.314 \frac{\text{L} \cdot \text{kPa}}{\text{mol} \cdot \text{K}} \times (273 + 27) \text{ K} \times 1000 \text{ mL}} = 1.67 \times 10^{-3} \text{ mol}$$

278. Given: $V = 425$ mL;
$T = 24°C$,
$P = 0.899$ atm

Unknown: n

$$n = \frac{PV}{RT} = \frac{0.899 \text{ atm} \times 425 \text{ mL} \times 1 \text{ L}}{0.0821 \frac{\text{L} \cdot \text{atm}}{\text{mol} \cdot \text{K}} \times (273 + 24) \text{ K} \times 1000 \text{ mL}} = 1.57 \times 10^{-2} \text{ mol}$$

279. Given: $m = 0.116$ g;
$V = 25.0$ mL;
$T = 127°C$;
$P = 155.3$ kPa;
$PV = \frac{mRT}{M}$

Unknown: M

$$M = \frac{mRT}{PV} = \frac{0.116 \text{ g} \times 8.314 \frac{\text{L} \cdot \text{kPa}}{\text{mol} \cdot \text{K}} \times (273 + 127) \text{ K} \times 1000 \text{ mL}}{155.3 \text{ kPa} \times 25.0 \text{ mL} \times 1 \text{ L}} = 99.4 \text{ g/mol}$$

280. Given: CO_2 gas;
$V = 7.10$ L;
$P = 1.11$ atm;
$T = 31°C$;
$PV = \frac{mRT}{M}$

Unknown: m

$M = 1 \text{ atom C} \times 12.01 \text{ amu/atom} + 2 \text{ atoms O} \times 16.00 \text{ amu/atom} = 44.01$ amu; $M = 44.01$ g/mol

$$m = \frac{MPV}{RT} = \frac{44.01 \text{ g/mol} \times 1.11 \text{ atm} \times 7.10 \text{ L}}{0.0821 \frac{\text{L} \cdot \text{atm}}{\text{mol} \cdot \text{K}} \times (273 + 31) \text{ K}} = 13.9 \text{ g}$$

281. Given: $T = 72°C$;
$P = 144.5$ kPa;
SiF_4 gas;
$D = \frac{MP}{RT}$

Unknown: D

$$D = \frac{MP}{RT} = \frac{104.09 \text{ g/mol} \times 144.5 \text{ kPa}}{8.314 \frac{\text{L} \cdot \text{kPa}}{\text{mol} \cdot \text{K}} \times (273 + 72) \text{ K}} = 5.24 \text{ g/L}$$

282. Given: $D = 1.13$ g/L;
$P = 1.09$ atm;
N_2 gas;
$D = \frac{MP}{RT}$

Unknown: T

$$T = \frac{MP}{DR} = \frac{28.02 \text{ g/mol} \times 1.09 \text{ atm}}{1.13 \text{ g/L} \times 0.0821 \frac{\text{L} \cdot \text{atm}}{\text{mol} \cdot \text{K}}} = 329 \text{ K}$$

283. a. Given: $P = 0.0477$ atm;
$V = 15\ 200$ L;
$T = -15°C$

Unknown: n

$$n = \frac{PV}{RT} = \frac{0.0477 \text{ atm} \times 15\ 200 \text{ L}}{0.0821 \dfrac{\text{L} \cdot \text{atm}}{\text{mol} \cdot \text{K}} \times (273 - 15) \text{ K}} = 34.2 \text{ mol}$$

b. Given: $V = 0.119$ mL;
$n = 0.000\ 350$ mol;
$T = 0°C$

Unknown: P in kPa

$$P = \frac{nRT}{V} = \frac{0.000\ 350 \text{ mol} \times 8.314 \dfrac{\text{L} \cdot \text{kPa}}{\text{mol} \cdot \text{K}} \times (273 + 0) \text{ K} \times 1000 \text{ mL}}{0.119 \text{ mL} \times 1 \text{ L}}$$

$= 6.68 \times 10^3$ kPa

c. Given: $P = 500.0$ kPa;
$V = 250.$ mL;
$n = 0.120$ mol

Unknown: T in °C

$$T = \frac{PV}{nR} = \frac{500.0 \text{ kPa} \times 250. \text{ mL} \times 1 \text{ L}}{0.120 \text{ mol} \times 8.314 \dfrac{\text{L} \cdot \text{kPa}}{\text{mol} \cdot \text{K}} \times 1000 \text{ mL}} = 125 \text{ K}$$

$125 \text{ K} - 273 = -148°C$

d. Given: $P = 19.5$ atm;
$n = 4.7 \times 10^4$ mol;
$T = 300.\ °C$

Unknown: V

$$V = \frac{nRT}{P} = \frac{4.7 \times 10^4 \text{ mol} \times 0.0821 \dfrac{\text{L} \cdot \text{atm}}{\text{mol} \cdot \text{K}} \times (273 + 300) \text{ K}}{19.5 \text{ atm}} = 1.1 \times 10^5 \text{ L}$$

---

284. Given: $PV = \dfrac{mRT}{M}$

a. Given: $P = 0.955$ atm;
$V = 3.77$ L;
$m = 8.23$ g;
$T = 25°C$

Unknown: M

$$M = \frac{mRT}{PV} = \frac{8.23 \text{ g} \times 0.0821 \dfrac{\text{L} \cdot \text{atm}}{\text{mol} \cdot \text{K}} \times (273 + 25) \text{ K}}{0.955 \text{ atm} \times 3.77 \text{ L}} = 55.9 \text{ g/mol}$$

b. Given: $P = 105.0$ kPa;
$V = 50.0$ mL;
$M = 48.02$ g/mol;
$T = 0°C$

Unknown: m

$$m = \frac{PVM}{RT} = \frac{105.0 \text{ kPa} \times 50.0 \text{ mL} \times 48.02 \text{ g/mol} \times 1 \text{ L}}{8.314 \dfrac{\text{L} \cdot \text{kPa}}{\text{mol} \cdot \text{K}} \times (273 + 0) \text{ K} \times 1000 \text{ mL}} = 0.111 \text{ g}$$

c. Given: $P = 0.782$ atm;
$m = 3.20 \times 10^{-3}$ g;
$M = 2.02$ g/mol;
$T = -5°C$

Unknown: V in L

$$V = \frac{mRT}{PM} = \frac{3.20 \times 10^{-3} \text{ g} \times 0.0821 \dfrac{\text{L} \cdot \text{atm}}{\text{mol} \cdot \text{K}} \times (273 - 5) \text{ K}}{0.782 \text{ atm} \times 2.02 \text{ g/mol}} = 4.46 \times 10^{-2} \text{ L}$$

d. Given: $V = 2.00$ L;
$m = 7.19$ g;
$M = 159.8$ g/mol;
$T = 185°C$

Unknown: P in atm

$$P = \frac{mRT}{MV} = \frac{7.19 \text{ g} \times 0.0821 \dfrac{\text{L} \cdot \text{atm}}{\text{mol} \cdot \text{K}} \times (273 + 185) \text{ K}}{159.8 \text{ g/mol} \times 2.00 \text{ L}} = 0.846 \text{ atm}$$

e. Given: $P = 107.2$ kPa;
  $V = 26.1$ mL;
  $m = 0.414$ g;
  $T = 45°C$

Unknown: M

$$M = \frac{mRT}{PV} = \frac{0.414 \text{ g} \times 8.314 \frac{\text{L} \cdot \text{kPa}}{\text{mol} \cdot \text{K}} \times (273 + 45) \text{ K} \times 1000 \text{ mL}}{107.2 \text{ kPa} \times 26.1 \text{ mL} \times 1 \text{ L}}$$

$$= 391 \text{ g/mol}$$

---

285. Given: $n = 1.00$ mol;
  $T = 25°C$;
  $P = 0.915$ kPa

Unknown: V

$$V = \frac{nRT}{P} = \frac{1.00 \text{ mol} \times 8.314 \frac{\text{L} \cdot \text{kPa}}{\text{mol} \cdot \text{K}} \times (273 + 25) \text{ K}}{0.915 \text{ kPa}} = 2.71 \times 10^3 \text{ L}$$

---

286. $D = \frac{MP}{RT}$

a. Given: $P = 1.12$ atm;
  $D = 2.40$ g/L;
  $T = 2°C$

Unknown: M

$$M = \frac{DRT}{P} = \frac{2.40 \text{ g/L} \times 0.0821 \frac{\text{L} \cdot \text{atm}}{\text{mol} \cdot \text{K}} \times (273 + 2) \text{ K}}{1.12 \text{ atm}} = 48.4 \text{ g/mol}$$

b. Given: $P = 7.50$ atm;
  $M = 30.07$ g/mol;
  $T = 20.°C$

Unknown: D in g/L

$$D = \frac{30.07 \text{ g/mol} \times 7.50 \text{ atm}}{0.0821 \frac{\text{L} \cdot \text{atm}}{\text{mol} \cdot \text{K}} \times (273 + 20.) \text{ K}} = 9.38 \text{ g/L}$$

c. Given: $P = 97.4$ kPa;
  $M = 104.09$ g/mol;
  $D = 4.37$ g/L

Unknown: T in °C

$$T = \frac{MP}{DR} = \frac{104.09 \text{ g/mol} \times 97.4 \text{ kPa}}{4.37 \text{ g/L} \times 8.314 \frac{\text{L} \cdot \text{kPa}}{\text{mol} \cdot \text{K}}} = 279 \text{ K}$$

$279 \text{ K} - 273 = 6°C$

d. Given: $M = 77.95$ g/mol;
  $D = 6.27$ g/L;
  $T = 66°C$

Unknown: P in atm

$$P = \frac{DRT}{M} = \frac{6.27 \text{ g/L} \times 0.0821 \frac{\text{L} \cdot \text{atm}}{\text{mol} \cdot \text{K}} \times (273 + 66) \text{ K}}{77.95 \text{ g/mol}} = 2.24 \text{ atm}$$

---

287. Given: $m = 1.36$ kg;
  N_2O gas;
  $V = 25.0$ L;
  $T = 59°C$

Unknown: P in atm

$$P = \frac{mRT}{MV} = \frac{1.36 \text{ kg} \times 0.0821 \frac{\text{L} \cdot \text{atm}}{\text{mol} \cdot \text{K}} \times (273 + 59) \text{ K} \times 1000 \text{ g}}{44.02 \text{ g/mol} \times 25.0 \text{ L} \times 1 \text{ kg}} = 33.7 \text{ atm}$$

---

288. Given: $AlCl_3$ vapor;
  $T = 225°C$;
  $P = 0.939$ atm

Unknown: D

$$D = \frac{MP}{RT} = \frac{133.33 \text{ g/mol} \times 0.939 \text{ atm}}{0.0821 \frac{\text{L} \cdot \text{atm}}{\text{mol} \cdot \text{K}} \times (273 + 225) \text{ K}} = 3.06 \text{ g/L}$$

---

289. Given: $D = 0.0262$ g/mL;
  $P = 0.918$ atm;
  $T = 10.°C$

Unknown: M

$$M = \frac{DRT}{P} = \frac{0.0262 \text{ g/mL} \times 0.0821 \frac{\text{L} \cdot \text{atm}}{\text{mol} \cdot \text{K}} \times (273 + 10) \text{ K} \times 1000 \text{ mL}}{0.918 \text{ atm} \times 1 \text{ L}}$$

$$= 663 \text{ g/mol}$$

290. Given: $m = 11.7$g;
He gas;
$P = 0.262$ atm;
$T = -50.°C$
Unknown: V

$$V = \frac{mRT}{MP} = \frac{11.9 \text{ g} \times 0.0821 \frac{\text{L} \cdot \text{atm}}{\text{mol} \cdot \text{K}} \times (273 - 50) \text{ K}}{4.00 \text{ g/mol} \times 0.262 \text{ atm}} = 208 \text{ L}$$

291. Given: $T = 15°C$; $P_{H_2O} =$
1.5988 kPa; $P_T =$
100.0 kPa; C_2H_6
gas; $V = 245$ mL
Unknown: n

$$P_{C_2H_6} = P_T - P_{H_2O} = 100.0 \text{ kPa} - 1.5988 \text{ kPa} = 98.4 \text{ kPa}$$

$$n = \frac{PV}{RT} = \frac{98.4 \text{ kPa} \times 245 \text{ mL} \times 1 \text{ L}}{8.314 \frac{\text{L} \cdot \text{kPa}}{\text{mol} \cdot \text{K}} \times (273 + 15) \text{ K} \times 1000 \text{ mL}} = 0.0101 \text{ mol}$$

292. Given: $V = 3.75$ L; NO
gas; $T = 19°C$;
$P = 1.10$ atm
Unknown: m

$$m = \frac{MPV}{RT} = \frac{30.01 \text{ g/mol} \times 1.10 \text{ atm} \times 3.75 \text{ L}}{0.0821 \frac{\text{L} \cdot \text{atm}}{\text{mol} \cdot \text{K}} \times (273 + 19) \text{ K}} = 5.16 \text{ g}$$

293. Given: theoretical yield
$NH_3 = 8.83$ g;
actual yield
NH_3 10.24 L;
$T_1 = 52°C$;
$P_1 = 105.3$ kPa;
1 mole gas at
STP = 22.4 L;
STP = 0°C, 101.3
kPa

Unknown: percent yield

$$V_{STP} = \frac{P_1 V_1 T_{STP}}{T_1 P_{STP}} = \frac{105.3 \text{ kPa} \times 10.24 \text{ L} \times (273 + 0) \text{ K}}{(273 + 52) \text{ K} \times 101.3 \text{ kPa}} = 8.94 \text{ L}$$

$$8.94 \text{ L} \times \frac{1 \text{ mol}}{22.4 \text{ L}} \times \frac{17.04 \text{ g}}{1 \text{ mol}} = 6.80 \text{ g actual yield}$$

$$\frac{6.80 \text{ g}}{8.83 \text{ g}} \times 100 = 77.0\% \text{ yield}$$

294. Given: $D = 0.405$ g/L;
$P = 0.889$ atm;
$T = 7°C$
Unknown: molar mass

$$M = \frac{DRT}{P} = \frac{0.405 \text{ g/L} \times 0.0821 \frac{\text{L} \cdot \text{atm}}{\text{mol} \cdot \text{K}} \times (273 + 7) \text{ K}}{0.889 \text{ atm}} = 10.5 \text{ g/mol}$$

295. Given: $V = 90.0$ L;
$P = 1780$ kPa;
$T = 18°C$;
mass empty
tank = 39.2 kg ;
mass tank +
gas = 50.5 kg

Unknown: molar mass
(M) of gas

$$m = 50.5 \text{ kg} - 39.2 \text{ kg} = 11.3 \text{ kg}$$

$$M = \frac{mRT}{PV} = \frac{11.3 \text{ kg} \times 8.314 \frac{\text{L} \cdot \text{kPa}}{\text{mol} \cdot \text{K}} \times (273 + 18) \text{ K} \times 1000 \text{ g}}{1780 \text{ kPa} \times 90.0 \text{ L} \times 1 \text{ kg}} = 171 \text{ g/mol}$$

296. Given: $V = 1.20 \times 10^3$ L;
$m = 12.0$ kg; HCl
gas; $T = 18°C$
Unknown: P

$$P = \frac{mRT}{MV} = \frac{12.0 \text{ kg} \times 0.0821 \frac{\text{L} \cdot \text{atm}}{\text{mol} \cdot \text{K}} \times (273 + 18) \text{ K} \times 1000 \text{ g}}{36.46 \text{ g/mol} \times 1.20 \times 10^3 \text{ L} \times 1 \text{ kg}} = 6.55 \text{ atm}$$

297. Given: $T = 20.°C$; Ne
gas; $D = 2.70$ g/L
Unknown: P in kPa

$$P = \frac{DRT}{M} = \frac{2.70 \text{ g/L} \times 8.314 \frac{\text{L} \cdot \text{kPa}}{\text{mol} \cdot \text{K}} \times (273 + 20) \text{ K}}{20.18 \text{ g/mol}} = 326 \text{ kPa}$$

298. Given: $V = 658$ mL; $m = 1.50$ g; Ne gas; $P = 4.50 \times 10^2$ kPa

Unknown: T

$$T = \frac{MPV}{mR} = \frac{20.18 \text{ g/mol} \times 4.50 \times 10^2 \text{ kPa} \times 658 \text{ mL} \times 1 \text{ L}}{1.50 \text{ g} \times 8.314 \frac{\text{L} \cdot \text{kPa}}{\text{mol} \cdot \text{K}} \times 1000 \text{ mL}} = 479 \text{ K}$$

---

299. Given: $m = 1.00$ g; H_2 gas; $P = 6.75$ millibars; 1 bar = 100 kPa = 0.9869 atm; $T_1 = -75°C$; $T_2 = -8°C$

Unknown : V at T_1 and T_2

$$V = \frac{TmR}{MP} = \frac{(273 - 75) \text{ K} \times 1.00 \text{ g} \times 8.314 \frac{\text{L} \cdot \text{kPa}}{\text{mol} \cdot \text{K}}}{2.02 \text{ g/mol} \times 0.675 \text{ kPa}} = 1210 \text{ L at } -75°C$$

$$V = \frac{TmR}{MP} = \frac{(273 - 8) \text{ K} \times 1.00 \text{ g} \times 8.314 \frac{\text{L} \cdot \text{kPa}}{\text{mol} \cdot \text{K}}}{2.02 \text{ g/mol} \times 0.675 \text{ kPa}} = 1620 \text{ L at } -8°C$$

---

300. Given: $n = 3.95$ mol; $V = 850.$ mL; $T = 15°C$

Unknown: P in kPa

$$P = \frac{nRT}{V} = \frac{3.95 \text{ mol} \times 8.314 \frac{\text{L} \cdot \text{kPa}}{\text{mol} \cdot \text{K}} \times (273 + 15) \text{ K} \times 1000 \text{ mL}}{850. \text{ mL} \times 1 \text{ L}} = 1.11 \times 10^4 \text{ kPa}$$

---

301. Given: $n = 0.00660$ mol; $P = 0.907$ atm; $T = 9°C$

Unknown: V in mL

$$V = \frac{nRT}{P} = \frac{0.00660 \text{ mol} \times 0.0821 \frac{\text{L} \cdot \text{atm}}{\text{mol} \cdot \text{K}} \times (273 + 9) \text{ K} \times 1000 \text{ mL}}{0.907 \text{ atm} \times 1 \text{ L}} = 168 \text{ mL}$$

---

302. Given: $m = 8.47$ kg; SO_2 gas; $P = 89.4$ kPa; $T = 40.°C$

Unknown: V

$$V = \frac{mRT}{MP} = \frac{8.47 \text{ kg} \times 8.314 \frac{\text{L} \cdot \text{kPa}}{\text{mol} \cdot \text{K}} \times (273 + 40) \text{ K} \times 1000 \text{ g}}{64.07 \text{ g/mol} \times 89.4 \text{ kPa} \times 1 \text{ kg}} = 3.85 \times 10^3 \text{ L}$$

---

303. Given: $m = 908$ g; He gas; $P = 128.3$ kPa; $T = 2°C$

Unknown: V

$$V = \frac{mRT}{MP} = \frac{908 \text{ g} \times 8.314 \frac{\text{L} \cdot \text{kPa}}{\text{mol} \cdot \text{K}} \times (273 + 2) \text{ K}}{4.00 \text{ g/mol} \times 128.3 \text{ kPa}} = 4.05 \times 10^3 \text{ L}$$

---

304. Given: $D = 1.162$ g/L; $T = 27°C$; $P = 100.0$ kPa

Unknown: M

$$M = \frac{DRT}{P} = \frac{1.162 \text{ g/L} \times 8.314 \frac{\text{L} \cdot \text{kPa}}{\text{mol} \cdot \text{K}} \times (273 + 27) \text{ K}}{100.0 \text{ kPa}} = 29.0 \text{ g/mol}$$

---

305. Given: balanced equation; 2800 L NH_3

Unknown: V of NO; V of O_2

$$2800 \text{ L NH}_3 \times \frac{5 \text{ L O}_2}{4 \text{ L NH}_3} = 3500 \text{ L O}_2$$

$$2800 \text{ L NH}_3 \times \frac{4 \text{ L NO}}{4 \text{ L NH}_3} = 2800 \text{ L NO}$$

---

306. Given: balanced equation; 3.60×10^4 mL F_2

Unknown: V of O_3: V of HF

$$3.60 \times 10^4 \text{ mL F}_2 \times \frac{1 \text{ mL O}_3}{3 \text{ mL F}_2} = 1.20 \times 10^4 \text{ mL O}_3$$

$$3.60 \times 10^4 \text{ mL F}_2 \times \frac{6 \text{ mL HF}}{3 \text{ mL F}_2} = 7.20 \times 10^4 \text{ mL HF}$$

307. Given: balanced equation; $P_1 = 2.26$ atm; $T_1 = 40°C$; $V_1 = 55.8$ mL

Unknown: V_{CO_2} produced at STP

$$V_2 \text{ (at STP)} = \frac{P_1 V_1 T_2}{T_1 P_2} = \frac{2.26 \text{ atm} \times 55.8 \text{ mL} \times (273 + 0) \text{ K}}{(273 + 40) \text{ K} \times 1.00 \text{ atm}} = 110. \text{ mL}$$

$$110. \text{ mL O}_2 \times \frac{2 \text{ mol CO}_2}{3 \text{ mol O}_2} = 73.3 \text{ mL CO}_2$$

---

308. Given: reactants and products: V_1 (of N_2O_5 at STP) = 5.00 L; $T_2 = 64.5°C$; $P_2 = 1.76$ atm

Unknown: balanced equation; V_2 for N_2O_5; V of NO_2

$$2N_2O_5 \rightarrow 4NO_2 + O_2$$

$$V_2 = \frac{V_1 P_1 T_2}{T_1 P_2} = \frac{5.00 \text{ L} \times 1.00 \text{ atm} \times (273 + 64.5) \text{ K}}{(273 + 0) \text{ K} \times 1.76 \text{ atm}} = 3.51 \text{ L N}_2\text{O}_5$$

$$3.51 \text{ L N}_2\text{O}_5 \times \frac{4 \text{ L NO}_2}{2 \text{ L N}_2\text{O}_5} = 7.02 \text{ NO}_2$$

---

309. Given: balanced equation

a. Given: excess Al; STP; mass $AlCl_3$ = 7.15 g

Unknown: V of Cl_2

$$7.15 \text{ g AlCl}_3 \times \frac{1 \text{ mol AlCl}_3}{133.33 \text{ g AlCl}_3} \times \frac{3 \text{ mol Cl}_2}{2 \text{ mol AlCl}_3} \times \frac{22.4 \text{ L Cl}_2}{1 \text{ mol Cl}_2} = 1.80 \text{ L Cl}_2$$

b. Given: 19.4 g Al, STP

Unknown: V of Cl_2

$$19.4 \text{ g Al} \times \frac{1 \text{ mol Al}}{26.98 \text{ g Al}} \times \frac{3 \text{ mol Cl}_2}{2 \text{ mol Al}} \times \frac{22.4 \text{ L Cl}_2}{1 \text{ mol Cl}_2} = 24.2 \text{ L Cl}_2$$

c. Given: 1.559 kg Al; $T = 20.°C$; $P = 0.945$ atm

Unknown: V of Cl_2

$$1.559 \text{ kg Al} \times \frac{1 \text{ mol Al}}{26.98 \text{ g Al}} \times \frac{1000 \text{ g}}{1 \text{ kg}} \times \frac{3 \text{ mol Cl}_2}{2 \text{ mol Al}} \times \frac{22.4 \text{ L Cl}_2}{1 \text{ mol Cl}_2} = 1940 \text{ L Cl}_2$$

$$V_2 = \frac{P_1 V_1 T_2}{T_1 P_2} = \frac{1.00 \text{ atm} \times 1940 \text{ L} \times (273 + 20) \text{ K}}{(273 + 0) \text{ K} \times 0.945 \text{ atm}} = 2.21 \times 10^3 \text{ L Cl}_2$$

d. Given: excess Al; 920. L Cl_2; STP

Unknown: mass $AlCl_3$ in g

$$920 \text{ L Cl}_2 \times \frac{1 \text{ mol}}{22.4 \text{ L}} \times \frac{2 \text{ mol AlCl}_3}{3 \text{ mol Cl}_2} \times \frac{133.33 \text{ g AlCl}_3}{1 \text{ mol AlCl}_3} = 3.65 \times 10^3 \text{ g AlCl}_3$$

e. Given: $V_1 = 1.049$ mL Cl_2; $T_1 = 37°C$; $P_1 = 5.00$ atm

Unknown: mass Al in g

Find V at STP:

$$V_2 = \frac{P_1 V_1 T_2}{T_1 P_2} = \frac{5.00 \text{ atm} \times 1.049 \text{ mL} \times (273 + 0) \text{ K}}{(273 + 37) \text{ K} \times 1.00 \text{ atm}} = 4.62 \text{ mL}$$

$$4.62 \text{ mL Cl}_2 \times \frac{1 \text{ mol Cl}_2}{22\,400 \text{ mL Cl}_2} \times \frac{2 \text{ mol Al}}{3 \text{ mol Cl}_2} \times \frac{26.98 \text{ g Al}}{1 \text{ mol Al}} = 3.71 \times 10^{-3} \text{ g Al}$$

f. Given: 500.00 kg Al; $T_2 = 15°C$; $P_2 = 83.0$ kPa

Unknown: V of Cl_2 in m^3

$$500.00 \text{ kg Al} \times \frac{1 \text{ mol Al}}{26.98 \text{ g Al}} \times \frac{3 \text{ mol Cl}_2}{2 \text{ mol Al}} \times \frac{1000 \text{ g}}{1 \text{ kg}} \times \frac{22.4 \text{ L}}{1 \text{ mol}} \times \frac{1 \text{ m}^3}{1000 \text{ L}}$$

$$= 623 \text{ m}^3 \text{ Cl}_2 \text{ at STP}$$

$$V_2 = \frac{P_1 V_1 T_2}{T_1 P_2} = \frac{101.3 \text{ kPa} \times 623 \text{ m}^3 \times (273 + 15) \text{ K}}{(273 + 0) \text{ K} \times 83.0 \text{ kPa}} = 802 \text{ m}^3$$

310. a. Given: balanced equation; STP; 57.0 mL H_2

Unknown: V of N_2

$$57.0 \text{ mL } H_2 \times \frac{1 \text{ mL } N_2}{3 \text{ mL } H_2} = 19.0 \text{ mL } N_2$$

b. Given: balanced equation; STP; $6.39 \times 10^4 \text{ L } H_2$

Unknown: V of NH_3

$$6.39 \times 10^4 \text{ L } H_2 \times \frac{2 \text{ L } NH_3}{3 \text{ L } H_2} = 4.26 \times 10^4 \text{ L } NH_3$$

c. Given: balanced equation; 20.0 mol N_2; STP

Unknown: V of NH_3

$$20.0 \text{ mol } N_2 \times \frac{2 \text{ mol } NH_3}{1 \text{ mol } N_2} \times \frac{22.4 \text{ L } NH_3}{1 \text{ mol } NH_3} = 896 \text{ L } NH_3$$

d. Given: balanced equation; $V_1 = 800.$ L NH_3; $T_1 = 55°C$; $P_1 = 0.900$ atm

Unknown: V of H_2 at STP

V of NH_3 at STP =

$$V_2 = \frac{P_1 V_1 T_2}{T_1 P_2} = \frac{0.900 \text{ atm} \times 800. \text{ L } NH_3 \times (273 + 0) \text{ K}}{(273 + 55) \text{ K} \times 1.00 \text{ atm}} = 599 \text{ L } NH_3$$

$$599 \text{ L } NH_3 \times \frac{3 \text{ L } H_2}{2 \text{ L } NH_3} = 899 \text{ L } H_2$$

311. a. Given: balanced equation; $V_{C_3H_8} = 3$ L at STP; $T_2 = 250.°C$; $P_2 = 1.00$ atm

Unknown: V of H_2O

$$3.0 \text{ L } C_3H_8 \times \frac{4 \text{ L } H_2O}{1 \text{ L } C_3H_8} = 12 \text{ L } H_2O \text{ at STP}$$

$$V_2 = \frac{P_1 V_1 T_2}{T_1 P_2} = \frac{1.00 \text{ atm} \times 12 \text{ L} \times (273 + 250) \text{ K}}{(273 + 0) \text{ K} \times 1.00 \text{ atm}} = 23 \text{ L}$$

b. Given: balanced equation; 640. L CO_2

Unknown: V of O_2

$$640. \text{ L } CO_2 \times \frac{5 \text{ L } O_2}{3 \text{ L } CO_2} = 1070 \text{ L } O_2$$

c. Given: 465 mL O_2 at STP; balanced equation; $T_2 = 37°C$; $P_2 = 0.973$ atm

Unknown: V_2 of CO_2

$$465 \text{ mL } O_2 \times \frac{3 \text{ mL } CO_2}{5 \text{ mL } O_2} = 279 \text{ mL } CO_2 \text{ at STP}$$

$$V_2 = \frac{P_1 V_1 T_2}{T_1 P_2} = \frac{1.00 \text{ atm} \times 279 \text{ mL} \times (273 + 37) \text{ K}}{(273 + 0) \text{ K} \times 0.973 \text{ atm}} = 326 \text{ mL}$$

d. Given: 2.50 L of C_3H_8 at STP; balanced equation; $T_2 = 175°C$; $P_2 = 1.14$ atm

Unknown: V of products at T_2 and P_2 (V_2)

$$2.50 \text{ L } C_3H_8 \times \frac{3 \text{ L } CO_2}{1 \text{ L } C_3H_8} = 7.50 \text{ L } CO_2 \text{ at STP}$$

$$2.50 \text{ L } C_3H_8 \times \frac{4 \text{ L } H_2O}{1 \text{ L } C_3H_8} = 10.0 \text{ L } H_2O$$

V_1 at STP = 750 L + 10.0 L = 17.5 L

$$V_2 = \frac{P_1 V_1 T_2}{T_1 P_2} = \frac{1.00 \text{ atm} \times 17.5 \text{ L} \times (273 + 175) \text{ K}}{(273 + 0) \text{ K} \times 1.14 \text{ atm}} = 25.2 \text{ L}$$

312. Given: balanced equation; $V_1 = 3500.$ L CO; $T_1 = 20.°C$; $P_1 = 0.953$ atm

Unknown: V of O_2 at STP

$$V_2 = \frac{P_1V_1T_2}{T_1P_2} = \frac{0.953 \text{ atm} \times 3500. \text{ L} \times (273 + 0) \text{ K}}{(273 + 20) \text{ K} \times 1.00 \text{ atm}} = 3110 \text{ L CO at STP}$$

$$V \text{ of } O_2 = 3110 \text{ L CO} \times \frac{1 \text{ L } O_2}{2 \text{ L CO}} = 1550 \text{ L } O_2$$

313. Given: balanced equation; $V_1 = 1.00$ L HF; $P_1 = 3.48$ atm; $T_1 = 25°C$; $T_2 = 15°C$; $P_2 = 0.940$ atm

Unknown: V of SiF_4 at V_2 and P_2

$$V_2 = \frac{P_1V_1T_2}{T_1P_2} = \frac{3.48 \text{ atm} \times 1.00 \text{ L} \times (273 + 15) \text{ K}}{(273 + 25) \text{ K} \times 0.940 \text{ atm}} = 3.58 \text{ L HF}$$

$$3.58 \text{ L HF} \times \frac{1 \text{ L } SiF_4}{4 \text{ L HF}} = 0.894 \text{ L } SiF_4$$

314. Given: balanced equation

a. Given: 6.28 g Fe

Unknown: V of H_2 at STP

$$6.28 \text{ g Fe} \times \frac{1 \text{ mol Fe}}{55.85 \text{ g Fe}} \times \frac{4 \text{ mol } H_2}{3 \text{ mol Fe}} \times \frac{22.4 \text{ L}}{1 \text{ mol}} = 3.36 \text{ L } H_2$$

b. Given: $V_1 = 500.$ L H_2O; $T_1 = 250.°C$; $P_1 = 1.00$ atm

Unknown: mass Fe

Convert to STP:

$$V_2 = \frac{P_1V_1T_2}{T_1P_2} = \frac{1.00 \text{ atm} \times 500. \text{ L} \times (273 + 0) \text{ K}}{(273 + 250) \text{ K} \times 1.00 \text{ atm}} = 261 \text{ L}$$

$$261 \text{ L } H_2O \times \frac{1 \text{ mol}}{22.4 \text{ L}} \times \frac{3 \text{ mol Fe}}{4 \text{ mol } H_2O} \times \frac{55.85 \text{ g Fe}}{1 \text{ mol Fe}} = 488 \text{ g Fe}$$

c. Given: 285 g Fe_3O_4

Unknown: V of H_2 at 20.°C and 1.06 atm

$$285 \text{ g } Fe_3O_4 \times \frac{1 \text{ mol } Fe_3O_4}{231.55 \text{ g } Fe_3O_4} \times \frac{4 \text{ mol } H_2}{1 \text{ mol } Fe_3O_4} \times \frac{22.4 \text{ L}}{1 \text{ mol}} = 110. \text{ L } H_2 \text{ at STP}$$

$$V_2 = \frac{P_1V_1T_2}{T_1P_2} = \frac{1.00 \text{ atm} \times 110. \text{ L} \times (273 + 20) \text{ K}}{(273 + 0) \text{ K} \times 1.06 \text{ atm}} = 111 \text{ L}$$

315. Given: balanced equation; 0.027 g Na; excess H_2O

Unknown: V of H_2 at STP

$$0.027 \text{ g Na} \times \frac{1 \text{ mol Na}}{22.99 \text{ g Na}} \times \frac{1 \text{ mol } H_2}{2 \text{ mol Na}} \times \frac{22.4 \text{ L}}{1 \text{ mol}} = 0.013 \text{ L } H_2$$

316. Given: balanced equation; $V_1 = 7.15$ L CO_2; $T_1 = 125°C$; $P_1 = 1.02$ atm

Unknown: V of O_2 at STP; mass $C_4H_{10}O$

$$V_2 = \frac{P_1V_1T_2}{T_1P_2} = \frac{1.02 \text{ atm} \times 7.15 \text{ L} \times (273 + 0) \text{ K}}{(273 + 125) \text{ K} \times 1.00 \text{ atm}} = 5.00 \text{ L } CO_2 \text{ at STP}$$

$$5.00 \text{ L } CO_2 \times \frac{6 \text{ L } O_2}{4 \text{ L } CO_2} = 7.50 \text{ L } O_2$$

$$5.00 \text{ L } CO_2 \times \frac{1 \text{ mol}}{22.4 \text{ L}} \times \frac{1 \text{ mol } C_4H_{10}O}{4 \text{ mol } CO_2} \times \frac{74.14 \text{ g } C_4H_{10}O}{1 \text{ mol } C_4H_{10}O} = 4.14 \text{ g } C_4H_{10}O$$

317. Given: balanced equation

a. Given: 0.100 mol $C_3H_5N_3O_9$

Unknown: V of products at STP

$$0.100 \text{ mol } C_3H_5N_3O_9 \times \frac{6 \text{ mol } N_2}{4 \text{ mol } C_3H_5N_3O_9} \times \frac{22.4 \text{ L}}{1 \text{ mol}} = 3.36 \text{ L } N_2$$

$$0.100 \text{ mol } C_3H_5N_3O_9 \times \frac{12 \text{ mol } CO_2}{4 \text{ mol } C_3H_5N_3O_9} \times \frac{22.4 \text{ L}}{1 \text{ mol}} = 6.72 \text{ L } CO_2$$

$$0.100 \text{ mol } C_3H_5N_3O_9 \times \frac{10 \text{ mol } H_2O}{4 \text{ mol } C_3H_5N_3O_9} \times \frac{22.4 \text{ L}}{1 \text{ mol}} = 5.60 \text{ L } H_2O$$

$$0.100 \text{ mol } C_3H_5N_3O_9 \times \frac{1 \text{ mol } O_2}{4 \text{ mol } C_3H_5N_3O_9} \times \frac{22.4 \text{ L}}{1 \text{ mol}} = 0.560 \text{ L } O_2$$

b. Given: 10.0 g $C_3H_5N_3O_9$

Unknown: total V gases produced at 300.°C and 1.00 atm

V_T from **a** $= 3.36 \text{ L} + 6.72 \text{ L} + 5.60 \text{ L} + 0.560 \text{ L} = 16.24 \text{ L}$

$$10.0 \text{ g } C_3H_5N_3O_9 \times \frac{1 \text{ mol } C_3H_5N_3O_9}{227.11 \text{ g } C_3H_5N_3O_9} \times \frac{16.24 \text{ L gases}}{0.100 \text{ mol } C_3H_5N_3O_9}$$

$= 7.15 \text{ L gases at STP}$

$$V_2 = \frac{V_1 P_1 T_2}{T_1 P_2} = \frac{7.15 \text{ L} \times 1.00 \text{ atm} \times (273 + 300) \text{ K}}{(273 + 0) \text{ K} \times 1.00 \text{ atm}} = 15.0 \text{ L gases}$$

---

318. Given: balanced equation; 250. mL N_2O at STP

Unknown: mass NH_4NO_3

$$250. \text{ mL } N_2O \times \frac{1 \text{ L}}{1000 \text{ mL}} \times \frac{1 \text{ mol}}{22.4 \text{ L}} \times \frac{1 \text{ mol } NH_4NO_3}{1 \text{ mol } N_2O} \times \frac{80.06 \text{ g } NH_4NO_3}{1 \text{ mol } NH_4NO_3}$$

$= 0.894 \text{ g } NH_4NO_3$

---

319. Given: balanced equation; 8.46 g Ca_3P_2

Unknown: V of PH_3 at 18°C and 102.4 kPa

$$8.46 \text{ g } Ca_3P_2 \times \frac{1 \text{ mol } Ca_3P_2}{182.18 \text{ g } Ca_3P_2} \times \frac{2 \text{ mol } PH_3}{1 \text{ mol } C_3P_2} \times \frac{22.4 \text{ L}}{1 \text{ mol}} = 2.08 \text{ L } PH_3 \text{ at STP}$$

$$V_2 = \frac{P_1 V_1 T_2}{T_1 P_2} = \frac{101.3 \text{ kPa} \times 2.08 \text{ L} \times (273 + 18) \text{ K}}{(273 + 0) \text{ K} \times 102.4 \text{ kPa}} = 2.19 \text{ PH}_3$$

---

320. Given: balanced equation; 6.0×10^3 kg $AlCl_3$

Unknown: mass Al; V of HCl at 4.71 atm + 43°C

$$6.0 \times 10^3 \text{ kg } AlCl_3 \times \frac{1 \text{ mol } AlCl_3}{133.33 \text{ g } AlCl_3} \times \frac{2 \text{ mol Al}}{2 \text{ mol } AlCl_3} \times \frac{26.98 \text{ g Al}}{1 \text{ mol Al}}$$

$= 1.2 \times 10^3 \text{ kg Al}$

$$6.0 \times 10^3 \text{ kg } AlCl_3 \times \frac{1 \text{ mol } AlCl_3}{133.33 \text{ g } AlCl_3} \times \frac{6 \text{ mol HCl}}{2 \text{ mol } AlCl_3} \times \frac{22.4 \text{ L}}{1 \text{ mol}} \times \frac{1000 \text{ g}}{1 \text{ kg}}$$

$= 3.0 \times 10^6 \text{ L HCl at STP}$

$$V_2 = \frac{P_1 V_1 T_2}{T_1 P_2} = \frac{1.00 \text{ atm} \times 3.0 \times 10^6 \text{ L} \times (273 + 43) \text{ K}}{(273 + 0) \text{ K} \times 4.71 \text{ atm}} = 7.4 \times 10^5 \text{ L HCl}$$

---

321. Given: balanced equation; actual yield = 8.50×10^4 kg $(NH_2)_2CO$; 89.5% yield

Unknown: V of NH_3

$$\text{theoretical yield } (NH_2)_2CO = 8.50 \times 10^4 \text{ kg } (NH_2)_2CO \times \frac{100\%}{89.5\%}$$

$= 9.50 \times 10^4 \text{ kg } (NH_2)_2CO$

$$9.50 \times 10^4 \text{ kg } (NH_2)_2CO \times \frac{1000 \text{ g}}{1 \text{ kg}} \times \frac{1 \text{ mol } (NH_2)_2CO}{60.07 \text{ g } (NH_2)_2CO} \times \frac{2 \text{ mol } NH_3}{1 \text{ mol } (NH_2)_2CO}$$

$$\times \frac{22.4 \text{ L}}{1 \text{ mol}} = 7.08 \times 10^7 \text{ L } NH_3$$

322. Given: $V_1 = 265$ mL O_2; $T_1 = 10.°C$; $P_1 = 0.975$ atm; balanced equation

Unknown: mass of BaO_2

$$P_{O_2} = P_T - P_{H_2O} = 0.975 \text{ atm} - 1.23 \text{ kPa} \times \frac{1 \text{ atm}}{101.3 \text{ kPa}} = 0.963 \text{ atm}$$

$$V_2 = \frac{P_1 V_1 T_2}{T_1 P_2} = \frac{0.963 \text{ atm} \times 265 \text{ mL} \times (273 + 0) \text{ K}}{(273 + 10) \text{ K} \times 1.00 \text{ atm}} = 246 \text{ mL } O_2 \text{ at STP}$$

$$246 \text{ mL } O_2 \times \frac{1 \text{ L}}{1000 \text{ mL}} \times \frac{1 \text{ mol}}{22.4 \text{ L}} \times \frac{2 \text{ mol } BaO_2}{1 \text{ mol } O_2} \times \frac{169.33 \text{ g } BaO_2}{1 \text{ mol } BaO_2}$$

$$= 3.72 \text{ g } BaO_2$$

323. Given: balanced equation; 15.0 g $KMnO_4$

Unknown: V of Cl_2 at 15°C and 0.959 atm

$$15.0 \text{ g } KMnO_4 \times \frac{1 \text{ mol } KMnO_4}{158.04 \text{ g } KMnO_4} \times \frac{5 \text{ mol } Cl_2}{2 \text{ mol } KMnO_4} \times \frac{22.4 \text{ L}}{1 \text{ mol}}$$

$$= 5.32 \text{ L } Cl_2 \text{ at STP}$$

$$V_2 = \frac{P_1 V_1 T_2}{T_1 P_2} = \frac{1.00 \text{ atm} \times 5.32 \text{ L} \times (273 + 15) \text{ K}}{(273 + 0) \text{ K} \times 0.959 \text{ atm}} = 5.85 \text{ L } Cl_2$$

324. Given: balanced equations; 35.0 kL O_2 at STP

Unknown: V of NH_3 at STP; V of NO_2 at STP

$$35.0 \text{ kL } O_2 \times \frac{4 \text{ L } NH_3}{5 \text{ L } O_2} = 28.0 \text{ kL } NH_3$$

$$28.0 \text{ kL } NH_3 \times \frac{4 \text{ L } NO}{4 \text{ L } NH_3} \times \frac{2 \text{ L } NO_2}{2 \text{ L } NO} = 28.0 \text{ kL } NO_2$$

325. Given: balanced equation; 5.00 L O_2 at STP

Unknown: mass of $KClO_3$

$$5.00 \text{ L } O_2 \times \frac{1 \text{ mol } O_2}{22.4 \text{ L } O_2} \times \frac{2 \text{ mol } KClO_3}{3 \text{ mol } O_2} \times \frac{122.55 \text{ g } KClO_3}{1 \text{ mol } KClO_3} = 18.2 \text{ g } KClO_3$$

326. Given: balanced equation

a. Given: 38 000 L CO_2

Unknown: V of NH_3 under the same conditions

$$38\,000 \text{ L } CO_2 \times \frac{1 \text{ L } NH_3}{1 \text{ L } CO_2} = 38\,000 \text{ L } NH_3$$

b. Given: 38 000 L CO_2 at 25°C and 1.00 atm

Unknown: mass of $NaHCO_3$

$$V_2 = \frac{P_1 V_1 T_2}{T_1 P_2} = \frac{1.00 \text{ atm} \times 38\,000 \text{ L} \times (273 + 0) \text{ K}}{(273 + 25) \text{ K} \times 1.00 \text{ atm}}$$

$$= 34\,800 \text{ L } CO_2 \text{ at STP}$$

$$34\,800 \text{ L } CO_2 \times \frac{1 \text{ mol}}{22.4 \text{ L}} \times \frac{1 \text{ mol } NaHCO_3}{1 \text{ mol } CO_2} \times \frac{84.01 \text{ g } NaHCO_3}{1 \text{ mol } NaHCO_3}$$

$$= 1.30 \times 10^5 \text{ g } NaHCO_3$$

c. Given: 46.0 kg $NaHCO_3$

Unknown: V of NH_3 at STP

$$46.0 \text{ kg } NaHCO_3 \times \frac{1000 \text{ g}}{1 \text{ kg}} \times \frac{1 \text{ mol } NaHCO_3}{84.01 \text{ g } NaHCO_3} \times \frac{1 \text{ mol } NH_3}{1 \text{ mol } NaHCO_3} \times \frac{22.4 \text{ L}}{1 \text{ mol}}$$

$$= 1.23 \times 10^4 \text{ L } NH_3$$

d. Given: 100.00 kg
NaHCO$_3$

Unknown: V of CO$_2$
at 5.50
atm and
42°C

$$100.00 \text{ kg NaHCO}_3 \times \frac{1000 \text{ g}}{1 \text{ kg}} \times \frac{1 \text{ mol NaHCO}_3}{84.01 \text{ g NaHCO}_3} \times \frac{1 \text{ mol CO}_2}{1 \text{ mol NaHCO}_3} \times \frac{22.4 \text{ L}}{1 \text{ mol}}$$

$$= 2.67 \times 10^4 \text{ L CO}_2 \text{ at STP}$$

$$V_2 = \frac{P_1V_1T_2}{T_1P_2} = \frac{1.00 \text{ atm} \times 2.67 \times 10^4 \text{ L} \times (273 + 42) \text{ K}}{(273 + 0) \text{ K} \times 5.50 \text{ atm}} = 5.60 \times 10^3 \text{ L CO}_2$$

---

327. Given: balanced
equation

a. Given: 4.74 g C$_4$H$_{10}$;
excess O$_2$

$$4.74 \text{ g C}_4\text{H}_{10} \times \frac{1 \text{ mol C}_4\text{H}_{10}}{58.14 \text{ g C}_4\text{H}_{10}} \times \frac{8 \text{ mol CO}_2}{2 \text{ mol C}_4\text{H}_{10}} \times \frac{22.4 \text{ L}}{1 \text{ mol}} = 7.30 \text{ L CO}_2 \text{ at STP}$$

Unknown: V of CO$_2$
at 150.°C
and 1.14
atm

$$V_2 = \frac{P_1V_1T_2}{T_1P_2} = \frac{1.00 \text{ atm} \times 7.30 \text{ L} \times (273 + 150) \text{ K}}{(273 + 0) \text{ K} \times 1.14 \text{ atm}} = 9.92 \text{ L CO}_2$$

b. Given: 0.500 g C$_4$H$_{10}$

Unknown: V of O$_2$ at
0.980 atm
and 75°C

$$0.500 \text{ g C}_4\text{H}_{10} \times \frac{1 \text{ mol C}_4\text{H}_{10}}{58.14 \text{ g C}_4\text{H}_{10}} \times \frac{13 \text{ mol O}_2}{2 \text{ mol C}_4\text{H}_{10}} \times \frac{22.4 \text{ L}}{1 \text{ mol}} = 1.25 \text{ L O}_2 \text{ at STP}$$

$$V_2 = \frac{P_1V_1T_2}{T_1P_2} = \frac{1.00 \text{ atm} \times 1.25 \text{ L} \times (273 + 75) \text{ K}}{(273 + 0) \text{ K} \times 0.980 \text{ atm}} = 1.63 \text{ L O}_2$$

c. Given: mass$_1$ (torch
+ fuel) =
876.2 g;
mass$_2$ (torch
+ fuel) =
859.3 g

mass butane reacted = 876.2 g − 859.3 g = 16.9 g

$$16.9 \text{ g C}_4\text{H}_{10} \times \frac{1 \text{ mol C}_4\text{H}_{10}}{58.14 \text{ g C}_4\text{H}_{10}} \times \frac{8 \text{ mol CO}_2}{2 \text{ mol C}_4\text{H}_{10}} \times \frac{22.4 \text{ L}}{1 \text{ mol}} = 26.0 \text{ L CO}_2$$

Unknown: V of CO$_2$
at STP

d. Given: 3720 L of CO$_2$
at 35°C and
0.993 atm

$$V_2 = \frac{V_1P_1T_2}{T_1P_2} = \frac{3720 \text{ L} \times 0.993 \text{ atm} \times (273 + 0) \text{ K}}{(273 + 35) \text{ K} \times 1.00 \text{ atm}} = 3270 \text{ L CO}_2 \text{ at STP}$$

Unknown: mass H$_2$O

$$3270 \text{ L CO}_2 \times \frac{1 \text{ mol}}{22.4 \text{ L}} \times \frac{10 \text{ mol H}_2\text{O}}{8 \text{ mol CO}_2} \times \frac{18.02 \text{ g H}_2\text{O}}{1 \text{ mol H}_2\text{O}} = 3290 \text{ g H}_2\text{O}$$

---

328. Given: 75.0 g ethanol;
500.0 g H$_2$O

$$\frac{75.0 \text{ g ethanol}}{(500.0 + 75.0) \text{ g}} \times 100 = 13.0\% \text{ ethanol}$$

Unknown: percentage
concentra-
tion

---

329. Given: 3.50 g KIO$_3$;
6.23 g KOH;
805.05 g H$_2$O

$$\frac{3.50 \text{ g KIO}_3}{(3.50 + 6.23 + 805.05) \text{ g}} \times 100 = 0.430\% \text{ KIO}_3$$

Unknown: percentage
concentra-
tion of KIO$_3$
and KOH

$$\frac{6.23 \text{ g KOH}}{(3.50 + 6.23 + 805.05) \text{ g}} \times 100 = 0.765\% \text{ KOH}$$

330. Given: 0.377 g RbCl to make a 5.00% solution

Unknown: mass of H_2O

$$0.377 \text{ g RbCl} \times \frac{100 \text{ g solution}}{5 \text{ g RbCl}} = 7.54 \text{ g solution}$$

$$7.54 \text{ g solution} - 0.377 \text{ g RbCl} = 7.16 \text{ g } H_2O$$

---

331. Given: 30.0 g H_2O; 18.0% $LiNO_3$ solution

Unknown: mass of $LiNO_3$

$$\frac{x}{30.0 \text{ g} + x} = 0.18 \; ; \; x = 6.59 \text{ g } LiNO_3$$

---

332. Given: 141.6 g $C_3H_5O(COOH)_3$; V of solution = 3500.0 mL

Unknown: molarity

$$141.6 \text{ g } C_3H_5O(COOH)_3 \times \frac{1 \text{ mol } C_3H_5O(COOH)_3}{192.14 \text{ g } C_3H_5O(COOH)_3} = 0.7370 \text{ mol}$$

$$\frac{0.7370 \text{ mol}}{3500.0 \text{ mL}} \times \frac{1000 \text{ mL}}{1 \text{ L}} = 0.2106 \text{ M}$$

---

333. Given: 280.0 mg NaCl; 2.00 mL H_2O

Unknown: molarity

$$280.0 \text{ mg NaCl} \times \frac{1 \text{ g}}{1000 \text{ mg}} \times \frac{1 \text{ mol NaCl}}{58.44 \text{ g NaCl}} = 0.00479 \text{ mol NaCl}$$

$$\frac{0.00479 \text{ mol NaCl}}{2.00 \text{ mL solution}} \times \frac{1000 \text{ mL}}{1 \text{ L}} = 2.40 \text{ M}$$

---

334. Given: 390.0 g CH_3COOH; 1000.0 mL solution

Unknown: molarity

$$390.0 \text{ g } CH_3COOH \times \frac{1 \text{ mol } CH_3COOH}{60.06 \text{ g } CH_3COOH} = 6.494 \text{ mol } CH_3COOH$$

$$\frac{6.494 \text{ mol } CH_3COOH}{1000.0 \text{ mL solution}} \times \frac{1000 \text{ mL}}{1 \text{ L}} = 6.494 \text{ M}$$

---

335. Given: 5.000×10^3 L; 0.215 M

Unknown: mass of $C_6H_{12}O_6$

$$0.215 \text{ mol/L} \times (5.00 \times 10^3 \text{ L}) \times \frac{180.18 \text{ g } C_6H_{12}O_6}{1 \text{ mol } C_6H_{12}O_6} = 1.94 \times 10^5 \text{ g } C_6H_{12}O_6$$

---

336. Given: 720. mL solution; 0.0939 M

Unknown: mass of $MgBr_2$

$$\frac{0.0939 \text{ mol}}{L} \times 720. \text{ mL} \times \frac{1 \text{ L}}{1000 \text{ mL}} \times \frac{184.10 \text{ g } MgBr_2}{1 \text{ mol } MgBr_2} = 12.4 \text{ g } MgBr_2$$

---

337. Given: 300. mL solution; 0.875 M

Unknown: mass of NH_4Cl

$$\frac{0.875 \text{ mol}}{L} \times 300. \text{ mL} \times \frac{1 \text{ L}}{1000 \text{ mL}} \times \frac{53.50 \text{ g } NH_4Cl}{1 \text{ mol } NH_4Cl} = 14.0 \text{ g } NH_4Cl$$

---

338. Given: 560 g CH_3COCH_3 solute; 620 g H_2O solvent

Unknown: molality

$$560 \text{ g } CH_3COCH_3 \times \frac{1 \text{ mol } CH_3COCH_3}{58.09 \text{ g } CH_3COCH_3} = 9.64 \text{ mol } CH_3COCH_3$$

$$\frac{9.64 \text{ mol } CH_3COCH_3}{0.620 \text{ kg solvent}} = 16 \text{ m}$$

339. Given: 12.9 g $C_6H_{12}O_6$ solute; 31.0 g H_2O solvent

Unknown: molality

$$12.9 \text{ g } C_6H_{12}O_6 \times \frac{1 \text{ mol } C_6H_{12}O_6}{180.18 \text{ g } C_6H_{12}O_6} = 0.0716 \text{ mol } C_6H_{12}O_6$$

$$\frac{0.0716 \text{ mol } C_6H_{12}O_6}{31.0 \text{ g solvent}} \times \frac{1000 \text{ g}}{1 \text{ kg}} = 2.31 \text{ m}$$

340. Given: 125 g solvent; 12.0 m solution

Unknown: moles of solute $(CH_3CHOHCH_2CH_3)$; mass of solute

$$125 \text{ g solvent} \times \frac{12.0 \text{ mol solute}}{1 \text{ kg solvent}} \times \frac{1 \text{ kg}}{1000 \text{ g}} = 1.50 \text{ mol solute}$$

$$1.50 \text{ mol } CH_3CHOHCH_2CH_3 \times \frac{74.14 \text{ g } CH_3CHOHCH_2CH_3}{1 \text{ mol } CH_3CHOHCH_2CH_3}$$

$$= 111 \text{ g } CH_3CHOHCH_2CH_3$$

341. a. Given: 12.0% $KMnO_4$; 500.0 g solution

Unknown: mass solute; mass solvent (H_2O)

$$500.0 \text{ g} \times 0.120 = 60.0 \text{ g } KMnO_4$$

$$500.0 \text{ g} - 60.0 \text{ g} = 440.0 \text{ g } H_2O$$

b. Given: 0.60 M $BaCl_2$; 1.750 L solution

Unknown: mass solute

$$\frac{0.60 \text{ mol } BaCl_2}{1.00 \text{ L solution}} \times 1.750 \text{ L solution} = 1.1 \text{ mol } BaCl_2$$

$$1.1 \text{ mol } BaCl_2 \times \frac{208.23 \text{ g } BaCl_2}{1 \text{ mol } BaCl_2} = 230 \text{ g } BaCl_2$$

c. Given: 6.20 m glycerol $(HOCH_2CHOHCH_2OH)$; 800.0 g H_2O solvent

Unknown: mass glycerol in g

$$\frac{6.20 \text{ mol glycerol}}{1 \text{ kg solvent}} \times 800.0 \text{ g solvent} \times \frac{1 \text{ kg}}{1000 \text{ g}} = 4.96 \text{ mol glyercol}$$

$$4.96 \text{ mol glycerol} \times \frac{92.11 \text{ glycerol}}{1 \text{ mol glycerol}} = 457 \text{ g glycerol}$$

d. Given: 12.27 g solute $(K_2Cr_2O_7)$; 650. mL solution

Unknown: molarity

$$\frac{12.27 \text{ g } K_2Cr_2O_7}{650. \text{ mL solution}} \times \frac{1000 \text{ mL}}{1 \text{ L}} \times \frac{1 \text{ mol } K_2Cr_2O_7}{294.20 \text{ g } K_2Cr_2O_7} = 0.0642 \text{ M } K_2Cr_2O_7$$

e. Given: 288 g $CaCl_2$ solute: 2.04 kg H_2O solvent

Unknown: molality

$$\frac{288 \text{ g } CaCl_2}{2.04 \text{ kg } H_2O} \times \frac{1 \text{ mol } CaCl_2}{110.98 \text{ g } CaCl_2} = 1.27 \text{ m}$$

f. Given: 0.160 M NaCl solution; 25.0 mL solution

$$\frac{0.160 \text{ mol NaCl}}{1.00 \text{ L solution}} \times \frac{1 \text{ L}}{1000 \text{ mL}} \times 25.0 \text{ mL solution} = 0.00400 \text{ mol NaCl}$$

Unknown: mass solute in g

$$0.00400 \text{ mol NaCl} \times \frac{58.44 \text{ g NaCl}}{1 \text{ mol NaCl}} = 0.234 \text{ g NaCl}$$

g. Given: 2.00 m $C_6H_{12}O_6$; 1.50 kg H_2O solvent

$$\frac{2.00 \text{ mol } C_6H_{12}O_6}{1.00 \text{ kg } H_2O} \times 1.50 \text{ kg } H_2O = 3.00 \text{ mol } C_6H_{12}O_6$$

Unknown: mass of solute and total mass of solution

$$3.00 \text{ mol } C_6H_{12}O_6 \times \frac{180.18 \text{ g } C_6H_{12}O_6}{1 \text{ mol } C_6H_{12}O_6} = 541 \text{ g } C_6H_{12}O_6$$

$$1.50 \text{ kg} \times \frac{1000 \text{ g}}{1 \text{ kg}} + 541 \text{ g} = 2040 \text{ g total}$$

---

342. Given: 2.50 L of 4.25 M solution of H_2SO_4

$$2.50 \text{ L solution} \times \frac{4.25 \text{ mol } H_2SO_4}{1.00 \text{ L solution}} = 10.6 \text{ mol } H_2SO_4$$

Unknown: moles of H_2SO_4

---

343. Given: 71.5 g $C_{18}H_{32}O_2$ solute; 525 g solvent

$$71.5 \text{ g } C_{18}H_{32}O_2 \times \frac{1 \text{ mol } C_{18}H_{32}O_2}{280.50 \text{ g } C_{18}H_{32}O_2} = 0.255 \text{ mol } C_{18}H_{32}O_2$$

Unknown: molality

$$\frac{0.255 \text{ mol } C_{18}H_{32}O_2}{525 \text{ g solvent}} \times \frac{1000 \text{ g}}{1 \text{ kg}} = 0.486 \text{ } m$$

---

344. Given: 16.2% $Na_2S_2O_3$ solution by mass

a. Unknown: mass $Na_2S_2O_3$ in 80.0 g solution

$$80.0 \text{ g} \times \frac{16.2\%}{100\%} = 13.0 \text{ g } Na_2S_2O_3$$

b. Unknown: moles $Na_2S_2O_3$ in 80.0 g solution

$$80.0 \text{ g} \times \frac{16.2\%}{100\%} Na_2S_2O_3 \times \frac{1 \text{ mol } Na_2S_2O_3}{158.12 \text{ g } Na_2S_2O_3}$$

$$= 0.0820 \text{ mol } Na_2S_2O_3$$

c. Given: 80.0 g of 16.2% $Na_2S_2O_3$ solution (see **b**) diluted to 250.0 mL with H_2O

$$\frac{0.0820 \text{ mol } Na_2S_2O_3}{250.0 \text{ mL solution}} \times \frac{1000 \text{ mL}}{1 \text{ L}} = 0.328 \text{ M}$$

Unknown: molarity of final solution

345. Given: $CoCl_2$ solute; 650.00 mL of 4.00 M solution

Unknown: mass of $CoCl_2$

$$\frac{4.00 \text{ mol } CoCl_2}{1.00 \text{ L solution}} \times 650.00 \text{ mL solution} \times \frac{1 \text{ L}}{1000 \text{ mL}} = 2.60 \text{ mol } CoCl_2$$

$$2.60 \text{ mol } CoCl_2 \times \frac{129.83 \text{ g } CoCl_2}{1.00 \text{ mol } CoCl_2} = 338 \text{ g } CoCl_2$$

---

346. Given: 11.27 g $AgNO_3$; 0.150 M solution

Unknown: volume of solution

$$11.27 \text{ g } AgNO_3 \times \frac{1 \text{ mol } AgNO_3}{169.88 \text{ g } AgNO_3} = 0.0663 \text{ mol } AgNO_3$$

$$0.0663 \text{ mol } AgNO_3 \times \frac{1 \text{ L solution}}{0.150 \text{ mol } AgNO_3} = 0.442 \text{ L solution}$$

---

347. Given: 2250 g H_2O solvent; 1.50 m solution

Unknown: mass of NH_2CONH_2

$$\frac{1.50 \text{ mol } NH_2CONH_2}{1.00 \text{ kg solvent}} \times 2250 \text{ g solvent} \times \frac{1 \text{ kg}}{1000 \text{ g}} = 3.38 \text{ mol } NH_2CONH_2$$

$$3.38 \text{ mol } NH_2CONH_2 \times \frac{60.07 \text{ g } NH_2CONH_2}{1 \text{ mol } NH_2CONH_2} = 203 \text{ g } NH_2CONH_2$$

---

348. Given: 21.29 mL of a 3.38 M $Ba(NO_3)_2$ solution

Unknown: mass of $Ba(NO_3)_2$

$$21.29 \text{ mL} \times \frac{1 \text{ L}}{1000 \text{ mL}} \times \frac{3.38 \text{ mol } Ba(NO_3)_2}{1 \text{ L}} = 0.0720 \text{ mol } Ba(NO_3)_2$$

$$0.0720 \text{ mol } Ba(NO_3)_2 \times \frac{261.35 \text{ g } Ba(NO_3)_2}{1 \text{ mol } Ba(NO_3)_2} = 18.8 \text{ g } Ba(NO_3)_2$$

---

349. Given: 100.0 g of a 3.5% $(NH_4)_2SO_4$ solution

Unknown: description of preparation

$$100.0 \text{ g} \times \frac{3.5\%}{100\%} (NH_4)_2SO_4 = 3.5 \text{ g } (NH_4)_2SO_4$$

$$100.0 \text{ g solution} - 3.5 \text{ g solute} = 96.5 \text{ g solvent}$$

Add 3.5 g $(NH_4)_2SO_4$ to 96.5 g H_2O

---

350. Given: 590.0 g water solvent; 0.82 m solution

Unknown: mass $CaCl_2$ solute

$$\frac{0.82 \text{ mol } CaCl_2}{1.00 \text{ kg } H_2O} \times 590.0 \text{ g } H_2O \times \frac{1 \text{ kg}}{1000 \text{ g}} = 0.48 \text{ mol } CaCl_2$$

$$0.48 \text{ mol } CaCl_2 \times \frac{110.98 \text{ g } CaCl_2}{1 \text{ mol } CaCl_2} = 53 \text{ g } CaCl_2$$

---

351. Given: 0.250 L of 5.00 M NH_3 diluted to 1.000 L

Unknown: moles NH_3; final molarity

$$0.250 \text{ L} \times \frac{5.00 \text{ mol } NH_3}{1 \text{ L}} = 1.25 \text{ mol } NH_3$$

$$\frac{1.25 \text{ mol } NH_3}{1.000 \text{ L}} = 1.25 \text{ M}$$

---

352. Given: 62.0 g solute; 125 g H_2O; 5.3 m solution

Unknown: molar mass of solute

$$\frac{5.3 \text{ mol solute}}{1.00 \text{ kg } H_2O} \times 125 \text{ g } H_2O \times \frac{1 \text{ kg}}{1000 \text{ g}} = 0.662 \text{ mol solute}$$

$$M = \frac{62.0 \text{ g solute}}{0.662 \text{ mol solute}} = 93.7 \text{ g/mol}$$

---

353. Given: 0.9% NaCl

Unknown: masses of NaCl and H_2O to prepare 50. L

$$50. \text{ L} \times \frac{1000 \text{ mL}}{1 \text{ L}} \times \frac{1.000 \text{ g}}{1 \text{ mL}} = 50\,000 \text{ g} = 50 \text{ kg}$$

$$\frac{0.9\%}{100\%} \times 50 \text{ kg} = 0.45 \text{ kg NaCl}; 50 \text{ kg} - 0.45 = 49.6 \text{ kg } H_2O$$

354. Given: mass beaker = 68.60 g; mass beaker + H_2O = 115.12 g; 4.08 g glucose solute

Unknown: percentage concentration glucose

mass H_2O = 115.12 g − 68.60 g = 46.52 g

total mass of solution = 46.52 g + 4.08 g = 50.60 g

$$\frac{4.08 \text{ g glucose}}{50.60 \text{ g solution}} \times 100 = 8.06\% \text{ glucose}$$

355. Given: D = 0.902 g/mL at 20°C for ethyl acetate solvent; cellulose nitrate solute

Unknown: V of solvent to prepare a 2.0% solution using 25 g of solute

$$\frac{25 \text{ g}}{x + 25 \text{ g}} = 0.020$$

$$x = \frac{25 \text{ g}}{0.020} - 25 \text{ g} = 1200 \text{ g solvent}$$

$$1200 \text{ g solvent} \times \frac{1 \text{ mL}}{0.902 \text{ g}} = 1400 \text{ mL or } 1.4 \text{ L solvent}$$

356. Given: reactants and products

Unknown: balanced equation

$$CdCl_2 + Na_2S \rightarrow CdS + 2NaCl$$

a. Given: 50.00 mL of a 3.91 M solution

Unknown: moles $CdCl_2$

$$\frac{3.91 \text{ mol } CdCl_2}{1 \text{ L}} \times 50.00 \text{ mL} \times \frac{1 \text{ L}}{1000 \text{ mL}} = 0.196 \text{ mol } CdCl_2$$

b. Given: 0.196 mol $CdCl_2$ from **a**; balanced equation; excess Na_2S

Unknown: moles CdS

$$0.196 \text{ mol } CdCl_2 \times \frac{1 \text{ mol CdS}}{1 \text{ mol } CdCl_2} = 0.196 \text{ mol CdS}$$

c. Given: 0.196 mol CdS from **b**

Unknown: mass CdS

$$0.196 \text{ mol CdS} \times \frac{144.48 \text{ g CdS}}{1 \text{ mol CdS}} = 28.3 \text{ g CdS}$$

357. Given: 60.00 mL of 5.85 M H_2SO_4 solution

Unknown: mass H_2SO_4

$$\frac{5.85 \text{ mol } H_2SO_4}{1.00 \text{ L}} \times 60.00 \text{ mL} \times \frac{1 \text{ L}}{1000 \text{ mL}} = 0.351 \text{ mol } H_2SO_4$$

$$0.351 \text{ mol } H_2SO_4 \times \frac{98.09 \text{ g } H_2SO_4}{1 \text{ mol } H_2SO_4} = 34.4 \text{ g } H_2SO_4$$

358. Given: 22.5 kL of 6.83 M HCl

Unknown: moles HCl

$$\frac{6.83 \text{ mol HCl}}{1.00 \text{ L}} \times 22.5 \text{ kL} \times \frac{1000 \text{ L}}{1 \text{ kL}} = 1.54 \times 10^5 \text{ mol HCl}$$

359. Given: balanced equation; excess H_2SO_4; 0.600 M $BaCl_2$ solution

Unknown: V $BaCl_2$ solution to produce 12.00 g $BaSO_4$

$$12.00 \text{ g BaSO}_4 \times \frac{1 \text{ mol BaSO}_4}{233.40 \text{ g BaSO}_4} = 0.05141 \text{ mol BaSO}_4$$

$$0.05141 \text{ mol BaSO}_4 \times \frac{1 \text{ mol BaCl}_2}{1 \text{ mol BaSO}_4} = 0.05141 \text{ mol BaCl}_2$$

$$0.05141 \text{ mol BaCl}_2 \times \frac{1.00 \text{ L}}{0.600 \text{ mol BaCl}_2} = 0.0857 \text{ L BaCl}_2 = 85.7 \text{ mL BaCl}_2$$

360. Given: $CuSO_4 \cdot 5H_2O$ solute

$$100. \text{ g} \times \frac{6.00\%}{100\%} \text{ CuSO}_4 = 6.00 \text{ g CuSO}_4$$

a. Given: 100. g of a 6.00% $CuSO_4$ solution

Unknown: preparation of solution

$$6.00 \text{ g CuSO}_4 \times \frac{1 \text{ mol CuSO}_4}{159.62 \text{ g CuSO}_4} \times \frac{1 \text{ mol CuSO}_4 \cdot 5H_2O}{1 \text{ mol CuSO}_4}$$

$$\times \frac{249.72 \text{ g CuSO}_4 \cdot 5H_2O}{1 \text{ mol CuSO}_4 \cdot 5H_2O} = 9.39 \text{ g CuSO}_4 \cdot 5H_2O \text{ in } 100. \text{ g} - 9.39 \text{ g}$$

$$= 90.61 \text{ g H}_2O$$

b. Given: 1.00 L of a 0.800 M $CuSO_4$ solution

Unknown: preparation of solution

$$1.00 \text{ L} \times \frac{0.800 \text{ mol CuSO}_4}{1.00 \text{ L}} \times \frac{1 \text{ mol CuSO}_4 \cdot 5H_2O}{1 \text{ mol CuSO}_4}$$

$$\times \frac{249.72 \text{ g CuSO}_4 \cdot 5H_2O}{1 \text{ mol CuSO}_4 \cdot 5H_2O} = 200. \text{ g CuSO}_4 \cdot 5H_2O \text{ in water to make } 1.00 \text{ L}$$

of solution

c. Given: 3.5 m solution of $CuSO_4$ in 1.0 kg H_2O

Unknown: preparation of solution

$$\frac{3.5 \text{ mol CuSO}_4}{1.0 \text{ kg H}_2O} \times 1.0 \text{ kg H}_2O \times \frac{1 \text{ mol CuSO}_4 \cdot 5H_2O}{1 \text{ mol CuSO}_4} \times \frac{249.72 \text{ g CuSO}_4 \cdot 5H_2O}{1 \text{ mol CuSO}_4 \cdot 5H_2O}$$

$$= 870 \text{ g CuSO}_4 \cdot 5H_2O$$

$$3.5 \text{ mol CuSO}_4 \times \frac{159.62 \text{ g CuSO}_4}{1 \text{ mol CuSO}_4} = 560 \text{ g CuSO}_4$$

$$870 \text{ g CuSO}_4 \cdot 5H_2O - 560 \text{ g CuSO}_4 = 310 \text{ g H}_2O$$

$$1.0 \text{ kg} \times \frac{1000 \text{ g}}{1 \text{ kg}} - 310 \text{ g} = 690 \text{ g added water}$$

361. Given: 700.0 mL of 2.50 M $CaCl_2$ solution

Unknown: mass $CaCl_2 \cdot 6H_2O$

$$700.0 \text{ mL} \times \frac{1 \text{ L}}{1000 \text{ mL}} \times \frac{2.50 \text{ mol CaCl}_2}{1 \text{ L}} \times \frac{1 \text{ mol CaCl}_2 \cdot 6H_2O}{1 \text{ mol CaCl}_2}$$

$$\times \frac{219.10 \text{ g CaCl}_2 \cdot 6H_2O}{1 \text{ mol CaCl}_2 \cdot 6H_2O} = 383 \text{ g CaCl}_2 \cdot 6H_2O$$

362. Given: 1.250 L of 0.00205 M $C_6H_{14}N_4O_2$

Unknown: mass of $C_6H_{14}N_4O_2$

$$1.250 \text{ L} \times \frac{0.00205 \text{ mol C}_6H_{14}N_4O_2}{1 \text{ L}} = 0.00256 \text{ mol C}_6H_{14}N_4O_2$$

$$0.00256 \text{ mol C}_6H_{14}N_4O_2 \times \frac{174.24 \text{ g C}_6H_{14}N_4O_2}{1 \text{ mol C}_6H_{14}N_4O_2} = 0.446 \text{ g C}_6H_{14}N_4O_2$$

363. Given: 2.402 kg $NiSO_4 \cdot 6H_2O$; 25% solution

Unknown: mass of water

$$2.402 \text{ kg } NiSO_4 \cdot 6H_2O \times \frac{1000 \text{ g}}{1 \text{ kg}} \times \frac{1 \text{ mol } NiSO_4 \cdot 6H_2O}{262.88 \text{ g } NiSO_4 \cdot 6H_2O}$$

$$\times \frac{1 \text{ mol } NiSO_4}{1 \text{ mol } NiSO_4 \cdot 6H_2O} \times \frac{154.76 \text{ g } NiSO_4}{1 \text{ mol } NiSO_4} = 1414 \text{ g } NiSO_4$$

$$\frac{1414 \text{ g}}{x + 1414 \text{ g}} = 0.25; \; x = \frac{1414 \text{ g}}{0.25} - 1414 \text{ g} = 4242 \text{ g } H_2O \text{ in solution}$$

$$4242 \text{ g } H_2O - (2402 \text{ g} - 1414 \text{ g}) = 3254 \text{ g } H_2O \text{ added}$$

---

364. Given: $KAl(SO_4)_2 \cdot 12H_2O$ solute; 35.0 g of a 15% $KAl(SO_4)_2$ solution

Unknown: mass of solute; mass of H_2O added

$$35.0 \text{ g} \times 0.15 \text{ } KAl(SO_4)_2 = 5.25 \text{ g } KAl(SO_4)_2$$

$$5.25 \text{ g } KAl(SO_4)_2 \times \frac{1 \text{ mol } KAl(SO_4)_2}{258.22 \text{ g } KAl(SO_4)_2} \times \frac{1 \text{ mol } KAl(SO_4)_2 \cdot 12H_2O}{1 \text{ mol } KAl(SO_4)_2}$$

$$\times \frac{474.46 \text{ g } KAl(SO_4)_2 \cdot 12H_2O}{1 \text{ mol } KAl(SO_4)_2 \cdot 12H_2O} = 9.646 \text{ g } KAl(SO_4)_2 \cdot 12H_2O$$

$$35.0 \text{ g solution} - 9.646 \text{ g solute} = 25.35 \text{ g water added}$$

---

365. a. Given: $M_S = 0.500$ M KBr; $V_S = 20.00$ mL; $V_D = 100.00$ mL; $M_S V_S = M_D V_D$

Unknown: M_D

$$M_D = \frac{M_S V_S}{V_D} = \frac{0.500 \text{ M KBr} \times 20.00 \text{ mL}}{100.00 \text{ mL}} = 0.100 \text{ M KBr}$$

b. Given: $M_S = 1.00$ M LiOH; $M_D = 0.075$ M LiOH; $V_D = 500.00$ mL; $M_S V_S = M_D V_D$

Unknown: V_S

$$V_S = \frac{M_D V_D}{M_S} = \frac{0.075 \text{ M LiOH} \times 500.00 \text{ mL}}{1.00 \text{ M LiOH}} = 38 \text{ mL}$$

c. Given: $V_S = 5.00$ mL; $M_D = 0.0493$ M HI; $V_D = 100.00$ mL; $M_S V_S = M_D V_D$

Unknown: M_S

$$M_S = \frac{M_D V_D}{V_S} = \frac{0.0493 \text{ M HI} \times 100.00 \text{ mL}}{5.00 \text{ mL}} = 0.986 \text{ M HI}$$

d. Given: $M_S = 12.0$ M HCl; $V_S = 0.250$ L; $M_D = 1.8$ M HCl; $M_S V_S = M_D V_D$

Unknown: V_D

$$V_D = \frac{M_S V_S}{M_D} = \frac{12.0 \text{ M HCl} \times 0.250 \text{ L}}{1.8 \text{ M HCl}} = 1.7 \text{ L}$$

e. Given: $M_S = 7.44$ M NH_3; $M_D = 0.093$ M NH_3; $V_D = 4.00$ L; $M_SV_S = M_DV_D$

Unknown: V_S

$$V_S = \frac{M_DV_D}{M_S} = \frac{0.093 \text{ M } NH_3 \times 4.00 \text{ L}}{7.44 \text{ M } NH_3} = 0.050 \text{ L} = 50. \text{ mL}$$

---

366. Given: $M_S = 0.0813$ M; $V_S = 16.5$ mL; $M_D = 0.0200$ M; $M_SV_S = M_DV_D$

Unknown: V_D; V of water added

$$V_D = \frac{M_SV_S}{M_D} = \frac{0.0813 \text{ M} \times 16.5 \text{ mL}}{0.0200 \text{ M}} = 67.1 \text{ mL}$$

$67.1 \text{ mL} - 16.5 \text{ mL} = 50.6 \text{ mL } H_2O \text{ added}$

---

367. Given: $M_S = 3.79$ M NH_4Cl; $V_S = 50.00$ mL; $V_D = 2.00$ L; $M_SV_S = M_DV_D$

Unknown: M_D

$$M_D = \frac{M_SV_S}{V_D} = \frac{3.79 \text{ M } NH_4Cl \times 50.00 \text{ mL}}{2000 \text{ mL}} = 0.0948 \text{ M } NH_4Cl$$

---

368. Given: 100.00 mL H_2O added; $M_D = 0.046$ M KOH; $M_S = 2.09$ M KOH; $M_SV_S = M_DV_D$

Unknown: V_S

$V_D = V_S + 100.00 \text{ mL}$

$M_SV_S = M_DV_D$

$2.09 \text{ M KOH} \times V_S = 0.046 \text{ M KOH } (V_S + 100.00 \text{ mL})$

$V_S = 2.3 \text{ mL}$

---

369. a. Given: $V_S = 20.00$ mL; $M_D = 0.50$ M; 100.00 mL H_2O added; $M_SV_S = M_DV_D$

Unknown: M_S

$$M_S = \frac{M_DV_D}{V_S} = \frac{0.50 \text{ M} \times (100.00 \text{ mL} + 20.00 \text{ mL})}{20.00 \text{ mL}} = 3.0 \text{ M}$$

b. Given: $V_D = 5.00$ L; $M_D = 3.0$ M; $M_S = 18.0$ M; $M_SV_S = M_DV_D$

Unknown: V_S

$$V_S = \frac{M_DV_D}{M_S} = \frac{3.0 \text{ M} \times 5.00 \text{ L}}{18.0 \text{ M}} = 0.83 \text{ L}$$

c. Given: V = 0.83 L, from **b**; D = 1.84 g/mL

Unknown: mass H_2SO_4

$$m = VD = 0.83 \text{ L} \times 1.84 \frac{\text{g}}{\text{mL}} \times \frac{1000 \text{ mL}}{1 \text{ L}} = 1.5 \times 10^3 \text{ g}$$

---

370. Given: $V_S = 1.19$ mL; $M_S = 8.00$ M; $M_D = 1.50$ M; $M_SV_S = M_DV_D$

Unknown: V_D

$$V_D = \frac{M_SV_S}{M_D} = \frac{8.00 \text{ M} \times 1.19 \text{ mL}}{1.50 \text{ M}} = 6.35 \text{ mL}$$

371. Given: $M_S = 5.75$ M; $V_D = 2.00$ L; $M_D = 1.00$ M; $M_S V_S = M_D V_D$

Unknown: V_S

$$V_S = \frac{M_D V_D}{M_S} = \frac{1.00 \text{ M} \times 2.00 \text{ L}}{5.75 \text{ M}} = 0.348 \text{ L or } 348 \text{ mL}$$

372. a. Given: $V_S = 25.00$ mL; $M_D = 0.186$ M; 50.00 mL H_2O added; $M_S V_S = M_D V_D$

Unknown: M_S

$$M_S = \frac{M_D V_D}{V_S} = \frac{0.186 \text{ M} \times (25.00 \text{ mL} + 50.00 \text{ mL})}{25.00 \text{ mL}} = 0.558 \text{ M}$$

373. a. Given: 36% HCl solution; $D = 1.18$ g/mL

Unknown: V_1 of 1.0 kg of HCl solution; V_2 that contains 1.0 g HCl; V_3 that contains 1.0 mol HCl

$$V_1 = \frac{m}{D} = 1.0 \text{ kg} \times \frac{1 \text{ mL}}{1.18 \text{ g}} \times \frac{1000 \text{ g}}{1 \text{ kg}} = 850 \text{ mL}$$

$$V_2 = \frac{100\% \times 1 \text{ g}}{36\%} \times \frac{1 \text{ mL}}{1.18 \text{ g}} = 2.4 \text{ mL}$$

$$V_3 = 36.46 \text{ g} \times \frac{100\%}{36\%} \times \frac{1 \text{ mL}}{1.18 \text{ g}} = 86 \text{ mL}$$

b. Given: $D = 1.42$ g/mL; 71% HNO_3 solution; $M_S V_S = M_D V_D$

Unknown: V of HNO_3 to prepare 10.0 L of 2.00 M HNO_3 (V_S)

$$\frac{71 \text{ g } HNO_3}{100 \text{ g}} \times \frac{1.42 \text{ g}}{1 \text{ mL}} \times \frac{1 \text{ mol } HNO_3}{63.02 \text{ g } HNO_3} \times \frac{1000 \text{ mL}}{1 \text{ L}} = 16 \frac{\text{mol } HNO_3}{\text{L}}$$
$$= 16 \text{ M } HNO_3$$

$$V_S = \frac{M_D V_D}{M_S} = \frac{2.00 \text{ M} \times 10.0 \text{ L}}{16 \text{ M}} = 1.2 \text{ L}$$

c. Given: 86 mL contains 1.0 mol (from **a**); $M_S V_S = M_D V_D$; $M_D = 3.0$ M; $V_D = 4.50$ L

Unknown: V_S

$$M_S = \frac{1 \text{ mol}}{86 \text{ mL}} \times \frac{1000 \text{ mL}}{1 \text{ L}} = 12 \text{ M}$$

$$V_S = \frac{M_D V_D}{M_S} = \frac{3.0 \text{ M} \times 4.50 \text{ L}}{12 \text{ M}} = 1.1 \text{ L}$$

374. Given: $M_S = 3.8$ M; $V_D = 8 V_S$; $M_S V_S = M_D V_D$

Unknown: M_D

$$M_D = \frac{M_S V_S}{V_D} = \frac{3.8 \text{ M} \times V_S}{8 V_S} = 0.48 \text{ M}$$

375. Given: $M_D = 2.50$ M;
$V_D = 480.$ mL;
39 mL H_2O
evaporated;
$M_SV_S = M_DV_D$

Unknown: M_S

$$M_S = \frac{M_DV_D}{V_S} = \frac{2.50 \text{ M} \times 480. \text{ mL}}{(480. - 39) \text{ mL}} = 2.72 \text{ M}$$

---

376. Given: $M_D = 1.22$ M;
$V_D = 25.00$ mL;
$M_S = 6.45$ M;
$M_SV_S = M_DV_D$

Unknown: V_S;
procedure

$$V_S = \frac{M_DV_D}{M_S} = \frac{1.22 \text{ M} \times 25.00 \text{ mL}}{6.45 \text{ M}} = 4.73 \text{ mL}$$

Dilute the 6.45 M acid by adding 4.73 mL of it to enough distilled water to make 25.00 mL of solution.

---

377. Given: 100.0 mL of a
2.41 M solution;
9.56 g solute

Unknown: molar mass
of solute

$$100.0 \text{ mL} \times \frac{2.41 \text{ mol}}{1 \text{ L}} \times \frac{1 \text{ L}}{1000 \text{ mL}} = 0.241 \text{ mol solute}$$

$$\text{molar mass} = \frac{9.56 \text{ g}}{0.241 \text{ mol}} = 39.7 \text{ g/mol}$$

---

378. Given: 34 g I_2; $V_S =$
25 mL; $V_D =$
500 mL; $M_SV_S =$
M_DV_D

Unknown: M_D

$$M_S = \frac{34 \text{ g } I_2}{25 \text{ mL}} \times \frac{1 \text{ mol } I_2}{253.8 \text{ g } I_2} \times \frac{1000 \text{ mL}}{1 \text{ L}} = 5.36 \text{ M}$$

$$M_D = \frac{M_SV_S}{V_D} = \frac{5.36 \text{ M} \times 25 \text{ mL}}{500 \text{ mL}} = 0.27 \text{ M}$$

---

379. Given: 85% H_3PO_4
solution;
$V = 600.0$ mL;
2.80 M

Unknown: mass of
solution

$$600.0 \text{ mL} \times \frac{2.80 \text{ mol}}{1 \text{ L}} \times \frac{1 \text{ L}}{1000 \text{ mL}} = 1.68 \text{ mol } H_3PO_4$$

$$1.68 \text{ mol } H_3PO_4 \times \frac{98.00 \text{ g } H_3PO_4}{1 \text{ mol } H_3PO_4} = 165 \text{ g } H_3PO_4$$

$$\text{mass of solution} = \frac{165 \text{ g } H_3PO_4 \times 100. \text{ g solution}}{85 \text{ g } H_3PO_4} = 190 \text{ g solution}$$

---

380. Given: $M_S = 18.0$ M;
$M_D = 4.0$ M;
$V_D = 3.00$ L;
$M_SV_S = M_DV_D$

Unknown: V_S

$$V_S = \frac{M_DV_D}{M_S} = \frac{4.0 \text{ M} \times 3.00 \text{ L}}{18.0 \text{ M}} = 0.67 \text{ L}$$

---

381. Given: $V_D = 1.00$ L; M_D
$= 0.495$ M;
$M_S = 3.07$ M;
$M_SV_S = M_DV_D$

Unknown: V_S

$$V_S = \frac{M_DV_D}{M_S} = \frac{0.495 \text{ M} \times 1.00 \text{ L}}{3.07 \text{ M}} = 0.161 \text{ L} = 161 \text{ mL}$$

Dilute 161 mL stock urea solution to 1.00 L.

---

382. a. Given: 76.2%
$C_6H_{12}O_6$

Unknown: molality

$$\frac{76.2 \text{ g } C_6H_{12}O_6}{(100. - 76.2) \text{ g } H_2O} \times \frac{1 \text{ mol } C_6H_{12}O_6}{180.18 \text{ g } C_6H_{12}O_6} \times \frac{1000 \text{ g}}{1 \text{ kg}} = 17.8 \text{ m}$$

b. Given: 76.2%
$C_6H_{12}O_6$;
$D =$
1.42 g/mL;
$V = 1.00$ L

Unknown: mass of
$C_6H_{12}O_6$;
molarity

$$\frac{1.42 \text{ g}}{1 \text{ mL}} \times 1.00 \text{ L} \times \frac{1000 \text{ mL}}{1 \text{ L}} \times \frac{76.2\%}{100\%} = 1080 \text{ g}$$

$$\frac{1080 \text{ g}}{1 \text{ L}} \times \frac{1 \text{ mol } C_6H_{12}O_6}{180.18 \text{ g } C_6H_{12}O_6} = 5.99 \text{ M}$$

---

383. Given: $M_D = 0.0890$ M;
$V_S = 10.00$ mL;
$V_D = 50.00$ mL;
$M_SV_S = M_DV_D$;
molar mass
$Na_2CO_3 =$
105.99 g

Unknown: M_S; percent-
age Na_2CO_3
in 50.00 g of
a material
used to make
1.000 L stock
solution

$$M_S = \frac{M_DV_D}{V_S} = \frac{0.0890 \text{ M} \times 50.00 \text{ mL}}{10.00 \text{ mL}} = 0.445 \text{ M}$$

$$\frac{0.445 \text{ mol}}{1 \text{ L}} \times 1.000 \text{ L} \times \frac{105.99 \text{ g}}{1 \text{ mol}} = 47.17 \text{ g } Na_2CO_3$$

$$\frac{47.17 \text{ g } Na_2CO_3}{50.00 \text{ g sample}} \times 100 = 94.34\% \text{ } Na_2CO_3$$

---

384. Given: V_T of $CuCl_2$
stock solution
= 0.600 L;
$V_S = 20.0$ mL;
$V_D = 150.0$ mL;
$M_D = 0.250$ M;
$M_SV_S = M_DV_D$

Unknown: mass $CuCl_2$
to make
stock
solution

$$M_S = \frac{M_DV_D}{V_S} = \frac{0.250 \text{ M} \times 150.0 \text{ mL}}{20.0 \text{ mL}} = 1.88 \text{ M}$$

$$\frac{1.88 \text{ mol } CuCl_2}{1 \text{ L}} \times 0.600 \text{ L} \times \frac{134.45 \text{ g } CuCl_2}{1 \text{ mol } CuCl_2} = 152 \text{ g } CuCl_2$$

---

385. Given: $M_S = 2.15$ M;
$M_D = 0.65$ M;
$M_SV_S = M_DV_D$

Unknown: dilution
factor

2.15 M $\times$ V = 0.65 $\times$ kV; k = 3.3; $V_D = 3.3 V_S$

$V_D - V_S = 3.3 V_S - 1.0 V_S = 2.3 V_S$; Add 2.3 volumes of H_2O per volume of stock solution.

---

386. a. Given: 18.2%
$Sr(NO_3)_2$
solution;
$D = 1.02$ g/ml
$V = 80.00$ mL

Unknown: mass of
$Sr(NO_3)_2$

$$80.00 \text{ mL} \times \frac{1.02 \text{ g}}{1 \text{ mL}} \times \frac{18.2 \text{ g } Sr(NO_3)_2}{100 \text{ g solution}} = 14.9 \text{ g } Sr(NO_3)_2$$

b. Given: 14.9 g
$Sr(NO_3)_2$
from **a**

Unknown: moles Sr
$(NO_3)_2$

$$14.9 \text{ g } Sr(NO_3)_2 \times \frac{1 \text{ mol } Sr(NO_3)_2}{211.64 \text{ g } Sr(NO_3)_2} = 7.04 \times 10^{-2} \text{ mol } Sr(NO_3)_2$$

c. Given: 7.04×10^{-2} mol $Sr(NO_3)_2$ from **b**; 420.0 mL H_2O added

Unknown: molarity (M_D)

$$M_S = \frac{7.04 \times 10^{-2} \text{ mol}}{80.0 \text{ mL}} \times \frac{1000 \text{ mL}}{1 \text{ L}} = 0.880 \text{ M}$$

$$M_D = \frac{M_S V_S}{V_D} = \frac{0.880 \text{ M} \times 80.0 \text{ mL}}{(80.0 + 420.0) \text{ mL}} = 0.141 \text{ M}$$

---

387. Given: 60.0 g $C_6H_{12}O_6$ in 80.0 g H_2O; K_f for water = $-1.86°C/m$; $\Delta t_f = K_f m$

Unknown: freezing point

$$60.0 \text{ g } C_6H_{12}O_6 \times \frac{1 \text{ mol } C_6H_{12}O_6}{180.18 \text{ g } C_6H_{12}O_6} = 0.333 \text{ mol } C_6H_{12}O_6$$

$$\frac{0.333 \text{ mol } C_6H_{12}O_6}{80.0 \text{ g } H_2O} \times \frac{1000 \text{ g}}{1 \text{ kg}} = 4.16 \, m$$

$$\Delta t_f = K_f m = \frac{-1.86°C}{m} \times 4.16 \, m = -7.74°C$$

$$\text{fp (solution)} = \text{fp (solvent)} + \Delta t_f = 0.00°C - 7.74°C = 7.74°C$$

---

388. Given: 645 g H_2NCONH_2; 980. g H_2O

Unknown: freezing point

$$645 \text{ g } H_2NCONH_2 \times \frac{1 \text{ mol } H_2NCONH_2}{60.07 \text{ g } H_2NCONH_2} = 10.7 \text{ mol } H_2NCONH_2$$

$$\frac{10.7 \text{ mol } H_2NCONH_2}{980. \text{ g } H_2O} \times \frac{1000 \text{ g}}{1 \text{ kg}} = 10.9 \, m$$

$$\Delta t_f = K_f m = -\frac{1.86°C}{m} \times 10.9 \, m = -20.3 \text{ °C}$$

$$f_p = 0.0°C - 20.3°C = -20.3°C$$

---

389. Given: 30.00 g KBr; 100.00 g H_2O

Unknown: boiling point

$$30.00 \text{ g KBr} \times \frac{1 \text{ mol KBr}}{119.00 \text{ g KBr}} = 0.252 \text{ mol KBr}$$

$$\Delta t_b = \frac{0.252 \text{ mol KBr}}{100.00 \text{ g } H_2O} \times \frac{1000 \text{ g}}{1 \text{ kg}} \times \frac{2 \text{ mol ions}}{1 \text{ mol KBr}} \times \frac{0.51°C}{\text{mol}} = 2.6 \text{ C}$$

$$\text{bp} = 100.0°C + 2.6°C = 102.6°C$$

---

390. Given: 385 g $CaCl_2$; 1.230×10^3 g H_2O

Unknown: boiling point

$$385 \text{ g } CaCl_2 \times \frac{1 \text{ mol } CaCl_2}{110.97 \text{ g } CaCl_2} = 3.47 \text{ mol } CaCl_2$$

$$\Delta t_b = \frac{3.47 \text{ mol } CaCl_2}{1.230 \times 10^3 \text{ g } H_2O} \times \frac{10^3 \text{ g}}{1 \text{ kg}} \times \frac{3 \text{ mol ions}}{1 \text{ mol } CaCl_2} \times \frac{0.51°C}{m} = 4.3°C$$

$$\text{bp} = 100.0°C + 4.3°C = 104.3°C$$

---

391. Given: 0.827 g nonelectrolyte; 2.500 g H_2O; fp = $-10.18°C$

Unknown: molar mass

$$m = \frac{\Delta t_f}{K_f} = \frac{-10.18°C}{-1.86°C/m} = 5.47 \, m$$

$$\frac{5.47 \text{ mol}}{1.00 \text{ kg } H_2O} \times 2.500 \text{ g } H_2O \times \frac{1 \text{ kg}}{1000 \text{ g}} = 0.0137 \text{ mol}$$

$$\frac{0.827 \text{ g}}{0.0137 \text{ mol}} = 60.4 \text{ g/mol}$$

392. Given: 0.171 g nonelectrolyte; ether solvent; mass of solution = 2.470 g; bp = 36.43°C

Unknown: molar mass

mass of ether solvent = 2.470 g − 0.171 g = 2.299 g

Δt_b = bp − normal bp = 36.43°C − 34.6°C = 1.83°C

$$m = \frac{\Delta t_b}{K_b} = \frac{1.83°C}{2.02°C/m} = 0.906\ m$$

$$\frac{0.906\ mol}{1.00\ kg\ ether} \times 2.299\ g\ ether \times \frac{1\ kg}{1000\ g} = 0.00208\ mol$$

$$\frac{0.171\ g}{0.00208\ mol} = 82.2\ g/mol$$

---

393. Given: 383 g glucose; 400. g H_2O

Unknown: freezing point; boiling point

$$383\ g\ C_6H_{12}O_6 \times \frac{1\ mol\ C_6H_{12}O_6}{180.18\ g\ C_6H_{12}O_6} = 2.13\ mol\ C_6H_{12}O_6$$

$$\frac{2.13\ mol}{400.\ g\ H_2O} \times \frac{1000\ g}{1\ kg} = 5.32\ m$$

$$fp = normal\ fp + (K_f m) = 0.00°C + \left(\frac{-1.86°C}{m} \times 5.32\ m\right) = -9.90°C$$

$$bp = normal\ bp + (K_b m) = 100.00°C + \left(\frac{0.51°C}{m} \times 5.32\ m\right) = 102.7°C$$

---

394. Given: 72.4 g glycerol; 122.5 g H_2O

Unknown: boiling point

$$72.4\ g\ glycerol \times \frac{1\ mol\ glycerol}{92.08\ g\ glycerol} = 0.786\ mol\ glycerol$$

$$\frac{0.786\ mol}{122.5\ g\ H_2O} \times \frac{1000\ g}{1\ kg} = 6.42\ m$$

$$bp = normal\ bp + (K_b m) = 100.00°C + \left(\frac{0.51°C}{m} \times 6.42\ m\right) = 103.3°C$$

---

395. Given: 30.20 g $HOCH_2CH_2OH$ solute; 88.40 g phenol

Unknown: boiling point

$$30.20\ g\ HOCH_2CH_2OH \times \frac{1\ mol\ HOCH_2CH_2OH}{62.08\ g\ HOCH_2CH_2OH}$$

$$= 0.4865\ mol\ HOCH_2CH_2OH$$

$$\frac{0.4865\ mol}{88.04\ g} \times \frac{1000\ g}{1\ kg} = 5.503\ m$$

$$bp = normal\ bp + (K_b m) = 181.8°C + \left(\frac{3.60°C}{m} \times 5.503\ m\right) = 201.6°C$$

---

396. Given: 450. g H_2O; fp = −4.5°C

Unknown: mass of ethanol solute

$$m = \frac{fp}{K_f} = \frac{-4.5°C}{-1.86°C/m} = 2.4\ m$$

$$\frac{2.4\ mol}{1\ kg} \times 450.\ g \times \frac{1\ kg}{1000\ g} = 1.1\ mol$$

$$1.1\ mol\ ethanol \times \frac{46.08\ g\ ethanol}{1\ mol\ ethanol} = 51\ g\ ethanol$$

397. Given: fp = –3.9°C 25.00 g H_2O; 4.27 g solute

Unknown: molar mass of solute

$$m = \frac{fp}{K_f} = \frac{-3.9°C}{-1.86°C/m} = 2.1\ m$$

$$\frac{2.1\ mol}{1\ kg\ H_2O} \times 25.00\ g\ H_2O \times \frac{1\ kg}{1000\ g} = 0.052\ mol$$

$$\frac{4.27\ g}{0.052\ mol} = 82\ g/mol$$

---

398. Given: 1.17 g $C_{10}H_8O$; 2.00 mL benzene; T = 20°C; D of benzene = 0.876 g/mL; K_f for benzene = –5.12°C/m; normal fp of benzene = 5.53°C

Unknown: freezing point

$$mass\ benzene = 2.00\ mL \times \frac{0.8769}{1\ mL} = 1.75\ g$$

$$mol\ C_{10}H_8O = 1.17\ g\ C_{10}H_8O \times \frac{1\ mol\ C_{10}H_8O}{144.18\ g\ C_{10}H_8O} = 0.00811\ mol\ C_{10}H_8O$$

$$\frac{0.00811\ mol\ C_{10}H_8O}{1.75\ g\ benzene} \times \frac{1000\ g}{1\ kg} = 4.63\ m$$

$$fp = normal\ fp + (K_fm) = 5.53°C + \left(\frac{-5.12°C}{m} \times 4.63\ m\right) = -18.2°C$$

---

399. Given: 10.44 g solute; 50.00 g CH_3COOH solvent; bp = 159.2°C

Unknown: molar mass

$$m = \frac{bp - normal\ bp}{K_b} = \frac{159.2°C - 117.9°C}{3.07°C/m} = 13.5\ m$$

$$\frac{13.5\ mol}{1\ kg\ solvent} \times 50.00\ g\ solvent \times \frac{1\ kg}{1000\ g} = 0.675\ mol$$

$$\frac{10.44\ g}{0.675\ mol} = 15.5\ g/mol$$

---

400. Given: 0.0355 g solute; 1.000 g camphor solvent; T = 200.0°C; fp = 157.7°C

Unknown: molar mass

$$m = \frac{fp - normal\ fp}{K_f} = \frac{157.7°C - 178.8°C}{-39.7°C/m} = 0.531\ m$$

$$\frac{0.531\ mol}{1\ kg\ solvent} \times 1.000\ g\ solvent \times \frac{1\ kg}{1000\ g} = 5.31 \times 10^{-4}\ mol$$

$$\frac{0.0355\ g}{5.31 \times 10^{-4}\ mol} = 66.8\ g/mol$$

---

401. Given: 22.5 g $C_6H_{12}O_6$; 294 g phenol

Unknown: boiling point

$$22.5\ g\ C_6H_{12}O_6 \times \frac{1\ mol\ C_6H_{12}O_6}{180.18\ g\ C_6H_{12}O_6} = 0.125\ mol\ C_6H_{12}O_6$$

$$\frac{0.125\ mol}{294\ g} \times \frac{1000\ g}{1\ kg} = 0.425\ m$$

$$bp = 181.8°C + (3.60°C/m \times 0.425\ m) = 183.3°C$$

---

402. Given: 50.0% solution of ethylene glycol in H_2O

$$\frac{50.0\ g\ ethylene\ glycol}{50.0\ g\ H_2O} \times \frac{1000\ g}{1\ kg} \times \frac{1\ mol\ ethylene\ glycol}{62.08\ g\ ethylene\ glycol} = 16.1\ m$$

a. Unknown: freezing point

$$fp = normal\ fp + (K_fm) = 0.00°C + (-1.86°C/m \times 16.1\ m) = -29.9°C$$

b. Unknown: boiling point

$$bp = normal\ bp + (K_bm) = 100.00°C + (0.51°C/m \times 16.1\ m) = 108.2°C$$

403. Given: $K_f = -20.0°C/m$; normal fp = 6.6°C; cyclohexane solvent; 1.604 g solute; 10.000 g cyclohexane; fp = -4.4°C

Unknown: molar mass

$$m = \frac{\text{fp} - \text{normal fp}}{K_f} = \frac{-4.4°C - 6.6°C}{-20.0°C/m} = 0.550\ m$$

$$\frac{0.550\ \text{mol}}{1.00\ \text{kg solvent}} \times 10.000\ \text{g solvent} \times \frac{1\ \text{kg}}{1000\ \text{g}} = 0.00550\ \text{mol}$$

$$\frac{1.604\ \text{g}}{0.00550\ \text{mol}} = 292\ \text{g/mol}$$

---

404. Given: 2.62 kg HNO_3; H_2O solvent; mass of solution = 5.91 kg

Unknown: freezing point

mass H_2O = 5.91 kg − 2.62 kg = 3.29 kg

$$2.62\ \text{kg}\ HNO_3 \times \frac{1\ \text{mol}\ HNO_3}{63.02\ \text{g}\ HNO_3} \times \frac{1000\ \text{g}}{1\ \text{kg}} = 41.6\ \text{mol}\ HNO_3 = 83.2\ \text{mol ions}$$

$$\frac{83.2\ \text{mol ions}}{3.29\ \text{kg}\ H_2O} = 25.3\ m$$

fp = normal fp + $(K_f m)$ = 0.00°C + (−1.86°C/m × 25.3 m) = −47.1°C

---

405. Given: 0.5190 g naphthalene solvent; mass solution = 0.5959 g; fp = 74.8°C

Unknown: molar mass

mass solute = 0.5959 g − 0.5190 g = 0.0769 g

$$m = \frac{\text{fp} - \text{normal fp}}{K_f} = \frac{74.8°C - 80.2°C}{-6.94°C/m} = 0.778\ m$$

$$\frac{0.778\ \text{mol}}{1.00\ \text{kg solvent}} \times 0.5190\ \text{g solvent} \times \frac{1\ \text{kg}}{1000\ \text{g}} = 4.04 \times 10^{-4}\ \text{mol}$$

$$\frac{0.0769\ \text{g}}{4.04 \times 10^{-4}\ \text{mol}} = 190.\ \text{g/mol}$$

---

406. Given: 8.69 g $NaCH_3COO$; 15.00 g H_2O

Unknown: boiling point

$$8.69\ \text{g}\ NaCH_3COO \times \frac{1\ \text{mol}\ NaCH_3COO}{82.04\ \text{g}\ NaCH_3COO} \times \frac{2\ \text{mol ions}}{1\ \text{mol}\ NaCH_3COO}$$

$$= 0.212\ \text{mol ions}$$

$$\frac{0.212\ \text{mol}}{15.00\ \text{g}\ H_2O} \times \frac{1000\ \text{g}}{.1\ \text{kg}} = 14.1\ m$$

bp = normal bp + $(K_b m)$ = 100.00°C + (0.51°C/m × 14.1 m) = 107.2°C

---

407. Given: 110.5 g H_2SO_4; 225 g H_2O

Unknown: freezing point

$$110.5\ \text{g}\ H_2SO_4 \times \frac{1\ \text{mol}\ H_2SO_4}{98.09\ \text{g}\ H_2SO_4} \times \frac{3\ \text{mol ions}}{1\ \text{mol}\ H_2SO_4} = 3.38\ \text{mol ions}$$

$$\frac{3.38\ \text{mol}}{225\ \text{g}\ H_2O} \times \frac{1000\ \text{g}}{1\ \text{kg}} = 15.0\ m$$

fp = normal fp + $(K_f m)$ = 0.00°C + (−1.86°C/m × 15.0 m) = −27.9°C

408. Given: empirical formula is C_8H_5; 4.04 g pyrene; 10.00 g benzene solvent; bp = 85.1°C; K_b = 2.53°C/m; normal bp = 80.1°C

Unknown: molar mass; molecular formula

$$m = \frac{bp - normal\ bp}{K_b} = \frac{85.1°C - 80.1°C}{2.53°C/m} = 1.98\ m$$

$$\frac{1.98\ mol}{1\ Kg\ solvent} \times 10.00\ g\ solvent \times \frac{1\ kg}{1000\ g} = 0.0198\ mol$$

$$\frac{4.04\ g}{0.0198\ mol} = 204\ g/mol$$

molar mass C_8H_5 = 101.13 g/mol

$$\frac{204\ g}{1\ mol} \times \frac{1\ mol}{101.13\ g} = 2.02 \approx 2$$

molecular formula = $C_{8 \times 2}H_{5 \times 2} = C_{16}H_{10}$

---

409. Given: $CaCl_2$ solute; 100.00 g H_2O; fp = –5.0°C

Unknown: mass $CaCl_2$; mass $C_6H_{12}O_6$ for same fp

$$m = \frac{fp - normal\ fp}{K_f} = \frac{-5.0°C - 0.0°C}{-1.86°C/m} = 2.7\ m\ (ions)$$

$$\frac{2.7\ mol\ ions}{1.0\ kg} \times \frac{1\ mol\ CaCl_2}{3\ mol\ ions} = 0.90\ m\ CaCl_2$$

$$\frac{0.90\ mol\ CaCl_2}{1.0\ kg\ H_2O} \times 100.00\ g\ H_2O \times \frac{1\ kg}{1000\ g} = 0.090\ mol\ CaCl_2$$

$$0.090\ mol\ CaCl_2 \times \frac{110.98\ g\ CaCl_2}{1\ mol\ CaCl_2} = 10.\ g\ CaCl_2$$

Because glucose is a nonelectrolyte, m of glucose = 2.7 m

$$\frac{2.7\ mol\ glucose}{1.0\ kg\ H_2O} \times 100.00\ g\ H_2O \times \frac{1\ kg}{1000\ g} = 0.27\ mol\ glucose$$

$$0.27\ mol\ C_6H_{12}O_6 \times \frac{180.18\ g\ C_6H_{12}O_6}{1\ mol\ C_6H_{12}O_6} = 49\ g\ glucose$$

---

410. Given: empirical formula is CH_2O; 0.0866 g solute; 1.000 g ether; bp = 36.5°C

Unknown: molecular formula

$$m = \frac{bp - normal\ bp}{K_b} = \frac{36.5°C - 34.6°C}{2.02°C/m} = 0.941\ m$$

$$\frac{0.941\ mol}{1.00\ kg\ solvent} \times 1.000\ g\ solvent \times \frac{1\ kg}{1000\ g} = 9.41 \times 10^{-4}\ mol$$

$$\frac{0.0866\ g}{9.41 \times 10^{-4}\ mol} = 92.0\ g/mol\ for\ the\ molecule$$

molar mass CH_2O = 30.03 g/mol

$$\frac{92.0\ g/mol}{30.03\ g.mol} = 3.06$$

molecular formula = $C_{1 \times 3}H_{2 \times 3}O_{1 \times 3} = C_3H_6O_3$

---

411. Given: 28.6% HCl by mass

Unknown: freezing point

$$\frac{28.6\ g\ HCl}{(100.0\ g - 28.6\ g)\ H_2O} \times \frac{1\ mol\ HCl}{36.46\ g\ HCl} \times \frac{2\ mol\ ions}{1\ mol\ HCl} \times \frac{1000\ g}{1\ kg} = 22.0\ m\ ions$$

$$fp = normal\ fp + (K_f m) = 0.00°C + (-1.86°C/m \times 22.0\ m) = -40.9°C$$

412. Given: 4.510 kg H_2O; fp = -18.0°C; $HOCH_2CH_2OH$ solute

Unknown: mass of solute; boiling point

$$m = \frac{fp - normal\ fp}{K_f} = \frac{-18.0°C - 0.0°C}{-1.86°C/m} = 9.68\ m$$

$$\frac{9.68\ mol}{1.00\ kg\ solvent} \times 4.510\ kg\ solvent = 43.7\ mol$$

$$43.7\ mol\ HOCH_2CH_2OH \times \frac{62.08\ g\ HOCH_2CH_2OH}{1\ mol\ HOCH_2CH_2OH}$$

$$= 2710\ g\ HOCH_2CH_2OH = 2.71\ kg\ HOCH_2CH_2OH$$

$$bp = normal\ bp \times (K_b m) = 100.00°C \times (0.51°C/m \times 9.68\ m) = 104.9°C$$

413. **a.** Given: 2.00 g solute; 10.00 g H_2O; fp = -4.0°C

Unknown: molality

$$\frac{fp - normal\ fp}{K_f} = \frac{-4.0°C - 0.0°C}{-1.86°C/m} = 2.2\ m$$

b. Given: 2.00 g solute; acetone solvent; bp = 58.9°C; normal bp = 56.00°C; K_b = 1.71°C/m

Unknown: molality

$$\frac{bp - normal\ bp}{K_b} = \frac{58.9°C - 56.00°C}{1.71°C/m} = 1.7\ m$$

414. Given: fp = -22.0°C; 100.00 g glycerol solute

Unknown: mass of H_2O

$$m = \frac{fp - normal\ fp}{K_f} = \frac{-22.0°C - 0.0°C}{-1.86°C/m} = 11.8\ m$$

$$100.00\ g\ C_3H_5(OH)_3 \times \frac{1\ mol\ C_3H_5(OH)_3}{92.11\ g\ C_3H_5(OH)_3} = 1.086\ mol\ C_3H_5(OH)_3$$

$$1.110\ mol\ C_3H_5(OH)_3 \times \frac{1\ kg\ H_2O}{11.8\ mol\ C_3H_5(OH)_3} \times \frac{1000\ g}{1\ kg} = 92.0\ g\ H_2O$$

415. Given: empirical formula is CH_2O; 0.515 g solute; 1.717 g acetic acid; fp = 8.8°C

Unknown: molar mass; molecular formula

$$m = \frac{fp - normal\ fp}{K_f} = \frac{8.8°C - 16.6°C}{-3.90°C/m} = 2.0\ m$$

$$\frac{2.0\ mol}{1.00\ kg\ acetic\ acid} \times 1.717\ g\ acetic\ acid \times \frac{1\ kg}{1000\ g} = 0.0034\ mol$$

$$\frac{0.515\ g}{0.0034\ mol} = 150\ g/mol$$

molar mass CH_2O = 30.03 g/mol

$$\frac{150\ g/mol}{30.03\ g/mol} = 5.0$$

molecular formula = $C_{1 \times 5}H_{2 \times 5}O_{1 \times 5} = C_5H_{10}O_5$

416. Given: empirical formula is C_2H_2O; 3.775 g solute; 12.00 g H_2O; fp = $-4.72°C$

Unknown: molar mass; molecular formula

$$m = \frac{fp - \text{normal fp}}{K_f} = \frac{-4.72°C - 0.00°C}{-1.86°C/m} = 2.54\ m$$

$$\frac{2.54\ \text{mol}}{1.00\ \text{kg}\ H_2O} \times 12.00\ \text{g}\ H_2O \times \frac{1\ \text{kg}}{1000\ \text{g}} = 0.0305\ \text{mol}$$

$$\frac{3.775\ \text{g}}{0.0305\ \text{mol}} = 124\ \text{g/mol}$$

molar mass C_2H_2O = 42.04 g/mol

$$\frac{124\ \text{g/mol}}{42.04\ \text{g/mol}} = 2.95 \approx 3$$

molecular formula = $C_{2 \times 3}H_{2 \times 3}O_{1 \times 3} = C_6H_6O_3$

---

417. Given: $[OH^-] = 6.4 \times 10^{-5}$ M

Unknown: $[H_3O^+]$

$$[H_3O^+][OH^-] = 1.0 \times 10^{-4}\ M^2$$

$$\frac{1.0 \times 10^{-4}\ M^2}{6.4 \times 10^{-5}\ M} = 1.6 \times 10^{-10}\ M$$

---

418. Given: 7.50×10^{-4} M HNO_3

Unknown: $[H_3O^+]$; $[OH^-]$

$$[H_3O^+] = 7.50 \times 10^{-4}\ M\ HNO_3 \times \frac{1\ M\ H_3O^+}{1\ M\ HNO_3} = 7.50 \times 10^{-4}\ M$$

$$[H_3O^+][OH^-] = 1.00 \times 10^{-14}\ M^2$$

$$[OH^-] = \frac{1.00 \times 10^{-14}\ M^2}{7.50 \times 10^{-4}\ M} = 1.33 \times 10^{-11}\ M$$

---

419. Given: 0.00118 M HBr

Unknown: pH

$$pH = -\log[H_3O^+] = -\log(1.18 \times 10^{-3}) = 2.928$$

---

420. a. Given: $[H_3O^+] = 1.0$ M

Unknown: pH

$$pH = -\log(1.0) = 0.0$$

b. Given: 2.0 M HCl solution

Unknown: pH

$$pH = -\log(2.0) = -0.30$$

c. Given: 10. M HCl solution

Unknown: pH

$$pH = -\log(10.) = -1.00$$

---

421. a. Given: $[OH^-] = 1 \times 10^{-5}$ M

Unknown: pH

$$[H_3O^+][OH^-] = 1 \times 10^{-14}\ M^2$$

$$[H_3O^+] = \frac{1 \times 10^{-14}\ M^2}{[OH^-]} = \frac{1. \times 10^{-14}\ M^2}{1 \times 10^{-5}\ M} = 1 \times 10^{-9}\ M$$

$$pH = -\log[H_3O^+] = -\log(1 \times 10^{-9}) = 9.0$$

b. Given: $[OH^-] = 5 \times 10^{-8}$ M

Unknown: pH

$[H_3O^+][OH^-] = 1 \times 10^{-14}$ M^2

$[H_3O^+] = \dfrac{1 \times 10^{-14} \text{ M}^2}{[OH^-]} = \dfrac{1 \times 10^{-14} \text{ M}^2}{5 \times 10^{-8} \text{ M}} = 2 \times 10^{-7}$ M

pH $= -\log [H_3O^+] = -\log (2 \times 10^{-7}) = 7 - 0.3 = 6.7$

c. Given: $[OH^-] = 2.90 \times 10^{-11}$ M

Unknown: pH

$[H_3O^+][OH^-] = 1 \times 10^{-14}$ M^2

$[H_3O^+] = \dfrac{1 \times 10^{-14} \text{ M}^2}{[OH^-]} = \dfrac{1.00 \times 10^{-14} \text{ M}^2}{2.90 \times 10^{-11} \text{ M}} = 3.45 \times 10^{-4}$ M

pH $= -\log [H_3O^+] = -\log (3.45 \times 10^{-4}) = 3.462$

---

422. Given: pH = 8.92

Unknown: pOH; (OH^-)

pH + pOH = 14

pOH $= 14.00 - $ pH $= 14.00 - 8.92 = 5.08$

$[OH^-] = $ antilog $(-$pOH$) = 1 \times 10^{-5.08} = 8.3 \times 10^{-6}$ M

---

423. a. Given: $[H_3O^+] = 2.51 \times 10^{-13}$ M

Unknown: pOH

$[OH^-] = \dfrac{1.00 \times 10^{-14} \text{ M}^2}{[H_3O^+]} = \dfrac{1.00 \times 1.0^{-14} \text{ M}^2}{2.51 \times 10^{-13} \text{ M}} = 3.98 \times 10^{-2}$ M

pOH $= -\log [OH^-] = -\log (3.98 \times 10^{-2}) = 1.400$

b. Given: $[H_3O^+] = 4.3 \times 10^{-3}$ M

Unknown: pOH

$[OH^-] = \dfrac{1.0 \times 10^{-14} \text{ M}^2}{[H_3O^+]} = \dfrac{1.0 \times 10^{-14} \text{ M}^2}{4.3 \times 10^{-3} \text{ M}} = 2.3 \times 10^{-12}$ M

pOH $= -\log [OH^-] = -\log (2.3 \times 10^{-12}) = 11.64$

c. Given: $[H_3O^+] = 9.1 \times 10^{-6}$ M

Unknown: pOH

$[OH^-] = \dfrac{1.0 \times 10^{-14} \text{ M}^2}{[H_3O^+]} = \dfrac{1.0 \times 10^{-14} \text{ M}^2}{9.1 \times 10^{-6} \text{ M}} = 1.1 \times 10^{-9}$ M

pOH $= -\log [OH^-] = -\log (1.1 \times 10^{-9}) = 8.96$

d. Given: $[H_3O^+] = 0.070$ M

Unknown: pOH

$[OH^-] = \dfrac{1.0 \times 10^{-14} \text{ M}^2}{[H_3O^+]} = \dfrac{1.0 \times 10^{-14} \text{ M}^2}{7.0 \times 10^{-2} \text{ M}} = 1.4 \times 10^{-13}$ M

pOH $= -\log [OH^-] = -\log (1.4 \times 10^{-13}) = 12.85$

---

424. Given: 3.50 g NaOH solute; $V = 2.50$ L

Unknown: $[OH^-]$; $[H_3O^+]$

3.50 g NaOH $\times \dfrac{1 \text{ mol NaOH}}{40.00 \text{ g NaOH}} = 0.0875$ mol NaOH

$[OH^-] = \dfrac{0.0875 \text{ mol}}{2.50 \text{ L}} = 0.0350$ M

$[H_3O^+] = \dfrac{1.00 \times 10^{-14} \text{ M}^2}{[OH^-]} = \dfrac{1.00 \times 10^{-14} \text{ M}^2}{3.50 \times 10^{-2} \text{ M}} = 2.86 \times 10^{-13}$ M

---

425. Given: $V_1 = 1.00$ L ; pH$_1$ = 12.90; $V_2 = 2.00$ L

Unknown: pH$_2$

$[H_3O^+] = $ antilog $(-$pH$) = 1 \times 10^{-12.90} = 1.3 \times 10^{-13}$ M

$M_2 = \dfrac{M_1 V_1}{V_2} = \dfrac{1.3 \times 10^{-13} \text{ M} \times 1.00 \text{ L}}{2.00 \text{ L}} = 6.5 \times 10^{-14}$ M

pH$_2 = -\log [H_3O^+] = -\log (6.5 \times 10^{-14}) = 13.19$

426. Unknown: $[H_3O^+]$; $[OH^-]$ $[OH^-] = 5 \times 10^{-2}$ M

   a. Given: 0.05 M NaOH $[H_3O^+] = \dfrac{1 \times 10^{-14} \text{ M}^2}{[OH^-]} = \dfrac{1 \times 10^{-14} \text{ M}^2}{5 \times 10^{-2} \text{ M}} = 2 \times 10^{-13}$ M

   b. Given: 0.0025 M H_2SO_4

$$[H_3O^+] = 0.0025 \text{ M H}_2\text{SO} \times \dfrac{2 \text{ M H}_3\text{O}^+}{1 \text{ M H}_2\text{SO}_4} = 0.0050 \text{ M} = 5.0 \times 10^{-3} \text{ M}$$

$$[OH^-] = \dfrac{1.0 \times 10^{-14} \text{ M}^2}{[H_3O^+]} = \dfrac{1.0 \times 10^{-14} \text{ M}^2}{5.0 \times 10^{-13} \text{ M}} = 2.0 \times 10^{-12} \text{ M}$$

   c. Given: 0.013 M LiOH

$$[OH-] = 1.3 \times 10^{-2} \text{ M}$$

$$[H_3O^+] = \dfrac{1.0 \times 10^{-14} \text{ M}^2}{1.3 \times 10^{-2} \text{ M}} = 7.7 \times 10^{-13} \text{ M}$$

   d. Given: 0.150 M HNO_3

$$[H_3O^+] = 1.50 \times 10^{-1} \text{ M}$$

$$[OH^-] = \dfrac{1.00 \times 10^{-14} \text{ M}^2}{1.50 \times 10^{-1} \text{ M}} = 6.67 \times 10^{-14} \text{ M}$$

   e. Given: 0.0200 M Ca $(OH)_2$

$$[OH^-] = 2[Ca(OH)_2] = 4.00 \times 10^{-2} \text{ M}$$

$$[H_3O^+] = \dfrac{1.00 \times 10^{-14} \text{ M}^2}{4.00 \times 10^{-2} \text{ M}} = 2.50 \times 10^{-13} \text{ M}$$

   f. Given: 0.390 M $HClO_4$

$$[H_3O^+] = 3.90 \times 10^{-1} \text{ M}$$

$$[OH^-] = \dfrac{1.00 \times 10^{-14} \text{ M}^2}{3.90 \times 10^{-1} \text{ M}} = 2.56 \times 10^{-14} \text{ M}$$

---

427. Unknown: pH

   a. Given: $[H_3O^+] = 2 \times 10^{-13}$ M $pH = -\log(2 \times 10^{-13}) = 12.7$

   b. Given: $[H_3O^+] = 5.0 \times 10^{-3}$ M $pH = -\log(5.0 \times 10^{-3}) = 2.30$

   c. Given: $[H_3O^+] = 7.7 \times 10^{-13}$ M $pH = -\log(7.7 \times 10^{-13}) = 12.11$

   d. Given: $[H_3O^+] = 1.50 \times 10^{-1}$ M $pH = -\log(1.50 \times 10^{-1}) = 0.824$

   e. Given: $[H_3O^+] = 2.50 \times 10^{-13}$ M $pH = -\log(2.50 \times 10^{-13}) = 12.602$

   f. Given: $[H_3O^+] = 3.90 \times 10^{-1}$ M $pH = -\log(3.90 \times 10^{-1}) = 0.409$

---

428. Given: 0.160 M KOH $[OH^-] = [KOH] = 1.60 \times 10^{-1}$ M

   Unknown: $[H_3O^+]$; $[OH^-]$ $[H_3O^+] = \dfrac{1.00 \times 10^{-14} \text{ M}^2}{1.60 \times 10^{-1} \text{ M}} = 6.25 \times 10^{-14} \text{ M}$

429. Given: pH = 12.9; NaOH solution

Unknown: molarity

pOH = 14.0 − 12.9 = 1.1

$[NaOH] = [OH^-] = antilog (- pOH) = 1.0 \times 10^{-1.1} = 0.08$ M

---

430. Given: 0.001 25 M HBr; V_1 = 175 mL; V_2 = 3.00 L; $M_1V_1 = M_2V_2$

Unknown: pH before and after dilution

$M_2 = \dfrac{M_1V_1}{V_2} = \dfrac{0.001\ 25\ M \times 175\ mL}{3.00\ L} \times \dfrac{1\ L}{1000\ mL} = 7.29 \times 10^{-5}$ M

$[HBr] = [H_3O^+]$

$pH_1 = - \log [H_3O^+] = - \log (1.25 \times 10^{-3}) = 2.903$

$pH_2 = - \log [H_3O^+] = - \log (7.29 \times 10^{-5}) = 4.137$

---

431. Given: NaOH solutions of 0.0001 M and 0.0005 M

Unknown: pH for both solutions

$[NaOH] = [OH^-] = 1 \times 10^{-4}$ M; $pOH = - \log (1 \times 10^{-4}) = 4.0$

$pH = 14.0 - 4.0 = 10.0$

$[NaOH] = [OH^-] = 5 \times 10^{-4}$ M; $pOH = - \log (5 \times 10^{-4}) = 3.3$

$pH = 14.0 - 3.3 = 10.7$

---

432. Given: V_1 = 15.0 mL; M_1 = 1.0 M HCl; V_2 = 20.0 mL; M_2 = 0.50 M HNO$_3$; V_F = 1.25 L

a. Unknown: $[H_3O^+]$ and $[OH^-]$ of final solution

Before dilution: $15.0\ mL \times \dfrac{1.0\ mol}{1\ L} \times \dfrac{1\ L}{1000\ mL} + 20.0\ mL \times \dfrac{0.50\ mol}{1\ L}$

$\times \dfrac{1\ L}{1000\ mL} = 0.0150\ mol + 0.0100\ mol = 0.0250$ mol

$[H_3O^+] = \dfrac{0.0250\ mol}{(15.0 + 20.0)\ mL} \times \dfrac{1000\ mL}{1\ L} = 0.714$ M

After dilution: $[H_3O^+] = M_F = \dfrac{0.714\ M \times 0.035\ L}{1.25\ L} = 0.020$ M

$[OH^-] = \dfrac{1.0 \times 10^{-14}\ M^2}{2.0 \times 10^{-2}\ M} = 5.0 \times 10^{-13}$ M

b. Unknown: pH of final solution

$pH = - \log [H_3O^+] = - \log (2.0 \times 10^{-2}) = 1.70$

---

433. a. Given: 0.001 57 M HNO$_3$

Unknown: pH

$[H_3O^+] = [HNO_3] = 1.57 \times 10^{-3}$ M

$pH = - \log [H_3O^+] = - \log (1.57 \times 10^{-3}) = 2.804$

b. Given: V_1 = 500.0 mL; M_1 = 0.001 57 M; V_2 = 447.0 mL

Unknown: pH at V_2

$M_2 = \dfrac{M_1V_1}{V_2} = \dfrac{1.57 \times 10^{-3}\ M \times 500.0\ mL}{447.0\ mL} = 1.76 \times 10^{-3}$ M

$pH = - \log [H_3O^+] = - \log (1.76 \times 10^{-3}) = 2.754$

---

434. Given: $[H_3O^+]$ = 0.00035 M

Unknown: $[OH^-]$

$[OH^-] = \dfrac{1.0 \times 10^{-14}\ M^2}{3.5 \times 10^{-4}\ M} = 2.9 \times 10^{-11}$ M

435. Given: NaOH solute;
$pH_1 = 12.14$;
$V_1 = 50.00$ mL;
$V_2 = 2.000$ L

Unknown: pH_2

$pOH_1 = 14.00 - pH = 14.00 - 12.14 = 1.86$

$[OH^-]_1 = $ antilog $(-pOH) = 1.0 \times 10^{-1.86} = 1.4 \times 10^{-2}$ M

$[OH^-]_2 = \dfrac{[OH^-]_1 V_1}{V_2} = \dfrac{1.4 \times 10^{-2} \text{ M} \times 50.00 \text{ mL}}{2.000 \text{ L}} \times \dfrac{1 \text{ L}}{1000 \text{ mL}} = 3.5 \times 10^{-4}$ M

$pOH_2 = -\log (3.5 \times 10^{-4}) = 3.46$

$pH_2 = 14.00 - 3.46 = 10.54$

---

436. Given: pH = 4.0

Unknown: $[H_3O^+]$;
$[OH^-]$

$[H_3O^+] = $ antilog $(-pH) = $ antilog $(-4.0) = 1 \times 10^{-4}$ M

$[OH^-] = \dfrac{1 \times 10^{-14} \text{ M}^2}{1 \times 10^{-4} \text{ M}} = 1 \times 10^{-10}$ M

---

437. Given: 0.000 460 M
$Ca(OH)_2$ solution

Unknown: pH

$[OH^-] = 4.60 \times 10^{-4}$ M $Ca(OH)_2 \times \dfrac{2 \text{ M OH}^-}{1 \text{ M Ca(OH)}_2} = 9.20 \times 10^{-4}$ M

$[H_3O^+] = \dfrac{1.00 \times 10^{-14} \text{ M}^2}{9.20 \times 10^{-4} \text{ M}} = 1.09 \times 10^{-11}$ M

$pH = -\log (1.09 \times 10^{-11}) = 10.963$

---

438. Given: $Sr(OH)_2$ solute;
pH = 11.4; 1.00 L

Unknown: mass
$Sr(OH)_2$

$pOH = 14.0 - 11.4 = 2.6$

$[OH^-] = $ antilog $(-pOH) = $ antilog $(-2.6) = 10^{-2.6} = 3 \times 10^{-3}$ M

$[Sr(OH)_2] = 3 \times 10^{-3}$ M $OH^- \times \dfrac{1 \text{ M Sr(OH)}_2}{2 \text{ M OH}^-} = 2 \times 10^{-3}$ M

$\dfrac{2 \times 10^{-3} \text{ mol}}{1 \text{ L}} \times 1.00 \text{ L} = 2 \times 10^{-3}$ mol

2×10^{-3} mol $Sr(OH)_2 \times \dfrac{121.64 \text{ g Sr(OH)}_2}{1 \text{ mol Sr(OH)}_2} = 0.2$ g $Sr(OH)_2$

---

439. Given: NH_3 solute;
pH = 11.00

Unknown: $[H_3O^+]$;
$[OH^-]$

$[H_3O^+] = $ antilog $(-11.00) = 1.0 \times 10^{-11}$ M

$[OH^-] = \dfrac{1.0 \times 10^{-14} \text{ M}^2}{1.0 \times 10^{-11} \text{ M}} = 1.0 \times 10^{-3}$ M

---

440. a. Given: 1.0 M
CH_3COOH;
pH = 2.40

Unknown: percent
ionization

$[H_3O^+] = $ antilog $(-2.40) = 1.00 \times 10^{-2.40} = 3.98 \times 10^{-3}$ M

$\dfrac{3.98 \times 10^{-3} \text{ M}}{1.0 \text{ M}} \times 100 = 0.40\%$ ionized

b. Given: 0.10 M
CH_3COOH;
pH = 2.90

Unknown: percent
ionization

$[H_3O^+] = $ antilog $(-2.90) = 1.00 \times 10^{-2.90} = 1.26 \times 10^{-3}$ M

$\dfrac{1.26 \times 10^{-3} \text{ M}}{0.10 \text{ M}} \times 100 = 1.3\%$ ionized

c. Given: 0.010 M
CH_3COOH;
pH = 3.40

Unknown: percent
ionization

$[H_3O^+] = $ antilog $(-3.40) = 1.00 \times 10^{-3.40} = 3.98 \times 10^{-4}$ M

$\dfrac{3.98 \times 10^{-4} \text{ M}}{1.0 \times 10^{-2} \text{ M}} \times 100 = 4.0\%$

441. Given: 5.00 g HNO_3;
2.00 L

Unknown: pH

$$5.00 \text{ g } HNO_3 \times \frac{1 \text{ mol } HNO_3}{63.02 \text{ g } HNO_3} = 0.0793 \text{ mol } HNO_3$$

$$[H_3O^+] = [HNO_3] = \frac{0.0793 \text{ mol}}{2.00 \text{ L}} = 0.0396 \text{ M}$$

$$pH = -\log(0.0396) = 1.402$$

---

442. Given: stock pH = 1.50;
HCl solute

Unknown: pH of diluted
solution

a. Given: $V_S = 1.00$ mL;
$V_D = 1000.$
mL

$$M_S = [H_3O^+] = [HCl] = \text{antilog } (-1.50) = 1.0 \times 10^{-1.50} \text{ M} = 3.16 \times 10^{-2} \text{ M}$$

$$M_D = \frac{M_S V_S}{V_D} = \frac{3.16 \times 10^{-2} \text{ M} \times 1.00 \text{ mL}}{1000. \text{ mL}} = 3.16 \times 10^{-5} \text{ M}$$

$$pH = -\log(3.16 \times 10^{-5}) = 4.50$$

b. Given: $V_S = 25.00$
mL; $V_D =$
200. mL

$$M_D = \frac{M_S V_S}{V_D} = \frac{3.16 \times 10^{-2} \text{ M} \times 25.00 \text{ mL}}{200. \text{ mL}} = 3.95 \times 10^{-3} \text{ M}$$

$$pH = -\log(3.95 \times 10^{-3}) = 2.40$$

c. Given: $V_S = 18.83$
mL; $V_D =$
4.000 L

$$M_D = \frac{M_S V_S}{V_D} = \frac{3.16 \times 10^{-2} \text{ M} \times 18.83 \text{ mL}}{4.000 \text{ L}} \times \frac{1 \text{ L}}{1000 \text{ mL}} = 1.49 \times 10^{-4} \text{ M}$$

$$pH = -\log(1.49 \times 10^{-4}) = 3.83$$

d. Given: $V_S = 1.50$ L;
$V_D = 20.0$ kL

$$M_D = \frac{M_S V_S}{V_D} = \frac{3.16 \times 10^{-2} \text{ M} \times 1.50 \text{ L}}{20.0 \text{ kL}} \times \frac{1 \text{ kL}}{1000 \text{ L}} = 2.37 \times 10^{-6} \text{ M}$$

$$pH = -\log(2.37 \times 10^{-6}) = 5.63$$

---

443. Given: $[H_3O^+] = 10\ 000$
$[OH^-]$; aqueous
solution

Unknown: $[H_3O^+]$;
$[OH^-]$

$$[H_3O^+][OH^-] = 10\ 000\ [OH^-][OH^-] = 1 \times 10^{-14} \text{ M}^2$$

$$[OH^-]^2 = \frac{1 \times 10^{-14} \text{ M}^2}{10^4} = 1 \times 10^{-18} \text{ M}^2$$

$$[OH^-] = 1 \times 10^{-9} \text{ M}$$

$$[H_3O^+] = 10^4 \, [OH^-] = 10^4 \times 1 \times 10^{-9} \text{ M} = 1 \times 10^{-5}$$

---

444. Given: KOH solute; pH
= 12.90; acid
reacts with half
of OH^-

Unknown: resulting pH

$$pOH = 14.00 - pH = 14.00 - 12.90 = 1.10$$

$$[OH^-] = \text{antilog } (-1.10) = 1.0 \times 10^{-1.10} = 0.079 \text{ M}$$

after reaction:

$$[OH^-] = \frac{0.079 \text{ M}}{2} = 0.040 \text{ M}$$

$$[H_3O^+] = \frac{1.0 \times 10^{-14} \text{ M}^2}{4.0 \times 10^2 \text{ M}} = 2.5 \times 10^{-13} \text{ M}$$

$$pH = -\log(2.5 \times 10^{-13}) = 12.60$$

---

445. Given: HCl solute;
pH = 1.70

Unknown: $[H_3O^+]$;
$[HCl]$

$$[H_3O^+] = \text{antilog } (-1.70) = 1.0 \times 10^{-1.70} = 0.020 \text{ M}$$

$$[HCl] = [H_3O^+] = 0.020 \text{ M}$$

446. Given: $Ca(OH)_2$ solute:
pH = 10.80

Unknown: molarity

pOH = 14.00 − pH = 14.00 − 10.80 = 3.20

$[OH^-]$ = antilog (−3.20) = $1.0 \times 10^{-3.20}$ = 6.3×10^{-4} M

$[Ca(OH)_2]$ = 6.3×10^{-4} M $OH^- \times \dfrac{1 \text{ M } Ca(OH)_2}{2 \text{ M } OH^-}$ = 3.2×10^{-4} M

---

447. Given: 1.00 M stock HCl

Unknown: pH

pH = − log (1.00×10^0) = 0.000

Given: pH = 4.00; 1.00 L stock HCl

Unknown: V_D

$[H_3O^+]$ = antilog (−4.00) = $1.0 \times 10^{-4.00}$ = 1.0×10^{-4} M

$V_D = \dfrac{M_S V_S}{M_D} = \dfrac{1.00 \text{ M} \times 1.00 \text{ L}}{1.0 \times 10^{-4} \text{ M}}$ = 1.0×10^{4} L = 10. kL

Given: 1.00 L of pH 4.00

Unknown: V at pH 6.00

$[H_3O^+]$ at pH 4.00 = 1.0×10^{-4} M

$[H_3O^+]$ at pH 6.00 = antilog (−6.00) = $1.0 \times 10^{-6.00}$ = 1.0×10^{-6} M

$V = \dfrac{1.0 \times 10^{-4} \text{ M} \times 1.00 \text{ L}}{1.0 \times 10^{-6} \text{ M}}$ = 1.0×10^{2} L

Given: 1.00 L of pH 4.00

Unknown: V at pH 8.00

$[H_3O^+]$ at pH 4.00 = 1.00×10^{-4} M

$[H_3O^+]$ at pH 8.00 = antilog (−8.00) = $1.0 \times 10^{-8.00}$ = 1.0×10^{-8} M

$V = \dfrac{1.0 \times 10^{-4} \text{ M} \times 1.00 \text{ L}}{1.0 \times 10^{-8} \text{ M}}$ = 1.0×10^{4} L = 10. kL

---

448. Given: pH = 1.28; 1.00 L $HClO_3$

Unknown: moles NaOH to react; mass NaOH

$HClO_3 + NaOH \rightarrow NaClO_3 + H_2O$

$[H_3O^+]$ = antilog (−1.28) = $1.0 \times 10^{-1.28}$ = 5.2×10^{-2} M

$\dfrac{5.2 \times 10^{-2} \text{ mol}}{1.0 \text{ L}} \times 1.00 \text{ L } HClO_3$ = 5.2×10^{-2} mol $HClO_3$

= 5.2×10^{-2} mol NaOH

0.052 mol NaOH $\times \dfrac{40.00 \text{ g NaOH}}{1.0 \text{ mol NaOH}}$ = 2.1 g NaOH

---

449. Given: NH_3 solute; pH = 11.90; 1.00 L NH_3 solution

Unknown: moles HCl to react

pOH = 14.00 − 11.90 = 2.10

$[OH^-]$ = antilog (−2.10) = $1.0 \times 10^{-2.10}$ = 7.9×10^{-3} M

$\dfrac{7.9 \times 10^{-3} \text{ mol}}{1.0 \text{ L}} \times 1.00 \text{ L}$ = 7.9×10^{-3} mol OH^- = 7.9×10^{-3} mol HCl

---

450. Given: pH = 3.15

Unknown: $[H_3O^+]$; $[OH^-]$

$[H_3O^+]$ = antilog (−3.15) = $1.0 \times 10^{-3.15}$ = 7.1×10^{-4} M

$[OH^-] = \dfrac{1.0 \times 10^{-14} \text{ M}^2}{7.1 \times 10^{-4} \text{ M}}$ = 1.4×10^{-11} M

451. Given: 20.00 mL HBr; 20.05 mL of 0.1819 M NaOH

Unknown: molarity HBr

$$HBr + NaOH \rightarrow NaBr + H_2O$$

$$\frac{0.1819 \text{ mol NaOH}}{L} \times 20.05 \text{ mL} \times \frac{1 \text{ L}}{1000 \text{ mL}} = 3.647 \times 10^{-3} \text{ mol NaOH}$$

$$3.647 \times 10^{-3} \text{ mol NaOH} \times \frac{1 \text{ mol HBr}}{1 \text{ mol NaOH}} = 3.647 \times 10^{-3} \text{ mol HBr}$$

$$\frac{3.647 \times 10^{-3} \text{ mol HBr}}{20.00 \text{ mL}} \times \frac{1000 \text{ mL}}{1 \text{ L}} = 0.1824 \text{ M HBr}$$

452. Given: 15.00 mL CH_3COOH; 22.70 mL of 0.550 M NaOH

Unknown: molarity of CH_3COOH

$$CH_3COOH + NaOH \rightarrow NaCH_3COO + H_2O$$

$$\frac{0.550 \text{ mol NaOH}}{L} \times 22.70 \text{ mL} \times \frac{1 \text{ L}}{1000 \text{ mL}} = 1.25 \times 10^{-2} \text{ mol NaOH}$$

$$1.25 \times 10^{-2} \text{ mol NaOH} \times \frac{1 \text{ mol } CH_3COOH}{1 \text{ mol NaOH}} = 1.25 \times 10^{-2} \text{ mol } CH_3COOH$$

$$\frac{1.25 \times 10^{-2} \text{ mol } CH_3COOH}{15.00 \text{ mL}} \times \frac{1000 \text{ mL}}{1 \text{ L}} = 0.833 \text{ M } CH_3COOH$$

453. Given: 20.00 mL $Sr(OH)_2$; 43.03 mL of 0.1159 M HCl

Unknown: molarity of $Sr(OH)_2$ solution

$$Sr(OH)_2 + 2HCl \rightarrow SrCl_2 + 2H_2O$$

$$\frac{0.1159 \text{ mol HCl}}{L} \times 43.03 \text{ mL} \times \frac{1 \text{ L}}{1000 \text{ mL}} = 4.987 \times 10^{-3} \text{ mol HCl}$$

$$4.987 \times 10^{-3} \text{ mol HCl} \times \frac{1 \text{ mol } Sr(OH)_2}{2 \text{ mol HCl}} = 2.494 \times 10^{-3} \text{ mol } Sr(OH)_2$$

$$\frac{2.494 \times 10^{-3} \text{ mol } Sr(OH)_2}{20.00 \text{ mL}} \times \frac{1000 \text{ mL}}{1 \text{ L}} = 0.1247 \text{ M } Sr(OH)_2$$

454. Given: 35.00 mL NH_3 solution; 54.95 mL of 0.400 M H_2SO_4

Unknown: molarity of NH_3 solution

$$2NH_3 + H_2SO_4 \rightarrow (NH_4)_2SO_4$$

$$\frac{0.400 \text{ mol } H_2SO_4}{L} \times 54.95 \text{ mL} \times \frac{1 \text{ L}}{1000 \text{ mL}} = 2.20 \times 10^{-2} \text{ mol } H_2SO_4$$

$$2.20 \times 10^{-2} \text{ mol } H_2SO_4 \times \frac{2 \text{ mol } NH_3}{1 \text{ mol } H_2SO_4} = 4.40 \times 10^{-2} \text{ mol } NH_3$$

$$\frac{4.40 \times 10^{-2} \text{ mol } NH_3}{35.00 \text{ mL}} \times \frac{1000 \text{ mL}}{1 \text{ L}} = 1.26 \text{ M } NH_3$$

455. Given: 28.25 mL of 0.218 M NaOH; 2.000 g acetic acid diluted to 100.00 mL; 20.00 mL acetic acid

Unknown: % acetic acid in stock solution

$$CH_3COOH + NaOH \rightarrow NaCH_3COO + H_2O$$

$$\frac{0.218 \text{ mol NaOH}}{L} \times 28.25 \text{ mL} \times \frac{1 \text{ L}}{1000 \text{ mL}} = 6.16 \times 10^{-3} \text{ mol NaOH}$$

$$6.16 \times 10^{-3} \text{ mol NaOH} \times \frac{1 \text{ mol CH}_3COOH}{1 \text{ mol NaOH}} = 6.16 \times 10^{-3} \text{ mol CH}_3COOH$$

$$\frac{6.16 \times 10^{-3} \text{ mol CH}_3COOH}{20.00 \text{ mL}} \times \frac{1000 \text{ mL}}{1 \text{ L}} = 0.308 \text{ M CH}_3COOH$$

$$\frac{2.000 \text{ g CH}_3COOH}{100.00 \text{ mL}} \times \frac{1000 \text{ mL}}{1 \text{ L}} \times \frac{1 \text{ mol CH}_3COOH}{60.06 \text{ g CH}_3COOH}$$

$$= 0.3333 \text{ M CH}_3COOH$$

$$\frac{0.308 \text{ M}}{0.3333 \text{ M}} \times 100 = 92.5\% \text{ CH}_3COOH$$

456. Given: 9.709 g Na_2CO_3 diluted to 1.0000 L; 10.00 mL Na_2CO_3 solution; 16.90 mL of 0.1022 M HCl

Unknown: percentage of Na_2CO_3

$$Na_2CO_3 + 2HCl \rightarrow 2NaCl + H_2O + CO_2$$

$$\frac{0.1022 \text{ mol HCl}}{L} \times 16.90 \text{ mL} \times \frac{1 \text{ L}}{1000 \text{ mL}} = 1.727 \times 10^{-3} \text{ mol HCl}$$

$$1.727 \times 10^{-3} \text{ mol HCl} \times \frac{1 \text{ mol Na}_2CO_3}{2 \text{ mol HCl}} = 8.635 \times 10^{-4} \text{ mol Na}_2CO_3$$

$$\frac{8.635 \times 10^{-4} \text{ mol Na}_2CO_3}{10.00 \text{ mL}} \times \frac{1000 \text{ mL}}{1 \text{ L}} = 8.635 \times 10^{-2} \text{ M Na}_2CO_3$$

$$\frac{9.709 \text{ g Na}_2CO_3}{1.0000 \text{ L}} \times \frac{1 \text{ mol Na}_2CO_3}{105.99 \text{ g Na}_2CO_3} = 9.160 \times 10^{-2} \text{ M Na}_2CO_3$$

$$\frac{8.635 \times 10^{-2} \text{ M Na}_2CO_3}{9.160 \times 10^{-2} \text{ M Na}_2CO_3} \times 100 = 94.27\% \text{ Na}_2CO_3$$

457. Given: 50.00 mL KOH; 27.87 mL of 0.8186 M HCl

Unknown: molarity of KOH

$$KOH + HCl \rightarrow KCl + H_2O$$

$$\frac{0.8186 \text{ mol HCl}}{L} \times 27.87 \text{ mL} \times \frac{1 \text{ L}}{1000 \text{ mL}} = 2.281 \times 10^{-2} \text{ mol HCl}$$

$$2.281 \times 10^{-2} \text{ mol HCl} \times \frac{1 \text{ mol KOH}}{1 \text{ mol HCl}} = 2.281 \times 10^{-2} \text{ mol KOH}$$

$$\frac{2.281 \times 10^{-2} \text{ mol KOH}}{50.00 \text{ mL}} \times \frac{1000 \text{ mL}}{1 \text{ L}} = 0.4562 \text{ M KOH}$$

458. Given: 15.00 mL CH_3COOH; 34.13 mL of 0.9940 M NaOH

Unknown: molarity of CH_3COOH

$$CH_3COOH + NaOH \rightarrow NaCH_3COO + H_2O$$

$$\frac{0.9940 \text{ mol NaOH}}{L} \times 34.13 \text{ mL} \times \frac{1 \text{ L}}{1000 \text{ mL}} = 3.393 \times 10^{-2} \text{ mol NaOH}$$

$$3.393 \times 10^{-2} \text{ mol NaOH} \times \frac{1 \text{ mol CH}_3COOH}{1 \text{ mol NaOH}}$$

$$= 3.393 \times 10^{-2} \text{ mol CH}_3COOH$$

$$\frac{3.393 \times 10^{-2} \text{ mol CH}_3COOH}{15.00 \text{ mL}} \times \frac{1000 \text{ mL}}{1 \text{ L}} = 2.262 \text{ M CH}_3COOH$$

459. Given: 12.00 mL NH_3 solution; 19.48 mL of 1.499 M HNO_3

Unknown: molarity of NH_3 solution

$$NH_3 + HNO_3 \rightarrow NH_4NO_3$$

$$\frac{1.499 \text{ mol } HNO_3}{L} \times 19.48 \text{ mL} \times \frac{1 \text{ L}}{1000 \text{ mL}} = 2.920 \times 10^{-2} \text{ mol } HNO_3$$

$$2.920 \times 10^{-2} \text{ mol } HNO_3 \times \frac{1 \text{ mol } NH_3}{1 \text{ mol } HNO_3} = 2.920 \times 10^{-2} \text{ mol } NH_3$$

$$\frac{2.920 \times 10^{-2} \text{ mol } NH_3}{12.00 \text{ mL}} \times \frac{1000 \text{ mL}}{1 \text{ L}} = 2.433 \text{ M } NH_3$$

460. a. Given: 1 mol acid : 1 mol base; $M_A = M_B$; 20.00 mL base

Unknown: V of acid

20.00 mL base because $M \times V$ provides number of moles, which are in a 1 : 1 ratio

b. Given: $M_A = 2M_B$; 20.00 mL base

Unknown: V of acid

$$M_A \times V_A = M_B \times 20.00 \text{ mL}$$

$$2M_B \times V_A = M_B \times 20.00 \text{ mL}$$

$$V_A = \frac{M_B \times 20.00 \text{ mL base}}{2M_B} = 10.00 \text{ mL}$$

c. Given: $M_B = 4M_A$; 20.00 mL base

Unknown: V of acid

$$M_A \times V_A = M_B \times 20.00 \text{ mL}$$

$$M_A \times V_A = 4M_A \times 20.00 \text{ mL}$$

$$V_A = \frac{4M_A \times 20.00 \text{ mL}}{M_A} = 80.00 \text{ mL}$$

461. Given: 10.00 mL stock HF diluted to 500.00 mL; 20.00 mL HF; 13.51 mL of 0.1500 M NaOH

Unknown: molarity of stock HF

$$HF + NaOH \rightarrow NaF + H_2O$$

$$\frac{0.1500 \text{ mol NaOH}}{L} \times 13.51 \text{ mL} \times \frac{1 \text{ L}}{1000 \text{ mL}} = 2.026 \times 10^{-3} \text{ mol NaOH}$$

$$2.026 \times 10^{-3} \text{ mol NaOH} \times \frac{1 \text{ mol HF}}{1 \text{ mol NaOH}} = 2.026 \times 10^{-3} \text{ mol HF}$$

$$\frac{2.026 \times 10^{-3} \text{ mol HF}}{20.00 \text{ mL}} \times \frac{1000 \text{ mL}}{1 \text{ L}} = 0.1013 \text{ M HF}$$

$$\frac{0.1013 \text{ mol HF}}{L} \times 500.00 \text{ mL} \times \frac{1 \text{ L}}{1000 \text{ mL}} = 0.05065 \text{ mol HF}$$

$$\frac{0.05065 \text{ mol HF}}{10.00 \text{ mL}} \times \frac{1000 \text{ mL}}{L} = 5.065 \text{ M HF}$$

462. Given: 16.22 mL of 0.5030 M KOH; 18.41 mL diprotic acid

Unknown: molarity of acid

$$\frac{0.5030 \text{ mol KOH}}{L} \times 16.22 \text{ mL} \times \frac{1 \text{ L}}{1000 \text{ mL}} = 8.159 \times 10^{-3} \text{ mol KOH}$$

$$8.159 \times 10^{-3} \text{ mol KOH} \times \frac{1 \text{ mol acid}}{2 \text{ mol KOH}} = 4.080 \times 10^{-3} \text{ mol acid}$$

$$\frac{4.080 \times 10^{-3} \text{ mol acid}}{18.41 \text{ mL}} \times \frac{1000 \text{ mL}}{1 \text{ L}} = 0.2216 \text{ M acid}$$

463. Given: 42.27 mL of
1.209 M NaOH;
25.00 mL H_2SO_4

Unknown: molarity of
the H_2SO_4

$$H_2SO_4 + 2NaOH \rightarrow Na_2SO_4 + 2H_2O$$

$$\frac{1.209 \text{ mol NaOH}}{L} \times 42.27 \text{ mL} \times \frac{1 \text{ L}}{1000 \text{ mL}} = 5.110 \times 10^{-2} \text{ mol NaOH}$$

$$5.110 \times 10^{-2} \text{ mol NaOH} \times \frac{1 \text{ mol } H_2SO_4}{2 \text{ mol NaOH}} = 2.555 \times 10^{-2} \text{ mol } H_2SO_4$$

$$\frac{2.555 \times 10^{-2} \text{ mol } H_2SO_4}{25.00 \text{ mL}} \times \frac{1000 \text{ mL}}{1 \text{ L}} = 1.022 \text{ M } H_2SO_4$$

---

464. Given: 1 mol acid: 1 mol
base; 0.7025 g
$KHC_8H_4O_4$;
20.18 mL KOH

Unknown: molarity of
KOH

$$0.7025 \text{ g } KHC_8H_4O_4 \times \frac{1 \text{ mol } KHC_8H_4O_4}{204.23 \text{ g } KHC_8H_4O_4}$$

$$= 3.440 \times 10^{-3} \text{ mol } KHC_8H_4O_4$$

$$3.440 \times 10^{-3} \text{ mol } KHC_8H_4O_4 \times \frac{1 \text{ mol KOH}}{1 \text{ mol } KHC_8H_4O_4} = 3.440 \times 10^{-3} \text{ mol KOH}$$

$$\frac{3.440 \times 10^{-3} \text{ mol KOH}}{20.18 \text{ mL}} \times \frac{1000 \text{ mL}}{1 \text{ L}} = 0.1705 \text{ M KOH}$$

---

465. Given: 20.00 mL
triprotic acid;
17.03 mL of
2.025 M NaOH

Unknown: molarity of
acid

$$\frac{2.025 \text{ mol NaOH}}{L} \times 17.03 \text{ mL} \times \frac{1 \text{ L}}{1000 \text{ mL}} = 3.449 \times 10^{-2} \text{ mol NaOH}$$

$$3.449 \times 10^{-2} \text{ mol NaOH} \times \frac{1 \text{ mol acid}}{3 \text{ mol NaOH}} = 1.150 \times 10^{-2} \text{ mol acid}$$

$$\frac{1.150 \times 10^{-2} \text{ mol acid}}{20.00 \text{ mL}} \times \frac{1000 \text{ mL}}{1 \text{ L}} = 0.5750 \text{ M acid}$$

---

466. Given: 41.04 mL KOH;
21.65 mL of
0.6515 M HNO_3

Unknown: molarity of
KOH

$$KOH + HNO_3 \rightarrow KNO_3 + H_2O$$

$$\frac{0.6515 \text{ mol } HNO_3}{L} \times 21.65 \text{ mL} \times \frac{1 \text{ L}}{1000 \text{ mL}} = 1.410 \times 10^{-2} \text{ mol } HNO_3$$

$$1.410 \times 10^{-2} \text{ mol } HNO_3 \times \frac{1 \text{ mol KOH}}{1 \text{ mol } HNO_3} = 1.410 \times 10^{-2} \text{ mol KOH}$$

$$\frac{1.410 \times 10^{-2} \text{ mol KOH}}{41.04 \text{ mL}} \times \frac{1000 \text{ mL}}{1 \text{ L}} = 0.3436 \text{ M KOH}$$

---

467. Given: 20.00 mL of
2.00 M H_2SO_4;
1.85 M NaOH

Unknown: V of NaOH

$$H_2SO_4 + 2NaOH \rightarrow Na_2SO_4 + 2H_2O$$

$$\frac{2.00 \text{ mol } H_2SO_4}{L} \times 20.00 \text{ mL} \times \frac{1 \text{ L}}{1000 \text{ mL}} = 4.00 \times 10^{-2} \text{ mol } H_2SO_4$$

$$4.00 \times 10^{-2} \text{ mol } H_2SO_4 \times \frac{2 \text{ mol NaOH}}{1 \text{ mol } H_2SO_4} = 8.00 \times 10^{-2} \text{ mol NaOH}$$

$$\frac{8.00 \times 10^{-2} \text{ mol NaOH}}{1.85 \text{ mol/L}} = 0.0432 \text{ L NaOH} = 43.2 \text{ mL NaOH}$$

468. Given: 0.5200 M H_2SO_4; 100.00 mL of 0.1225 M $Sr(OH)_2$

Unknown: V of H_2SO_4

$H_2SO_4 + Sr(OH)_2 \rightarrow SrSO_4 + 2H_2O$

$$\frac{0.1225 \text{ mol Sr(OH)}_2}{L} \times 100.00 \text{ mL} \times \frac{1 \text{ L}}{1000 \text{ mL}} = 1.225 \times 10^{-2} \text{ mol Sr(OH)}_2$$

$$1.225 \times 10^{-2} \text{ mol Sr(OH)}_2 \times \frac{1 \text{ mol H}_2SO_4}{1 \text{ mol Sr(OH)}_2} = 1.225 \times 10^{-2} \text{ mol H}_2SO_4$$

$$\frac{1.225 \times 10^{-2} \text{ mol H}_2SO_4}{0.5200 \text{ mol/L}} = 0.02356 \text{ L H}_2SO_4 = 23.56 \text{ mL H}_2SO_4$$

469. Given: 4.005 g KOH in 200.00 mL solution; 25.00 mL KOH; 19.93 mL of 0.4388 M HCl

Unknown: moles KOH in 4.005 g; mass KOH; percent KOH

$KOH + HCl \rightarrow KCl + H_2O$

$$\frac{0.4388 \text{ mol HCl}}{L} \times 19.93 \text{ mL} \times \frac{1 \text{ L}}{1000 \text{ mL}} = 8.745 \times 10^{-3} \text{ mol HCl}$$

$$8.745 \times 10^{-3} \text{ mol HCl} \times \frac{1 \text{ mol KOH}}{1 \text{ mol HCl}} = 8.745 \times 10^{-3} \text{ mol KOH in 25.00 mL}$$

$$8.745 \times 10^{-3} \text{ mol KOH} \times \frac{200.00 \text{ mL}}{25.00 \text{ mL}} = 6.996 \times 10^{-2} \text{ mol KOH}$$

in 4.005 g KOH

$$6.996 \times 10^{-2} \text{ mol KOH} \times \frac{56.11 \text{ g KOH}}{1 \text{ mol KOH}} = 3.925 \text{ g KOH}$$

$$\frac{3.925 \text{ g}}{4.005 \text{ g}} \times 100 = 98.00\% \text{ KOH}$$

470. Given: 558 mL of 3.18 M HCl

Unknown: mass of $Mg(OH)_2$ to react

$Mg(OH)_2 + 2HCl \rightarrow MgCl_2 + 2H_2O$

$$\frac{3.18 \text{ mol HCl}}{L} \times 558 \text{ mL} \times \frac{1 \text{ L}}{1000 \text{ mL}} = 1.77 \text{ mol HCl}$$

$$1.77 \text{ mol HCl} \times \frac{1 \text{ mol Mg(OH)}_2}{2 \text{ mol HCl}} = 0.885 \text{ mol Mg(OH)}_2$$

$$0.885 \text{ mol Mg(OH)}_2 \times \frac{58.32 \text{ g Mg(OH)}_2}{1 \text{ mol Mg(OH)}_2} = 51.6 \text{ g Mg(OH)}_2$$

471. Given: 12.61 mL NH_3 solution; 5.19 mL of 1.25 M HCl

Unknown: molarity of NH_3 solution

$$\frac{1.25 \text{ mol HCl}}{L} \times 5.19 \text{ mL} \times \frac{1 \text{ L}}{1000 \text{ mL}} = 6.49 \times 10^{-3} \text{ mol HCl}$$

$$6.49 \times 10^{-3} \text{ mol HCl} \times \frac{1 \text{ mol NH}_3}{1 \text{ mol HCl}} = 6.49 \times 10^{-3} \text{ mol NH}_3$$

$$\frac{6.49 \times 10^{-3} \text{ mol NH}_3}{12.61 \text{ mL}} \times \frac{1000 \text{ mL}}{1 \text{ L}} = 0.515 \text{ M NH}_3$$

472. Given: 5.090 g sample of 92.10% NaOH; 2.811 M diprotic acid

Unknown: V of acid

$$5.090 \text{ g NaOH} \times 0.9210 = 4.688 \text{ g NaOH}$$

$$4.688 \text{ g NaOH} \times \frac{1 \text{ mol NaOH}}{40.00 \text{ g NaOH}} \times \frac{1 \text{ mol acid}}{2 \text{ mol NaOH}} = 0.05860 \text{ mol acid}$$

$$\frac{0.05860 \text{ mol acid}}{2.811 \text{ mol/L}} = 0.02085 \text{ L acid} = 20.85 \text{ mL acid}$$

473. Given: 43.09 mL of 0.1529 M $Ba(OH)_2$; 26.06 mL HCl for $Ba(OH)_2$; 27.05 mL HCl for 15.00 mL RbOH

$$Ba(OH)_2 + 2HCl \rightarrow BaCl_2 + 2H_2O$$

$$\frac{0.1529 \text{ mol } Ba(OH)_2}{L} \times 43.09 \text{ mL} \times \frac{1 \text{ L}}{1000 \text{ mL}} = 6.588 \times 10^{-3} \text{ mol } Ba(OH)_2$$

$$6.588 \times 10^{-3} \text{ mol } Ba(OH)_2 \times \frac{2 \text{ mol HCl}}{1 \text{ mol } Ba(OH)_2} = 1.318 \times 10^{-2} \text{ mol HCl}$$

a. Unknown: molarity of HCl

$$\frac{1.318 \times 10^{-2} \text{ mol HCl}}{26.06 \text{ mL}} \times \frac{1000 \text{ mL}}{1 \text{ L}} = 0.5058 \text{ M HCl}$$

b. Unknown: molarity of RbOH

$$HCl + RbOH \rightarrow RbCl + H_2O$$

$$\frac{0.5058 \text{ mol HCl}}{L} \times 27.05 \text{ mL} \times \frac{1 \text{ L}}{1000 \text{ mL}} = 1.368 \times 10^{-2} \text{ mol HCl}$$

$$1.368 \times 10^{-2} \text{ mol HCl} \times \frac{1 \text{ mol RbOH}}{1 \text{ mol HCl}} = 1.368 \times 10^{-2} \text{ mol RbOH}$$

$$\frac{1.368 \times 10^{-2} \text{ mol RbOH}}{15.00 \text{ mL}} \times \frac{1000 \text{ mL}}{1 \text{ L}} = 0.9120 \text{ M RbOH}$$

---

474. Given: 2800 kg of 6.0 M HCl; $D_{HCl} = 1.10$ g/mL

Unknown: mass $Ca(OH)_2$

$$Ca(OH)_2 + 2HCl \rightarrow CaCl_2 + 2H_2O$$

$$2800 \text{ kg HCl} \times \frac{1 \text{ mL}}{1.10 \text{ g}} \times \frac{1000 \text{ g}}{1 \text{ kg}} \times \frac{1 \text{ L}}{1000 \text{ mL}} = 2500 \text{ L HCl}$$

$$\frac{6.0 \text{ mol HCl}}{L} \times 2500 \text{ L} = 1.5 \times 10^4 \text{ mol HCl}$$

$$1.5 \times 10^4 \text{ mol HCl} \times \frac{1 \text{ mol } Ca(OH)_2}{2 \text{ mol HCl}} = 7.5 \times 10^3 \text{ mol } Ca(OH)_2$$

$$7.5 \times 10^3 \text{ mol } Ca(OH)_2 \times \frac{74.10 \text{ g } Ca(OH)_2}{1 \text{ mol } Ca(OH)_2} = 5.6 \times 10^5 \text{ g } Ca(OH)_2$$

$$= 560 \text{ kg } Ca(OH)_2$$

---

475. Given: 1.00 mL HNO_3 diluted to 200.00 mL; 10.00 mL of diluted HNO_3; 23.94 mL of 0.0177 M $Ba(OH)_2$

Unknown: molarity of original HNO_3

$$Ba(OH)_2 + 2HNO_3 \rightarrow Ba(NO_3)_2 + 2H_2O$$

$$\frac{0.0177 \text{ mol } Ba(OH)_2}{L} \times 23.94 \text{ mL} \times \frac{1 \text{ L}}{1000 \text{ mL}} = 4.24 \times 10^{-4} \text{ mol } Ba(OH)_2$$

$$4.24 \times 10^{-4} \text{ mol } Ba(OH)_2 \times \frac{2 \text{ mol } HNO_3}{1 \text{ mol } Ba(OH)_2} = 8.48 \times 10^{-4} \text{ mol } HNO_3$$

$$\frac{8.48 \times 10^{-4} \text{ mol } HNO_3}{10.00 \text{ mL}} \times \frac{1000 \text{ mL}}{1 \text{ L}} = 8.48 \times 10^{-2} \text{ M } HNO_3$$

$$\frac{8.48 \times 10^{-2} \text{ mol } HNO_3}{1 \text{ L}} \times 200.00 \text{ mL} \times \frac{1 \text{ L}}{1000 \text{ mL}} = 1.70 \times 10^{-2} \text{ mol } HNO_3$$

$$\frac{1.70 \times 10^{-2} \text{ mol } HNO_3}{1.00 \text{ mL}} \times \frac{1000 \text{ mL}}{L} = 17.0 \text{ M } HNO_3$$

476. Given: 4.494 M H_2SO_4; 7.2280 g LiOH

Unknown: V of H_2SO_4

$H_2SO_4 + 2LiOH \rightarrow Li_2SO_4 + 2H_2O$

$7.2280 \text{ g LiOH} \times \dfrac{1 \text{ mol LiOH}}{23.95 \text{ g LiOH}} = 0.3018 \text{ mol LiOH}$

$0.3018 \text{ mol LiOH} \times \dfrac{1 \text{ mol } H_2SO_4}{2 \text{ mol LiOH}} = 0.1509 \text{ mol } H_2SO_4$

$\dfrac{0.1509 \text{ mol } H_2SO_4}{4.494 \text{ mol/L}} = 0.03358 \text{ L } H_2SO_4 = 33.58 \text{ mL } H_2SO_4$

---

477. Given: $5CO_2(g) + Si_3N_4(s) \rightarrow 3SiO(s) + 2N_2O(g) + 5CO(g)$

Unknown: reaction enthalpy for the given reaction

(1) $CO(g) + SiO_2(s) \rightarrow SiO(g) + CO_2(g)$

(2) $8CO_2(g) + Si_3N_4(s) \rightarrow 3SiO_2(s) + 2N_2O(g) + 8CO(g)$

$\Delta H_{\text{reaction 1}} = +520.9 \text{ kJ}$

$\Delta H_{\text{reaction 2}} = +461.05 \text{ kJ}$

$3[CO(g) + SiO_2(s) \rightarrow SiO(g) + CO_2(g)] \quad \Delta H = 3(+520.9) = +1562.7 \text{ kJ}$

$8CO_2(g) + Si_3N_4(s) \rightarrow 3SiO_2(g) + 2N_2O(g) + 8CO(g) \quad \Delta H = +461.05 \text{ kJ}$

$5CO_2(g) + Si_3N_4(s) \rightarrow 3SiO(s) + 2N_2O(g) + 5CO(g)$

$\Delta H = 2024 \text{ kJ}$

---

478. Given: $CaCO_3(s) \rightarrow CaO(s) + CO_2(g)$

Unknown: ΔH

$CaCO_3(s) \rightarrow Ca(s) + C(s) + \dfrac{3}{2}O_2(g) \quad \Delta H = 1207.6 \text{ kJ/mol}$

$Ca(s) + \dfrac{1}{2}O_2(g) \rightarrow CaO(s) \quad \Delta H = -634.9 \text{ kJ/mol}$

$C(s) + O_2(g) \rightarrow CO_2(g) \quad \Delta H = -393.5 \text{ kJ/mol}$

$CaCO_3(s) \rightarrow CaO(s) + CO_2(g) \quad \Delta H = 179.2 \text{ kJ/mol}$

---

479. Given: $2FeO(s) + O_2(g) \rightarrow Fe_2O_3(s)$

Unknown: ΔH

$4Fe(s) + 3O_2(g) \rightarrow 2Fe_2O_3(s) \quad \Delta H = -1118.4 \text{ kJ/mol}$

$2[2FeO(s) \rightarrow 2Fe(s) + O_2(g)] \quad \Delta H = 2(+825.5) = +1651.0$

$4FeO(s) + O_2(g) \rightarrow 2Fe_2O_3(s) \quad \Delta H = 533 \text{ kJ/mol}$

---

480. Given: $NH_3(g) + HF(g) \rightarrow NH_4F(s)$

Unknown: ΔH

$NH_3(g) \rightarrow N(g) + \dfrac{3}{2}H_2(g) \quad \Delta H = 45.9 \text{ kJ/mol}$

$HF(g) \rightarrow \dfrac{1}{2}H_2(g) + F(s) \quad \Delta H = 273.3 \text{ kJ/mol}$

$N(g) + 2H_2(g) + F(s) \rightarrow NH_4F(s) \quad \Delta H = -125 \text{ kJ/mol}$

$NH_3(g) + HF(g) \rightarrow NH_4F(s) \quad \Delta H = 194 \text{ kJ/mol}$

---

481. Given: $H_2S(g) + O_2(g) \rightarrow H_2O(l) + SO_2(g)$

$\Delta H_{\text{reaction}} = -562.1 \text{ kJ/mol}$

$\Delta S_{\text{reaction}} = -0.092\ 78 \text{ kJ/mol} \cdot \text{K}$

$T = 25°C = 298 \text{ K}$

Unknown: ΔG

$\Delta G = \Delta H - T\Delta S$

$= -562.1 \text{ kJ/mol} - [(298 \text{ K})(-0.092\ 78 \text{ kJ/mol} \cdot \text{K})]$

$= -534.5 \text{ kJ/mol}$

482. Given: $NaClO_3(s) \rightarrow$
$NaCl(s) + O_2(g)$
$\Delta H_{reaction} =$
-19.1 kJ/mol
$\Delta S_{reaction} =$
0.1768 kJ/mol · K
$T = 25°C = 298$ K

Unknown: ΔG

$\Delta G = \Delta H - T\Delta S$

$= -19.1$ kJ/mol $-$ [(298 K)(0.1768 kJ/mol · K)]

$= -71.8$ kJ/mol

---

483. Given: $C_2H_6(g) + O_2(g)$
$\rightarrow 2CO_2(g) +$
$3\ H_2O(l)$
$\Delta H_{reaction} =$
-1561 kJ/mol
$\Delta S_{reaction} =$
-1.4084 kJ/mol · K
$T = 25°C = 298$ K

Unknown: ΔG for combustion of 1 mole of C_2H_6

$\Delta G = \Delta H - T\Delta S$

$= -1561$ kJ/mol $-$ [(298 K)(-0.4084 kJ/mol · K)]

$= -1683$ kJ/mol

---

484. Given: $F_2(g) + H_2O(l) \rightarrow$
$2HF(g) + O_2(g)$

Unknown: ΔH

$2[H_2 + F_2 \rightarrow 2\ HF] \quad \Delta H = 2(-273.3) = -546.6$ kJ/mol

$2H_2O \rightarrow 2H_2 + O_2 \quad \Delta H = +285.8$

$2F_2(g) + 2H_2O(l) \rightarrow 4HF(g) + O_2(g) \quad \Delta H = -260.8$ kJ/mol

---

485. Given: $CaO(s) + SO_3(g)$
$\rightarrow CaSO_4(s)$
$H_2O(l) + SO_3(g)$
$\rightarrow H_2SO_4(l)$
$\Delta H = -132.5$
kJ/mol
$H_2SO_4(l) + Ca(g)$
$\rightarrow CaSO_4(s) +$
$H_2(g)\ \Delta H =$
-602.5 kJ/mol
$Ca(s) + O_2(g) \rightarrow$
$CaO(s)\ \Delta H =$
-634.9 kJ/mol
$H_2(g) + O_2(g) \rightarrow$
$H_2O(l)\ \Delta H =$
-285.8 kJ/mol

Unknown: ΔH for reaction of CaO $+ SO_3$

$CaO(s) \rightarrow Ca(s) + \frac{1}{2}O_2(g) \quad \Delta H = +634.9$ kJ/mol

$H_2O(l) + SO_3(g) \rightarrow H_2SO_4(l) \quad \Delta H = -132.5$ kJ/mol

$H_2SO_4(l) + Ca(s) \rightarrow CaSO_4(s) + H_2(g) \quad \Delta H = -602.5$ kJ/mol

$H_2 + \frac{1}{2}O_2 \rightarrow H_2O(l) \quad \Delta H = -285.8$ kJ/mol

---

$CaO(s) + SO_3(g) \rightarrow CaSO_4(s) \quad \Delta H = -385.9$ kJ/mol

---

486. Given: $Na_2O(s) + SO_2(g)$
$\rightarrow Na_2SO_3(s)$

Unknown: ΔH

$Na_2O(s) \rightarrow 2Na(s) + \frac{1}{2}O_2(g) \quad \Delta H = +414.2$ kJ/mol

$SO_2(g) \rightarrow S(s) + O_2(g) \quad \Delta H = +296.8$ kJ/mol

$2Na(s) + S(s) + \frac{3}{2}O_2(g) \rightarrow Na_2SO_3(s) \quad \Delta H = -1101$ kJ/mol

---

$Na_2O(s) + SO_2(g) \rightarrow Na_2SO_3(s) \quad \Delta H = -390.$ kJ/mol

487. Given: $C_4H_9OH(l)$ $+ O_2(g) \rightarrow$ $C_3H_7COOH(l)$ $+ H_2O(l);$ $C_4H_9OH(l) +$ $6O_2(g) \rightarrow 4CO_2(g)$ $+ 5H_2O(l)$ $\Delta H_c =$ -2675.9 kJ/mol; $C_3H_7COOH(l)$ $+ 5O_2(g) \rightarrow$ $4CO_2(g)$ $+ 4H_2O(l)$ $\Delta H_c =$ -2183.6 kJ/mol

Unknown: ΔH for oxidation of C_4H_9OH to make C_3H_7COOH

$C_4H_9OH(l) + 6O_2(g) \rightarrow 4CO_2(g) + 5H_2O(l)$ $\quad \Delta H_c = -2675.9$ kJ/mol

$4CO_2(g) + 4H_2O(l) \rightarrow C_3H_7COOH(l) + 5O_2(g)$ $\quad \Delta H_c = 2183.6$ kJ/mol

---

$C_4H_9OH(l) + O_2(g) \rightarrow C_3H_7COOH(l) + H_2O(l)$ $\quad \Delta H = -492.3$ kJ/mol

488. Given: $CuO(s) + H_2(g)$ $\rightarrow Cu(s) + H_2O(l)$ $\Delta H =$ -128.5 kJ/mol $\Delta S = -70.1$ J/mol•K $T = 25°C = 298$ K

Unknown ΔG

$\Delta G = \Delta H - T\Delta S$

$\Delta S = (-70.1 \text{ J/mol} \cdot \text{K})\left(\dfrac{\text{kJ}}{1000 \text{ J}}\right) = -0.0701 \text{ kJ/mol} \cdot \text{K}$

$\Delta G = -128.5 \text{ kJ/mol} - [(298 \text{ K})(-0.0701 \text{ kJ/mol} \cdot \text{K})]$

$\quad = -107.6 \text{ kJ/mol}$

489. Given: $NaI(s) + Cl_2(g)$ $\rightarrow NaCl(s) + I_2(l)$ $\Delta S = -79.9$ J/mol•K $\Delta G =$ -98.0 kJ/mol $T = 25°C = 298$ K

Unknown: ΔH

$\Delta G = \Delta H - T\Delta S$

$\Delta H + \Delta G + T\Delta S$

$\Delta S = (-79.9 \text{ J/mol} \cdot \text{K})\left(\dfrac{\text{kJ}}{1000 \text{ J}}\right) = -0.0799 \text{ kJ/mol} \cdot \text{K}$

$\Delta H = -98.0 \text{ kJ/mol} + [(298 \text{ K})(-0.0799 \text{ kJ/mol} \cdot \text{K})] = -121.8 \text{ kJ/mol}$

490. Given: $4HBr(g) +$ $MnO_2(s) \rightarrow$ $MnBr_2(s) +$ $2H_2O(l) + Br_2(l)$ $\Delta H = -291.3$ kJ/mol; $T = 25°C = 298$ K $\Delta H^o_{f\,HBr} = -36.29$ kJ/mol $\Delta H^o_{f\,MnO_2} =$ -520.0 kJ/mol $\Delta H^o_{f\,H_2O} = -285.8$ kJ/mol $\Delta H^o_{f\,Br_2} = 0.00$ kJ/mol

Unknown: ΔH^o_f of $MnBr_2(s) = x$

Net ΔH = [Sum of ΔH_f of products] – [Sum of ΔH_f of reactants]

$-291.3 = \left[\Delta H_{f\,MnBr_2} + 2\,\Delta H_{f\,H_2O} + \Delta H_{f\,Br_2} \right] -$

$\left[4\,\Delta H_{f\,HBr} + \Delta H_{f\,MnO_2} \right]$

$-291.3 = [x + (2)(-258.8) + (0)] - [(4)(-36.29) + (-520)]$

$-291.3 = x + 93.56$

$-291.3 - 93.56 = x = -384.9$ kJ/mol

491. Given: $CaC_2(s) +$
$2H_2O(l) \rightarrow$
$C_2H_2(g) +$
$Ca(OH)_2(s)$
$\Delta G =$
-147.7 kJ/mol
$\Delta H =$
-125.6 kJ/mol
$T = 25°C = 298$ K

Unknown: ΔS

$\Delta G = \Delta H - T\Delta S$

$\Delta S = (\Delta H - \Delta G)/T$

$\quad = [-125.6 \text{ kJ/mol} - (-147.7 \text{ kJ/mol})]/298 \text{ K}$

$\quad = 0.0742 \text{ kJ/mol}$

---

492. Given: $NH_4NO_3(s) \rightarrow$
$N_2O(g) +$
$2H_2O(g)$
$\Delta S = 446.4$
J/mol·K
$T = 25°C = 298$ K

Unknown: ΔG

$2N(g) + \frac{1}{2}O_2(g) \rightarrow N_2O(g) \quad \Delta H = 82.1 \text{ kJ/mol}$

$2[H_2(g) + \frac{1}{2}O_2(g) \rightarrow H_2O(g)] \quad \Delta H = (2)(-241.82) = -483.64 \text{ kJ/mol}$

$2[H_2O(l) \rightarrow H_2(g) + \frac{1}{2}O_2(g)] \quad \Delta H = (2)(285.8) = 571.6 \text{ kJ/mol}$

$NH_4NO_3(s) \rightarrow N_2(g) + 2H_2O(l) + \frac{1}{2}O_2 \quad \Delta H = 365.56 \text{ kJ/mol}$

$NH_4NO_3(s) \rightarrow N_2O(g) + 2H_2O(g) \quad \Delta H = -35.98 \text{ kJ/mol}$

$\Delta S = (446.4 \text{ J/mol·K})(\text{kJ}/1000 \text{ J}) = 0.4464 \text{ kJ/mol·K}$

$\Delta G = \Delta H - T\Delta S$

$\quad = -35.98 \text{ kJ/mol} - [(298 \text{ K})(0.4464 \text{ kJ/mol·K})] = -169.0 \text{ kJ/mol}$

---

493. **a.** Unknown: Chemical equations for combustion of (1) 1 mol of methane (CH_4) and (2) 1 mol of propane (C_3H_8)

1. *methane*: $CH_4(g) + 2O_2(g) \rightarrow CO_2(g) + 2H_2O(l)$
2. *propane*: $C_3H_8(g) + 5O_2(g) \rightarrow 3CO_2(g) + 4H_2O(g)$

b. Unknown: Enthalpy change (ΔH) for each reaction

1. *methane*: $CH_4(g) \rightarrow C(s) + 2H_2(g) \quad \Delta H = 74.9 \text{ kJ/mol}$

$C(s) + O_2(g) \rightarrow CO_2(g) \quad \Delta H = -393.5 \text{ kJ/mol}$

$2[H_2(g) + \frac{1}{2}O_2(g) \rightarrow H_2O(g)] \quad \Delta H = (2)(-241.82) = -483.64 \text{ kJ/mol}$

$CH_4(g) + 2O_2(g) \rightarrow CO_2(g) + 2H_2O(g) \quad \Delta H = -802.2 \text{ kJ/mol}$

2. *propane*: $3[C(s) + O_2(g) \rightarrow CO_2(g)] \quad \Delta H = (3)(-393.5) = -1180.5 \text{ kJ/mol}$

$4[H_2(g) + \frac{1}{2}O_2(g) \rightarrow H_2O(g)] \quad \Delta H = (4)(-241.82) = -967.28 \text{ kJ/mol}$

$C_3H_8(g) \rightarrow 3C(s) + 4H_2(g) \quad \Delta H = 104.7 \text{ kJ/mol}$

$C_3H_8(g) + 5O_2(g) \rightarrow 3CO_2(g) + 4H_2O(g) \quad \Delta H = -2043 \text{ kJ/mol}$

c. Unknown: Heat output per kilogram of each fuel

1. *methane*: $(1000 \text{ g } CH_4)\left(\dfrac{\text{mol } CH_4}{16.05 \text{ g } CH_4}\right) = 62.3 \text{ mol } CH_4$

$(62.3 \text{ mol } CH_4)(-802.2 \text{ kJ/mol}) = -4.998 \times 10^{-4} \text{ kJ/kg}$

2. *propane*: $(1000 \text{ g/}C_3H_8)\left(\dfrac{\text{mol } C_3H_8}{44.11 \text{ g } C_3H_8}\right) = 22.67 \text{ mol } C_3H_8$

$(22.67 \text{ mol } C_3H_8)(-2043 \text{ kJ/mol}) = -4.632 \times 10^4 \text{ kJ/kg}$

494. Given: $C_2H_2(g) + H_2O(l)$ $\rightarrow CH_3CHO(l)$; $C_2H_2(g) + 2O_2(g) \rightarrow 2CO_2(g) + H_2O(l)$ $\Delta H = -1299.6$ kJ/mol; $CH_3CHO(l) + 2O_2(g) \rightarrow 2CO_2(g) + 2H_2O(l)$ $\Delta H = -1166.9$ kJ/mol

$C_2H_2(g) + 2O_2(g) \rightarrow 2CO_2(g) + H_2O(l)$ $\quad \Delta H = -1299.6$ kJ/mol

$2CO_2(g) + 2H_2O(l) \rightarrow CH_3CHO(l) + 2O_2(g)$ $\quad \Delta H = 1166.9$ kJ/mol

$\overline{C_2H_2(g) + H_2O(l) \rightarrow CH_3CHO(l) \quad \Delta H = -132.7 \text{ kJ/mol}}$

Unknown: Enthalpy (ΔH) for reaction of acetylene with water

495. Given: $C_{10}H_{22}(l) + 15O_2(g) \rightarrow 10CO_2(g) + 11H_2O(l)$ ΔH_f^0 for liquid decane $(C_{10}H_{22})$ $= -300.9$ kJ/mol

$10[C(s) + O_2(g) \rightarrow CO_2(g)]$ $\quad \Delta H = (10)(-393.5) = -3935$ kJ/mol

$11[H_2(g) + \frac{1}{2}O_2(g) \rightarrow H_2O(l)]$ $\quad \Delta H = (11)(-285.8) = -3143.8$ kJ/mol

$C_{10}H_{22}(l) \rightarrow 10C(s) + 11H_2(g)$ $\quad \Delta H = 300.9$ kJ/mol

$\overline{C_{10}H_{22}(l) + \frac{31}{2}O_2(g) \rightarrow 10CO_2(g) + 11H_2O(l) \quad \Delta H = -6777.9 \text{ kJ/mol}}$

Unknown: Enthalpy (ΔH) for combustion of decane

496. Given: $MgO(s) + 2HCl(g) \rightarrow MgCl_2(s) + H_2O(l)$; $Mg(s) + 2HCl(g) \rightarrow MgCl_2(s) + H_2(g)$ $\Delta H = -456.9$ kJ/mol; $Mg(s) + O_2(g) \rightarrow MgO(s)$ $\Delta H = -601.6$ kJ/mol; $H_2O(l) \rightarrow H_2(g) + O_2(g)$ $\Delta H = +285.8$ kJ/mol

$Mg(s) + 2HCl(g) \rightarrow MgCl_2(s) + H_2(g)$ $\quad \Delta H = -456.9$ kJ/mol

$MgO(s) \rightarrow Mg(s) + \frac{1}{2}O_2(g)$ $\quad \Delta H = 601.6$ kJ/mol

$H_2(g) + \frac{1}{2}O_2(g) \rightarrow H_2O(l)$ $\quad \Delta H = -285.8$ kJ/mol

$\overline{MgO(s) + 2HCl(g) \rightarrow MgCl_2(s) + H_2O(l) \quad \Delta H = -141.1 \text{ kJ/mol}}$

Unknown: Enthalpy (ΔH) of reaction of MgO with HCl

497. Given: $2NaOH(s) + 2Na(s) \xrightarrow{\Delta} 2Na_2O(s) + H_2(g)$ $\Delta S = 10.6$ J/mol·K $\Delta H^o{}_{fNaOH} = -425.9$ kJ/mol $T = 25^oC = 298$ K

$2[2Na(s) + \frac{1}{2}O_2(g) \rightarrow Na_2O(s)]$ $\quad \Delta H = (2)(-414.2) = -828.4$ kJ/mol

$2[NaOH(s) \rightarrow 2Na(s) + O_2(g) + H_2(g)]$ $\quad \Delta H = (2)(425.9 = 851.8$ kJ/mol

$\overline{2NaOH(s) + 2Na(s) \rightarrow 2Na_2O(s) + H_2(g) \quad \Delta H = 23.4 \text{ kJ/mol}}$

$\Delta S = (10.6 \text{ J/mol·K})(\text{kJ}/1000 \text{ J}) = 0.0106$ kJ/mol

$\Delta G = \Delta H - T\Delta S$

$\quad = 23.4 \text{ kJ/mol} - [(298 \text{ K})(0.0106 \text{ kJ/mol·K})]$

$\quad = 20.2$ kJ/mol

Unknown: ΔG

498. Given: $NH_3(g) + HCl(g)$
$\rightarrow NH_4Cl(s)$
$T = 25°C = 298$ K
$\Delta G =$
-91.2 kJ/mol

Unknown: Entropy
change (ΔS)
in J/mol·K

$\frac{1}{2}N_2(g) + 2H_2(g) + \frac{1}{2}Cl_2(g) \rightarrow NH_4Cl(s) \quad \Delta H = -314.4$ kJ/mol

$NH_3(g) \rightarrow \frac{1}{2}N_2(g) + \frac{3}{2}H_2(g) \quad \Delta H = 45.9$ kJ/mol

$HCl(s) \rightarrow \frac{1}{2}H_2(g) + \frac{1}{2}Cl_2(g) \quad \Delta H = 92.3$ kJ/mol

---

$NH_3(g) + HCl(g) \rightarrow NH_4Cl(s) \quad \Delta H = -176.2$ kJ/mol

$\Delta G = \Delta H - T\Delta S$

$\Delta S = \Delta H - \Delta G/T$

$\quad = (-176.2 \text{ kJ/mol}) - (-91.2 \text{ kJ/mol})/298$ K

$\quad = (-0.285 \text{ kJ/mol} \cdot \text{K})\left(\dfrac{1000 \text{ J}}{\text{kJ}}\right) = -285$ J/mol·K

---

499. a. Given: $3C(s) +$
$Fe_2O_3(s) \rightarrow$
$3CO(g) + Fe(s)$
$\Delta H^\circ_{fCO(g)} =$
-110.53
kJ/mol

Unknown: Enthalpy
(ΔH)

$3C(s) + \frac{3}{2}O_2(g) \rightarrow 3CO(g) \quad \Delta H = (3)(-110.53) = -331.59$ kJ/mol

$Fe_2O_3(s) \rightarrow 2Fe(s) + \frac{3}{2}O_2(g) \quad \Delta H = +1118.4$ kJ/mol

---

$3C(s) + Fe_2O_3(s) \rightarrow 3CO(g) + 2Fe(s) \quad \Delta H = 786.8$ kJ/mol

b. Given: $3Mn(s) +$
$Fe_2O_3(s) \rightarrow$
$3MnO(s) +$
$2Fe(s)$
$\Delta H^\circ_{fMnO(s)} =$
-384.9 kJ/mol

Unknown: ΔH

$3[Mn(s) + \frac{1}{2}O_2(g) \rightarrow MnO(s)] \quad \Delta H = (3)(-384.9) = -1154.7$ kJ/mol

$Fe_2O_3(s) \rightarrow 2Fe(s) + \frac{3}{2}O_2(g) \quad \Delta H = +1118.4$ kJ/mol

---

$3Mn(s) + Fe_2O_3(s) \rightarrow 3MnO(s) + 2Fe(s) \quad \Delta H = -36$ kJ/mol

c. Given: $12P(s) +$
$10Fe_2O_3(s) \rightarrow$
$3P_4O_{10}(s)$
$+ 20Fe(s)$
$\Delta H^\circ_{fP_4O_{10}}(s) =$
-3009.9
kJ/mol

Unknown: ΔH

$3[4P(s) + 5O_2(g) \rightarrow P_4O_{10}(s)] \quad \Delta H = (3)(-3009.9) = -9029.7$ kJ/mol

$F10[Fe_2O_3(s) \rightarrow 2Fe(s) + \frac{3}{2}O_2(g)] \quad \Delta H = (10)(1118.4) = 11\,184.$ kJ/mol

---

$12P(s) + 10Fe_2O_3(s) \rightarrow 3P_4O_{10}(s) + 20Fe(s) \quad \Delta H = +2154$ kJ/mol

d. Given: $3Si(s) +$
$2Fe_2O_3(s) \rightarrow$
$3 SiO_2(s) +$
$4Fe(s)$
$\Delta H^\circ_{fSiO_2}(s) =$
-910.9 kJ/mol

Unknown: ΔH

$3[Si(s) + O_2(g) \rightarrow SiO_2(s)] \quad \Delta H = (3)(-910.9) = 2732.7$ kJ/mol

$2[Fe_2O_3(s) \rightarrow 2Fe(s) + \frac{3}{2}O_2(g)] \quad \Delta H = (2)(1118.4) = 2236.8$ kJ/mol

---

$3Si(s) + 2Fe_2O_3(s) \rightarrow 3SiO_2(s) + 4Fe(s) \quad \Delta H = -496$ kJ/mol

e. Given: $3S(s) +$
$2 Fe_2O_3(s) \rightarrow$
$3 SO_2(g) +$
$4 Fe(s)$

Unknown: ΔH

$3[S(s) + O_2(g) \rightarrow SO_2(g)] \quad \Delta H = (3)(-296.8) = -890.4$ kJ/mol

$2[Fe_2O_3(s) \rightarrow 2Fe(s) + \frac{3}{2}O_2(g)] \quad \Delta H = (2)(1118.4) = 2236.8$ kJ/mol

---

$3S(s) + 2Fe_2O_3(s) \rightarrow 3SO_2(g) + 4Fe(s) \quad \Delta H +1346.4$ kJ/mol

500. a. Given: $A \rightleftharpoons C + D$
$[A] = 2.24 \times 10^{-2}$ M
$[C] = 6.41 \times 10^{-3}$ M
$[D] = 6.41 \times 10^{-3}$ M

Unknown: K

$$K = \frac{[C][D]}{[A]} = \frac{(6.41 \times 10^{-3}\text{ M})^2}{2.24 \times 10^{-2}\text{ M}} = 1.83 \times 10^{-3}$$

b. Given: $A + B \rightleftharpoons C + D$
$[A] = 3.23 \times 10^{-5}$ M $= [B]$
$[C] = 1.27 \times 10^{-2}$ M $= [D]$

Unknown: K

$$K = \frac{[C][D]}{[A][B]} = \frac{(1.27 \times 10^{-2}\text{ M})^2}{(3.23 \times 10^{-5}\text{M})^2} = 1.55 \times 10^5$$

c. Given: $A + B \rightleftharpoons 2\,C$
$[A] = 7.02 \times 10^{-3}$ M $= [B]$
$[C] = 2.16 \times 10^{-2}$ M

Unknown: K

$$K = \frac{[C]^2}{[A][B]} = \frac{(2.16 \times 10^{-2}\text{ M})^2}{(7.02 \times 10^{-3}\text{ M})^2} = 9.47$$

d. Given: $2A \rightleftharpoons 2C + D$
$[A] = 6.59 \times 10^{-4}$ M
$[C] = 4.06 \times 10^{-3}$ M
$[D] = 2.03 \times 10^{-3}$ M

Unknown: K

$$K = \frac{[C]^2[D]}{[A]^2} = \frac{(4.06 \times 10^{-3}\text{ M})^2(2.03 \times 10^{-3}\text{ M})}{(6.59 \times 10^{-4}\text{ M})^2} = 7.71 \times 10^{-2}$$

e. Given: $A + B \rightleftharpoons C + D + E$
$[A] = 3.73 \times 10^{-4}$ M $= [B]$
$[C] = 9.35 \times 10^{-4}$ M $= [D]$ $= [E]$

Unknown: K

$$K = \frac{[C][D][E]}{[A][B]} = \frac{(9.35 \times 10^{-4}\text{ M})^3}{(3.73 \times 10^{-4}\text{ M})^2} = 5.88 \times 10^{-3}$$

f. Given: $2A + B \rightleftharpoons 2C$
$[A] = 5.50 \times 10^{-3}$ M
$[B] = 2.25 \times 10^{-3}$ M
$[C] = 1.02 \times 10^{-2}$ M

Unknown: K

$$K = \frac{[C]^2}{[A]^2[B]} = \frac{(1.02 \times 10^{-2}\text{ M})^2}{(5.50 \times 10^{-3}\text{ M})^2(2.25 \times 10^{-3}\text{ M})} = 1.53 \times 10^3$$

501. Given: $2A(g) \rightleftharpoons 2C(g)$
+ D(g)
[A] = 1.88×10^{-1} M
[C] = 6.56 M
$K = 2.403 \times 10^2$

Unknown: [D]

$K = \dfrac{[C]^2[D]}{[A]^2}$

[D] = (K) [A]^2/[C]^2

$= (2.403 \times 10^2)\,(1.88 \times 10^{-1}\text{ M})^2/(6.56\text{ M})^2$

$= 0.197$ M

---

502. Given: $T = 700$ K
$K = 3.164 \times 10^3$
$C_2H_4(g) + H_2(g)$
$\rightleftharpoons C_2H_6(g)$

Unknown: [C_2H_4] if
[H_2] = 0.0619 M and
[C_2H_6] = 1.055 M

$K = \dfrac{[C_2H_6]}{[C_2H_4][H_2]}$

$[C_2H_4] = \dfrac{[C_2H_6]}{[H_2]\ (K)} = \dfrac{1.055\text{ M}}{(0.0619\text{ M})(3.164 \times 10^3)} = 5.39 \times 10^{-3}$ M

---

503. Given: A + 2B $\rightleftharpoons$ C + 2D
[A] = 0.0567 M
[B] = 0.1171 M
[C] = 0.000 3378 M
[D] = 0.000 6756 M

Unknown: K

$K = \dfrac{[C][D]^2}{[A][B]^2} = \dfrac{(0.000\,3378\text{ M})(0.000\,6756\text{ M})^2}{(0.0567\text{ M})(0.1171\text{ M})^2} = 1.98 \times 10^{-7}$

---

504. Given: $2A \rightleftharpoons 2C + 2D$
[A] = 0.1077 M
[C] = 0.000 4104 M
[D] = 0.000 4104 M

Unknown: K

$K = \dfrac{[C]^2[D]^2}{[A]^2} = \dfrac{(0.000\,4104\text{ M})^2(0.000\,4104\text{ M})^2}{0.1077\text{ M}^2} = 2.446 \times 10^{-12}$

---

506. a. Given: $COCl_2(g) \rightleftharpoons$ CO(g) + $Cl_2(g)$
$T = 25°C$
$K = 4.282 \times 10^{-2}$
[CO] = 5.90×10^{-3} M = [Cl_2]

Unknown: [$COCl_2$]

$K = \dfrac{[CO][Cl_2]}{[COCl_2]}$

$[COCl_2] = \dfrac{[CO][Cl_2]}{K} = \dfrac{(5.90 \times 10^{-3}\text{ M})^2}{4.282 \times 10^{-2}} = 8.13 \times 10^{-4}$ M

b. Given: $COCl_2(g) \rightleftharpoons$ CO(g) + $Cl_2(g)$
$K = 4.282 \times 10^{-2}$
[$COCl^2$] = 0.003 70 M
[CO] = [Cl_2]

Unknown: [CO] and [Cl_2]

$K = \dfrac{[CO][Cl_2]}{[COCl_2]}$

$K = \dfrac{x^2}{[COCl_2]}$

$x^2 = (K)\,[COCl_2]$

$x = \sqrt{(K)\,[COCl_2]} = \sqrt{(4.282 \times 10^{-2})(0.003\,70\text{ M})} = 0.0126$ M

507. Given: $A(g) + B(s) \rightleftharpoons$
$C(g) + D(s)$
$K = 1$
$T = 500$ K

B and D are solids; therefore their concentrations = 1.

$$K = \frac{[C][1]}{[A][1]}$$

a. Unknown: [A] and [C]

If $K = 1$ [C][D] = [A][B]

$$K = 1 = \frac{[C][1]}{[A][1]} = \frac{[C]}{[A]}$$

Therefore, [A] = [C]

---

508. Given: $C(s) + H_2O(g) \rightleftharpoons$
$CO(g) + H_2(g)$
$K = 4.251 \times 10^{-2}$
$T = 800$ K
$[H_2O] = 0.1990$ M

Unknown: [CO] and [H_2]

C is a solid; [C] = 1

$$K = \frac{[CO][H_2]}{[1][H_2O]}$$

$[CO][H_2] = (K)[H_2O]$

$x^2 = (4.251 \times 10^{-2})(0.1990 \text{ M})$

$x = \sqrt{8.459 \times 10^{-3}}$ M

$= 0.0918$ M

---

509. a. Given: $2NO(g) + O_2(g)$
$\rightleftharpoons 2NO_2(g)$
$T = 500$ K
$K = 1.671 \times 10^4$
$[NO] = 6.200 \times 10^{-2}$ M
$[O^2] = 8.305 \times 10^{-3}$ M

Unknown: [NO_2]

$$K = \frac{[NO_2]^2}{[NO]^2[O_2]}$$

$[NO_2]^2 = K[NO]^2[O_2]$

$[NO_2] = \sqrt{K[NO]^2[O_2]}$

$= \sqrt{(1.671 \times 10^4)(6.200 \times 10^{-2} \text{ M})^2(8.305 \times 10^{-3} \text{ M})}$

$= 0.7304$ M

b. Given: $T = 1000$ K
$K = 1.315 \times 10^{-2}$
$[NO] = 6.200 \times 10^{-2}$ M
$[O_2] = 8.305 \times 10^{-3}$ M

Unknown: [NO_2]

$[NO_2] \sqrt{K[NO]^2[O_2]}$

$= \sqrt{(1.315 \times 10^{-2})(6.200 \times 10^{-2} \text{ M})^2(8.305 \times 10^{-3} \text{ M})}$

$= 6.479 \times 10^{-4}$ M

---

511. b. Given: $H_2(g) + Br_2(g)$
$\rightleftharpoons 2HBr(g)$
$K = 5.628 \times 10^{18}$ $[H_2]_{initial}$
$= [Br_2]_{initial}$
$[HBr] = 0.500$ M

Unknown: [H_2]

$$K = \frac{[HBr]^2}{[H_2][Br_2]}$$

$[H_2] = [Br_2] = x$

$$[H_2] = \frac{[HBr]^2}{(K)(x)}$$

$$x^2 = \frac{(0.500 \text{ M})^2}{(5.628 \times 10^{18})}$$

$$x = \sqrt{\frac{(0.500 \text{ M})^2}{(5.628 \times 10^{18})}} = 2.11 \times 10^{-10} \text{ M}$$

512. Given: $N_2F_4(g) \rightleftharpoons 2$
$NF_2(g)$
$T = 25°C$
$[N_2F_4] = 0.9989$
M
$[NF_2] = 1.131 \times 10^{-3}$ M

Unknown: K

$K = \dfrac{[NF_2]^2}{[N_2F_4]} = \dfrac{(1.131 \times 10^{-3} \text{ M})^2}{0.9989 \text{ M}} = 1.281 \times 10^{-6}$

513. Given: $N_2O_4(g) \rightleftharpoons$
$2NO_2(g)$
$T = 25°C$
$[N_2O_4] = 5.95 \times 10^{-1}$ M
$[NO_2] = 5.24 \times 10^{-2}$ M

Unknown: K

$K = \dfrac{[NO_2]^2}{[N_2O_4]} = \dfrac{(5.24 \times 10^{-2} \text{ M})^2}{(5.95 \times 10^{-1} \text{ M})} = 4.61 \times 10^{-3}$

514. a. Given: $NaCN(s) +$
$HCl(g) \rightleftharpoons$
$HCN(g) +$
$NaCl(s)$

Unknown: Expression for equilibrium constant (K)

$K = \dfrac{[HCN][NaCl]}{[NaCN][HCl]}$

NaCN and NaCl are solids; therefore their concentrations equal 1.

$K = \dfrac{[HCN]}{[HCl]}$

b. Given: $K = 2.405 \times 10^6$
$[HCN] = 0.8959$ M

Unknown: $[HCl]$

$K = \dfrac{[HCN]}{[HCl]}$

$[HCl] = \dfrac{[HCN]}{K} = \dfrac{0.8959 \text{ M}}{2.405 \times 10^6} = 3.725 \times 10^{-7}$ M

515. a. Given: $CH_4(g) +$
$H_2O(g) \rightleftharpoons$
$CO(g) +$
$3 H_2(g)$
At 1100 K, $K = 3.112 \times 10^2$

b. Temperature = 110
K, $K = 3.112 \times 10^2$
$[H_2] = 1.56$ M
$[CH_4] = 3.70 \times 10^{-2}$ M
$[H_2O] = 8.27 \times 10^{-1}$ M

Unknown: $[CO]$

$K = \dfrac{[CO][H_2]^3}{[CH_4][H_2O]}$

$[CO] = (K) \dfrac{[CH_4][H_2O]}{[H_2]} = \dfrac{(3.112 \times 10^2)\,(3.70 \times 10^{-2} \text{ M})(8.27 \times 10^{-1} \text{ M})}{(1.56 \text{ M})^3}$

$= 2.51$ M

516. Given: $N_2O_4 \rightleftharpoons NO_2$
   $T = 20°C = 293$ K
   $[N_2O_4] = 2.55 \times 10^{-3}$ M
   $[NO_2] = 10.4 \times 10^{-3}$ M
   Unknown: K

$N_2O_4 \rightleftharpoons 2NO_2$

$$K = \frac{[NO_2]^2}{[N_2O_4]} = \frac{(10.4 \times 10^{-3} \text{ M})^2}{(2.55 \times 10^{-3} \text{ M})} = 0.0424$$

---

517. Given: $N_2O_4 \rightleftharpoons NO_2$
   $T = 20°C = 293$ K
   $[N_2O_4] = 2.67 \times 10^{-3}$ M
   $[NO_2] = 10.2 \times 10^{-3}$ M
   Unknown: K

$N_2O_4 \rightleftharpoons 2NO_2$

$$K = \frac{[NO_2]^2}{[N_2O_4]} = \frac{(10.2 \times 10^{-3} \text{ M})^2}{2.67 \times 10^{-3} \text{ M}} = 0.0390$$

---

518. Given: $T = 25°C$
   $[HCOOH] = 0.025$ M
   $[H_3O^+] = 2.03 \times 10^{-3}$ M
   Unknown: K_a

$HCOOH + H_2O \rightleftharpoons H_3O^+ + HCOO^-$

$$K_a = \frac{[H_3O^+][HCOO^-]}{[HCOOH]}$$

$[H_3O^+] = [HCOO^-] = 2.03 \times 10^{-3}$ M

$[HCOOH] = 0.025 - 2.03 \times 10^{-3} = 0.022\ 97$ M

$$K_a = \frac{(2.03 \times 10^{-3})^2}{0.022\ 97} = 1.8 \times 10^{-4}$$

---

519. Given: $[HIO_3] = 0.400$ M
   pH = 0.726
   $T = 25°C$
   Unknown: K_a

$pH = -\log [H_3O^+]$

$\log [H_3O^+] = -pH$

$[H_3O^+] = \text{antilog} (-pH)$

$[H_3O^+] = 1 \times 10^{-pH}$

$\qquad = 1 \times 10^{-0.726}$

$\qquad = 0.1879$ M

$HIO_3 + H_2O \rightleftharpoons H_3O^+ + IO_3^-$

$[H_3O^+] = [IO_3^-] = 0.1879$ M

$[HIO_3] = 0.400 - 0.1879 = 0.212$ M

$$K_a = \frac{[H_3O^+][IO_3^-]}{[HIO_3]} = \frac{(0.1879)^2}{0.212} = 0.167$$

520. Given: $[HClO] = 0.150$ M
pH = 4.55
$T = 25°C$

Unknown: K_a

$[H_3O^+] = $ antilog $(-pH)$

$[H_3O^+] = 1 \times 10^{-pH} = 1 \times 10^{-4.55} = 2.8 \times 10^{-5}$

$HClO + H_2O \rightleftharpoons H_3O^+ + ClO^-$

$[H_3O^+] = [ClO^-] = 2.8 \times 10^{-5}$ M

$[HClO] = 0.150 - 2.8 \times 10^{-5} = 0.15$ M

$$K_a = \frac{[H_3O^+][ClO^-]}{[HClO]} = \frac{(2.8 \times 10^{-5})^2}{0.15} = 5.2 \times 10^{-9}$$

---

521. Given: $[CH_3CH_2CH_2NH_2] = 0.039$ M
$[OH^-] = 3.74 \times 10^{-3}$ M

Unknown: (a) pH of solution;
(b) K_b for propylamine

a. pH = $-\log [H_3O^+]$
$[H_3O^+][OH^-] = 1 \times 10^{-14}$ M^2

$$[H_3O^+] = \frac{1.0 \times 10^{-14} \text{ M}^2}{3.74 \times 10^{-3} \text{ M}} = 2.67 \times 10^{-12} \text{ M}$$

pH = $-\log (2.67 \times 10^{-12}) = 11.573$

b. $CH_3CH_2CH_2NH_2 + H_2O \rightleftharpoons CH_3CH_2CH_2NH_3^+ + OH^-$

$$K_b = \frac{[CH_3CH_2CH_2NH_3^+][OH^-]}{[CH_3CH_2CH_2NH_2]}$$

$[OH^-] = [CH_3CH_2CH_2NH_3^+] = 3.74 \times 10^{-3}$ M

$[CH_3CH_2CH_2NH_2] = 0.039 - 3.74 \times 10^{-3}$ M $= 0.03526$

$$K_b = \frac{(3.74 \times 10^{-3})^2}{0.03526} = 4.0 \times 10^{-4}$$

---

522. Given: K_a of $HNO_2 = 4.6 \times 10^{-4}$
$T = 25°C$
$[HNO_2] = 0.0450$ M

Unknown: $[H_3O^+]$

$HNO_2 + H_2O \rightleftharpoons H_3O^+ + NO_2^-$

$$K_a = \frac{[H_3O^+][NO_2^-]}{[HNO_2]}$$

$[H_3O^+] = [NO_2^-] = x$

$x^2 = (K_a)[HNO_2] = (4.6 \times 10^{-4})(0.0450 \text{ M}) = 2.07 \times 10^{-5}$ M

$x = \sqrt{2.07 \times 10^{-5} \text{ M}} = 4.5 \times 10^{-3}$ M

523. Given: $[HN_3] = 0.102$ M
$[H_3O^+] = 1.39 \times 10^{-3}$ M
$T = 25°C$

Unknown: **a.** pH
b. K_a

a. $pH = -\log [H_3O^+] = -\log (1.39 \times 10^{-3}) = 2.857$

b. $HN_3 + H_2O \rightleftharpoons H_3O^+ + N_3^-$

$$K_a = \frac{[H_3O^+][N_3^-]}{[HN_3]}$$

$[H_3O^+] = [N_3^-] = 1.39 \times 10^{-3}$ M

$[HN_3] = 0.102$ M $- 1.39 \times 10^{-3}$ M $= 0.10061$ M

$$K_a = \frac{(1.39 \times 10^{-3})^2}{0.10061} = 1.92 \times 10^{-5}$$

---

524. Given: $[BrCH_2COOH] = 0.200$ M
$[H_3O^+] = 0.0192$ M
$T = 25°C$

Unknown: **a.** pH
b. K_a

a. $pH = -\log [H_3O^+] = -\log (0.0192) = 1.717$

b. $BrCH_2COOH + H_2O \rightleftharpoons H_3O^+ + BrCH_2COO^-$

$$K_a = \frac{[H_3O^+][BrCH_2COO^-]}{[BrCH_2COOH]}$$

$[H_3O^+] = [BrCH_2COO^-] = 0.0192$ M

$[BrCH_2COOH] = 0.200$ M $- 0.0192$ M $= 0.1808$ M

$$K_a = \frac{(0.0192)^2}{0.1808} = 2.04 \times 10^{-3}$$

---

525. a. Given: $B + H_2O \rightleftharpoons BH^+ + OH^-$
$[B]_{initial} = 0.400$ M
$[OH^-] = 2.70 \times 10^{-4}$ M

Unknown: (1) $[H_3O^+]$
(2) pH
(3) K_b

(1) $[H_3O^+][OH^-] = 1.00 \times 10^{-14}$ M^2

$$[H_3O^+] = \frac{1.00 \times 10^{-14} \text{ M}^2}{2.70 \times 10^{-4} \text{ M}} = 3.70 \times 10^{-11} \text{ M}$$

(2) $pH = -\log (3.70 \times 10^{-11}) = 10.431$

(3) $B + H_2O \rightleftharpoons BH^+ + OH^-$

$$K_b = \frac{[BH^+][OH^-]}{[B]}$$

$[OH^-] = [BH^+] = 2.70 \times 10^{-4}$ M

$[B] = 0.400$ M $- 2.70 \times 10^{-4}$ M $= 0.399\ 73$ M

$$K_b = \frac{(2.70 \times 10^{-4})^2}{0.399\ 73} = 1.82 \times 10^{-7}$$

b. Given: $B_{initial} = 0.005\ 50\ M$

$[OH^-] = 8.45 \times 10^{-4}\ M$

Unknown: (1) [B] at equilibrium
(2) K_b
(3) pH

(1) [B] at equilibrium $= 0.005\ 50\ M - 8.45 \times 10^{-4}\ M = 4.66 \times 10^{-3}\ M$

(2) $B + H_2O \rightleftharpoons BH^+ + OH^-$

$$K_b = \frac{[BH^+][OH^-]}{[B]}$$

$[OH^-] = [BH^+] = 8.45 \times 10^{-4}\ M$

$$K_b = \frac{(8.45 \times 10^{-4}\ M)^2}{4.66 \times 10^{-3}\ M} = 1.53 \times 10^{-4}$$

(3) $pH = -\log[H_3O^+]$

$[H_3O^+][OH^-] = 1 \times 10^{-14}\ M^2$

$$[H_3O^+] = \frac{1 \times 10^{-14}\ M^2}{8.45 \times 10^{-4}\ M} = 1.18 \times 10^{-11}\ M$$

$pH = -\log(1.18 \times 10^{-11}) = 10.93$

c. Given: $[B]_{initial} = 0.0350\ M$

$pH = 11.29$

Unknown: (1) $[H_3O^+]$
(2) $[OH^-]$
(3) [B] at equilibrium
(4) K_b

(1) $[H_3O^+] = $ antilog $(-pH) = 1 \times 10^{-pH} = 1 \times 10^{-11.29} = 5.13 \times 10^{-12}\ M$

(2) $[H_3O^+][OH^-] = 1 \times 10^{-14}\ M^2$

$$[OH^-] = \frac{1 \times 10^{-14}\ M^2}{[H_3O^+]} = \frac{1 \times 10^{-14}\ M^2}{5.13 \times 10^{-12}\ M} = 1.9 \times 10^{-3}\ M$$

(3) [B] at equilibrium $= 0.0350\ M - 1.9 \times 10^{-3}\ M = 0.0331\ M$

(4) $K_b = \dfrac{[BH^+][OH^-]}{[B]}$

$[OH^-] = [BH^+] = 1.9 \times 10^{-3}\ M$

$$K_b = \frac{(1.9 \times 10^{-3})^2}{0.0331} = 1.1 \times 10^{-4}$$

d. Given: [B] at equilibrium $= 0.006\ 28\ M$

$[OH^-] = 0.000\ 92\ M$

Unknown: (1) $[B]_{initial}$
(2) K_b
(3) pH

(1) $[B]_{eq} = [B]_{initial} - [OH^-]$

$[B]_{initial} = [B]_{eq} + [OH^-] = 0.006\ 28\ M + 0.000\ 92\ M = 7.2 \times 10^{-3}\ M$

(2) $K_b = \dfrac{[BH^+][OH^-]}{[B]}$

$[OH^-] = [BH^+] = 0.000\ 92\ M$

$$K_b = \frac{(0.000\ 92\ M)^2}{0.006\ 28\ M} = 1.35 \times 10^{-4}$$

(3) $pH = -\log[H_3O^+]$

$[H_3O^+][OH^-] = 1 \times 10^{-14}\ M^2$

$$[H_3O^+] = \frac{1 \times 10^{14}\ M^2}{0.000\ 92\ M} = 1.1 \times 10^{-11}$$

$pH = -\log(1.1 \times 10^{-11}) = 10.96$

526. Given: Solubility of
C_6H_5COOH in
water = 2.9 g/L
pH = 2.92
$T = 25°C$

Unknown: K_a

$C_6H_5COOH + H_2O \rightleftharpoons H_3O^+ + C_6H_5COO^-$

$pH = -\log [H_3O^+]$

$\log [H_3O^+] = -pH$

$[H_3O^+] = \text{antilog} (-pH)$

$[H_3O^+] = 1 \times 10^{-pH} = 1 \times 10^{-2.92} = 1.2 \times 10^{-3} \text{ M}$

$[H_3O^+] = [C_6H_5COO^-] = 1.2 \times 10^{-3} \text{ M}$

$\left(\dfrac{2.9 \text{ g } C_6H_5COOH}{L} \right)\left(\dfrac{1 \text{ mol } C_6H_5COOH}{122.11 \text{ g } C_6H_5COOH} \right) = 0.02375 \text{ M}$

$= [C_6H_5COOH]_{initial}$

$[C_6H_5COOH] = 0.02375 - 1.2 \times 10^{-3} = 0.02255$

$K_a = \dfrac{[H_3O^+][C_6H_5COO^-]}{[C_6H_5COOH]} = \dfrac{(1.2 \times 10^{-2} \text{ M})^2}{0.022\,55 \text{ M}} = 6.4 \times 10^{-5}$

---

527. Given: $[H_2NCH_2CH_2OH]_{initial} =$
0.006 50 M
pH = 10.64
$T = 25°C$

Unknown: **a.** $[H_2NCH_2CH_2OH]$ at
equilibrium
b. K_b

a. $H_2NCH_2CH_2OH + H_2O \rightleftharpoons H_3NCH_2CH_2OH^+ + OH^-$

$pH = -\log [H_3O^+]$

$\log [H_3O^+] = -pH$

$[H_3O^+] = \text{antilog} (-pH)$

$[H_3O^+] = 1 \times 10^{-pH} = 1 \times 10^{-10.64} = 2.3 \times 10^{-11} \text{ M}$

$[H_3O^+][OH^-] = 1 \times 10^{-14} \text{ M}^2$

$[OH^-] = \dfrac{1 \times 10^{-14} \text{ M}^2}{[H_3O^+]} = \dfrac{1 \times 10^{-14} \text{ M}^2}{2.3 \times 10^{-11} \text{ M}} = 4.35 \times 10^{-4} \text{ M}$

$[H_2NCH_2CH_2OH] = 0.006\,50 \text{ M} - 4.35 \times 10^{-4} \text{ M} = 6.06 \times 10^{-3} \text{ M}$

$[H_3NCH_2CH_2OH^+] = [OH^-] = 4.35 \times 10^{-4} \text{ M}$

b. $K_b = \dfrac{[H_3NCH_2CH_2OH^+][OH^-]}{[H_2NCH_2CH_2OH]} = \dfrac{(4.35 \times 10^{-4} \text{ M})^2}{6.06 \times 10^{-3} \text{ M}} = 3.1 \times 10^{-5}$

---

528. Given: $[H_2Se] = 0.060$ M
$[H_3O^+] = 2.72 \times 10^{-3}$ M
$T = 25°C$

Unknown: K_a

$H_2Se + H_2O \rightleftharpoons H_3O^+ + HSe^-$

$K_a = \dfrac{[H_3O^+][HSe^-]}{H_2Se}$

$[HSe^-] = [H_3O^+] = 2.72 \times 10^{-3} \text{ M}$

$H_2Se = 0.060 \text{ M} - 2.72 \times 10^{-3} \text{ M} = 0.05728 \text{ M}$

$K_a = \dfrac{(2.72 \times 10^{-3} \text{ M})^2}{0.05728 \text{ M}} = 1.3 \times 10^{-4}$

529. Given: K_b of C_5H_5N
$= 1.78 \times 10^{-9}$
$[C_5H_5N] = 0.140$ M

Unknown: **a.** $[OH^-]$
b. pH

a. $C_5H_5N + H_2O \rightleftharpoons C_5H_5NH^+ + OH^-$

$$K_b = \frac{[C_5H_5NH^+]\,[OH^-]}{C_5H_5N}$$

$[C_5H_5NH^+] = [OH^-] = x$

$x^2 = K_b[C_5H_5N] = (1.78 \times 10^{-9})\,(0.140 \text{ M}) = 2.5 \times 10^{-10}$

$x = \sqrt{2.5 \times 10^{-10}} = 1.58 \times 10^{-5} \text{ M} = [OH^-]$

b. $pH = -\log [H_3O^+]$

$[H_3O^+][OH^-] = 1 \times 10^{-14} \text{ M}^2$

$$[H_3O^+] = \frac{1 \times 10^{-14} \text{ M}^2}{[OH^-]}$$

$$= \frac{1 \times 10^{-14} \text{ M}^2}{1.58 \times 10^{-5} \text{ M}} = 6.329 \times 10^{-10} \text{ M}$$

$pH = -\log [6.329 \times 10^{-10} \text{ M}] = 9.20$

---

530. Given: $[HA] = 0.0208$ M
pH = 2.17

Unknown: **a.** $[HA]_{initial}$
b. K_a

a. $[HA] + [H_2O] \rightleftharpoons H_3O^+ + A^-$

$pH = -\log [H_3O^+]$

$\log [H_3O^+] = -pH$

$[H_3O^+] = \text{antilog}\,(-pH) = 1 \times 10^{-pH} = 1 \times 10^{-2.17} = 6.76 \times 10^{-3} \text{ M}$

$[HA] = [HA]_{initial} - [H_3O^+]$

$[HA]_{initial} = [HA] + [H_3O^+]$

$= 0.0208 \text{ M} + 6.76 \times 10^{-3} \text{ M} = 0.02756 \text{ M}$

b. $K_a = \dfrac{[H_3O^+][A^-]}{[HA]}$

$[H_3O^+] = [A^-] = 6.76 \times 10^{-3} \text{ M}$

$$K_a = \frac{(6.76 \times 10^{-3} \text{ M})^2}{0.0208 \text{ M}} = 2.2 \times 10^{-3}$$

531. Given: Mass of solute $(CH_3COCOOH)$ = 438 mg
volume of solvent (H_2O) = 10.00 mL
pH = 1.34

Unknown: K_a

$$CH_3COCOOH + H_2O \rightleftharpoons H_3O^+ + CH_3COCOO^-$$

$$pH = -\log [H_3O^+]$$

$$\log [H_3O^+] = -pH$$

$$[H_3O^+] = \text{antilog } (-pH)$$

$$[H_3O^+] = 1 \times 10^{-pH} = 1 \times 10^{-1.34} = 0.0457 \text{ M}$$

$$[H_3O^+] = [CH_3COCOO^-] = 0.0457 \text{ M}$$

$$\left(\frac{438 \text{ mg } CH_3COCOOH}{10.00 \text{ mL}}\right)\left(\frac{g}{1000 \text{ mg}}\right)\left(\frac{1000 \text{ mL}}{L}\right)\left(\frac{1 \text{ mol } CH_3COCOOH}{88.04 \text{ g } CH_3COCOOH}\right)$$

$$= 0.4975 \text{ M} = [CH_3COCOOH]_{initial}$$

$$[CH_3COCOOH] = 0.4975 - .0457 = 0.4518 \text{ M}$$

$$K_a = \frac{[H_3O^+][CH_3COCOO^-]}{[CH^3COCOOH]} = \frac{(0.0457 \text{ M})^2}{0.4518 \text{ M}} = 4.63 \times 10^{-3}$$

---

532. Given: $[H_3O^+]$ of solution of acetoacetic acid (CH_3COCH_2COOH) = 4.38 $\times 10^{-3}$ M
$[CH_3COCH_2COOH]$ (nonionized) = 0.0731 M

Unknown: K_a

$$CH_3COCH_2COOH + H_2O \rightleftharpoons H_3O^+ \; CH_3COCH_2COO^-$$

$$K_a = \frac{[H_3O^+][CH_3COCH_2COO^-]}{[CH_3COCH_2COOH]}$$

$$[CH_3COCH_2COO^-] = [H_3O^+] = 4.38 \times 10^{-3} \text{ M}$$

$$[CH_3COCH_2COOH] = 0.0731 \text{ M} - 4.38 \times 10^{-3} \text{ M} = 0.068\,72 \text{ M}$$

$$K_a = \frac{(4.38 \times 10^{-3} \text{ M})^2}{0.0731 \text{ M}} = 2.62 \times 10^{-4}$$

---

533. Given: K_a of $CH_3CHClCOOH$ = 1.48 $\times 10^{-3}$
$[CH_3CHClCOOH]_{initial}$ = 0.116 M

Unknown: **a.** $[H_3O^+]$
b. pH

a. $$CH_3CHClCOOH + H_2O \rightleftharpoons H_3O^+ + CH_3CHClCOO^-$$

$$K_a = \frac{[H_3O^+][CH_3CHClCOO^-]}{[CH_3CHClCOOH]}$$

$$[H_3O^+] = x = [CH_3CHClCOO^-]$$

$$[CH_3CHClCOOH] = 0.116 - x$$

$$K_a = \frac{(x)(x)}{0.116} - x = \frac{x^2}{0.116 - x}$$

$$K_a = 1.48 \times 10^{-3}$$

$$1.48 \times 10^{-3} = \frac{x^2}{0.116 - x}$$

By the quadratic equation, x = 0.0124 M.

b. $$pH = -\log [H_3O^+] = -\log (0.0124) = 1.907$$

534. Given: First ionization:
$$H_2SO_4 + H_2O \rightarrow H_3O^+ + HSO_4^-$$
Ionization
$= 100\%$
Second ioniza-
tion: $HSO_4^- + H_2O \rightleftharpoons H_3O^+ + SO_4^{2-}$
$K_{a_2} = 1.3 \times 10^{-2}$
$[H_2SO_4] = 0.0788$ M

Unknown: **a.** total $[H_3O^+]$
b. pH of H_2SO_4 solution

a. $K_{a_2} = 1.3 \times 10^{-2} = \dfrac{[H_3O^+][SO_4^{2-}]}{HSO_4^-}$

$[H_3O^+] = 0.0788 + x$

$[SO_4^{2-}] = x$

$[HSO_4^-] = 0.0788 - x$

$1.3 \times 10^{-2} = \dfrac{(0.0788 + x)(x)}{(0.0788 - x)}$

$(1.3 \times 10^{-2})(0.0788 - x) = (0.0788 + x)(x)$

$(1.0244 \times 10^{-3}) - (1.3 \times 10^{-2})\,x = (7.88 \times 10^{-2})\,x + x^2$

$x^2 + (9.18 \times 10^{-2})\,x - (1.0244 \times 10^{-3}) = 0$

By the quadratic formula, $x = 0.010\,024$.

$[H_3O^+] = 0.0788 + 0.01 = 0.0888$

b. $pH = -\log [H_3O^+] = -\log (0.0888) = 1.05$

---

535. Given: $[HOCN] = 0.100$ M
$[H_3O^+] = 5.74 \times 10^{-3}$ M

Unknown: **a.** K_a
b. pH

a. $HOCN + H_2O \rightleftharpoons H_3O^+ + OCN^-$

$K_a = \dfrac{[H_3O^+][OCN^-]}{[HOCN]}$

$[H_3O^+] = [OCN^-] = 5.74 \times 10^{-3}$ M

$[HOCN] = 0.100 \text{ M} - 5.74 \times 10^{-3} \text{ M} = 0.094$ M

$K_a = \dfrac{(5.74 \times 10^{-3})^2}{0.094} = 3.5 \times 10^{-4}$

b. $pH = -\log [H_3O^+] = -\log (5.74 \times 10^{-3}) = 2.241$

---

536. Given: $[HCN] = 0.025$ M
$[CN^-] = 3.16 \times 10^{-6}$ M

$HCN + H_2O \rightleftharpoons H_3O^+ + CN^-$

a. Unknown: $[H_3O^+]$

$[CN^-] = [H_3O^+] = 3.16 \times 10^{-6}$ M

b. Unknown: pH

$pH = -\log [H_3O^+] = -\log (3.16 \times 10^{-6}) = 5.500$

d. Unknown: K_a

$K_a = \dfrac{[H_3O^+][CN^-]}{[HCN]}$

$[HCN] = 0.025 \text{ M} - 3.16 \times 10^{-6} \text{ M} = 0.0249$ M

$K_a = \dfrac{(3.16 \times 10^{-6} \text{ M})^2}{0.0249 \text{ M}} = 4.0 \times 10^{-10}$

f. Given: $[HCN] = 0.085$ M

Unknown: $[H_3O^+]$

$K_a = \dfrac{x^2}{0.085}$

$x^2 = (K_a)(0.085)$

$x = \sqrt{(K_a)(0.085)} = \sqrt{(4.0 \times 10^{-10})(0.085)} = \sqrt{3.4 \times 10^{-11}} = 5.8 \times 10^{-6}$

537. Given: $[CCl_2HCOOH] =$ 1.20 M
$[H_3O^+] = 0.182$ M

a. Unknown: pH.

$pH = -\log [H_3O^+] = -\log (0.182) = 0.740$

b. Unknown: K_a

$CCl_2HCOOH + H_2O \;] \rightleftharpoons H_3O^+ + CCl_2HCOO^-$

$$K_a = \frac{[H_3O^+]\,[CCl_2HCOO^-]}{[CCl_2HCOOH]}$$

$[H_3O^+] = [CCl_2HCOO^-] = 0.182$ M

$[CCl_2HCOOH] = 1.20$ M $- 0.182$ M $= 1.018$ M

$$K_a = \frac{(0.182)^2}{1.018} = 0.0325$$

538. Given: $[C_6H_5OH] =$ 0.215 M
pH $= 5.61$
Unknown: K_a

$C_6H_5OH + H_2O \;] = \; H_3O^+ + C_6H_5O^-$

$$K_a = \frac{[H_3O^+][C_6H_5O^-]}{[C_6H_5OH]}$$

$pH = -\log [H_3O^+]$

$\log [H_3O^+] = -pH$

$[H_3O^+] = $ antilog $(-pH)$

$[H_3O^+] = 1 \times 10^{-pH} = 1 \times 10^{-5.61} = 2.45 \times 10^{-6}$ M

$[H_3O^+] = [C_6H_5O^-] = 2.45 \times 10^{-6}$ M

$[C_6H_5OH] = 0.215 - 2.45 \times 10^{-6} = 0.215$ M

$$K_a = \frac{(2.45 \times 10^{-6})^2}{0.215} = 2.80 \times 10^{-11}$$

539. Given: Solution of NH_2CH_2COOH is 3.75 g in 250.0 mL H_2O
pH $= 0.890$

a. Unknown: molarity of NH_2CH_2COOH

$\left(\dfrac{3.75 \text{ g } NH_2CH_2COOH}{250 \text{ mL}} \right)\left(\dfrac{1000 \text{ mL}}{L} \right)\left(\dfrac{1 \text{ mol } NH_2CH_2COOH}{75.06 \text{ g } NH_2CH_2COOH} \right)$

$= 0.200$ M NH_2CH_2COOH

b. Unknown: K_a

$$NH_2CH_2COOH + H_2O \rightleftharpoons H_3O^+ + NH_2CH_2COO^-$$

$$K_a = \frac{[H_3O^+]\,[NH_2CH_2COO^-]}{[NH_2CH_2COOH]}$$

$$pH = -\log[H_3O^+]$$

$$\log[H_3O^+] = -pH$$

$$[H_3O^+] = \text{antilog}(-pH)$$

$$[H_3O^+] = 1 \times 10^{-pH} = 1 \times 10^{-0.890} = 0.1288\ M$$

$$[H_3O^+] = [NH_2CH_2COO^-] = 0.1288\ M$$

$$[NH_2CH_2COOH] = 0.200\ M - 0.1288\ M = 0.0712\ M$$

$$K_a = \frac{(0.1288)^2}{0.0712} = 0.233$$

---

540. Given: $(CH_3)_3N + H_2O$] $\rightleftharpoons CH_3NH^+ + OH^-$
$[(CH_3)_3N] = 0.0750\ M$
$[OH^-] = 2.32 \times 10^{-3}\ M$

Unknown: **a.** pH
         b. K_b

a. $[H_3O^+][OH^-] = 1 \times 10^{-14}\ M^2$

$$[H_3O^+] = \frac{1 \times 10^{-14}\ M^2}{[OH^-]} = \frac{1 \times 10^{-14}\ M^2}{2.32 \times 10^{-3}\ M} = 4.31 \times 10^{-12}\ M$$

$$pH = -\log[H_3O^+] = -\log(4.31 \times 10^{-12}) = 11.37$$

b. $K_b = \dfrac{[CH_3NH^+][OH^-]}{[(CH_3)_3N]}$

$$[OH^-] = [CH_3NH^+] = 2.32 \times 10^{-3}\ M$$

$$[(CH_3)_3N] = 0.0750\ M - 2.32 \times 10^{-3}\ M = 0.07268\ M$$

$$K_b = \frac{(2.32 \times 10^{-3})^2}{0.07268} = 7.41 \times 10^{-5}$$

---

541. Given: $[(CH_3)_2NH] = 5.00 \times 10^{-3}\ M$
pH = 11.20

Unknown: **a.** K_b
         b. Which base is stronger: $(CH_3)_2NH$ or $(CH_3)_3N$?

a. $(CH_3)_2NH + H_2O$] $\rightleftharpoons (CH_3)_2NH_2^+ + OH^-$

$$K_b = \frac{[(CH_3)_2NH_2^+][OH^-]}{[(CH_3)_2NH]}$$

$$pH = -\log[H_3O^+]$$

$$\log[H_3O^+] = -pH$$

$$[H_3O^+] = \text{antilog}(-pH) = 1 \times 10^{-pH} = 1 \times 10^{-11.20} = 6.31 \times 10^{-12}\ M$$

$$[H_3O^+][OH^-] = 1 \times 10^{-14}\ M^2$$

$$[OH^-] = \frac{1 \times 10^{-14}\ M^2}{[H_3O^+]} = \frac{1 \times 10^{-14}\ M^2}{6.31 \times 10^{-12}\ M} = 1.585 \times 10^{-3}\ M$$

$$[OH^-] = [(CH_3)_2NH_2^+] = 1.585 \times 10^{-3}\ M$$

$$[(CH_3)_2NH] = 5.00 \times 10^{-3}\ M - 1.585 \times 10^{-3}\ M = 3.415 \times 10^{-3}\ M$$

$$K_b = \frac{(1.585 \times 10^{-3})^2}{3.415 \times 10^{-3}} = 7.36 \times 10^{-4}$$

b. K_b of $(CH_3)_3N = 7.41 \times 10^{-5}$

K_b of $(CH_3)_2NH = 7.36 \times 10^{-4}$

$$7.36 \times 10^{-4} > 7.41 \times 10^{-5}$$

Therefore $(CH_3)_2NH$ (dimethylamine) is the stronger base.

542. Given: $H_2NNH_2 +$
$H_2O(l) \rightleftharpoons$
$H_2NNH_3^+ (aq)$
$+ OH^- (aq)$
$H_2NNH_3^+ (aq)$
$+ H_2O(l) \rightleftharpoons$
$H_3NNH_3^{2+} (aq)$
$+ OH^- (aq)$
$K_{b_2} = 8.9 \times 10^{-16}$

$$K_{b_1} = \frac{[H_2NNH_3^+][OH^-]}{[H_2NNH_2]}$$

$[H_3O^+] = \text{antilog} (-pH)$

$[H_3O^+] = 1 \times 10^{-pH}$

$= 1 \times 10^{-10.50}$

a. $[H_2NNH_2] = 0.120$ M
pH = 10.50

Unknown: K_{b_1}
(Assume
that
$[H_2NNH_2]$
initial does
not
change.)

$= 3.16 \times 10^{-11}$ M

$[H_3O^+][OH^-] = 1 \times 10^{-14}$ M^2

$[OH^-] = \frac{1 \times 10^{-14} \text{ M}^2}{[H_3O^+]} = \frac{1 \times 10^{-14} \text{ M}^2}{3.16 \times 10^{-11} \text{ M}}$

$= 3.16 \times 10^{-4}$ M

$[OH^-] = 3.16 \times 10^{-4}$ M $= [H_2NNH_3^+]$

$$K_{b_1} = \frac{(3.16 \times 10^{-4})^2}{0.120 \text{ M}} = 8.3 \times 10^{-7}$$

b. Given: $[H_2NNH_2] =$
0.020 M

Unknown: $[OH^-]$

$$K_{b_1} = \frac{[H_2NNH_3^+] [OH^-]}{[H_2NNH_2]}$$

$8.3 \times 10^{-7} = \dfrac{x^2}{0.020}$

$x = \sqrt{(8.3 \times 10^{-7})(0.020)} = 1.3 \times 10^{-4}$ M $= [OH^-]$

c. Unknown: pH of
0.020 M
$[H_2NNH_2]$
solution

$[H_3O^+][OH^-] = 1 \times 10^{-14}$ M^2

$[H_3O^+] = \frac{1 \times 10^{-14} \text{ M}^2}{[OH^-]} = \frac{1 \times 10^{-14} \text{ M}^2}{1.3 \times 10^{-4} \text{ M}} = 7.7 \times 10^{-11}$ M

$pH = -\log [H_3O^+] = -\log (7.7 \times 10^{-11}) = 10.11$

---

543. Given: Saturated solution: 0.276 g
$AgBrO_3$ in
150.0 mL H_2O

Unknown: K_{sp}

$\text{solubility} = \left(\frac{0.276 \text{ g AgBrO}_3}{150.0 \text{ mL H}_2O}\right)\left(\frac{1000 \text{ mL}}{L}\right)\left(\frac{1 \text{ mol AgBrO}_3}{235.74 \text{ g AgBrO}_3}\right)$

$= 7.80 \times 10^{-3}$ M $AgBrO_3$

$AgBrO_3(s) \rightleftharpoons Ag^+(aq) + BrO_3^-(aq)$

$K_{sp} = [Ag^+][BrO_3^-]$

$[Ag^+] = 7.80 \times 10^{-3}$ M

$[BrO_3^-] = 7.80 \times 10^{-3}$ M

$K_{sp} = (7.80 \times 10^{-3})^2 = 6.08 \times 10^{-5}$

544. Given: solubility of CaF_2
= 0.0427 g/2.50 L

Unknown: K_{sp}

$$\left(\frac{0.0427 \text{ g } CaF_2}{2.50 \text{ L}}\right)\left(\frac{1 \text{ mol } CaF_2}{78.06 \text{ g } CaF_2}\right) = 2.19 \times 10^{-4} \text{ M } CaF_2$$

$$CaF_2(s) \rightleftharpoons Ca^{2+}(aq) + 2F^-(aq)$$

$$K_{sp} = [Ca^{2+}][F^-]^2$$

$$[Ca^{2+}] = 2.19 \times 10^{-4} \text{ M}$$

$$[F^-] = (2)(2.19 \times 10^{-4}) = 4.38 \times 10^{-4} \text{ M}$$

$$K_{sp} = (2.19 \times 10^{-4})(4.38 \times 10^{-4})^2$$

$$= 4.20 \times 10^{-11}$$

---

545. Given: K_{sp} of $CaSO_4$
= 9.1×10^{-6}

Unknown: $[CaSO_4]$ in a saturated solution

$$CaSO_4(s) \rightleftharpoons Ca^{2+}(aq) + SO_4^{2-}(aq)$$

$$K_{sp} = [Ca^{2+}][SO_4^{2-}]$$

$$[Ca^{2+}] = [SO_4^{2-}] = x$$

$$K_{sp} = x^2 = 9.1 \times 10^{-6}$$

$$x = \sqrt{9.1 \times 10^{-6}}$$

$$= 3.0 \times 10^{-3} \text{ M} = [CaSO_4]$$

---

546. Given: A salt = X_2Y
$K_{sp} = 4.25 \times 10^{-7}$

Unknown: **a.** molarity of a saturated solution of the salt
b. molarity of a solution of AZ with the same K_{sp}

a. $X_2Y(s) \rightleftharpoons 2X(aq) + Y(aq)$

$$K_{sp} = [X]^2[Y]$$

$$[X] = 2x$$

$$[Y] = x$$

$$K_{sp} = 4.25 \times 10^{-7} = (2x)^2(x) = 4x^3$$

$$x = 4.74 \times 10^{-3} \text{ M} = [X_2Y]$$

b. $AZ(s) \rightleftharpoons A(aq) + Z(aq)$

$$K_{sp} = [A][Z] = x^2$$

$$x = \sqrt{4.25 \times 10^{-7}} = 6.52 \times 10^{-4} \text{ M}$$

547. Given: V NaOH = 0.320 L
$\quad$ [NaOH] = 0.046 M
$\quad$ V CaCl$_2$ = 0.400 L
$\quad$ [CaCl$_2$] = 0.085 M
$\quad$ K_{sp} Ca(OH)$_2$
$\quad$ = 5.5 × 10^{-6}

Unknown: whether a pre-
$\quad$ cipitate
$\quad$ of Ca(OH)$_2$
$\quad$ forms

$$2NaOH + CaCl_2 \rightarrow 2NaCl + Ca(OH)_2$$

$$Ca(OH)_2(s) \rightleftharpoons Ca^{2+}(aq) + 2OH^-(aq)$$

$$K_{sp} = [Ca^{2+}][OH^-]^2 = 5.5 \times 10^{-6}$$

$$(0.400 \text{ L})\left(\frac{0.085 \text{ mol Ca}^{2+}}{\text{L}}\right) = 0.034 \text{ mol Ca}^{2+}$$

$$(0.320 \text{ L})\left(\frac{0.046 \text{ mol OH}^-}{\text{L}}\right) = 0.0147 \text{ mol OH}^-$$

Total volume = 0.320 L + 0.400 L = 0.720 L

$$\frac{0.034 \text{ mol Ca}^{2+}}{0.720 \text{ L}} = 0.0472 \text{ mol/L Ca}^{2+}$$

$$\frac{0.0147 \text{ mol OH}^-}{0.720 \text{ L}} = 0.0204 \text{ mol/L OH}^-$$

$$[Ca^{2+}][OH^-]^2 = (0.0472)(0.0204)^2$$

$$= 1.9 \times 10^{-5} = \text{ion product}$$

$1.9 \times 10^{-5} > K_{sp}$; precipitation occurs

---

548. Given: V AgNO$_3$ = 0.020 L
$\quad$ [AgNO$_3$] = 0.077 M
$\quad$ V NaC$_2$H$_3$O$_2$
$\quad$ = 0.030 L
$\quad$ [NaC$_2$H$_3$O$_2$]
$\quad$ = 0.043 M
$\quad$ K_{sp} AgC$_2$H$_3$O$_2$
$\quad$ = 2.5 × 10^{-3}

Unknown: whether a pre-
$\quad$ cipitate forms

$$AgNO_3 + NaC_2H_3O_2 \rightarrow AgC_2H_3O_2 + NaNO_3$$

$$AgC_2H_3O_2(s) \rightleftharpoons Ag^+(aq) + C_2H_3O_2^-(aq)$$

$$K_{sp} = [Ag^+][C_2H_3O_2^-] = 2.5 \times 10^{-3}$$

$$(0.020 \text{ L})\left(\frac{0.077 \text{ mol Ag}^+}{\text{L}}\right) = 1.54 \times 10^{-3} \text{ mol Ag}^+$$

$$(0.030 \text{ L})\left(\frac{0.043 \text{ mol C}_2\text{H}_3\text{O}_2}{\text{L}}\right) = 1.29 \times 10^{-3} \text{ mol C}_2\text{H}_3\text{O}_2$$

Total volume = 0.020 L + 0.030 L = 0.050 L

$$\frac{1.54 \times 10^{-3} \text{ mol Ag}^+}{0.050 \text{ L}} = 0.031 \text{ mol/L Ag}^+$$

$$\frac{1.29 \times 10^{-3} \text{ mol C}_2\text{H}_3\text{O}_2^-}{0.050 \text{ L}} = 0.026 \text{ mol/L C}_2\text{H}_3\text{O}_2^-$$

$$[Ag^+][C_2H_3O_2^-] = (0.031)(0.026) = 8.1 \times 10^{-4} = \text{ion product}$$

$8.1 \times 10^{-4} < 2.5 \times 10^{-3}$; no precipitation

549. Given: V $Pb(C_2H_3O_2)_2$
$= 0.100$ L
$[Pb(C_2H_3O_2)]$
$= 0.036$ M
V $NaCl = 0.050$ L
$[NaCl] = 0.074$ M
K_{sp} $PbCl_2$
$= 1.9 \times 10^{-4}$

Unknown: whether a
precipitate
forms

$Pb(C_2H_3O_2)_2 + 2NaCl \rightarrow PbCl_2 + 2Na(C_2H_3O_2)$

$PbCl_2(s) \rightleftharpoons Pb^+(aq) + 2Cl^-(aq)$

$K_{sp} = [Pb^+][Cl^-]^2 = 1.9 \times 10^{-4}$

$(0.100 \text{ L})\left(\dfrac{0.036 \text{ mol Pb}^+}{L}\right) = 3.6 \times 10^{-3} \text{ mol Pb}^+$

$(0.050 \text{ L})\left(\dfrac{0.074 \text{ mol Cl}^-}{L}\right) = 3.7 \times 10^{-3} \text{ mol Cl}^-$

Total volume = 0.1 L + 0.05 L = 0.15 L

$\dfrac{3.6 \times 10^{-3} \text{ mol Pb}^+}{0.15 \text{ L}} = 0.024 \text{ mol/L Pb}^+$

$\dfrac{3.7 \times 10^{-3} \text{ mol Cl}^-}{0.15 \text{ L}} = 0.025 \text{ mol/L Cl}^-$

$[Pb^+][Cl^-]^2 = (0.024)(0.025)^2 = 1.5 \times 10^{-5} =$ ion product

$1.5 \times 10^{-5} < 1.9 \times 10^{-4}$; no precipitation

---

550. Given: V $(NH_4)_2S$
$= 0.020$ L
$[(NH_4)_2S]$
$= 0.0090$ M
V $Al(NO_3)_3$
$= 0.120$ L
$[Al(NO_3)_3]$
$= 0.0082$ M
K_{sp} Al_2S_3
$= 2.00 \times 10^{-7}$

Unknown: whether a
precipitate
forms

$3(NH_4)_2S + 2Al(NO_3)_3 \rightarrow Al_2S_3 + 6NH_4NO_3$

$Al_2S_3(s) \rightleftharpoons 2Al^{3+}(aq) + 3S^{2-}(aq)$

$K_{sp} = [Al^{3+}]^2[S^{2-}]^3 = 2.00 \times 10^{-7}$

$(0.120 \text{ L})\left(\dfrac{0.0082 \text{ mol Al}^{3+}}{L}\right) = 9.8 \times 10^{-4} \text{ mol Al}^{3+}$

$(0.020 \text{ L})\left(\dfrac{0.0090 \text{ mol S}^{2-}}{L}\right) = 1.8 \times 10^{-4} \text{ mol S}^{2-}$

Total volume = 0.120 L + 0.020 L = 0.140 L

$\dfrac{9.8 \times 10^{-4} \text{ mol Al}^{3+}}{0.140 \text{ L}} = 7.0 \times 10^{-3} \text{ mol/L Al}^{3+}$

$\dfrac{1.8 \times 10^{-4} \text{ mol S}^{2-}}{0.140 \text{ L}} = 1.3 \times 10^{-3} \text{ mol/L S}^{2-}$

$[Al^{3+}]^2[S^{2-}]^3 = (7.0 \times 10^{-3})^2(1.3 \times 10^{-3})^3 = 1.1 \times 10^{-13} =$ ion product

$1.1 \times 10^{-13} < 2.00 \times 10^{-7}$; no precipitation

---

551. Given: $[CaCrO_4] =$
0.010 M
Unknown: K_{sp}

$CaCrO_4(s) \rightleftharpoons Ca^{2+} + CrO_4^{2-}$

$K_{sp} = [Ca^{2+}][CrO_4^{2-}]$

$[Ca^{2+}] = 0.010$ M

$[CrO_4^{2-}] = 0.010$ M

$K_{sp} = (0.010)^2 = 1.0 \times 10^{-4}$

552. Given: Solubility of $PbSeO_4 = 0.001\ 36$ g/10.00 mL

Unknown: K_{sp}

$$\left(\frac{0.001\ 36\ \text{g } PbSeO_4}{10.00\ \text{mL}}\right)\left(\frac{1000\ \text{mL}}{\text{L}}\right)\left(\frac{1\ \text{mol } PbSeO_4}{350.12\ \text{g } PbSeO_4}\right) = 3.88 \times 10^{-4}\ \text{M } PbSeO_4$$

$$PbSeO_4(s) \rightleftharpoons Pb^{2+}(aq) + SeO_4^{2-}(aq)$$

$$K_{sp} = [Pb^{2+}][SeO_4^{2-}]$$

$$[Pb^{2+}] = [SeO_4^{2-}] = 3.88 \times 10^{-4}\ \text{M}$$

$$K_{sp} = (3.88 \times 10^{-4})^2 = 1.51 \times 10^{-7}$$

---

553. Given: V of CuSCN $= 0.0225$ L
[CuSCN] $= 4.0 \times 10^{-6}$ M

Unknown: **a.** K_{sp}
b. mass of CuSCN dissolved in 1×10^{-3} L of solution

a. $CuSCN(s) \rightleftharpoons Cu^{1+}(aq) + SCN^{1-}(aq)$

$$K_{sp} = [Cu^{1+}][SCN^{1-}]$$

$$[Cu^{1+}] = [SCN^{1-}] = 4.0 \times 10^{-6}\ \text{M}$$

$$K_{sp} = (4.0 \times 10^{-6})^2 = 1.6 \times 10^{-11}$$

b. solubility =
$$4.0 \times 10^{-6}\ \text{M} = \left(\frac{x\ \text{g CuSCN}}{1 \times 10^3\ \text{L}}\right)\left(\frac{1\ \text{mol CuSCN}}{121.64\ \text{g CuSCN}}\right)$$

$$x = (4.0 \times 10^{-6}\ \text{M})(1000\ \text{L})(121.64\ \text{g})/1\ \text{mol} = 0.49\ \text{g}$$

---

554. Given: $[Ag_2Cr_2O_7] = 3.684 \times 10^{-3}$ M

Unknown: K_{sp}

$$Ag_2Cr_2O_7(s) \rightleftharpoons 2Ag^+(aq) + Cr_2O_7^{2-}(aq)$$

$$K_{sp} = [Ag^+]^2[Cr_2O_7^{2-}]$$

$$[Ag^+] = (2)(3.684 \times 10^{-3}\ \text{M}) = 7.368 \times 10^{-3}\ \text{M}$$

$$[Cr_2O_7^-] = 3.684 \times 10^{-3}\ \text{M}$$

$$K_{sp} = (7.368 \times 10^{-3})^2(3.684 \times 10^{-3}) = 2.000 \times 10^{-7}$$

---

555. Given: K_{sp} BaSO$_3$ = 8.0×10^{-7}

Unknown: **a.** [BaSO$_3$]
b. mass of BaSO$_3$ dissolved in 500. mL H$_2$O

a. $BaSO_3(s) \rightleftharpoons Ba^{2+}(aq) + SO_3^{2-}(aq)$

$$K_{sp} = [Ba^{2+}][SO_3^{2-}]$$

$$[Ba^{2+}] = [SO_3^{2-}] = x$$

$$K_{sp} = x^2 = 8.0 \times 10^{-7}$$

$$x = \sqrt{8.0 \times 10^{-7}} = 8.9 \times 10^{-4}\ \text{M} = [BaSO_3]$$

b. solubility =
$$8.9 \times 10^{-4}\ \text{M} = \left(\frac{x\ \text{g BaSO}_3}{500\ \text{mL}}\right)\left(\frac{1000\ \text{mL}}{1\ \text{L}}\right)\left(\frac{1\ \text{mol BaSO}_3}{217.37\ \text{g BaSO}_3}\right)$$

$$x = \frac{(8.9 \times 10^{-4}\ \text{M})(500\ \text{mL})(1\ \text{L})(217.37\ \text{g})}{(1000\ \text{mL})(1\ \text{mol})}$$

$$= 0.097\ \text{g}$$

---

556. Given: K_{sp} PbCl$_2$ = 1.9×10^{-4}

Unknown: [PbCl$_2$]

$$PbCl_2(s) \rightleftharpoons Pb^{2+}(aq) + 2Cl^-$$

$$K_{sp} = [Pb^{2+}][Cl^-]^2$$

$$[Pb^{2+}] = x$$

$$[Cl^-] = 2x$$

$$K_{sp} = 1.9 \times 10^{-4} = (x)(2x)^2 = 4x^3$$

$$x = \sqrt[3]{1.9 \times 10^{-4}/4} = 0.036\ \text{M} = [PbCl_2]$$

557. Given: K_{sp} BaCO$_3$ = 1.2×10^{-8}

Unknown: **a.** [BaCO$_3$]
b. volume of water needed to dissolve 0.10 g BaCO$_3$

a. $BaCO_3(s) \rightleftharpoons Ba^{2+}(aq) + CO_3^{2-}(aq)$

$K_{sp} = [Ba^{2+}][CO_3^{2-}] = 1.2 \times 10^{-8}$

$1.2 \times 10^{-8} = x^2$

$x = 1.1 \times 10^{-4}$ M = [BaCO$_3$]

b. solubility =
1.1×10^{-4} M $= \left(\dfrac{0.10 \text{ g BaCO}_3}{x}\right)\left(\dfrac{1 \text{ mol BaCO}_3}{197.31 \text{ g BaCO}_3}\right)$

$x = (0.10 \text{ g BaCO}_3)\left(\dfrac{1 \text{ mol BaCO}_3}{197.31 \text{ g BaCO}_3}\right)\left(\dfrac{1}{1.1 \times 10^{-4} \text{ M}}\right)$

$x = 4.6$ L

558. Given: K_{sp} SrSO$_4$ = 3.2×10^{-7}

Unknown: **a.** [SrSO$_4$]
b. mass of SrSO$_4$ remaining after 20.0 L saturated solution is evaporated

a. $SrSO_4(s) \rightleftharpoons Sr^{2+}(aq) + SO_4^{2-}(aq)$

$K_{sp} = [Sr^{2+}][SO_4^{2-}] = 3.2 \times 10^{-7}$

$3.2 \times 10^{-7} = x^2$

$x = 5.7 \times 10^{-4}$ M = [SrSO$_4$]

b. solubility =
5.7×10^{-4} M $= \left(\dfrac{x \text{ g SrSO}_4}{20.0 \text{ L}}\right)\left(\dfrac{1 \text{ mol SrSO}_4}{183.65 \text{ g SrSO}_4}\right)$

$x = (5.7 \times 10^{-4} \text{ M})(20.0 \text{ L})(183.65 \text{ g SrSO}_4/\text{mol})$

$= 2.1$ g

559. Given: K_{sp} SrSO$_3$ = 4.0×10^{-8}
solubility = 1.0000 g/5.0 L H$_2$O

Unknown: mass of SrSO$_3$ remaining after saturated solution is filtered

$SrSO_3(s) \rightleftharpoons Sr^{2+}(aq) + SO_3^{2-}(aq)$

$K_{sp} = [Sr^{2+}][SO_3^{2-}] = 4.0 \times 10^{-8}$

$4.0 \times 10^{-8} = x^2$

$x = 2.0 \times 10^{-4} = [SrSO_3]$

solubility =

2.0×10^{-4} M $= \left(\dfrac{x}{5 \text{ L}}\right)\left(\dfrac{1 \text{ mol}}{167.66 \text{ g SrSO}_3}\right)$

$x = (2.0 \times 10^{-4} \text{ M})(5 \text{ L})\left(\dfrac{167.66 \text{ g SrSO}_3}{1 \text{ mol}}\right)$

$= 0.17$ g SrSO$_3$

$1.000 \text{ g} - 0.17 \text{ g} = 0.83 \text{ g SrSO}_3$

560. Given: K_{sp} Mn$_3$(AsO$_4$)$_2$ = 1.9×10^{-11}

Unknown: [Mn$_3$(AsO$_4$)$_2$] in a saturated solution

$Mn_3(AsO_4)_2(s) \rightleftharpoons 3Mn^{2+}(aq) + 2AsO_4^{3-}(aq)$

$K_{sp} = [Mn^{2+}]^3[AsO_4^{3-}]^2$

$[Mn^{2+}] = 3x$

$[AsO_4^{3-}] = 2x$

$K_{sp} = 1.9 \times 10^{-11} = (3x)^3(2x)^2 = 108x^5$

$x = 2.8 \times 10^{-3}$ M = [Mn$_3$(AsO$_4$)$_2$]

561. Given: V $Sr(NO_3)_2 =$ 0.030 L

$[Sr(NO_3)_2] =$ 0.0050 M

V $K_2SO_4 = 0.020$ L

$[K_2SO_4] = 0.010$ M

K_{sp} $SrSO_4 = 3.2 \times 10^{-7}$

Unknown: **a.** ion product of the ions that can form a precipitate (b) whether a precipitate forms

a. $Sr(NO_3)_2 + K_2SO_4 \rightarrow SrSO_4 + 2KNO_3$

$SrSO_4(s)$ $Sr^{2+}(aq) + SO_4^{2-}(aq)$

$K_{sp} = [Sr^{2+}][SO_4^{2-}] = 3.2 \times 10^{-7}$

$(0.030 \text{ L})\left(\dfrac{0.0050 \text{ mol } Sr^{2+}}{L}\right) = 1.5 \times 10^{-4} \text{ mol } Sr^{2+}$

$(0.020 \text{ L})\left(\dfrac{0.010 \text{ mol } SO_4^{2-}}{L}\right) = 2.0 \times 10^{-4} \text{ mol } SO_4^{2-}$

Total volume = 0.030 L + 0.020 L = 0.050 L

$\dfrac{1.5 \times 10^{-4} \text{ mol } Sr^{2+}}{0.050 \text{ L}} = 3.0 \times 10^{-3} \text{ mol/L } Sr^{2+}$

$\dfrac{2.0 \times 10^{-4} \text{ mol } SO_4^{2-}}{0.050 \text{ L}} = 4.0 \times 10^{-3} \text{ mol/L } SO_4^{2-}$

$[Sr^{2+}][SO_4^{2-}] = (3.0 \times 10^{-3})(4.0 \times 10^{-3})$

$= 1.2 \times 10^{-5} = \text{ion product}$

b. $1.2 \times 10^{-5} > 3.2 \times 10^{-7}$; precipitation occurs

---

562. Given: K_{sp} $PbBr_2 =$ 6.3×10^{-6}

V $MgBr_2$ $= 0.120$ L

$[MgBr_2]$ $= 0.0035$ M

V $Pb(C_2H_3O_2)_2$ $= 0.180$ L

$[Pb(C_2H_3O_2)_2]$ $= 0.0024$ M

Unknown: **a.** ion product of Br^- and Pb^{2+} in the mixed solution

b. whether a precipitate forms

a. $MgBr_2 + Pb(C_2H_3O_2)_2 \rightarrow PbBr_2 + Mg(C_2H_3O_2)_2$

$PbBr_2(s)$ $Pb^{2+}(aq) + 2Br^-(aq)$

$K_{sp} = [Pb^{2+}][Br^-]^2 = 6.3 \times 10^{-6}$

$(0.180 \text{ L})\left(\dfrac{0.0024 \text{ mol } Pb^{2+}}{L}\right) = 4.3 \times 10^{-4} \text{ mol } Pb^{2+}$

$(0.120 \text{ L})\left(\dfrac{0.0035 \text{ mol } Br^-}{L}\right) = 4.2 \times 10^{-4} \text{ mol } Br^-$

Total volume = 0.180 L + 0.120 L = 0.3 L

$\dfrac{4.3 \times 10^{-4} \text{ mol } Pb^{2+}}{0.3 \text{ L}} = 1.4 \times 10^{-3} \text{ mol/L } Pb^{2+}$

$\dfrac{4.2 \times 10^{-4} \text{ mol } Br^-}{0.3 \text{ L}} = 1.4 \times 10^{-3} \text{ mol/L } Br^-$

$[Br^-] = (2)(1.4 \times 10^{-3}) = 2.8 \times 10^{-3}$

ion product $= [Pb^{2+}][Br^-]^2 = (1.4 \times 10^{-3})(2.8 \times 10^{-3})^2$

$= 1.1 \times 10^{-8}$

b. $1.1 \times 10^{-8} < 6.3 \times 10^{-6}$; no precipitation occurs

563. Given: K_{sp} Mg(OH)$_2$ = 1.5×10^{-11}

Unknown: **b.** volume of H$_2$O required to dissolve 0.10 g Mg(OH)$_2$

b. $K_{sp} = [Mg^{2+}][OH^-]^2$

$[Mg^{2+}] = x$

$[OH^-] = 2x$

$K_{sp} = 1.5 \times 10^{-11} = (x)(2x)^2 = 4x^3$

$x = 1.6 \times 10^{-4}$ M = [Mg(OH)$_2$]

solubility =

$1.6 \times 10^{-4} \text{ M} = \left(\dfrac{0.10 \text{ g Mg(OH)}_2}{x}\right)\left(\dfrac{1 \text{ mol Mg(OH)}_2}{58.3 \text{ g Mg(OH)}_2}\right)$

$x = (0.10 \text{ g Mg(OH)}_2)\left(\dfrac{1 \text{ mol Mg(OH)}_2}{58.3 \text{ g Mg(OH)}_2}\right)\left(\dfrac{1}{1.6 \times 10^{-4} \text{ M}}\right)$

$= 11$ L

564. Given: K_{sp} Li$_2$CO$_3$ = 2.51×10^{-2}

Unknown: **a.** [Li$_2$CO$_3$]
b. mass of Li$_2$CO$_3$ dissolved to make 3440 mL of saturated solution

a. Li$_2$CO$_3$ 2Li$^+$ + CO$_3^{2-}$

$K_{sp} = [Li^+]^2[CO_3^{2-}]$

$[Li^+] = 2x$

$[CO_3^{2-}] = x$

$K_{sp} = 2.51 \times 10^{-2} = (2x)^2(x) = 4x^3$

$x = 0.184$ M = [Li$_2$CO$_3$]

b. solubility =

$0.184 \text{ M} = \left(\dfrac{x}{3440 \text{ mL}}\right)\left(\dfrac{1000 \text{ mL}}{L}\right)\left(\dfrac{1 \text{ mol Li}_2\text{CO}_3}{73.86 \text{ g Li}_2\text{CO}_3}\right)$

$x = (0.184 \text{ M})(3440 \text{ mL})\left(\dfrac{1L}{1000 \text{ mL}}\right)\left(\dfrac{73.86 \text{ g Li}_2\text{CO}_3}{1 \text{ mol}}\right)$

$= 46.8$ g

565. Given: V Ba(OH)$_2$ = 0.050 L
V HCl = 0.03161 L
[HCl] = 0.3417 M

Unknown: K_{sp} Ba(OH)$_2$

Ba(OH)$_2$ + 2HCl → BaCl$_2$ + 2H$_2$O

BaCl$_2$ Ba^{2+} + 2Cl$^-$

$(0.03161 \text{ L})\left(\dfrac{0.3417 \text{ mol HCl}}{L}\right) = 0.01080$ mol HCl

$\left(\dfrac{1 \text{ mol Ba(OH)}_2}{2 \text{ mol HCl}}\right)(0.01080 \text{ mol HCl}) = 5.400 \times 10^{-3}$ mol Ba(OH)$_2$

$\dfrac{5.400 \times 10^{-3} \text{ mol Ba(OH)}_2}{0.050 \text{ L}} = 0.1080$ M Ba(OH)$_2$

$K_{sp} = [Ba^{2+}][Cl^-]^2$

[Ba(OH)$_2$] = 0.1080 M

$[Ba^{2+}]$ = 0.1080 M

$[Cl^-]$ = (2)(0.1080) = 0.2160 M

$K_{sp} = (0.1080)(0.2160)^2$

$= 5.040 \times 10^{-3}$

566. $QR \rightarrow Q^+ + R^-$

    a. Given: $[QR] = 1.0$ M $K_{sp} = [Q^+][R^-]$

          Unknown: K_{sp} $= (1.0)(1.0) = 1.0$

    b. Given: $[QR] = 0.50$ M $K_{sp} = [Q^+][R^-]$

          Unknown: K_{sp} $= (0.50)(0.50) = 0.25$

    c. Given: $[QR] = 0.1$ M $K_{sp} = (0.1)(0.1) = 0.01$

          Unknown: K_{sp}

    d. Given: $[QR] = 0.001$ M $K_{sp} = (0.001)(0.001) = 1 \times 10^{-6}$

          Unknown: K_{sp}

---

567. Given: Saturated solutions of the salts QR, X_2Y, KL_2, A_3Z, and D_2E_3 are 0.02 M

     Unknown: K_{sp} for each salt

    a. $QR \rightarrow Q^+ + R^-$

$$K_{sp} = [Q^+][R^-] = (0.02)^2 = 4 \times 10^{-4}$$

    b. $X_2Y \rightarrow 2X^+ + Y^-$

$$K_{sp} = [X^+]^2[Y^-]$$

$$[X^+] = (2)(0.02) = 0.04 \text{ M}$$

$$[Y^-] = 0.02 \text{ M}$$

$$K_{sp} = (0.04)^2(0.02) = 3 \times 10^{-5}$$

    c. $KL_2 \rightarrow K^+ + 2L^-$

$$K_{sp} = [K^+][L^-]^2$$

$$[K^+] = 0.02 \text{ M}$$

$$[L^-] = (2)(0.02) = 0.04 \text{ M}$$

$$K_{sp} = (0.02)(0.04)^2 = 3 \times 10^{-5}$$

    d. $A_3Z \rightarrow 3A^+ + Z^-$

$$K_{sp} = [A^+]^3[Z^-]$$

$$[A^+] = (3)(0.02) = 0.06 \text{ M}$$

$$[Z^-] = 0.02 \text{ M}$$

$$K_{sp} = (0.06)^3(0.02) = 4 \times 10^{-6}$$

    e. $D_2E_3 \rightarrow 2D^+ + 3E^-$

$$K_{sp} = [D^+]^2[E^-]^3$$

$$[D^+] = (2)(0.02) = 0.04 \text{ M}$$

$$[E^-] = (3)(0.02) = 0.06 \text{ M}$$

$$K_{sp} = (0.04)^2(0.06)^3 = 3 \times 10^{-7}$$

568. Given: K_{sp} of AgBr = 5.0×10^{-13}

Unknown: **a.** [AgBr]
b. mass of AgBr in 10.0 L of saturated solution

a. $AgBr(s) \rightleftharpoons Ag^+(aq) + Br^-(aq)$

$K_{sp} = [Ag^+][Br^-]$

$[Ag^+] = [Br^-] = x$

$K_{sp} = x^2 = 5.0 \times 10^{-13}$

$x = 7.1 \times 10^{-7}$ M = [AgBr]

b. solubility =

$$7.1 \times 10^{-7} \text{ M} = \left(\frac{x \text{ AgBr}}{10.0 \text{ L}}\right)\left(\frac{1 \text{ mol AgBr}}{187.87 \text{ g AgBr}}\right)$$

$x = (7.1 \times 10^{-7} \text{ M})(10.0 \text{ L})(187.87 \text{ g})/1 \text{ mol}$

$= 1.3 \times 10^{-3}$ g

---

569. Given: K_{sp} of $Ca(OH)_2$ = 5.5×10^{-6}

Unknown: **a.** molarity of saturated $Ca(OH)_2$ solution
b. [OH$^-$]
c. pH

a. $Ca(OH)_2(s) \rightleftharpoons Ca^{2+}(aq) + 2OH^-(aq)$

$K_{sp} = [Ca^{2+}][OH^-]^2$

$[Ca^{2+}] = x$

$[OH^-] = 2x$

$K_{sp} = 5.5 \times 10^{-6} = (x)(2x)^2 = 4x^3$

$x = 0.011$ M = $[Ca(OH)_2]$

b. $[OH^-] = (2)(x) = (2)(0.011 \text{ M}) = 0.022$ M

c. $[H_3O^+][OH^-] = 1 \times 10^{-14}$ M^2

$[H_3O^+] = \dfrac{1 \times 10^{-14} \text{ M}^2}{0.022 \text{ M}}$

$= 4.5 \times 10^{-13}$

$\text{pH} = -\log [H_3O^+]$

$= -\log (4.5 \times 10^{-13})$

$= 12.35$

---

570. Given: K_{sp} of $MgCO_3$ = 3.5×10^{-8}

Unknown: mass of $MgCO_3$ dissolved in 4.00 L of water

$MgCO_3(s) \rightleftharpoons Mg^{2+}(aq) + CO_3^{2-}(aq)$

$K_{sp} = [Mg^{2+}][CO_3^{2-}]$

$[Mg^{2+}] = [CO_3^{2-}] = x$

$K_{sp} = x^2 = 3.5 \times 10^{-8}$

$x = 1.9 \times 10^{-4}$ M = $[MgCO_3]$

solubility =

$$1.9 \times 10^{-4} \text{ M} = \left(\frac{x}{4.00 \text{ L}}\right)\left(\frac{1 \text{ mol MgCO}_3}{84.29 \text{ g MgCO}_3}\right)$$

$x = (1.9 \times 10^{-4} \text{ M})(4.00 \text{ L})(84.29 \text{ g})/1 \text{ mol}$

$= 0.064$ g

571. *Formula equation:*

$$Fe + SnCl_4 \rightarrow FeCl_3 + SnCl_2$$

Ionic equation:

$$\overset{0}{Fe} + \overset{+4}{Sn}{}^{4+} + \overset{-1}{4Cl^-} \rightarrow \overset{+3}{Fe}{}^{3+} + \overset{-1}{3Cl^-} + \overset{+2}{Sn}{}^{2+} + \overset{-1}{2Cl^-}$$

Oxidation half-reaction:

$$2[\overset{0}{Fe} \rightarrow \overset{+3}{Fe}{}^{3+} + 3e^-] = 2Fe \rightarrow 2Fe^{3+} + 6e^-$$

Reduction half-reaction:

$$3[\overset{+4}{SnCl_4} + 2e^- \rightarrow \overset{+2}{SnCl_2} + 2Cl^-] = 3SnCl_4 + 6e^- \rightarrow 3SnCl_2 + 6Cl^-$$

Combine half-reactions:

$$2Fe \rightarrow 2Fe^{3+} + 6e^-$$
$$3SnCl_4 + 6e^- \rightarrow 3SnCl_2 + 6Cl^-$$
$$\overline{3SnCl_4 + 2Fe \rightarrow 3SnCl_2 + 2Fe^{3+} + 6Cl^-}$$

Combine ions to form balanced equation:

$$2Fe + 3SnCl_4 \rightarrow 2FeCl_3 + 3SnCl_2$$

---

572. *Formula equation:*

$$H_2O_2 + FeSO_4 + H_2SO_4 \rightarrow Fe_2(SO_4)_3 + H_2O$$

Ionic equation:

$$\overset{+1\ -1}{H_2O_2} + \overset{+2}{Fe}{}^{2+} + \overset{+6-2}{(SO_4^{2-}} + \overset{+1}{2H^+} + \overset{+6-2}{(SO_4^{2-}} \rightarrow \overset{+3}{2Fe}{}^{3+} + \overset{+6-2}{3(SO_4^{2-})} + \overset{+1\ -2}{H_2O}$$

Oxidation half-reaction:

$$\overset{+2}{2Fe}{}^{2+} \rightarrow \overset{+3}{2Fe}{}^{3+} + 2e^-$$

Reduction half-reaction:

$$\overset{+1\ -1}{H_2O_2} + 2H^+ + 2e^- \rightarrow \overset{+1\ -2}{2H_2O}$$

Combine half-reactions:

$$2Fe^{2+} \rightarrow 2F^{3+} + 2e^-$$
$$H_2O_2 + 2H^+ + 2e^- \rightarrow H_2O + H_2O$$
$$\overline{H_2O_2 + 2H^+ + 2Fe^{2+} \rightarrow 2Fe^{3+} + 2H_2O}$$

Combine ions to form balanced equation:

$$H_2O_2 + 2FeSO_4 + H_2SO_4 \rightarrow Fe_2(SO_4)_3 + 2H_2O$$

573. *Formula equation:*

$$CuS + HNO_3 \rightarrow Cu(NO_3)_2 + NO + S + H_2O$$

Ionic equation:

$$Cu^{2+} + S^{2-} + H^+ + \overset{+5-2}{NO_3^-} \rightarrow Cu^{2+} + 2\overset{+5-2}{NO_3^-} + \overset{+2-2}{NO} + \overset{0}{S} + \overset{+1-2}{H_2O}$$

Oxidation half-reaction:

$$3[\overset{-2}{CuS} \rightarrow 2e^- + Cu^{2+} + \overset{0}{S}] = 3CuS \rightarrow 6e^- + 3Cu^{2+} + 3S$$

Reduction half-reaction:

$$2[4\overset{+5}{HNO_3} + 3e^- \rightarrow 3NO_3^- + \overset{+2}{NO} + 2H_2O]$$

$$= 8HNO_3 + 6e^- \rightarrow 6NO_3^- + 2NO + 4H_2O$$

Combine half-reactions:

$$3CuS \rightarrow 6e^- + 3Cu^{2+} + 3S$$

$$8HNO_3 + 6e^- \rightarrow 6NO_3^- + 2NO + 4H_2O$$

$$3CuS + 8HNO_3 \rightarrow 3Cu^{2+} + 3S + 6NO_3^- + 2NO + 4H_2O$$

Combine ions to form balanced equation:

$$3CuS + 8HNO_3 \rightarrow 3Cu(NO_3)_2 + 2NO + 3S + 4H_2O$$

---

574. *Formula equation:*

$$K_2Cr_2O_7 + HI \rightarrow CrI_3 + KI + I_2 + H_2O$$

Ionic equation:

$$2\overset{+1}{K^+} + \overset{+6}{Cr_2}\overset{-2}{O_7^{2-}} + \overset{+1-1}{H\,I} \rightarrow \overset{+3}{Cr^{3+}} + 3\overset{-1}{I^-} + \overset{+1-1}{K\,I} + \overset{0}{I_2} + \overset{+1-2}{H_2O}$$

Oxidation half-reaction:

$$3[2\overset{-1}{I^-} \rightarrow \overset{0}{I_2} + 2e^-] = 6I^- \rightarrow 3I_2 + 6e^-$$

Reduction half-reaction:

$$\overset{+6}{K_2Cr_2O_7} + 14H^+ + 8I^- + 6e^- \rightarrow 2\overset{+3}{CrI_3} + 2KI + 7H_2O$$

Combine half-reactions:

$$6I^- \rightarrow 3I_2 + 6e^-$$

$$K_2Cr_2O_7 + 14H^+ + 8I^- + 6e^- \rightarrow 2CrI_3 + 2KI + 7H_2O$$

$$K_2Cr_2O_7 + 14H^+ + 14I^- \rightarrow 2CrI_3 + 2KI + 3I_2 + 7H_2O$$

Combine ions to form balanced equation:

$$K_2Cr_2O_7 + 14HI \rightarrow 2CrI_3 + 2KI + 3I_2 + 7H_2O$$

575. *Formula equation:*

$$CO_2 + NH_2OH \rightarrow CO + N_2 + H_2O$$

Ionic equation:

$$\overset{+4-2}{CO_2} + \overset{-1+1-2+1}{NH_2OH} \rightarrow \overset{+2-2}{CO} + \overset{0}{N_2} + \overset{+1-2}{H_2O}$$

Oxidation half-reaction:

$$2\overset{-1}{NH_2OH} + 2OH^- \rightarrow \overset{0}{N_2} + 4H_2O + 2e^-$$

Reduction half-reaction:

$$\overset{+4}{CO_2} + H_2O + 2e^- \rightarrow \overset{+2}{CO} + 2OH^-$$

Combine half-reactions:

$$2NH_2OH + 2OH^- \rightarrow N_2 + 4H_2O + 2e^-$$

$$\underline{CO_2 + H_2O + 2e^- \rightarrow CO + 2OH^-}$$

$$CO_2 + 2NH_2OH \rightarrow CO + N_2 + 3H_2O$$

Combine ions to form balanced equation:

$$CO_2 + 2NH_2OH \rightarrow CO + N_2 + 3H_2O$$

---

576. *Formula equation:*

$$Bi(OH)_3 + K_2SnO_2 \rightarrow Bi + K_2SnO_3$$

Ionic equation:

$$\overset{+3}{Bi^{3+}} + 3\overset{-2+1}{OH^-} + 2\overset{+1}{K^+} + \overset{+2-2}{SnO_2^{2-}} \rightarrow \overset{0}{Bi} + 2\overset{+1}{K^+} + \overset{+4-2}{SnO_3^{2-}}$$

Oxidation half-reaction:

$$3[2K^+ + \overset{+2}{SnO_2^{2-}} + H_2O \rightarrow 2K^+ + \overset{+4}{SnO_3^{2-}} + 2H^+ + 2e^-]$$

$$= 6K^+ + 3SnO_2^{2-} + 3H_2O \rightarrow 6K^+ + 3SnO_3^{2-} + 6H^+ + 6e^-$$

Reduction half-reaction:

$$2[\overset{+3}{Bi^{3+}} + 3OH^- + 3H^+ + 3e^- \rightarrow \overset{0}{Bi} + 3H_2O]$$

$$= 2Bi^{3+} + 6OH^- + 6H^+ + 6e^- \rightarrow 2Bi + 6H_2O$$

Combine half-reactions:

$$6K^+ + 3SnO_2^{2-} + 3H_2O \rightarrow 6K^+ + 3SnO_3^{2-} + 6H^+ + 6e^-$$

$$\underline{2Bi^{3+} + 6OH^- + 6H^+ + 6e^- \rightarrow 2Bi + 6H_2O}$$

$$6K^+ + 2Bi^{3+} + 6OH^- + 3SnO_2^{2-} \rightarrow 6K^+ + 2Bi + H_2O + 3SnO_3^{2-}$$

Combine ions to form balanced equation:

$$2Bi(OH)_3 + 3K_2SnO_2 \rightarrow 2Bi + 3K_2SnO_3 + 3H_2O$$

577. *Formula equation:*

$$Mg + N_2 \rightarrow Mg_3N_2$$

Ionic equation:

$$\overset{0}{Mg} + \overset{0}{N_2} \rightarrow 3\overset{+2}{Mg}{}^{2+} + 2\overset{-3}{N}{}^{3-}$$

Oxidation half-reaction:

$$3\overset{0}{Mg} \rightarrow 3\overset{+2}{Mg}{}^{2+} + 6e^-$$

Reduction half-reaction:

$$\overset{0}{N_2} + 6e^- \rightarrow 2\overset{-3}{N}{}^{3-}$$

Combine half-reactions:

$$3Mg \rightarrow 3Mg^{2+} + 6e^-$$

$$\underline{N_2 + 6e^- \rightarrow 2N^{3-}}$$

$$3Mg + N_2 \rightarrow 3Mg^{2+} + 2N^{3+}$$

Combine ions to form balanced equation:

$$3Mg + N_2 \rightarrow Mg_3N_2$$

---

578. *Formula equation:*

$$SO_2 + Br_2 + H_2O \rightarrow HBr + H_2SO_4$$

Ionic equation:

$$\overset{+4-2}{SO_2} + \overset{0}{Br_2} + \overset{+1-2}{H_2O} \rightarrow \overset{+1}{H}{}^+ + \overset{-1}{Br}{}^- + 2\overset{+1}{H}{}^+ + \overset{+6-2}{SO_4^{2-}}$$

Oxidation half-reaction:

$$\overset{+4}{SO_2} + 2H_2O \rightarrow \overset{+6}{SO_4^{2-}} + 4H^+ + 2e^-$$

Reduction half-reaction:

$$\overset{0}{Br_2} + 2e^- \rightarrow 2\overset{-1}{Br}{}^-$$

Combine half-reactions:

$$SO_2 + 2H_2O \rightarrow SO_4^{2-} + 4H^+ + 2e^-$$

$$\underline{Br_2 + 2e^- \rightarrow 2Br^-}$$

$$SO_2 + 2H_2O + Br_2 \rightarrow 2Br^- + SO_4^{2-} + 4H^+$$

Combine ions to form balanced equation:

$$SO_2 + Br_2 + 2H_2O \rightarrow 2HBr + H_2SO_4$$

579. *Formula equation:*

$$H_2S + Cl_2 \rightarrow S + HCl$$

Ionic equation:

$$2\overset{+1}{H_2^+} + \overset{-2}{S^{2-}} + \overset{0}{Cl_2} \rightarrow \overset{0}{S} + \overset{+1}{H^+} + \overset{-1}{Cl^-}$$

Oxidation half-reaction:

$$\overset{-2}{S^{2-}} + 2H^+ \rightarrow \overset{0}{S} + 2H^+ + 2e^-$$

Reduction half-reaction:

$$\overset{0}{Cl_2} + 2e^- \rightarrow 2\overset{-1}{Cl^-}$$

Combine half-reactions:

$$S^{2-} + 2H^+ \rightarrow S + 2H^+ + 2e^-$$

$$Cl_2 + 2e^- \rightarrow 2Cl^-$$

$$\overline{S^{2-} + 2H^+ + Cl_2 \rightarrow S + 2Cl^- + 2H^+}$$

Combine ions to form balanced equation:

$$H_2S + Cl_2 \rightarrow S + 2HCl$$

---

580. *Formula equation:*

$$PbO_2 + HBr \rightarrow PbBr_2 + Br_2 + \overset{-2}{H_2O}$$

Ionic equation:

$$\overset{+4\ -2}{PbO_2} + \overset{+1}{H^+} + \overset{-1}{Br^-} \rightarrow \overset{+2\ -1}{PbBr_2} + \overset{0}{Br_2} + \overset{+1\ -2}{H_2O}$$

Oxidation half-reaction:

$$2\overset{-1}{Br^-} \rightarrow \overset{0}{Br_2} + 2e^-$$

Reduction half-reaction:

$$2Br^- + \overset{+4}{PbO_2} + 4H^+ + 2e^- \rightarrow \overset{+2}{PbBr_2} + 2H_2O$$

Combine half-reactions:

$$2Br^- \rightarrow Br_2 + 2e^-$$

$$2Br^- + PbO_2 + 4H^+ + 2e^- \rightarrow PbBr_2 + 2H_2O$$

$$\overline{4Br^- + PbO_2 + 4H^+ \rightarrow PbBr_2 + Br_2 + 2H_2O}$$

Combine ions to form balanced equation:

$$PbO_2 + 4HBbr \rightarrow PbBr_2 + Br_2 + 2H_2O$$

581. *Formula equation:*

$$S + HNO_3 \rightarrow NO_2 + H_2SO_4 + H_2O$$

Ionic equation:

$$\overset{0}{S} + \overset{+1+5-2}{HNO_3} \rightarrow \overset{+4-2}{NO_2} + \overset{+1}{2H^+} + \overset{+6-2}{SO_4^{2-}} + \overset{+1-2}{H_2O}$$

Oxidation half-reaction:

$$\overset{0}{S} + 4H_2O \rightarrow \overset{+6}{SO_4^{2-}} + 8H^+ + 6e^-$$

Reduction half-reaction:

$$6[\overset{+5}{HNO_3^-} + H^+ + 1e^- \rightarrow \overset{+4}{NO_2} + H_2O] = 6HNO_3 + 6H^+ + 6e^- \rightarrow 6NO_2 + 6H_2O$$

Combine half-reactions:

$$S + 4H_2O \rightarrow SO_4^{2-} + 8H^+ + 6e^-$$
$$\underline{6HNO_3 + 6H^+ + 6e^- \rightarrow 6NO_2 + 6H_2O}$$
$$S + 6HNO_3 \rightarrow SO_4^{2-} + 2H^+ + 6NO_2 + 2H_2O$$

Combine ions to form balanced equation:

$$S + 6HNO_3 \rightarrow 6NO_2 + H_2SO_4 + 2H_2O$$

---

582. *Formula equation:*

$$NaIO_3 + N_2H_4 + HCl \rightarrow N_2 + NaICl_2 + H_2O$$

Ionic equation:

$$\overset{+1+5-2}{NaIO_3} + \overset{-2+1}{N_2H_4} + \overset{+1}{H^+} + \overset{-1}{Cl^-} \rightarrow \overset{0}{N_2} + \overset{+1+1-1}{NaICl_2} + \overset{+1-2}{H_2O}$$

Oxidation half-reaction:

$$\overset{-2}{N_2H_4} \rightarrow \overset{0}{N_2} + 4H^+ + 4e^-$$

Reduction half-reaction:

$$\overset{+5}{NaIO_3} + 6H^+ + 2Cl^- + 4e^- \rightarrow \overset{+1}{NaICl_2} + 3H_2O$$

Combine half-reactions:

$$N_2H_4 \rightarrow N_2 + 4H^+ + 4e^-$$
$$\underline{NaIO_3 + 6H^+ + 2Cl^- + 4e^- \rightarrow NaICl_2 + 3H_2O}$$
$$NaIO_3 + 2H^+ + 2Cl^- + N_2H_4 \rightarrow NaICl_2 + 3H_2O + N_2$$

Combine ions to form balanced equation:

$$NaIO_3 + N_2H_4 + 2HCl \rightarrow N_2 + NaICl_2 + 3H_2O$$

583. *Formula equation:*

$$MnO_2 + H_2O_2 + HCl \rightarrow MnCl_2 + O_2 + H_2O$$

Ionic equation:

$$\overset{+4\ -2}{MnO_2} + \overset{+1\ -1}{H_2O_2} + \overset{+1}{H^+} + \overset{-1}{Cl^-} \rightarrow \overset{+2}{Mn^{2+}} + 2\overset{-1}{Cl^-} + \overset{0}{O_2} + \overset{+1\ -2}{H_2O}$$

Oxidation half-reaction:

$$\overset{-1}{H_2O_2} \rightarrow \overset{0}{O_2} + 2H^+ + 2e^-$$

Reduction half-reaction:

$$\overset{+4}{MnO_2} + 4H^+ + 2Cl^- + 2e^- \rightarrow \overset{+2}{Mn^{2+}} + 2H_2O + 2Cl^-$$

Combine half-reactions:

$$H_2O_2 \rightarrow O_2 + 2H^+ + 2e^-$$
$$\underline{MnO_2 + 4H^+ + 2Cl^- + 2e^- \rightarrow Mn^{2+} + 2H_2O + 2Cl^-}$$
$$MnO_2 + 2H^+ + H_2O_2 + 2Cl^- \rightarrow Mn^{2+} + 2H_2O + O_2 + 2Cl^-$$

Combine ions to form balanced equation:

$$MnO_2 + H_2O_2 + 2HCl \rightarrow MnCl_2 + O_2 + 2H_2O$$

---

584. *Formula equation:*

$$AsH_3 + NaClO_3 \rightarrow H_3AsO_4 + NaCl$$

Ionic equation:

$$\overset{-3\ +1}{AsH_3} + \overset{+1}{Na^+} + \overset{+5\ -2}{ClO_3^-} \rightarrow \overset{+1}{3H^+} + \overset{+5\ -2}{AsO_4^{3-}} + \overset{+1}{Na^+} + \overset{-1}{Cl^-}$$

Oxidation half-reaction:

$$3[\overset{-3}{AsH_3} + 4H_2O \rightarrow \overset{+5}{AsO_4^{3-}} + 11H^+ + 8e^-]$$
$$= 3AsH_3 + 12H_2O \rightarrow 3AsO_4 + 33H^+ + 24e^-$$

Reduction half-reaction:

$$4[\overset{+5}{ClO_3} + 6H^+ + Na^+ + 6e^- \rightarrow \overset{-1}{Cl^-} + 3H_2O + Na^+]$$
$$= 4ClO_3 + 24H^+ + 4Na^+ + 24e^- \rightarrow 4Cl^- + 12H_2O + 4Na^+$$

Combine half-reactions:

$$3AsH_3 + 12H_2O \rightarrow 3AsO_4 + 33H^+ + 24e^-$$
$$\underline{4ClO_3 + 24H^+ + 4Na^+ + 24e^- \rightarrow 4Cl^- + 12H_2O + 4Na^+}$$
$$3AsH_3 + 4ClO_3 + 4Na^+ \rightarrow 3AsO_4 + 9H^+ + 4Na^+ + 4Cl^-$$

Combine ions to form balanced equation:

$$3AsH_3 + 4NaClO_3 \rightarrow 3H_3AsO_4 + 4NaCl$$

585. *Formula equation:*

$$K_2Cr_2O_7 + H_2C_2O_4 + HCl \rightarrow CrCl_3 + CO_2 + KCl + H_2O$$

Ionic equation:

$$\overset{+1}{2K^+} + \overset{+6\;-2}{Cr_2O_7^{2-}} + \overset{+1}{2H^+} + \overset{+3\,-2}{C_2O_4^{2-}} + \overset{+1}{H^+} + \overset{-1}{Cl^-} \rightarrow$$

$$\overset{+3}{Cr^{3+}} + \overset{-1}{3Cl^-} + \overset{+4\,-2}{CO_2} + \overset{+1}{K^+} + \overset{-1}{Cl^-} + \overset{+1\,-2}{H_2O}$$

Oxidation half-reaction:

$$3[\overset{+3}{C_2O_4} \rightarrow \overset{+4}{2CO_2} + 2e^-] = 3C_2O_4 \rightarrow 6CO_2 + 6e^-$$

Reduction half-reaction:

$$\overset{+6}{Cr_2O_7} + 14H^+ + 6e^- \rightarrow \overset{+3}{2Cr^{3+}} + 7H_2O$$

Combine half-reactions:

$$3C_2O_4 \rightarrow 6CO_2 + 6e^-$$

$$\underline{Cr_2O_7 + 14H^+ + 6e^- \rightarrow 2Cr^{3+} + 7H_2O}$$

$$Cr_2O_7 + 14H^+ + 3C_2O_4 \rightarrow 2Cr^{3+} + 6CO_2 + 7H_2O$$

Combine ions to form balanced equation:

$$K_2Cr_2O_7 + 3H_2C_2O_4 + 8HCl \rightarrow 2CrCl_3 + 6CO_2 + 2KCl + 7H_2O$$

---

586. *Formula equation:*

$$\overset{+2\;\;+5-2}{Hg(NO_3)_2} \rightarrow \overset{+2\,-2}{HgO} + \overset{+4-2}{NO_2} + \overset{0}{O_2}$$

Oxidation half-reaction:

$$\overset{-2}{2O} \rightarrow \overset{0}{O_2} + 4e^-$$

Reduction half-reaction:

$$4[\overset{+5}{N} + 1e^- \rightarrow \overset{+4}{N}] = 4N + 4e^- \rightarrow 4N$$

Balanced equation:

$$2Hg(NO_3)_2 \rightarrow 2HgO + 4NO_2 + O_2$$

587. *Formula equation:*

$$HAuCl_4 + N_2H_4 \rightarrow Au + N_2 + HCl$$

Ionic equation:

$$\overset{+1}{H^+} + \overset{+3\ -1}{AuCl_4^-} + \overset{-2\ +1}{N_2H_4} \rightarrow \overset{0}{Au} + \overset{0}{N_2} + \overset{+1}{H^+} + \overset{-1}{Cl^-}$$

Oxidation half-reaction:

$$3[\overset{-2}{N_2H_4} \rightarrow \overset{0}{N_2} + 4H^+ + 4e^-] = 3N_2H_4 \rightarrow 3N_2 + 12H^+ + 12e^-$$

Reduction half-reaction:

$$4[\overset{+3}{HAuCl_4} + 3e^- \rightarrow \overset{0}{Au} + 4H^+ + 4Cl^-] = 4HAuCl_4 + 12e^- \rightarrow 4Au + 16Cl^- + 4H^+$$

Combine half-reactions:

$$3N_2H_4 \rightarrow 3N_2 + 12H^+ + 12e^-$$

$$\underline{4HAuCl_4^- + 12e^- \rightarrow 4Au + 16Cl^- + 4H^+}$$

$$4AuCl_4^- + 3N_2H_4 \rightarrow 4Au + 16Cl^- + 3N_2 + 16H^+$$

Combine ions to form balanced equation:

$$4HAuCl_4 + 3N_2H_4 \rightarrow 4Au + 3N_2 + 16HCl$$

---

588. *Formula equation:*

$$Sb_2(SO_4)_3 + KMnO_4 + H_2O \rightarrow H_3SbO_4 + K_2SO_4 + MnSO_4 + H_2SO_4$$

Ionic equation:

$$2\overset{+3}{Sb^{3+}} + 3\overset{+6-2}{SO_4^{2-}} + \overset{+1}{K^+} + \overset{+7\ -2}{MnO_4^-} + \overset{+1-2}{H_2O} \rightarrow$$

$$3\overset{+1}{H^+} + \overset{+5-2}{SbO_4^{3-}} + 2\overset{+1}{K^+} + \overset{+6-2}{SO_4^{2-}} + \overset{+2}{Mn^{2+}} + \overset{+6-2}{SO_4^{2-}} + 2\overset{+1}{H^+} + \overset{+6-2}{SO_4^{2-}}$$

Oxidation half-reaction:

$$5[2\overset{+3}{Sb^{3+}} + 3SO_4^{2-} + 8H_2O \rightarrow 2\overset{+5}{SbO_4^{3-}} + 3SO_4^{2-} + 16H^+ + 4e^-]$$

$$= 10Sb^{3+} + 15SO_4^{2-} + 40H_2O \rightarrow 10SbO_4^{3-} + 15SO_4^{2-} + 80H^+ + 20e^-$$

Reduction half-reaction:

$$4[K^+ + \overset{+7}{MnO_4^-} + 8H^+ + 5e^- \rightarrow K^+ + \overset{+2}{Mn^{2+}} + 4H_2O]$$

$$= 4K^+ + 4MnO_4 + 32H^+ + 20e^- \rightarrow 4K^+ + 4Mn^{2+} + 16H_2O$$

Combine half-reactions:

$$10Sb^{3+} + 15SO_4^{2-} + 40H_2O \rightarrow 10SbO_4^{3-} + 15SO_4^{2-} + 80H^+ + 20e^-$$

$$\underline{4MnO_4^- + 4K^+ + 32H^+ + 20e^- \rightarrow 4Mn^{2+} + 4K^+ + 16H_2O}$$

$$10Sb^{3+} + 24H_2O + 4MnO_4^- + 15SO_4^{2-} + 4K^+ \rightarrow$$

$$10SbO_4^{3-} + 48H^+ + 4Mn^{2+} + 15SO_4^{2-} + 4K^+$$

Combine ions to form balanced equation:

$$5Sb_2(SO_4)_3 + 4KMnO_4 + 24H_2O \rightarrow 10H_3SbO_4 + 2K_2SO_4 + 4MnSO_4 + 9H_2SO_4$$

589. *Formula equation:*

$$Mn(NO_3)_2 + NaBiO_3 + HNO_3 \rightarrow Bi(NO_3)_2 + HMnO_4 + NaNO_3 + H_2O$$

Ionic equation:

$$\overset{+2}{Mn}{}^{2+} + 2\overset{+5-2}{NO_3^-} + \overset{+1}{Na}\overset{+5-2}{BiO_3} + \overset{+1}{H^+} + \overset{+5-2}{NO_3^-}$$

$$\rightarrow \overset{+2}{Bi}{}^{2+} + 2\overset{+5-2}{NO_3^-} + \overset{+1+7}{H}\overset{-2}{MnO_4} + \overset{+1}{Na^+} + \overset{+5-2}{NO_3^-} + \overset{+1-2}{H_2O}$$

Oxidation half-reaction:

$$3[\overset{+2}{Mn}{}^{2+} + 4H_2O \rightarrow \overset{+7}{H}MnO_4 + 7H^+ + 5e^-]$$

$$= 3Mn^{2+} + 12H_2O \rightarrow 3HMnO_4 + 21H^+ + 15e^-$$

Reduction half-reaction:

$$5[Na\overset{+5}{Bi}O_3 + 6H^+ + 3e^- \rightarrow \overset{+2}{Bi}{}^{2+} + Na^+ + 3H_2O]$$

$$= 5NaBiO_3 + 30H^+ + 15e^- \rightarrow 5Bi^{2+} + 5Na^+ + 15H_2O$$

Combine half-reactions:

$$3Mn^{2+} + 12H_2O \rightarrow 3HMnO_4 + 21H^+ + 15e^-$$

$$5NaBiO_3 + 30H^+ + 15e^- \rightarrow 5Bi^{2+} + 5Na^+ + 15H_2O$$

$$\overline{3Mn^{2+} + 5NaBiO_3 + 9H^+ \rightarrow 3MnO_4 + 5Na^+ + 5Bi^{2+} + 3H_2O}$$

Combine ions to form balanced equation:

$$3Mn(NO_3)_2 + 5NaBiO_3 + 9HNO_3 \rightarrow 5Bi(NO_3)_2 + 3HMnO_4 + 5NaNO_3 + 3H_2O$$

---

590. *Formula equation:*

$$H_3AsO_4 + Zn + HCl \rightarrow AsH_3 + ZnCl_2 + H_2O$$

Ionic equation:

$$3\overset{+1}{H^+} + \overset{+5-2}{AsO_4^{3-}} + \overset{0}{Zn} + \overset{+1}{H^+} + \overset{-1}{Cl^-} \rightarrow \overset{-3+1}{AsH_3} + \overset{+2}{Zn}{}^{2+} + 2\overset{-1}{Cl^-} + \overset{+1-2}{H_2O}$$

Oxidation half-reaction:

$$4[\overset{0}{Zn} \rightarrow \overset{+2}{Zn}{}^{2+} + 2e^-] = 4Zn \rightarrow 4Zn^{2+} + 8e^-$$

Reduction half-reaction:

$$\overset{+5}{AsO_4} + 11H^+ + 8Cl^- + 8e^- \rightarrow \overset{-3}{AsH_3} + 4H_2O + 8Cl^-$$

Combine half-reactions:

$$4Zn \rightarrow 4Zn^{2+} + 8e^-$$

$$AsO_4 + 11H^+ + 8Cl^- + 8e^- \rightarrow AsH_3 + 4H_2O + 8Cl^-$$

$$\overline{AsO_4 + 11H^+ + 4Zn + 8Cl^- \rightarrow AsH_3 + 4H_2O + 4Zn^{2+} + 8Cl^-}$$

Combine ions to form balanced equation:

$$H_3AsO_4 + 4Zn + 8HCl \rightarrow AsH_3 + 4ZnCl_2 + 4H_2O$$

591. *Formula equation:*

$$KClO_3 + HCl \rightarrow Cl_2 + H_2O + KCl$$

Ionic equation:

$$\overset{+1}{K^+} + \overset{+5\,-2}{ClO_3^-} + \overset{+1}{H^+} + \overset{-1}{Cl^-} \rightarrow \overset{0}{Cl_2} + \overset{+1\,-2}{H_2O} + \overset{+1}{K^+} + \overset{-1}{Cl^-}$$

Oxidation half-reaction:

$$3[\overset{-1}{2Cl^-} \rightarrow \overset{0}{Cl_2} + 2e^-] = 6Cl^- \rightarrow 3Cl_2 + 6e^-$$

Reduction half-reaction:

$$K^+ + \overset{+5}{ClO_3^-} + 6H^+ + 6e^- \rightarrow K^+ + \overset{-1}{Cl^-} + 3H_2O$$

Combine half-reactions:

$$6Cl^- \rightarrow 3Cl_2 + 6e^-$$

$$K^+ + ClO_3^- + 6H^+ + 6e^- \rightarrow K^+ + Cl^- + 3H_2O$$
$$\overline{K^+ + ClO_3^- + 6H^+ + 6Cl^- \rightarrow K^+ + Cl^- + 3H_2O + 3Cl_2}$$

Combine ions to form balanced equation:

$$KClO_3 + 6HCl \rightarrow 3Cl_2 + 3H_2O + KCl$$

---

592. *Formula equation:*

$$KClO_3 + HCl \rightarrow Cl_2 + ClO_2 + H_2O + KCl$$

Ionic equation:

$$\overset{+1+5\,-2}{KClO_3} + \overset{+1-1}{HCl^-} \rightarrow \overset{0}{Cl_2} + \overset{+4\,-2}{ClO_2} + \overset{+1\,-2}{H_2O} + \overset{+1}{K^+} + \overset{-1}{Cl^-}$$

Oxidation half-reaction:

$$2[\overset{-1}{2HCl} + 2H_2O \rightarrow \overset{+4}{ClO_2} + 6H^+ + Cl^- + 5e^-]$$
$$= 4HCl + 4H_2O \rightarrow 2ClO_2 + 12H^+ + 2Cl^- + 10e^-$$

Reduction half-reaction:

$$\overset{+5}{2KClO_3} + 12H^+ + 10e^- \rightarrow \overset{0}{Cl_2} + 2K^+ + 6H_2O$$

Combine half-reactions:

$$4HCl + 4H_2O \rightarrow 2ClO_2 + 12H^+ + 2Cl^- + 10e^-$$

$$2KClO_3 + 12H^+ + 10e^- \rightarrow Cl_2 + 2K^+ + 6H_2O$$
$$\overline{4HCl + 2KClO_3 \rightarrow 2ClO_2 + 2K^+ + Cl_2 + 2H_2O + 2Cl^-}$$

Combine ions to form balanced equation:

$$2KClO_3 + 4HCl \rightarrow Cl_2 + 2ClO_2 + 2H_2O + 2KCl$$

593. *Formula equation:*

$$MnCl_3 + H_2O \rightarrow MnCl_2 + MnO_2 + HCl$$

Ionic equation:

$$\overset{+3}{Mn^{3+}} + \overset{-1}{3Cl^-} + \overset{+1}{H_2}\overset{-2}{O} \rightarrow \overset{+2}{Mn^{2+}} + \overset{-1}{2Cl^-} + \overset{+4}{Mn}\overset{-2}{O_2} + \overset{+1}{H^+} + \overset{-1}{Cl^-}$$

Oxidation half-reaction:

$$\overset{+3}{Mn^{3+}} + 3Cl^- + 2H_2O \rightarrow \overset{+4}{Mn}O_2 + 3Cl^- + 4H^+ + 1e^-$$

Reduction half-reaction:

$$\overset{+3}{Mn^{3+}} + 3Cl^- + 1e^- \rightarrow \overset{+2}{Mn^{2+}} + 3Cl^-$$

Combine half-reactions:

$$Mn^{3+} + 3Cl^- + 2H_2O \rightarrow MnO_2 + 3Cl^- + 4H^+ + 1e^-$$
$$\underline{Mn^{3+} + 3Cl^- + 1e^- \rightarrow Mn^{2+} + 3Cl^-}$$
$$2Mn^{3+} + 6Cl^- + 2H_2O \rightarrow Mn^{2+} + 6Cl^- + MnO_2 + 4H^+$$

Combine ions to form balanced equation:

$$2MnCl_3 + 2H_2O \rightarrow MnCl_2 + MnO_2 + 4HCl$$

---

594. *Formula equation:*

$$NaOH + H_2O + Al \rightarrow NaAl(OH)_4 + H_2 \text{ (in basic solution)}$$

Ionic equation:

$$\overset{+1}{Na^+} + \overset{-2+1}{OH^-} + \overset{+1}{H_2}\overset{-2}{O} + \overset{0}{Al} \rightarrow \overset{+1}{Na^+}\overset{+3}{Al}\overset{-2+1}{(OH)_4^-} + \overset{0}{H_2}$$

Oxidation half-reaction:

$$2[\overset{0}{Al} + Na^+ + 4OH^- \rightarrow \overset{+3}{Al}(OH)_4^- + Na^+ + 3e^-]$$
$$= 2Al + 2Na^+ + 8OH^- \rightarrow 2Al(OH)_4^- + 2Na^+ + 6e^-$$

Reduction half-reaction:

$$3[2\overset{+1}{H_2}O + 2e^- \rightarrow \overset{0}{H_2} + 2OH^-] = 6H_2O + 6e^- \rightarrow 3H_2 + 6OH^-$$

Combine half-reactions:

$$2Al + 2Na^+ + 8OH^- \rightarrow 2Al(OH)_4^- + 2Na^+ + 6e^-$$
$$\underline{6H_2O + 6e^- \rightarrow 3H_2 + 6OH^-}$$
$$2Al + 2Na^+ + 2OH^- + 6H_2O \rightarrow 2Al(OH)_4^- + 2Na^+ + 3H_2$$

Combine ions to form balanced equation:

$$2NaOH + 6H_2O + 2Al \rightarrow 2NaAl(OH)_4 + 3H_2$$

595. *Formula equation:*

$$Br_2 + Ca(OH)_2 \rightarrow CaBr_2 + Ca(BrO_3)_2 + H_2O \text{ (in basic solution)}$$

Ionic equation:

$$\overset{0}{Br_2} + \overset{+2}{Ca^{2+}} + \overset{-2+1}{2OH^-} \rightarrow \overset{+2}{Ca^{2+}} + \overset{-1}{2Br^-} + \overset{+2}{Ca^{2+}} + \overset{+5\ -2}{2BrO_3^-} + \overset{+1\ -2}{H_2O}$$

Oxidation half-reaction:

$$\overset{0}{Br_2} + 6Ca^{2+} + 12OH^- \rightarrow \overset{+5}{2BrO_3^-} + 6Ca^{2+} + 6H_2O + 10e^-$$

Reduction half-reaction:

$$5[\overset{0}{Br_2} + 2e^- \rightarrow \overset{-1}{2Br^-}] = 5Br_2 + 10e \rightarrow 10Br^-$$

Combine half-reactions:

$$Br_2 + Ca^{2+} + 12OH^- \rightarrow 2BrO_3 + Ca^{2+} + 6H_2O + 10e^-$$

$$\underline{5Br_2 + 10e^- \rightarrow 10Br^-}$$

$$6Br_2 + 12OH^- \rightarrow 10Br^- + 2BrO_3 + 6H_2O$$

Combine ions to form balanced equation:

$$6Br_2 + 6Ca(OH)_2 \rightarrow 5CaBr_2 + Ca(BrO_3)_2 + 6H_2O$$

---

596. *Formula equation:*

$$N_2O + NaClO + NaOH \rightarrow NaCl + NaNO_2 + H_2O \text{ (in basic solution)}$$

Ionic equation:

$$\overset{+1\ -2}{N_2O} + \overset{+1\ +1-2}{NaClO} + \overset{+1}{Na^+}\overset{-2+1}{OH^-} \rightarrow \overset{+1}{Na^+} + \overset{-1}{Cl^-} + \overset{+1\ +3-2}{NaNO_2} + \overset{+1\ -2}{H_2O}$$

Oxidation half-reaction:

$$2Na + \overset{+1}{N_2O} + 6OH^- \rightarrow \overset{+3}{2NaNO_2} + 3H_2O + 4e^-$$

Reduction half-reaction:

$$2[\overset{+1}{NaClO} + H_2O + 2e^- \rightarrow Cl^- + 2OH^- + Na^+]$$

$$= 2NaClO + 2H_2O + 4e^- \rightarrow 2Cl^- + 4OH^- + 2Na^+$$

Combine half-reactions:

$$2Na^+ + N_2O + 6OH^- \rightarrow 2NaNO_2 + 3H_2O + 4e^-$$

$$\underline{2NaClO + 2H_2O + 4e^- \rightarrow 2Cl^- + 4OH^- + 2Na^+}$$

$$2Na^+ + N_2O + 2OH^- + 2NaClO \rightarrow 2NaNO_2 + H_2O + 2Cl^- + 2Na^+$$

Combine ions to form balanced equation:

$$N_2O + 2NaClO + 2NaOH \rightarrow 2NaCl + 2NaNO_2 + H_2O$$

597. *Formula equation:*

$$HBr + MnO_2 \rightarrow MnBr_2 + H_2O + Br_2$$

Ionic equation:

$$\overset{+1}{H^+} + \overset{-1}{Br^-} + \overset{+4\ -2}{MnO_2} \rightarrow \overset{+2\ -1}{MnBr_2} + \overset{+1\ -2}{H_2O} + \overset{0}{Br_2}$$

Oxidation half-reaction:

$$2\overset{-1}{Br^-} \rightarrow \overset{0}{Br_2} + 2e^-$$

Reduction half-reaction:

$$2Br^- + \overset{+4}{MnO_2} + 4H^+ + 2e^- \rightarrow \overset{+2}{MnBr_2} + 2H_2O$$

Combine half-reactions:

$$2Br^- \rightarrow Br_2 + 2e^-$$

$$\underline{2Br^- + MnO_2 + 4H^+ + 2e^- \rightarrow MnBr_2 + 2H_2O}$$

$$4Br^- + MnO_2 + 4H^+ \rightarrow Br_2 + MnBr_2 + 2H_2O$$

Combine ions to form balanced equation:

$$4HBr + MnO_2 \rightarrow MnBr_2 + 2H_2O + Br_2$$

---

598. *Formula equation:*

$$Au + HCl + HNO_3 \rightarrow HAuCl_4 + NO + H_2O \text{ (in } aqua\ regia^*)$$

Ionic equation:

$$\overset{0}{Au} + \overset{+1}{H^+} + \overset{-1}{Cl^-} + \overset{+1}{H^+} + \overset{+5\ -2}{NO_3} \rightarrow \overset{+1+3\ -1}{HAuCl_4} + \overset{+2-2}{NO} + \overset{+1\ -2}{H_2O}$$

Oxidation half-reaction:

$$\overset{0}{Au} + 4Cl^- + H^+ \rightarrow \overset{+3}{HAuCl_4} + 3e^-$$

Reduction half-reaction:

$$\overset{+5}{NO_3^-} + 4H^+ + 3e^- \rightarrow \overset{+2}{NO} + 2H_2O$$

Combine half-reactions:

$$Au + 4Cl^- + H^+ \rightarrow HAuCl_4 + 3e^-$$

$$\underline{NO_3^- + 4H^+ + 3e^- \rightarrow NO + 2H_2O}$$

$$Au + 4Cl^- + 5H^+ + NO_3^- \rightarrow HAuCl_4 + NO + 2H_2O$$

Combine ions to form balanced equation:

$$Au + 4HCl + HNO_3 \rightarrow HAuCl_4 + NO + 2H_2O$$

*Aqua regia = concentrated HCl + concentrated HNO_3.

599. $\overset{+2}{Cu}{}^{2+} + \overset{0}{Fe} \rightarrow \overset{+2}{Fe}{}^{2+} + \overset{0}{Cu}$

Anode = Fe (oxidation)

Cathode = Cu (reduction)

Half-reactions:

$Fe \rightleftharpoons Fe^{2+} + 2e^-$ $\qquad\qquad\qquad$ $E^0 = +0.45$ V

$Cu^{2+} + 2e^- \rightleftharpoons Cu$ $\qquad\qquad$ $E^0 = +0.34$ V

$\overline{\qquad\qquad\qquad\qquad\qquad\qquad\qquad\qquad\qquad}$

$\qquad\qquad\qquad\qquad\qquad E^0{}_{cell} = +0.79$ V; spontaneous

---

600. $\overset{+2}{Pb}{}^{2+} + \overset{+2}{Fe}{}^{2+} \rightarrow \overset{+3}{Fe}{}^{3+} + \overset{0}{Pb}$

Anode = Fe (oxidation)

Cathode = Pb (reduction)

Half-reactions:

$Fe^{2+} \rightleftharpoons Fe^{3+} + 1e^-$ $\qquad\qquad$ $E^0 = -0.77$ V

$Pb^{2+} + 2e^- \rightleftharpoons Pb$ $\qquad\qquad$ $E^0 = -0.13$ V

$\overline{\qquad\qquad\qquad\qquad\qquad\qquad\qquad\qquad\qquad}$

$\qquad\qquad\qquad\qquad\qquad E^0{}_{cell} = -0.90$ V; not spontaneous

---

601. $\overset{+2}{Mn}{}^{2+} + 3H_2O + \overset{+2}{Sn}{}^{2+} \rightarrow \overset{+7}{MnO_4^-} + 8H^+ + \overset{0}{Sn}$

Anode = Mn (oxidation)

Cathode = Sn (reduction)

Half-reactions:

$Mn^{2+} + 4H_2O \; MnO_4^- + 8H^+ + 5e^-$ $\qquad$ $E^0 = -1.50$ V

$Sn^{2+} + 2e^- \rightleftharpoons Sn$ $\qquad\qquad\qquad\qquad$ $E^0 = -0.14$ V

$\overline{\qquad\qquad\qquad\qquad\qquad\qquad\qquad\qquad\qquad}$

$\qquad\qquad\qquad\qquad\qquad E^0{}_{cell} = -1.64$ V; not spontaneous

---

602. $\overset{+6}{MnO_4^{2-}} + \overset{0}{Cl_2} \rightarrow \overset{+7}{MnO_4^-} + \overset{-1}{2Cl^-}$

Anode = Mn (oxidation)

Cathode = Cl (reduction)

Half-reactions:

$MnO_4^{2-} \rightleftharpoons MnO_4^- + e^-$ $\qquad\qquad$ $E^0 = -0.56$ V

$Cl_2 + 2e^- \rightleftharpoons 2Cl^-$ $\qquad\qquad\qquad$ $E^0 = +1.36$ V

$\overline{\qquad\qquad\qquad\qquad\qquad\qquad\qquad\qquad\qquad}$

$\qquad\qquad\qquad\qquad\qquad E^0{}_{cell} = +0.80$ V; spontaneous

603. $\overset{+1}{Hg_2^{2+}} + 2\overset{+6}{MnO_4^{2-}} \rightarrow 2\overset{0}{Hg} + 2\overset{+7}{MnO_4^-}$

Anode = Mn (oxidation)

Cathode = Hg (reduction)

Half-reactions:

$MnO_4^{2-} \rightleftharpoons MnO_4^- + e^-$ $\qquad\qquad E^0 = -0.56$ V

$Hg_2^{2+} + 2e^- \rightleftharpoons 2Hg$ $\qquad\qquad \underline{E^0 = +0.80}$ V

$\qquad\qquad\qquad\qquad\qquad\qquad E^0{}_{cell} = +0.24$ V; spontaneous

---

604. $2\overset{+1}{Li^+} + \overset{0}{Pb} \rightarrow 2\overset{0}{Li} + \overset{+2}{Pb^{2+}}$

Anode = Pb (oxidation)

Cathode = Li (reduction)

Half-reactions:

$Pb \rightleftharpoons Pb^{2+} + 2e^-$ $\qquad\qquad E^0 = +0.13$ V

$Li^+ + e^- \rightleftharpoons Li$ $\qquad\qquad \underline{E^0 = -3.04}$ V

$\qquad\qquad\qquad\qquad\qquad\qquad E^0{}_{cell} = -2.91$ V; not spontaneous

---

605. $\overset{0}{Br_2} + 2\overset{-1}{Cl^-} \rightarrow 2\overset{-1}{Br^-} + \overset{0}{Cl_2}$

Anode = Cl (oxidation)

Cathode = Br (reduction)

Half-reactions:

$2Cl^- \rightleftharpoons Cl_2 + 2e^-$ $\qquad\qquad E^0 = -1.36$ V

$Br_2 + 2e^- \rightleftharpoons 2Br^-$ $\qquad\qquad \underline{E^0 = +1.07}$ V

$\qquad\qquad\qquad\qquad\qquad\qquad E^0{}_{cell} = -0.29$ V; not spontaneous

---

606. $\overset{0}{S} + 2\overset{-1}{I^-} \rightarrow \overset{-2}{S^{2-}} + \overset{0}{I_2}$

Anode = I (oxidation)

Cathode = S (reduction)

Half-reactions:

$2I^- \rightleftharpoons I_2 + 2e^-$ $\qquad\qquad E^0 = -0.54$ V

$S + 2e^- \rightleftharpoons S^{2-}$ $\qquad\qquad \underline{E^0 = -0.48}$ V

$\qquad\qquad\qquad\qquad\qquad\qquad E^0{}_{cell} = -1.02$ V; not spontaneous

607. $Ca^{2+} + 2e^- \rightleftharpoons Ca$ $\qquad\qquad\qquad\qquad E^0 = -2.87\text{ V}$

$Fe^{3+} + 3e^- \rightleftharpoons Fe$ $\qquad\qquad\qquad\qquad E^0 = -0.04\text{ V}$

Anode = Ca (oxidation)
Cathode = Fe (reduction)

Anode reaction:

$Ca \rightleftharpoons Ca^{2+} + 2e^-$

Cathode reaction:

$Fe^{3+} + 3e^- \rightleftharpoons Fe$

$E^0{}_{cell} = E^0{}_{cathode} - E^0{}_{anode} = -0.04 - (-2.87) = +2.83\text{ V}$

---

608. $Ag^+ + e^- \rightleftharpoons Ag$ $\qquad\qquad\qquad\qquad E^0 = +0.80\text{ V}$

$S + 2H^+ + 2e^- \rightleftharpoons H_2S$ $\qquad\qquad\qquad E^0 = +0.14\text{ V}$

Anode = S (oxidation)
Cathode = Ag (reduction)

Anode reaction:

$H_2S \rightleftharpoons S + 2H^+ + 2e^-$

Cathode reaction:

$Ag^+ + e^- \rightleftharpoons Ag$

$E^0{}_{cell} = E^0{}_{cathode} - E^0{}_{anode} = +0.80 - (+0.14) = +0.66\text{ V}$

---

609. $Fe^{3+} + e^- \rightleftharpoons Fe^{2+}$ $\qquad\qquad\qquad E^0 = +0.77\text{ V}$

$Sn^{2+} + 2e^- \rightleftharpoons Sn$ $\qquad\qquad\qquad E^0 = -0.14\text{ V}$

Anode = Sn (oxidation)
Cathode = Fe (reduction)

Anode reaction:

$Sn \rightleftharpoons Sn^{2+} + 2e^-$

Cathode reaction:

$Fe^{3+} + e^- \rightleftharpoons Fe^{2+}$

$E^0{}_{cell} = E^0{}_{cathode} - E^0{}_{anode} = +0.77 - (-0.14) = +0.91\text{ V}$

610. $Cu^{2+} + 2e^- \rightleftharpoons Cu$ $\qquad\qquad\qquad E^0 = +0.34$ V

$Au^{3+} + 3e^- \rightleftharpoons Au$ $\qquad\qquad\qquad E^0 = +1.50$ V

Anode = Cu (oxidation)
Cathode = Au (reduction)

Anode reaction:

$Cu \rightleftharpoons Cu^{2+} + 2e^-$

Cathode reaction:

$Au^{3+} + 3e^- \rightleftharpoons Au$

$E^0_{cell} = E^0_{cathode} - E^0_{anode} = +1.50 - (+0.34) = +1.16$ V

---

611. $\overset{0}{Ba} + \overset{+2}{Sn^{2+}} \rightarrow \overset{+2}{Ba^{2+}} + \overset{0}{Sn}$

Anode = Ba (oxidation)
Cathode = Sn (reduction)

Half-reactions:

$Ba \rightleftharpoons Ba^{2+} + 2e^-$ $\qquad\qquad\qquad E^0 = +2.91$ V

$Sn^{2+} + 2e^- \rightleftharpoons Sn$ $\qquad\qquad\qquad \underline{E^0 = -0.14\ \text{V}}$

$\qquad\qquad\qquad\qquad\qquad\qquad E^0_{cell} = +2.77$ V; spontaneous

---

612. $\overset{0}{Ni} + \overset{+2}{Hg^{2+}} \rightarrow \overset{+2}{Ni^{2+}} + \overset{0}{Hg}$

Anode = Ni (oxidation)
Cathode = Hg (reduction)

Half-reactions:

$Ni \rightleftharpoons Ni^{2+} + 2e^-$ $\qquad\qquad\qquad E^0 = +0.26$ V

$Hg^{2+} + 2e^- \rightleftharpoons Hg$ $\qquad\qquad\qquad \underline{E^0 = +0.85\ \text{V}}$

$\qquad\qquad\qquad\qquad\qquad\qquad E^0_{cell} = +1.11$ V; spontaneous

---

613. $2\overset{+3}{Cr^{3+}} + 7H_2O + 6\overset{+3}{Fe^{3+}} \rightarrow \overset{+6}{Cr_2O_7^{2-}} + 14H^+ + 6\overset{+2}{Fe^{2+}}$

Anode = Cr (oxidation)
Cathode = Fe (reduction)

Half-reactions:

$2Cr^{3+} + 7H_2O \rightleftharpoons Cr_2O_7^{2-} + 14H^+ + 6e^-$ $\qquad E^0 = -1.23$ V

$Fe^{3+} + e^- \rightleftharpoons Fe^{2+}$ $\qquad\qquad\qquad\qquad\quad \underline{E^0 = +0.77\ \text{V}}$

$\qquad\qquad\qquad\qquad\qquad\qquad E^0_{cell} = -0.46$ V; not spontaneous

614. $\overset{0}{Cl_2} + \overset{0}{Sn} \rightarrow 2\overset{-1}{Cl^-} + \overset{+2}{Sn^{2+}}$

Anode = Sn (oxidation)

Cathode = Cl (reduction)

Half-reactions:

$Sn \rightleftharpoons Sn^{2+} + 2e^-$ $E^0 = +0.14$ V

$Cl_2 + 2e^- \rightleftharpoons 2Cl^-$ $E^0 = +1.36$ V

                     $E^0_{cell} = +1.50$ V; spontaneous

615. $\overset{0}{Al} + 3\overset{+3}{Ag^+} \rightarrow \overset{+3}{Al^{3+}} + 3\overset{0}{Ag}$

Anode = Al (oxidation)

Cathode = Ag (reduction)

Half-reactions:

$Al \rightleftharpoons Al^{3+} + 3e^-$ $E^0 = +1.66$ V

$Ag^+ + e^- \rightleftharpoons Ag$ $E^0 = +0.80$ V

                     $E^0_{cell} = +2.46$ V; spontaneous

616. $\overset{+1}{Hg_2^{2+}} + \overset{-2}{S^{2-}} \rightarrow 2\overset{0}{Hg} + \overset{0}{S}$

Anode = S (oxidation)

Cathode = Hg (reduction)

Half-reactions:

$S^{2-} \rightleftharpoons S + 2e^-$ $E^0 = +0.48$ V

$Hg_2^{2+} + 2e^- \rightleftharpoons 2Hg$ $E^0 = +0.80$ V

                     $E^0_{cell} = +1.28$ V; spontaneous

617. $\overset{0}{Ba} + 2\overset{+1}{Ag^+} \rightarrow \overset{+2}{Ba^{2+}} + 2\overset{0}{Ag}$

Anode = Ba (oxidation)

Cathode = Ag (reduction)

Half-reactions:

$Ba \rightleftharpoons Ba^{2+} + 2e^-$ $E^0 = +2.91$ V

$Ag^+ + e^- \rightleftharpoons Ag$ $E^0 = +0.80$ V

                     $E^0_{cell} = +3.71$ V; spontaneous

618. $\overset{-1}{2I^-} + \overset{+2}{Ca^{2+}} \rightarrow \overset{0}{I_2} + \overset{0}{Ca}$

Anode = I (oxidation)

Cathode = Ca (reduction)

Half-reactions:

$2I^- \rightleftharpoons I_2 + 2e^-$ $\qquad\qquad E^0 = -0.54$ V

$Ca^{2+} + 2e^- \rightleftharpoons Ca$ $\qquad\qquad E^0 = -2.87$ V

$\rule{5cm}{0.4pt}$

$E^0{}_{cell} = -3.41$ V; not spontaneous

---

619. $\overset{0}{Zn} + \overset{+7}{2MnO_4^-} \rightarrow \overset{+2}{Zn^{2+}} + \overset{+6}{2MnO_4^{2-}}$

Anode = Zn (oxidation)

Cathode = Mn (reduction)

Half-reactions:

$Zn \rightleftharpoons Zn^{2+} + 2e^-$ $\qquad\qquad E^0 = +0.76$ V

$MnO_4^- + e^- \rightleftharpoons MnO_4^{2-}$ $\qquad\qquad E^0 = +0.56$ V

$\rule{5cm}{0.4pt}$

$E^0{}_{cell} = +1.32$ V; spontaneous

---

620. $\overset{+3}{2Cr^{3+}} + \overset{+2}{3Mg^{2+}} + 7H_2O \rightarrow \overset{+6}{Cr_2O_7^{2-}} + 14H^+ + \overset{0}{3Mg}$

Anode = Cr (oxidation)

Cathode = Mg (reduction)

Half-reactions:

$2Cr^{3+} + 7H_2O \rightleftharpoons Cr_2O_7^{2-} + 14H^+ + 6e^-$ $\qquad E^0 = -1.23$ V

$Mg^{2+} + 2e^- \rightleftharpoons Mg$ $\qquad\qquad\qquad\qquad\quad E^0 = -2.37$ V

$\rule{5cm}{0.4pt}$

$E^0{}_{cell} = -3.60$ V; not spontaneous

---

621. $Cl_2 + 2e^- \rightleftharpoons 2Cl^-$ $\qquad\qquad\qquad E^0 = +1.36$ V

$Ni^{2+} + 2e^- \rightleftharpoons Ni$ $\qquad\qquad\qquad\quad E^0 = -0.26$ V

Anode = Ni (oxidation)

Cathode = Cl (reduction)

Anode reaction:

$Ni \rightleftharpoons Ni^{2+} + 2e^-$

Cathode reaction:

$Cl_2 + 2e^- \rightleftharpoons 2Cl^-$

$E^0_{cell} = E^0_{cathode} - E^0_{anode} = +1.36 - (-0.26) = +1.62$ V

Combine half-reactions:

$Ni \rightleftharpoons Ni^{2+} + 2e^-$

$Cl_2 + 2e^- \rightleftharpoons 2Cl^-$

$\rule{5cm}{0.4pt}$

$Cl_2 + Ni \rightleftharpoons Ni^{2+} + 2Cl^-$

622. $Fe^{3+} + 3e^- \rightleftharpoons Fe$ $E^0 = -0.04$ V

$Hg^{2+} + 2e^- \rightleftharpoons Hg$ $E^0 = +0.85$ V

Anode = Fe (oxidation)
Cathode = Hg (reduction)

Anode reaction:

$2[Fe \rightleftharpoons Fe^{3+} + 3e^-] = 2Fe \rightleftharpoons 2Fe^{3+} + 6e^-$

Cathode reaction:

$3[Hg^{2+} + 2e^- \rightleftharpoons Hg] = 3Hg^{2+} + 6e^- \rightleftharpoons 3Hg$

$E^0_{cell} = E^0_{cathode} - E^0_{anode} = +0.85 - (-0.04) = +0.89$ V

Combine half-reactions:

$2Fe \rightleftharpoons 2Fe^{3+} + 6e^-$

$3Hg^{2+} + 6e^- \rightleftharpoons 3Hg$

$3Hg^{2+} + 2Fe \rightarrow 3Hg + 2Fe^{3+}$

623. $MnO_4^- + e^- \rightleftharpoons MnO_4^{2-}$ $E^0 = +0.56$ V

$Al^{3+} + 3e^- \rightleftharpoons Al$ $E^0 = -1.66$ V

Anode = Al (oxidation)
Cathode = Mn (reduction)

Anode reaction:

$Al \rightleftharpoons Al^{3+} + 3e^-$

Cathode reaction:

$3[MnO_4^- + e^- \rightleftharpoons MnO_4^{2-}] = 3MnO_4^- + 3e^- \rightleftharpoons 3MnO_4^{2-}$

$E^0_{cell} = E^0_{cathode} - E^0_{anode} = +0.56 - (-1.66) = +2.22$ V

Combine half-reactions:

$Al \rightleftharpoons Al^{3+} + 3e^-$

$3MnO_4^- + 3e^- \rightleftharpoons 3MnO_4^{2-}$

$3MnO_4^- + Al \rightarrow 3MnO_4^{2-} + Al^{3+}$

624. $MnO_4^- + 8H^+ + 5e^- \rightleftharpoons Mn^{2+} + 4H_2O$ $\qquad E^0 = +1.50$ V

$S + 2H^+ + 2e^- \rightleftharpoons H_2S$ $\qquad\qquad E^0 = +0.14$ V

Anode = S (oxidation)
Cathode = Mn (reduction)

Anode reaction:

$5[H_2S \rightleftharpoons S + 2H^+ + 2e^-] = 5H_2S \rightleftharpoons 5S + 10H^+ + 10e^-$

Cathode reaction:

$2[MnO_4^- + 8H^+ + 5e^- \rightleftharpoons Mn^{2+} + 4H_2O]$

$= 2MnO_4^- + 16H^+ + 10e^- \rightleftharpoons 2Mn^{2+} + 8H_2O$

$E^0_{cell} = E^0_{cathode} - E^0_{anode} = +1.50 - (+0.14) = +1.36$ V

Combine half-reactions:

$$5H_2S \rightleftharpoons 5S + 10H^+ + 10e^-$$
$$2MnO_4^- + 16H^+ + 10e^- \rightleftharpoons 2Mn^{2+} + 8H_2O$$

_____

$$2MnO_4^- + 6H^+ + 5H_2S \rightarrow 2Mn^{2+} + 8H_2O + 5S$$

625. $Ca^{2+} + 2e^- \rightleftharpoons Ca$ $\qquad\qquad E^0 = -2.87$ V

$Li^+ + e^- \rightleftharpoons Li$ $\qquad\qquad E^0 = -3.04$ V

Anode = Li (oxidation)
Cathode = Ca (reduction)

Anode reaction:

$2[Li \rightleftharpoons Li^+ + e^-] = 2Li \rightleftharpoons 2Li^+ + 2e^-$

Cathode reaction:

$Ca^{2+} + 2e^- \rightleftharpoons Ca$

$E^0_{cell} = E^0_{cathode} - E^0_{anode} = -2.87 - (-3.04) = +0.17$ V

Combine half-reactions:

$$2Li \rightleftharpoons 2Li^+ + 2e^-$$
$$Ca^{2+} + 2e^- \rightleftharpoons Ca$$

_____

$$Ca^{2+} + 2Li \rightarrow Ca + 2Li^+$$

626. $Br_2 + 2e^- \rightleftharpoons 2Br^-$ $\qquad\qquad\qquad\qquad E^0 = +1.07$ V

$MnO_4^- + 8H^+ + 5e^- \rightleftharpoons Mn^{2+} + 4H_2O \qquad E^0 = +1.50$ V

Anode = Br (oxidation)
Cathode = Mn (reduction)

Anode reaction:

$5[2Br^- \rightleftharpoons Br_2 + 2e^-] = 10Br^- \rightleftharpoons 5Br_2 + 10e^-$

Cathode reaction:

$2[MnO_4^- + 8H^+ + 5e^- \rightleftharpoons Mn^{2+} + 4H_2O]$

$= 2MnO_4^- + 16H^+ + 10e^- \rightleftharpoons 2Mn^{2+} + 8H_2O$

$E^0_{cell} = E^0_{cathode} - E^0_{anode} = +1.50 - (+1.07) = +0.43$ V

Combine half-reactions:

$$10Br^- \rightleftharpoons 5Br_2 + 10e^-$$

$\underline{2MnO_4^- + 16H^+ + 10e^- \rightleftharpoons 2Mn^{2+} + 8H_2O \qquad\qquad}$

$2MnO_4^- + 16H^+ + 10Br^- \rightarrow 2Mn^{2+} + 8H_2O + 5Br_2$

---

627. $Sn^{2+} + 2e^- \rightleftharpoons Sn$ $\qquad\qquad\qquad\qquad E^0 = -0.14$ V

$Fe^{3+} + e^- \rightleftharpoons Fe^{2+}$ $\qquad\qquad\qquad\qquad E^0 = +0.77$ V

Anode = Sn (oxidation)
Cathode = Fe (reduction)

Anode reaction:

$Sn \rightleftharpoons Sn^{2+} + 2e^-$

Cathode reaction:

$2[Fe^{3+} + e^- \rightleftharpoons Fe^{2+}] = 2Fe^{3+} + 2e^- \rightleftharpoons 2Fe^{2+}$

$E^0_{cell} = E^0_{cathode} - E^0_{anode} = +0.77 - (-0.14) = +0.91$ V

Combine half-reactions:

$$Sn \rightleftharpoons Sn^{2+} + 2e^-$$

$\underline{2Fe^{3+} + 2e^- \rightleftharpoons 2Fe^{2+} \qquad\qquad\qquad}$

$2Fe^{3+} + Sn \rightarrow 2Fe^{2+} + Sn^{2+}$

628. $Zn^{2+} + 2e^- \rightleftharpoons Zn$ $\qquad\qquad\qquad\qquad E^0 = -0.76 \text{ V}$

$Cr_2O_7^{2-} + 14H^+ + 6e^- \rightleftharpoons 2Cr^{3+} + 7H_2O$ $\qquad E^0 = +1.23 \text{ V}$

Anode = Zn (oxidation)

Cathode = Cr (reduction)

Anode reaction:

$3[Zn \rightleftharpoons Zn^{2+} + 2e^-] = 3Zn \rightleftharpoons 3Zn^{2+} + 6e^-$

Cathode reaction:

$Cr_2O_7^{2-} + 14H^+ + 6e^- \rightleftharpoons 2Cr^{3+} + 7H_2O$

$E^0_{cell} = E^0_{cathode} - E^0_{anode} = +1.23 - (-0.76) = +1.99 \text{ V}$

Combine half-reactions:

$$3Zn \rightleftharpoons 3Zn^{2+} + 6e^-$$
$$Cr_2O_7^{2-} + 14H^+ + 6e^- \rightleftharpoons 2Cr^{3+} + 7H_2O$$

$$\overline{Cr_2O_7^{2-} + 14H^+ + 3Zn \rightarrow 2Cr^{3+} + 7H_2O + 3Zn^{2+}}$$

---

629. $Ba^{2+} + 2e^- \rightleftharpoons Ba$ $\qquad\qquad\qquad E^0 = -2.91 \text{ V}$

$Ca^{2+} + 2e^- \rightleftharpoons Ca$ $\qquad\qquad\qquad E^0 = -2.87 \text{ V}$

Anode = Ba (oxidation)

Cathode = Ca (reduction)

Anode reaction:

$Ba \rightleftharpoons Ba^{2+} + 2e^-$

Cathode reaction:

$Ca^{2+} + 2e^- \rightleftharpoons Ca$

$E^0_{cell} = E^0_{cathode} - E^0_{anode} = -2.87 - (-2.91) = +0.04 \text{ V}$

Combine half-reactions:

$$Ba \rightleftharpoons Ba^{2+} + 2e^-$$
$$Ca^{2+} + 2e^- \rightleftharpoons Ca$$

$$\overline{Ca^{2+} + Ba \rightarrow Ca + Ba^{2+}}$$

630. $Hg_2^{2+} + 2e^- \rightleftharpoons 2Hg$ $\qquad\qquad\qquad E^0 = +0.80$ V

$Cd^{2+} + 2e^- \rightleftharpoons Cd$ $\qquad\qquad\qquad E^0 = -0.40$ V

Anode = Cd (oxidation)
Cathode = Hg (reduction)

Anode reaction:

$Cd \rightleftharpoons Cd^{2+} + 2e^-$

Cathode reaction:

$Hg_2^{2+} + 2e^- \rightleftharpoons 2Hg$

$E^0_{cell} = E^0_{cathode} - E^0_{anode} = +0.80 - (-0.40) = +1.20$ V

Combine half-reactions:

$$Cd \rightleftharpoons Cd^{2+} + 2e^-$$

$$\underline{Hg_2^{2+} + 2e^- \rightleftharpoons 2Hg}$$

$$Hg_2^{2+} + Cd \rightarrow 2Hg + Cd^{2+}$$